Instructor's Resource

for

Discrete Mathematics and Its Applications

Fifth Edition

Kenneth H. Rosen
AT&T Laboratories

McGraw Hill

Boston   Burr Ridge, IL   Dubuque, IA   Madison, WI   New York   San Francisco   St. Louis
Bangkok   Bogotá   Caracas   Lisbon   London   Madrid
Mexico City   Milan   New Delhi   Seoul   Singapore   Sydney   Taipei   Toronto

McGraw-Hill Higher Education

*A Division of The **McGraw-Hill** Companies*

Instructor's Resource Guide for
DISCRETE MATHEMATICS AND ITS APPLICATIONS, FIFTH EDITION
KENNETH H. ROSEN

Published by McGraw-Hill Higher Education, an imprint of The McGraw-Hill Companies, Inc.,
1221 Avenue of the Americas, New York, NY 10020. Copyright © The McGraw-Hill Companies,
Inc., 2003, 1999, 1995. All rights reserved.

This book is printed on acid-free paper.

1 2 3 4 5 6 7 8 9 0 CUS CUS 0 9 8 7 6 5 4 3 2

ISBN 0-07-247480-7

www.mhhe.com

Preface

This *Instructor's Resource Guide for Discrete Mathematics and Its Applications*, fifth edition, consists of six items that an instructor of a course in discrete mathematics using the text should find useful.

- The bulk of this *Guide* consists of solutions to all the even-numbered exercises in the text, and thus complements the *Student Solutions Guide for Discrete Mathematics and Its Applications*, fifth edition, which contains solutions to the odd-numbered exercises. It is assumed that the user of the present manual has access to that *Guide* as well. The solutions presented here are not necessarily the only ways of solving these problems, of course, nor are the answers unique in all cases. These are complete solutions, although they are somewhat less expository than the student-oriented solutions in the *Student Solutions Guide*.

- Several detailed course outlines are shown, for courses with different emphases and different student backgrounds and ability levels. These suggested syllabi include courses with a mathematics emphasis, courses with a computer science emphasis, one-term courses, and two-term courses.

- To aid instructors in moving from the fourth edition to the fifth edition, we have provided tables showing where material and exercises appearing in the fourth edition can be found in the fifth edition.

- This *Guide* contains detailed teaching suggestions for instructors. There are chapter overviews, followed by remarks on each section. Goals and prerequisites are stated, advice on teaching the section is presented, and comments on the exercise sets are offered.

- Two sample tests are provided for each chapter and two sample final examinations—the first easier than the second in each case. Solutions for the test questions are included. Instructors can draw on these sample tests when constructing tests for their own classes, or they can provide them to students as samples with which to prepare for the actual exams.

- Finally, this *Guide* contains a test bank of over 1300 exam questions. Answers are included.

In addition to this *Guide*, you will find the website created for *Discrete Mathematics and Its Applications* an invaluable resource. Included at the site are a Web guide to discrete mathematics that provides useful links keyed to the text, additional examples and exercises, a bulletin board, *a shared course material link where other instructors using this text have posted their lecture notes*, and other material you may find useful. The address is `www.mhhe.com/rosen`.

I want to thank Jerry Grossman for his extensive advice and assistance in the preparation of this *Guide*, Paul Lorczak, Georgia Mederer, Lyndon Weberg, and Suzanne Zeitman for double-checking the solutions, and students at Monmouth College and Oakland University for their input on preliminary versions of solutions to the exercises. The test bank was produced by John Michaels, for whose excellent work I am most grateful. Some questions and answers for this bank were contributed by Tao Jiang, Nancy Kinnersley, Antonette Logar, Thomas Roe, Zoltan Szekely, and Bharti Temkin, to whom I also extend my appreciation.

It is possible that there are a few errors here, despite our best efforts at eliminating them. I would appreciate hearing about all that you find, be they typographical or mathematical. Any other comments that will improve subsequent editions of this book are always greatly appreciated. You can locate the link for reporting possible errors in the Information Center within the website www.mhhe.com/rosen.

Kenneth H. Rosen

Contents

CHAPTER 1
The Foundations: Logic and Proof, Sets, and Functions

SECTION 1.1   Logic

2. Propositions must have clearly defined truth values, so a proposition must be a declarative sentence with no free variables.

a) Not a proposition—a command.

b) Not a proposition—a question.

c) A proposition that is false, as anyone who has been to Maine knows.

d) Not a proposition—its truth value depends on the value of x.

e) Not a proposition—its truth value depends on the value of x (for example, if $x = 2$, then the statement is true).

f) On the surface, this should probably be classified as not a proposition, since it contains free variables. If, for example, x and z are both Bill Clinton, then it is not clear what the truth value would be. On the other hand, if it is assumed that the variables are all meant to represent real numbers, then one could make the observation that for all possible values of the variables, the statement is true. Hence we could call this a (true) proposition.

4. a) I did not buy a lottery ticket this week.

b) Either I bought a lottery ticket this week or [in the inclusive sense] I won the million dollar jackpot on Friday.

c) If I bought a lottery ticket this week, then I won the million dollar jackpot on Friday.

d) I bought a lottery ticket this week and I won the million dollar jackpot on Friday.

e) I bought a lottery ticket this week if and only if I won the million dollar jackpot on Friday.

f) If I did not buy a lottery ticket this week, then I did not win the million dollar jackpot on Friday.

g) I did not buy a lottery ticket this week, and I did not win the million dollar jackpot on Friday.

h) Either I did not buy a lottery ticket this week, or else I did buy one and won the million dollar jackpot on Friday.

6. a) The election is not decided.

b) The election is decided, or the votes have been counted.

c) The election is not decided, and the votes have been counted.

d) If the votes have been counted, then the election is decided.

e) If the votes have not been counted, then the election is not decided.

f) If the election is not decided, then the votes have not been counted.

g) The election is decided if and only if the votes have been counted.

h) Either the votes have not been counted, or else the election is not decided and the votes have been counted. Note that we were able to incorporate the parentheses by using the words *either* and *else*.

8. a) If you have the flu, then you miss the final exam.

b) You do not miss the final exam if and only if you pass the course.

c) If you miss the final exam, then you do not pass the course.

d) You have the flu, or miss the final exam, or pass the course.

e) It is either the case that if you have the flu then you do not pass the course or the case that if you miss the final exam then you do not pass the course (or both, it is understood).

f) Either you have the flu and miss the final exam, or you do not miss the final exam and do pass the course.

10. a) $r \wedge \neg q$ **b)** $p \wedge q \wedge r$ **c)** $r \to p$ **d)** $p \wedge \neg q \wedge r$ **e)** $(p \wedge q) \to r$ **f)** $r \leftrightarrow (q \vee p)$

12. a) This is $\mathbf{T} \leftrightarrow \mathbf{T}$, which is true.

b) This is $\mathbf{T} \leftrightarrow \mathbf{F}$, which is false.

c) This is true. In the winter this is $\mathbf{T} \leftrightarrow \mathbf{T}$, and in the other seasons it is $\mathbf{F} \leftrightarrow \mathbf{F}$, both of which are true.

d) This is $\mathbf{F} \leftrightarrow \mathbf{F}$, which is true.

e) This is $\mathbf{F} \leftrightarrow \mathbf{T}$, which is false.

14. a) The employer making this request would be happy if the applicant knew both of these languages, so this is clearly an inclusive *or*.

b) The restaurant would probably charge extra if the diner wanted both of these items, so this is an exclusive *or*.

c) If a person happened to have both forms of identification, so much the better, so this is clearly an inclusive *or*.

d) This could be argued either way, but the inclusive interpretation seems more appropriate. This phrase means that faculty members who do not publish papers in research journals are likely to be fired from their jobs during the probationary period. On the other hand, it may happen that they will be fired even if they do publish (for example, if their teaching is poor).

16. a) The necessary condition is the conclusion: If you get promoted, then you wash the boss's car.

b) If the winds are from the south, then there will be a spring thaw.

c) The sufficient condition is the hypothesis: If you bought the computer less than a year ago, then the warranty is good.

d) If Willy cheats, then he gets caught.

e) The "only if" condition is the conclusion: If you access the website, then you must pay a subscription fee.

f) If you know the right people, then you will be elected.

g) If Carol is on a boat, then she gets seasick.

18. a) If I am to remember to send you the address, then you will have to send me an e-mail message. (This has been slightly reworded so that the tenses make more sense.)

b) If you were born in the United States, then you are a citizen of this country.

c) If you keep your textbook, then it will be a useful reference in your future courses. (The word "then" is understood in English, even if omitted.)

d) If their goaltender plays well, then the Red Wings will win the Stanley Cup.

e) If you get the job, then you had the best credentials.

f) If there is a storm, then the beach erodes.

g) If you log on to the server, then you have a valid password.

20. a) You will get an A in this course if and only if you learn how to solve discrete mathematics problems.

b) You will be informed if and only if you read the newspaper every day. (It sounds better in this order; it would be logically equivalent to state this as "You read the newspaper every day if and only if you will be informed.")

c) It rains if and only if it is a weekend day.

d) You can see the wizard if and only if he is not in.

22. a) Converse: If I stay home, then it will snow tonight. Contrapositive: If I do not stay at home, then it will not snow tonight. Inverse: If it does not snow tonight, then I will not stay home.

b) Converse: Whenever I go to the beach, it is a sunny summer day. Contrapositive: Whenever I do not go to the beach, it is not a sunny summer day. Inverse: Whenever it is not a sunny day, I do not go to the beach.

c) Converse: If I sleep until noon, then I stayed up late. Contrapositive: If I do not sleep until noon, then I did not stay up late. Inverse: If I don't stay up late, then I don't sleep until noon.

24. To construct the truth table for a compound proposition, we work from the inside out. In each case, we will show the intermediate steps. In part **(d)**, for example, we first construct the truth tables for $p \wedge q$ and for $p \vee q$ and combine them to get the truth table for $(p \wedge q) \rightarrow (p \vee q)$. For parts **(a)** and **(b)** we have the following table (column three for part **(a)**, column four for part **(b)**).

p	$\neg p$	$p \rightarrow \neg p$	$p \leftrightarrow \neg p$
T	F	F	F
F	T	T	F

For parts **(c)** and **(d)** we have the following table.

p	q	$p \vee q$	$p \wedge q$	$p \oplus (p \vee q)$	$(p \wedge q) \rightarrow (p \vee q)$
T	T	T	T	F	T
T	F	T	F	F	T
F	T	T	F	T	T
F	F	F	F	F	T

For part **(e)** we have the following table.

p	q	$\neg p$	$q \rightarrow \neg p$	$p \leftrightarrow q$	$(q \rightarrow \neg p) \leftrightarrow (p \leftrightarrow q)$
T	T	F	F	T	F
T	F	F	T	F	F
F	T	T	T	F	F
F	F	T	T	T	T

For part **(f)** we have the following table.

p	q	$\neg q$	$p \leftrightarrow q$	$p \leftrightarrow \neg q$	$(p \leftrightarrow q) \oplus (p \leftrightarrow \neg q)$
T	T	F	T	F	T
T	F	T	F	T	T
F	T	F	F	T	T
F	F	T	T	F	T

26. For parts **(a)** and **(b)** we have the following table (column two for part **(a)**, column four for part **(b)**).

p	$p \oplus p$	$\neg p$	$p \oplus \neg p$
T	F	F	T
F	F	T	T

For parts **(c)** and **(d)** we have the following table (columns five and six).

p	q	$\neg p$	$\neg q$	$p \oplus \neg q$	$\neg p \oplus \neg q$
T	T	F	F	T	F
T	F	F	T	F	T
F	T	T	F	F	T
F	F	T	T	T	F

For parts (e) and (f) we have the following table (columns five and six). This time we have omitted the column explicitly showing the negation of q. Note that the first is a tautology and the second is a contradiction (see definitions in Section 1.2).

p	q	$p \oplus q$	$p \oplus \neg q$	$(p \oplus q) \vee (p \oplus \neg q)$	$(p \oplus q) \wedge (p \oplus \neg q)$
T	T	F	T	T	F
T	F	T	F	T	F
F	T	T	F	T	F
F	F	F	T	T	F

28. For parts (a) and (b), we have

p	q	r	$p \vee q$	$(p \vee q) \vee r$	$(p \vee q) \wedge r$
T	T	T	T	T	T
T	T	F	T	T	F
T	F	T	T	T	T
T	F	F	T	T	F
F	T	T	T	T	T
F	T	F	T	T	F
F	F	T	F	T	F
F	F	F	F	F	F

For parts (c) and (d), we have

p	q	r	$p \wedge q$	$(p \wedge q) \vee r$	$(p \wedge q) \wedge r$
T	T	T	T	T	T
T	T	F	T	T	F
T	F	T	F	T	F
T	F	F	F	F	F
F	T	T	F	T	F
F	T	F	F	F	F
F	F	T	F	T	F
F	F	F	F	F	F

Finally, for parts (e) and (f) we have

p	q	r	$\neg r$	$p \vee q$	$(p \vee q) \wedge \neg r$	$p \wedge q$	$(p \wedge q) \vee \neg r$
T	T	T	F	T	F	T	T
T	T	F	T	T	T	T	T
T	F	T	F	T	F	F	F
T	F	F	T	T	T	F	T
F	T	T	F	T	F	F	F
F	T	F	T	T	T	F	T
F	F	T	F	F	F	F	F
F	F	F	T	F	F	F	T

30. This time the truth table needs $2^4 = 16$ rows.

p	q	r	s	$p \to q$	$(p \to q) \to r$	$((p \to q) \to r) \to s$
T	T	T	T	T	T	T
T	T	T	F	T	T	F
T	T	F	T	T	F	T
T	T	F	F	T	F	T
T	F	T	T	F	T	T
T	F	T	F	F	T	F
T	F	F	T	F	T	T
T	F	F	F	F	T	F
F	T	T	T	T	T	T
F	T	T	F	T	T	F
F	T	F	T	T	F	T
F	T	F	F	T	F	T
F	F	T	T	T	T	T
F	F	T	F	T	T	F
F	F	F	T	T	F	T
F	F	F	F	T	F	T

32. a) Since the condition is true, the statement is executed, so x is incremented and now has the value 2.

b) Since the condition is false, the statement is not executed, so x is not incremented and now still has the value 1.

c) Since the condition is true, the statement is executed, so x is incremented and now has the value 2.

d) Since the condition is false, the statement is not executed, so x is not incremented and now still has the value 1.

e) Since the condition is true when it is encountered (since $x = 1$), the statement is executed, so x is incremented and now has the value 2. (It is irrelevant that the condition is now false.)

34. a) $1\ 1000 \wedge (0\ 1011 \vee 1\ 1011) = 1\ 1000 \wedge 1\ 1011 = 1\ 1000$

b) $(0\ 1111 \wedge 1\ 0101) \vee 0\ 1000 = 0\ 0101 \vee 0\ 1000 = 0\ 1101$

c) $(0\ 1010 \oplus 1\ 1011) \oplus 0\ 1000 = 1\ 0001 \oplus 0\ 1000 = 1\ 1001$

d) $(1\ 1011 \vee 0\ 1010) \wedge (1\ 0001 \vee 1\ 1011) = 1\ 1011 \wedge 1\ 1011 = 1\ 1011$

36. The truth value of "Fred and John are happy" is $\min(0.8, 0.4) = 0.4$. The truth value of "Neither Fred nor John is happy" is $\min(0.2, 0.6) = 0.2$, since this statement means "Fred is not happy, and John is not happy," and we computed the truth values of the two propositions in this conjunction in Exercise 35.

38. This cannot be a proposition, because it cannot have a truth value. Indeed, if it were true, then it would be truly asserting that it is false, a contradiction; on the other hand if it were false, then its assertion that it is false must be false, so that it would be true—again a contradiction. Thus this string of letters, while appearing to be a proposition, is in fact meaningless.

40. No. This is a classical paradox. (We will use the male pronoun in what follows, assuming that we are talking about males shaving their beards here, and assuming that all men have facial hair. If we restrict ourselves to beards and allow female barbers, then the barber could be female with no contradiction.) If such a barber existed, who would shave the barber? If the barber shaved himself, then he would be violating the rule that he shaves only those people who do not shave themselves. On the other hand, if he does not shave himself, then the rule says that he must shave himself. Neither is possible, so there can be no such barber.

42. a) If the explorer (a woman, so that our pronouns will not get confused here—the cannibals will be male) encounters a truth-teller, then he will honestly answer "no" to her question. If she encounters a liar, then the honest answer to her question is "yes," so he will lie and answer "no." Thus everybody will answer "no" to the question, and the explorer will have no way to determine which type of cannibal she is speaking to.

b) There are several possible correct answers. One is the following question: "If I were to ask you if you always told the truth, would you say that you did?" Then if the cannibal is a truth teller, he will answer yes (truthfully), while if he is a liar, then, since in fact he would have said that he did tell the truth if questioned, he will now lie and answer no.

44. **a)** "But" means "and": $r \wedge \neg p$.

   b) "Whenever" means "if": $(r \wedge p) \to q$.

   c) Access being denied is the negation of q, so we have $\neg r \to \neg q$.

   d) The hypothesis is a conjunction: $(\neg p \wedge r) \to q$.

46. We write these symbolically: $u \to \neg a$, $a \to s$, $\neg s \to \neg u$. Note that we can make all the conclusion true by making a false, s true, and u false. Therefore if the users cannot access the file system, they can save new files, and the system is not being upgraded, then all the implications are true. Thus the system is consistent.

48. This system is consistent. We use L, Q, N, and B to stand for the basic propositions here, "The file system is locked," "New messages will be queued," "The system is functioning normally," and "New messages will be sent to the message buffer," respectively. Then the given specifications are $\neg L \to Q$, $\neg L \leftrightarrow N$, $\neg Q \to B$, $\neg L \to B$, and $\neg B$. If we want consistency, then we had better have B false in order that $\neg B$ be true. This requires that both L and Q be true, by the two implications that have B as their consequence. The first implication therefore is of the form $F \to T$, which is true. Finally, the biconditional $\neg L \leftrightarrow N$ can be satisfied by taking N to be false. Thus this set of specifications is consistent. Note that there is just this one satisfying truth assignment.

50. This is similar to Example 14, about universities in New Mexico. To search for hiking in West Virginia, we could enter WEST **AND** VIRGINIA **AND** HIKING. If we enter (VIRGINIA **AND** HIKING) **NOT** WEST, then we'll get websites about hiking in Virginia but not in West Virginia, except for sites that happen to use the word "west" in a different context (e.g., "Follow the stream west until you come to a clearing").

52. If A is a knight, then his statement that both of them are knights is true, and both will be telling the truth. But that is impossible, because B is asserting otherwise (that A is a knave). If A is a knave, then B's assertion is true, so he must be a knight, and A's assertion is false, as it should be. Thus we conclude that A is a knave and B is a knight.

54. We can draw no conclusions. A knight will declare himself to be a knight, telling the truth. A knave will lie and assert that he is a knight. Since everyone will say "I am a knight," we can determine nothing.

56. **a)** We look at the three possibilities of who the innocent men might be. If Smith and Jones are innocent (and therefore telling the truth), then we get an immediate contradiction, since Smith said that Jones was a friend of Cooper, but Jones said that he did not even know Cooper. If Jones and Williams are the innocent truth-tellers, then we again get a contradiction, since Jones says that he did not know Cooper and was out of town, but Williams says he saw Jones with Cooper (presumably in town, and presumably if we was with him, then he knew him). Therefore it must be the case that Smith and Williams are telling the truth. Their statements do not contradict each other. Based on Williams' statement, we know that Jones is lying, since he said that he did not know Cooper when in fact he was with him. Therefore Jones is the murderer.

   b) This is just like part **(a)**, except that we are not told ahead of time that one of the men is guilty. Can none of them be guilty? If so, then they are all telling the truth, but this is impossible, because as we just saw, some of the statements are contradictory. Can more than one of them be guilty? If, for example, they are all guilty, then their statements give us no information. So that is certainly possible.

58. This information is enough to determine the entire system. Let each letter stand for the statement that the person whose name begins with that letter is chatting. Then the given information can be expressed symbolically as follows: $\neg K \to H$, $R \to \neg V$, $\neg R \to V$, $A \to R$, $V \to K$, $K \to V$, $H \to A$, $H \to K$. Note that we were able to convert all of these statements into implications. In what follows we will sometimes make use of the contrapositives of these implications as well. First suppose that H is true. Then it follows that A and K are true, whence it follows that R and V are true. But R implies that V is false, so we get a contradiction. Therefore H must be false. From this it follows that K is true; whence V is true, and therefore R is false, as is A. We can now check that this assignment leads to a true value for each implication. So we conclude that Kevin and Vijay are chatting but Heather, Randy, and Abby are not.

60. Note that Diana's statement is merely that she didn't do it.
    a) John did it. There are four cases to consider. If Alice is the sole truth-teller, then Carlos did it; but this means that John is telling the truth, a contradiction. If John is the sole truth-teller, then Diana must be lying, so she did it, but then Carlos is telling the truth, a contradiction. If Carlos is the sole truth-teller, then Diana did it, but that makes John truthful, again a contradiction. So the only possibility is that Diana is the sole truth-teller. This means that John is lying when he denied it, so he did it. Note that in this case both Alice and Carlos are indeed lying.
    b) Again there are four cases to consider. Since Carlos and Diana are making contradictory statements, the liar must be one of them (we could have used this approach in part **(a)** as well). Therefore Alice is telling the truth, so Carlos did it. Note that John and Diana are telling the truth as well here, and it is Carlos who is lying.

SECTION 1.2   Propositional Equivalences

2. There are two cases. If p is true, then $\neg(\neg p)$ is the negation of a false proposition, hence true. Similarly, if p is false, then $\neg(\neg p)$ is also false. Therefore the two propositions are logically equivalent.

4. **a)** We construct the relevant truth table and note that the fifth and seventh columns are identical.

p	q	r	$p \vee q$	$(p \vee q) \vee r$	$q \vee r$	$p \vee (q \vee r)$
T	T	T	T	T	T	T
T	T	F	T	T	T	T
T	F	T	T	T	T	T
T	F	F	T	T	F	T
F	T	T	T	T	T	T
F	T	F	T	T	T	T
F	F	T	F	T	T	T
F	F	F	F	F	F	F

   b) Again we construct the relevant truth table and note that the fifth and seventh columns are identical.

p	q	r	$p \wedge q$	$(p \wedge q) \wedge r$	$q \wedge r$	$p \wedge (q \wedge r)$
T	T	T	T	T	T	T
T	T	F	T	F	F	F
T	F	T	F	F	F	F
T	F	F	F	F	F	F
F	T	T	F	F	T	F
F	T	F	F	F	F	F
F	F	T	F	F	F	F
F	F	F	F	F	F	F

6. We see that the fourth and seventh columns are identical.

p	q	$p \wedge q$	$\neg(p \wedge q)$	$\neg p$	$\neg q$	$\neg p \vee \neg q$
T	T	T	F	F	F	F
T	F	F	T	F	T	T
F	T	F	T	T	F	T
F	F	F	T	T	T	T

8. We construct a truth table for each implication and note that the relevant column contains only T's. For part **(a)** we have the following table.

p	q	$\neg p$	$p \vee q$	$\neg p \wedge (p \vee q)$	$[\neg p \wedge (p \vee q)] \to q$
T	T	F	T	F	T
T	F	F	T	F	T
F	T	T	T	T	T
F	F	T	F	F	T

For part **(b)** we have the following table. We omit the columns showing $p \to q$ and $q \to r$ so that the table will fit on the page.

p	q	r	$(p \to q) \to (q \to r)$	$q \to r$	$[(p \to q) \to (q \to r)] \to (p \to r)$
T	T	T	T	T	T
T	T	F	F	T	T
T	F	T	T	T	F
T	F	F	F	F	T
F	T	T	T	T	T
F	T	F	F	T	F
F	F	T	T	T	F
F	F	F	T	T	T

For part **(c)** we have the following table.

p	q	$p \to q$	$p \wedge (p \to q)$	$[p \wedge (p \to q)] \to q$
T	T	T	T	T
T	F	F	F	T
F	T	T	F	T
F	F	T	F	T

For part **(d)** we have the following table. We have omitted some of the intermediate steps to make the table fit.

p	q	r	$(p \vee q) \wedge (p \to r) \wedge (p \to r)$	$[(p \vee q) \wedge (p \to r) \wedge (p \to r)] \to r$
T	T	T	T	T
T	T	F	F	T
T	F	T	T	T
T	F	F	F	T
F	T	T	T	T
F	T	F	F	T
F	F	T	F	T
F	F	F	F	T

10. We argue directly by showing that if the hypothesis is true, then so is the conclusion. An alternative approach, which we show only for part **(a)**, is to use the equivalences listed in the section and work symbolically.

a) Assume the hypothesis is true. Then p is false. Since $p \vee q$ is true, we conclude that q must be true. Here is a more "algebraic" solution: $[\neg p \wedge (p \vee q)] \to q \equiv \neg[\neg p \wedge (p \vee q)] \vee q \equiv \neg\neg p \vee \neg(p \vee q)] \vee q \equiv p \vee \neg(p \vee q) \vee q \equiv (p \vee q) \vee \neg(p \vee q) \equiv \mathbf{T}$. The reasons for these logical equivalences are, respectively, Table 6, line 1; De Morgan's law; double negation; commutative and associative laws; negation law.

b) We want to show that if the entire hypothesis is true, then the conclusion $p \to r$ is true. To do this, we need only show that if p is true, then r is true. Suppose p is true. Then by the first part of the hypothesis, we conclude that q is true. It now follows from the second part of the hypothesis that r is true, as desired.

c) Assume the hypothesis is true. Then p is true, and since the second part of the hypothesis is true, we conclude that q is also true, as desired.

d) Assume the hypothesis is true. Since the first part of the hypothesis is true, we know that either p or q is true. If p is true, then the second part of the hypothesis tells us that r is true; similarly, if q is true, then the third part of the hypothesis tells us that r is true. Thus in either case we conclude that r is true.

12. This is not a tautology. It is saying that knowing that the hypothesis of an implication is false allows us to conclude that the conclusion is also false, and we know that this is not valid reasoning. To show that it is not a tautology, we need to find truth assignments for p and q that make the entire proposition false. Since this is possible only if the conclusion if false, we want to let q be true; and since we want the hypothesis to be true, we must also let p be false. It is easy to check that if, indeed, p is false and q is true, then the implication is false. Therefore it is not a tautology.

14. The first of these propositions is true if and only if p and q have the same truth value. The second is true if and only if either p and q are both true, or p and q are both false. Clearly these two conditions are saying the same thing.

16. It is easy to see from the definitions of implication and negation that each of these propositions is false in the case in which p is true and q is false, and true in the other three cases. Therefore the two propositions are logically equivalent.

18. It is easy to see from the definitions of the logical operations involved here that each of these propositions is true in the cases in which p and q have the same truth value, and false in the cases in which p and q have opposite truth values. Therefore the two propositions are logically equivalent.

20. We could form truth tables and check that $(p \to q) \wedge (p \to r)$ and $p \to (q \wedge r)$ have the same truth value in all eight situations. Alternatively, we can reason as follows. Suppose that $(p \to q) \wedge (p \to r)$ is true. We want to show that $p \to (q \wedge r)$ is true, which means that we want to show that $q \wedge r$ is true whenever p is true. If p is true, since we know that both $p \to q$ and $p \to r$ are true from our assumption, we can conclude that q is true and that r is true. Therefore $q \wedge r$ is true, as desired. Conversely, suppose that $p \to (q \wedge r)$ is true. We need to show that $p \to q$ is true and that $p \to r$ is true, which means that if p is true, then so are q and r. But this follows from $p \to (q \wedge r)$.

22. We could do this by truth tables, but we can also argue explicitly as to exactly which rows of the truth table will have T as their entries. Now $(p \to q) \vee (p \to r)$ will be true when either of the implications is true. The implication will be true if p is false, or if q in one case or r in the other case is true, i.e., when $q \vee r$ is true, which is precisely when $p \to (q \vee r)$ is true. Since the two propositions are true in exactly the same situations, they are logically equivalent.

24. Applying the third and first equivalences in Table 6, we have $\neg p \to (q \to r) \equiv p \vee (q \to r) \equiv p \vee \neg q \vee r$. Applying the first equivalence in Table 6 to $q \to (p \vee r)$ shows that $\neg q \vee p \vee r$ is equivalent to it. But these are equivalent by the commutative and associative laws.

26. We know that $p \leftrightarrow q$ is true precisely when p and q have the same truth value. But this happens precisely when $\neg p$ and $\neg q$ have the same truth value, that is, $\neg p \leftrightarrow \neg q$.

28. We could prove this by constructing a truth table for $(p \vee q) \wedge (\neg p \vee r) \to (q \vee r)$ and finding T in all eight rows. Alternatively, we reason as follows. The conclusion $q \vee r$ will be true in every case except when q and r are both false. But if q and r are both false, then one of $p \vee q$ or $\neg p \vee r$ is false, because one of p or $\neg p$ is false. Thus in this case the hypothesis $(p \vee q) \wedge (\neg p \vee r)$ is false. An implication in which the conclusion is true or the hypothesis is false is true, and that completes the argument.

30. We apply the rules stated in the preamble.
     a) $p \vee \neg q \vee \neg r$ **b)** $(p \vee q \vee r) \wedge s$ **c)** $(p \wedge \mathbf{T}) \vee (q \wedge \mathbf{F})$

32. The table is in fact displayed so as to exhibit the duality. The two identity laws are duals of each other, the two domination laws are duals of each other, etc. The only law not listed with another, the double negation law, is its own dual, since there are no occurrences of $\wedge$, $\vee$, $\mathbf{T}$, or $\mathbf{F}$ to replace.

34. Following the hint, we easily see that the answer is $p \wedge q \wedge \neg r$.

36. The statement of the problem is really the solution. Each line of the truth table corresponds to exactly one combination of truth values for the n atomic propositions involved. We can write down a conjunction that is true precisely in this case, namely the conjunction of all the atomic propositions that are true and the negations of all the atomic propositions that are false. If we do this for *each* line of the truth table for which the value of the compound proposition is to be true, and take the disjunction of the resulting propositions, then we have the desired proposition in its disjunctive normal form.

38. Given a compound proposition p, we can, by Exercise 37, write down a proposition q that is logically equivalent to p and uses only $\neg$, $\wedge$, and $\vee$. Now by De Morgan's law we can get rid of all the $\vee$'s by replacing each occurrence of $p_1 \vee p_2 \vee \cdots \vee p_n$ with $\neg(\neg p_1 \wedge \neg p_2 \wedge \cdots \wedge \neg p_n)$.

40. We write down the truth table corresponding to the definition.

p	q	$p \mid q$
T	T	F
T	F	T
F	T	T
F	F	T

42. We write down the truth table corresponding to the definition.

p	q	$p \downarrow q$
T	T	F
T	F	F
F	T	F
F	F	T

44. **a)** From the definition (or as seen in the truth table constructed in Exercise 42), $p \downarrow p$ is false when p is true and true when p is false, exactly as $\neg p$ is; thus the two are logically equivalent.
     b) The proposition $(p \downarrow q) \downarrow (p \downarrow q)$ is equivalent, by part **(a)**, to $\neg(p \downarrow q)$, which from the definition (or truth table or Exercise 43) is clearly equivalent to $p \vee q$.
     c) By Exercise 39, every compound proposition is logically equivalent to one that uses only $\neg$ and $\vee$. But by parts **(a)** and **(b)** of the present exercise, we can get rid of all the negations and disjunctions by using *NOR*'s. Thus every compound proposition can be converted into a logically equivalent compound proposition involving only *NOR*'s.

46. This exercise is similar to Exercise 44. First we can see from the truth tables that $(p \mid p) \equiv (\neg p)$ and that $((p \mid p) \mid (q \mid q)) \equiv (p \vee q)$. Then we argue exactly as in part **(c)** of Exercise 44: by Exercise 39, every compound proposition is logically equivalent to one that uses only $\neg$ and $\vee$. But by our observations at the beginning of the present exercise, we can get rid of all the negations and disjunctions by using *NAND*'s. Thus every compound proposition can be converted into a logically equivalent compound proposition involving only *NAND*'s.

48. To show that these are *not* logically equivalent, we need only find one assignment of truth values to p, q, and r for which the truth values of $p \mid (q \mid r)$ and $(p \mid q) \mid r$ differ. One such assignment is T for p and F for q and r. Then computing from the truth tables (or definitions), we see that $p \mid (q \mid r)$ is false and $(p \mid q) \mid r$ is true.

50. To say that p and q are logically equivalent is to say that the truth tables for p and q are identical; similarly, to say that q and r are logically equivalent is to say that the truth tables for q and r are identical. Clearly if the truth tables for p and q are identical, and the truth tables for q and r are identical, then the truth tables for p and r are identical (this is a fundamental axiom of the notion of equality). Therefore p and r are logically equivalent. (We are assuming—and there is no loss of generality in doing so—that the same atomic variables appear in all three propositions.)

52. If we want the first two of these to be true, then p and q must have the same truth value. If q is true, then the third and fourth expressions will be true, and if r is false, the last expression will be true. So all five of these disjunctions will be true if we set p and q to be true, and r to be false.

54. In each case we hunt for truth assignments that make all the disjunctions true.
a) Since p occurs in four of the five disjunctions, we can make p true, and then make q false (and make r and s anything we please). Thus this proposition is satisfiable.
b) This is satisfiable by, for example, setting p to be false (that takes care of the first, second, and fourth disjunctions), s to be false (for the third and sixth disjunctions), q to be true (for the fifth disjunction), and r to be anything.
c) It is not hard to find a satisfying truth assignment, such as p, q, and s true, and r false.

SECTION 1.3   Predicates and Quantifiers

2. a) This is true, since there is an a in *orange*.   **b)** This is false, since there is no a in *lemon*.
c) This is false, since there is no a in *true*.   **d)** This is true, since there is an a in *false*.

4. a) Here x is still equal to 0, since the condition is false.
b) Here x is still equal to 1, since the condition is false.
c) This time x is equal to 1 at the end, since the condition is true, so the statement $x := 1$ is executed.

6. The answers given here are not unique, but care must be taken not to confuse nonequivalent sentences. Parts **(c)** and **(f)** are equivalent; and parts **(d)** and **(e)** are equivalent. But these two pairs are not equivalent to each other.
a) Some student in the school has visited North Dakota. (Alternatively, there exists a student in the school who has visited North Dakota.)
b) Every student in the school has visited North Dakota. (Alternatively, all students in the school have visited North Dakota.)

c) This is the negation of part **(a)**: No student in the school has visited North Dakota. (Alternatively, there does not exist a student in the school who has visited North Dakota.)

d) Some student in the school has not visited North Dakota. (Alternatively, there exists a student in the school who has not visited North Dakota.)

e) This is the negation of part **(b)**: It is not true that every student in the school has visited North Dakota. (Alternatively, not all students in the school have visited North Dakota.)

f) All students in the school have not visited North Dakota. (This is technically the correct answer, although common English usage takes this sentence to mean—incorrectly—the answer to part **(e)**. To be perfectly clear, one could say that every student in this school has failed to visit North Dakota, or simply that no student has visited North Dakota.)

8. Note that part **(b)** and part **(c)** are not the sorts of things one would normally say.

  a) If an animal is a rabbit, then that animal hops. (Alternatively, every rabbit hops.)

  b) Every animal is a rabbit and hops.

  c) There exists an animal such that if it is a rabbit, then it hops. (Note that this is trivially true, satisfied, for example, by lions, so it is not the sort of thing one would say.)

  d) There exists an animal that is a rabbit and hops. (Alternatively, some rabbits hop. Alternatively, some hopping animals are rabbits.)

10. **a)** We assume that this means that one student has all three animals: $\exists x (C(x) \wedge D(x) \wedge F(x))$.

  b) $\forall x (C(x) \vee D(x) \vee F(x))$ **c)** $\exists x (C(x) \wedge F(x) \wedge \neg D(x))$

  d) This is the negation of part **(a)**: $\neg \exists x (C(x) \wedge D(x) \wedge F(x))$.

  e) Here the owners of these pets can be different: $(\exists x\, C(x)) \wedge (\exists x\, D(x)) \wedge (\exists x\, F(x))$. There is no harm in using the same dummy variable, but this could also be written, for example, as $(\exists x\, C(x)) \wedge (\exists y\, D(y)) \wedge (\exists z\, F(z))$.

12. **a)** Since $0 + 1 > 2 \cdot 0$, we know that $Q(0)$ is true.

  b) Since $(-1) + 1 > 2 \cdot (-1)$, we know that $Q(-1)$ is true.

  c) Since $1 + 1 \not> 2 \cdot 1$, we know that $Q(1)$ is false.

  d) From part **(a)** we know that there is at least one x that makes $Q(x)$ true, so $\exists x\, Q(x)$ is true.

  e) From part **(c)** we know that there is at least one x that makes $Q(x)$ false, so $\forall x\, Q(x)$ is false.

  f) From part **(c)** we know that there is at least one x that makes $Q(x)$ false, so $\exists x\, \neg Q(x)$ is true.

  g) From part **(a)** we know that there is at least one x that makes $Q(x)$ true, so $\forall x\, \neg Q(x)$ is false.

14. **a)** Since $(-1)^3 = -1$, this is true.

  b) Since $(\frac{1}{2})^4 < (\frac{1}{2})^2$, this is true.

  c) Since $(-x)^2 = ((-1)x)^2 = (-1)^2 x^2 = x^2$, we know that $\forall x ((-x)^2 = x^2)$ is true.

  d) Twice a positive number is larger than the number, but this inequality is not true for negative numbers or 0. Therefore $\forall x (2x > x)$ is false.

16. **a)** true ($x = \sqrt{2}$)   **b)** false ($\sqrt{-1}$ is not a real number)

  c) true (the left-hand side is always at least 2)   **d)** false (not true for $x = 1$ or $x = 0$)

18. Existential quantifiers are like disjunctions, and universal quantifiers are like conjunctions. See Examples 7 and 13.

  a) We want to assert that $P(x)$ is true for some x in the universe, so either $P(-2)$ is true or $P(-1)$ is true or $P(0)$ is true or $P(1)$ is true or $P(2)$ is true. Thus the answer is $P(-2) \vee P(-1) \vee P(0) \vee P(1) \vee P(2)$. The other parts of this exercise are similar. Note that by De Morgan's laws, the expression in part **(c)** is logically equivalent to the expression in part **(f)**, and the expression in part **(d)** is logically equivalent to the expression in part **(e)**.

b) $P(-2) \wedge P(-1) \wedge P(0) \wedge P(1) \wedge P(2)$

c) $\neg P(-2) \vee \neg P(-1) \vee \neg P(0) \vee \neg P(1) \vee \neg P(2)$

d) $\neg P(-2) \wedge \neg P(-1) \wedge \neg P(0) \wedge \neg P(1) \wedge \neg P(2)$

e) This is just the negation of part **(a)**: $\neg(P(-2) \vee P(-1) \vee P(0) \vee P(1) \vee P(2))$

f) This is just the negation of part **(b)**: $\neg(P(-2) \wedge P(-1) \wedge P(0) \wedge P(1) \wedge P(2))$

20. Existential quantifiers are like disjunctions, and universal quantifiers are like conjunctions. See Examples 7 and 13.

a) We want to assert that $P(x)$ is true for some x in the universe, so either $P(-5)$ is true or $P(-3)$ is true or $P(-1)$ is true or $P(1)$ is true or $P(3)$ is true or $P(5)$ is true. Thus the answer is $P(-5) \vee P(-3) \vee P(-1) \vee P(1) \vee P(3) \vee P(5)$.

b) $P(-5) \wedge P(-3) \wedge P(-1) \wedge P(1) \wedge P(3) \wedge P(5)$

c) The formal translation is as follows: $((-5 \neq 1) \rightarrow P(-5)) \wedge ((-3 \neq 1) \rightarrow P(-3)) \wedge ((-1 \neq 1) \rightarrow P(-1)) \wedge ((1 \neq 1) \rightarrow P(1)) \wedge ((3 \neq 1) \rightarrow P(3)) \wedge ((5 \neq 1) \rightarrow P(5))$. However, since the hypothesis $x \neq 1$ is false when x is 1 and true when x is anything other than 1, we have more simply $P(-5) \wedge P(-3) \wedge P(-1) \wedge P(3) \wedge P(5)$.

d) The formal translation is as follows: $((-5 \geq 0) \wedge P(-5)) \vee ((-3 \geq 0) \wedge P(-3)) \vee ((-1 \geq 0) \wedge P(-1)) \vee ((1 \geq 0) \wedge P(1)) \vee ((3 \geq 0) \wedge P(3)) \vee ((5 \geq 0) \wedge P(5))$. Since only three of the x's in the universe meet the condition, the answer is equivalent to $P(1) \vee P(3) \vee P(5)$.

e) For the second part we again restrict the domain: $(\neg P(-5) \vee \neg P(-3) \vee \neg P(-1) \vee \neg P(1) \vee \neg P(3) \vee \neg P(5)) \wedge (P(-1) \wedge P(-3) \wedge P(-5))$. This is equivalent to $(\neg P(1) \vee \neg P(3) \vee \neg P(5)) \wedge (P(-1) \wedge P(-3) \wedge P(-5))$.

22. In order to do the translation the second way, we let $C(x)$ be the propositional function "x is in your class." Note that for the second way, we always want to use implications with universal quantifiers and conjunctions with existential quantifiers.

a) Let $P(x)$ be "x has a cellular phone." Then we have $\forall x\, P(x)$ the first way, or $\forall x (C(x) \rightarrow P(x))$ the second way.

b) Let $F(x)$ be "x has seen a foreign movie." Then we have $\exists x\, F(x)$ the first way, or $\exists x (C(x) \wedge F(x))$ the second way.

c) Let $S(x)$ be "x can swim." Then we have $\exists x\, \neg S(x)$ the first way, or $\exists x (C(x) \wedge \neg S(x))$ the second way.

d) Let $Q(x)$ be "x can solve quadratic equations." Then we have $\forall x\, Q(x)$ the first way, or $\forall x (C(x) \rightarrow Q(x))$ the second way.

e) Let $R(x)$ be "x wants to be rich." Then we have $\exists x\, \neg R(x)$ the first way, or $\exists x (C(x) \wedge \neg R(x))$ the second way.

24. In all of these, we will let $Y(x)$ be the propositional function that x is in your school or class, as appropriate.

a) If we let $U(x)$ be "x has visited Uzbekistan," then we have $\exists x\, U(x)$ if the universe is just your schoolmates, or $\exists x (Y(x) \wedge U(x))$ if the universe is all people. If we let $V(x, y)$ mean that person x has visited country y, then we can rewrite this last one as $\exists x (Y(x) \wedge V(x, \text{Uzbekistan}))$.

b) If we let $C(x)$ and $P(x)$ be the propositional functions asserting that x has studied calculus and C++, respectively, then we have $\forall x (C(x) \wedge P(x))$ if the universe is just your schoolmates, or $\forall x (Y(x) \rightarrow (C(x) \wedge P(x)))$ if the universe is all people. If we let $S(x, y)$ mean that person x has studied subject y, then we can rewrite this last one as $\forall x (Y(x) \rightarrow (S(x, \text{calculus}) \wedge S(x, \text{C++})))$.

c) If we let $B(x)$ and $M(x)$ be the propositional functions asserting that x owns a bicycle and a motorcycle, respectively, then we have $\forall x (\neg(B(x) \wedge M(x)))$ if the universe is just your schoolmates, or $\forall x (Y(x) \rightarrow \neg(B(x) \wedge$

$M(x)))$ if the universe is all people. Note that "no one" became "for all ... not." If we let $O(x, y)$ mean that person x owns item y, then we can rewrite this last one as $\forall x(Y(x) \rightarrow \neg(O(x, \text{bicycle}) \wedge O(x, \text{motorcycle}))))$.

d) If we let $H(x)$ be "x is happy," then we have $\exists x \neg H(x)$ if the universe is just your schoolmates, or $\exists x(Y(x) \wedge \neg H(x))$ if the universe is all people. If we let $E(x, y)$ mean that person x is in mental state y, then we can rewrite this last one as $\exists x(Y(x) \wedge \neg E(x, \text{happy}))$.

e) If we let $T(x)$ be "x was born in the twentieth century," then we have $\forall x \, T(x)$ if the universe is just your schoolmates, or $\forall x(Y(x) \rightarrow T(x))$ if the universe is all people. If we let $B(x, y)$ mean that person x was born in the yth century, then we can rewrite this last one as $\forall x(Y(x) \rightarrow B(x, 20))$.

26. Let $R(x)$ be "x is in the correct place"; let $E(x)$ be "x is in excellent condition"; let $T(x)$ be "x is a [or your] tool"; and let the universe of discourse be all things.

a) There exists something not in the correct place: $\exists x \neg R(x)$.

b) If something is a tool, then it is in the correct place place and in excellent condition: $\forall x \, (T(x) \rightarrow (R(x) \wedge E(x)))$.

c) $\forall x \, (R(x) \wedge E(x))$

d) This is saying that everything fails to satisfy the condition: $\forall x \neg (R(x) \wedge E(x))$.

e) There exists a tool with this property: $\exists x \, (T(x) \wedge \neg R(x) \wedge E(x))$.

28. a) $P(1, 3) \vee P(2, 3) \vee P(3, 3)$ **b)** $P(1, 1) \wedge P(1, 2) \wedge P(1, 3)$
    c) $\neg P(2, 1) \vee \neg P(2, 2) \vee \neg P(2, 3)$ **d)** $\neg P(1, 2) \wedge \neg P(2, 2) \wedge \neg P(3, 2)$

30. In each case we need to specify some propositional functions (predicates) and identify the universe of discourse.

a) Let $F(x)$ be "x has fleas," and let the universe of discourse be dogs. Our original statement is $\forall x \, F(x)$. Its negation is $\exists x \neg F(x)$. In English this reads "There is a dog that does not have fleas."

b) Let $H(x)$ be "x can add," where the universe of discourse is horses. Then our original statement is $\exists x \, H(x)$. Its negation is $\forall x \neg H(x)$. In English this is rendered most simply as "No horse can add."

c) Let $C(x)$ be "x can climb," and let the universe of discourse be koalas. Our original statement is $\forall x \, C(x)$. Its negation is $\exists x \neg C(x)$. In English this reads "There is a koala that cannot climb."

d) Let $F(x)$ be "x can speak French," and let the universe of discourse be monkeys. Our original statement is $\neg \exists x \, F(x)$ or $\forall x \neg F(x)$. Its negation is $\exists x \, F(x)$. In English this reads "There is a monkey that can speak French."

e) Let $S(x)$ be "x can swim" and let $C(x)$ be "x can catch fish," where the universe of discourse is pigs. Then our original statement is $\exists x \, (S(x) \wedge C(x))$. Its negation is $\forall x \neg (S(x) \wedge C(x))$, which could also be written $\forall x \, (\neg S(x) \vee \neg C(x))$ by De Morgan's law. In English this is "No pig can both swim and catch fish," or "Every pig either is unable to swim or is unable to catch fish."

32. a) Let $S(x)$ be "x obeys the speed limit," where the universe of discourse is drivers. The original statement is $\exists x \neg S(x)$, the negation is $\forall x \, S(x)$, "All drivers obey the speed limit."

b) Let $S(x)$ be "x is serious," where the universe of discourse is Swedish movies. The original statement is $\forall x \, S(x)$, the negation is $\exists x \neg S(x)$, "Some Swedish movies are not serious."

c) Let $S(x)$ be "x can keep a secret," where the universe of discourse is people. The original statement is $\neg \exists x \, S(x)$, the negation is $\exists x \, S(x)$, "Some people can keep a secret."

d) Let $A(x)$ be "x has a good attitude," where the universe of discourse is people in this class. The original statement is $\exists x \neg A(x)$, the negation is $\forall x \, A(x)$, "Everyone in this class has a good attitude."

34. a) Since $1^2 = 1$, this statement is false; $x = 1$ is a counterexample. So is $x = 0$ (these are the only two counterexamples).

   b) There are two counterexamples: $x = \sqrt{2}$ and $x = -\sqrt{2}$.

   c) There is one counterexample: $x = 0$.

36. a) Some system is open.   **b)** Every system is either malfunctioning or in a diagnostic state.

   c) Some system is open, or some system is in a diagnostic state.   **d)** Some system is unavailable.

   e) No system is working. (We could also say "Every system is not working," as long as we understood that this is different from "Not every system is working.")

38. There are many ways to write these, depending on what we use for predicates.

   a) Let $F(x)$ be "There is less than x megabytes free on the hard disk," with the universe of discourse being positive numbers, and let $W(x)$ be "User x is sent a warning message." Then we have $F(30) \rightarrow \forall x\, W(x)$.

   b) Let $O(x)$ be "Directory x can be opened," let $C(x)$ be "File x can be closed," and let E be the proposition "System errors have been detected." Then we have $E \rightarrow ((\forall x\, \neg O(x)) \wedge (\forall x\, \neg C(x)))$.

   c) Let B be the proposition "The file system can be backed up," and let $L(x)$ be "User x is currently logged on." Then we have $(\exists x\, L(x)) \rightarrow \neg B$.

   d) Let $D(x)$ be "Product x can be delivered," and let $M(x)$ be "There are at least x megabytes of memory available" and $S(x)$ be "The connection speed is at least x kilobits per second," where the universe of discourse for the last two propositional functions are positive numbers. Then we have $(M(8) \wedge S(56)) \rightarrow D(\text{video on demand})$.

40. There are many ways to write these, depending on what we use for predicates.

   a) Let $A(x)$ be "User x has access to an electronic mailbox." Then we have $\forall x\, A(x)$.

   b) Let $A(x, y)$ be "Group member x can access resource y," and let $S(x, y)$ be "System x is in state y." Then we have $S(\text{file system}, \text{locked}) \rightarrow \forall x\, A(x, \text{system mailbox})$.

   c) Let $S(x, y)$ be "System x is in state y." Recalling that "only if" indicates a necessary condition, we have $S(\text{firewall}, \text{diagnostic}) \rightarrow S(\text{proxy server}, \text{diagnostic})$.

   d) Let $T(x)$ be "The throughput is at least x kbps," where the universe of discourse is positive numbers, let $M(x, y)$ be "Resource x is in mode y," and let $S(x, y)$ be "Router x is in state y." Then we have $(T(100) \wedge \neg T(500) \wedge \neg M(\text{proxy server}, \text{diagnostic})) \rightarrow \exists x\, S(x, \text{normal})$.

42. Both propositions are asserting that both $P(x)$ and $Q(x)$ are true for all values of x.

44. a) There are two cases. If A is true, then $(\forall x P(x)) \vee A$ is true, and since $P(x) \vee A$ is true for all x, $\forall x (P(x) \vee A)$ is also true. Thus both sides of the logical equivalence are true (hence equivalent). Now suppose that A is false. If $P(x)$ is true for all x, then the left-hand side is true. Furthermore, the right-hand side is also true (since $P(x) \vee A$ is true for all x). On the other hand, if $P(x)$ is false for some x, then both sides are false. Therefore again the two sides are logically equivalent.

   b) There are two cases. If A is true, then $(\exists x P(x)) \vee A$ is true, and since $P(x) \vee A$ is true for some (really all) x, $\exists x (P(x) \vee A)$ is also true. [We need to assume implicitly that the universe of discourse has at least one object in it.] Thus both sides of the logical equivalence are true (hence equivalent). Now suppose that A is false. If $P(x)$ is true for at least one x, then the left-hand side is true. Furthermore, the right-hand side is also true (since $P(x) \vee A$ is true for that x). On the other hand, if $P(x)$ is false for all x, then both sides are false. Therefore again the two sides are logically equivalent.

46. It is enough to find a counterexample. It is intuitively clear that the first proposition is asserting much more than the second. It is saying that one of the two predicates, P or Q, is universally true; whereas the second proposition is simply saying that for every x either $P(x)$ or $Q(x)$ holds, but which it is may well depend on x. As a simple counterexample, let $P(x)$ be the statement that x is odd, and let $Q(x)$ be the statement that x is even. Let the universe of discourse be the positive integers. The second proposition is true, since every positive integer is either odd or even. But the first proposition is false, since it is neither the case that all positive integers are odd nor the case that all of them are even.

48. a) This is false, since there are many values of x that make $x > 1$ true.

b) This is false, since there are two values of x that make $x^2 = 1$ true.

c) This is true, since by algebra we see that the unique solution to the equation is $x = 3$.

d) This is false, since there are no values of x that make $x = x + 1$ true.

50. There are only three cases in which $\exists x! P(x)$ is true, so we form the disjunction of these three cases. The answer is thus $(P(1) \wedge \neg P(2) \wedge \neg P(3)) \vee (\neg P(1) \wedge P(2) \wedge \neg P(3)) \vee (\neg P(1) \wedge \neg P(2) \wedge P(3))$.

52. A Prolog query returns a yes/no answer if there are no variables in the query, and it returns the values that make the query true if there are.

a) None of the facts was that Kevin was enrolled in EE 222. So the response is **no**.

b) One of the facts was that Kiko was enrolled in Math 273. So the response is **yes**.

c) Prolog returns the names of the courses for which Grossman is the instructor, namely just **cs301**.

d) Prolog returns the names of the instructor for CS 301, namely **grossman**.

e) Prolog returns the names of the instructors teaching any course that Kevin is enrolled in, namely **chan**, since Chan is the instructor in Math 273, the only course Kevin is enrolled in.

54. Following the idea and syntax of Example 21, we have the following rule:
`grandfather(X,Y) :- father(X,Z), father(Z,Y); father(X,Z), mother(Z,Y).`
Note that we used the comma to mean "and" and the semicolon to mean "or." For X to be the grandfather of Y, X must be either Y's father's father or Y's mother's father.

56. a) $\forall x(P(x) \to Q(x))$ **b)** $\exists x(R(x) \wedge \neg Q(x))$ **c)** $\exists x(R(x) \wedge \neg P(x))$

d) Yes. The unsatisfactory excuse guaranteed by part **(b)** cannot be a clear explanation by part **(a)**.

58. a) $\forall x(P(x) \to \neg S(x))$ **b)** $\forall x(R(x) \to S(x))$ **c)** $\forall x(Q(x) \to P(x))$ **d)** $\forall x(Q(x) \to \neg R(x))$

e) Yes. If x is one of my poultry, then he is a duck (by part **(c)**), hence not willing to waltz (part **(a)**). Since officers are always willing to waltz (part **(b)**), x is not an officer.

SECTION 1.4   Nested Quantifiers

2. a) There exists a real number x such that for every real number y, $xy = y$. This is asserting the existence of a multiplicative identity for the real numbers, and the statement is true, since we can take $x = 1$.

b) For every real number x and real number y, if x is nonnegative and y is negative, then the difference $x - y$ is positive. Or, more simply, a nonnegative number minus a negative number is positive (which is true).

c) For every real number x and real number y, there exists a real number z such that $x = y + z$. This is a true statement, since we can take $z = x - y$ in each case.

4. a) Some student in your class has taken some computer science course.

   b) There is a student in your class who has taken every computer science course.

   c) Every student in your class has taken at least one computer science course.

   d) There is a computer science course that every student in your class has taken.

   e) Every computer science course has been taken by at least one student in your class.

   f) Every student in your class has taken every computer science course.

6. a) Randy Goldberg is enrolled in CS 252.

   b) Someone is enrolled in Math 695.

   c) Carol Sitea is enrolled in some course.

   d) Some student is enrolled simultaneously in Math 222 and CS 252.

   e) There exist two distinct people, the second of whom is enrolled in every course that the first is enrolled in.

   f) There exist two distinct people enrolled in exactly the same courses.

8. a) $\exists x \exists y Q(x, y)$

   b) This is the negation of part (**a**), and so could be written either $\neg\exists x \exists y Q(x, y)$ or $\forall x \forall y \neg Q(x, y)$.

   c) We assume from the wording that the statement means that the same person appeared on both shows: $\exists x [Q(x, \text{Jeopardy}) \wedge Q(x, \text{Wheel of Fortune})]$

   d) $\forall y \exists x Q(x, y)$ **e)** $\exists x_1 \exists x_2 [Q(x_1, \text{Jeopardy}) \wedge Q(x_2, \text{Jeopardy}) \wedge x_1 \neq x_2]$

10. a) $\forall x F(x, \text{Fred})$ **b)** $\forall y F(\text{Evelyn}, y)$ **c)** $\forall x \exists y F(x, y)$ **d)** $\neg\exists x \forall y F(x, y)$ **e)** $\forall y \exists x F(x, y)$

   f) $\neg\exists x [F(x, \text{Fred}) \wedge F(x, \text{Jerry})]$

   g) $\exists y_1 \exists y_2 [F(\text{Nancy}, y_1) \wedge F(\text{Nancy}, y_2) \wedge y_1 \neq y_2 \wedge \forall y (F(\text{Nancy}, y) \rightarrow (y = y_1 \vee y = y_2))]$

   h) $\exists y [\forall x F(x, y) \wedge \forall z (\forall x F(x, z) \rightarrow z = y)]$ **i)** $\neg\exists x F(x, x)$

   j) $\exists x \exists y [x \neq y \wedge F(x, y) \wedge \forall z ((F(x, z) \wedge z \neq x) \rightarrow z = y)]$ (We do not assume that this sentence is asserting that this person can fool her/himself.)

12. The answers to this exercise are not unique; there are many ways of expressing the same propositions symbolically. Note that $C(x, y)$ and $C(y, x)$ say the same thing.

   a) $\neg I(\text{Jerry})$ **b)** $\neg C(\text{Rachel}, \text{Chelsea})$ **c)** $\neg C(\text{Jan}, \text{Sharon})$ **d)** $\neg\exists x\, C(x, \text{Bob})$

   e) $\forall x (x \neq \text{Joseph} \leftrightarrow C(x, \text{Sanjay}))$ **f)** $\exists x\, \neg I(x)$ **g)** $\neg\forall x\, I(x)$ (same as (**f**))

   h) $\exists x \forall y (x = y \leftrightarrow I(y))$ **i)** $\exists x \forall y (x \neq y \leftrightarrow I(y))$ **j)** $\forall x (I(x) \rightarrow \exists y (x \neq y \wedge C(x, y)))$

   k) $\exists x (I(x) \wedge \forall y (x \neq y \rightarrow \neg C(x, y)))$ **l)** $\exists x \exists y (x \neq y \wedge \neg C(x, y))$ **m)** $\exists x \forall y\, C(x, y)$

   n) $\exists x \exists y (x \neq y \wedge \forall z \, \neg(C(x, z) \wedge C(y, z)))$ **o)** $\exists x \exists y (x \neq y \wedge \forall z (C(x, z) \vee C(y, z)))$

14. The answers to this exercise are not unique; there are many ways of expressing the same propositions symbolically. Our universe of discourse for persons here consists of people in this class. We need to make up a predicate in each case.

   a) Let $S(x, y)$ mean that person x can speak language y. Then our statement is $\exists x\, S(x, \text{Hindi})$.

   b) Let $P(x, y)$ mean that person x plays sport y. Then our statement is $\forall x \exists y\, P(x, y)$.

   c) Let $V(x, y)$ mean that person x has visited state y. Then our statement is $\exists x (V(x, \text{Alaska}) \wedge \neg V(x, \text{Hawaii}))$.

   d) Let $L(x, y)$ mean that person x has learned programming language y. Then our statement is $\forall x \exists y\, L(x, y)$.

   e) Let $T(x, y)$ mean that person x has taken course y, and let $O(y, z)$ mean that course y is offered by department z. Then our statement is $\exists x \exists z \forall y (O(y, z) \rightarrow T(x, y))$.

   f) Let $G(x, y)$ mean that persons x and y grew up in the same town. Then our statement is $\exists x \exists y (x \neq y \wedge G(x, y) \wedge \forall z (G(x, z) \rightarrow (x = y \vee x = z)))$.

g) Let $C(x, y, z)$ mean that persons x and y have chatted with each other in chat group z. Then our statement is $\forall x \exists y \exists z (x \neq y \wedge C(x, y, z))$.

16. We let $P(s, c, m)$ be the statement that student s has class standing c and is majoring in m. The variable s ranges over students in the class, the variable c ranges over the four class standings, and the variable m ranges over all possible majors.

a) The proposition is $\exists s \exists m P(s, \text{junior}, m)$. It is true from the given information.

b) The proposition is $\forall s \exists c P(s, c, \text{computer science})$. This is false, since there are some mathematics majors.

c) The proposition is $\exists s \exists c \exists m (P(s, c, m) \wedge (c \neq \text{junior}) \wedge (m \neq \text{mathematics}))$. This is true, since there is a sophomore majoring in computer science.

d) The proposition is $\forall s (\exists c P(s, c, \text{computer science}) \vee \exists m P(s, \text{sophomore}, m))$. This is false, since there is a freshman mathematics major.

e) The proposition is $\exists m \forall c \exists s P(s, c, m)$. This is false. It cannot be that m is mathematics, since there is no senior mathematics major, and it cannot be that m is computer science, since there is no freshman computer science major. Nor, of course, can m be any other major.

18. a) $\forall f (H(f) \rightarrow \exists c\, A(c))$, where $A(x)$ means that console x is accessible, and $H(x)$ means that fault condition x is happening

b) $(\forall u \exists m (A(m) \wedge S(u, m))) \rightarrow \forall u\, R(u)$, where $A(x)$ means that the archive contains message x, $S(x, y)$ means that user x sent message y, and $R(x)$ means that the e-mail address of user x can be retrieved

c) $(\forall b \exists m\, D(m, b)) \leftrightarrow \exists p \neg C(p)$, where $D(x, y)$ means that mechanism x can detect breach y, and $C(x)$ means that process x has been compromised

d) $\forall x \forall y (x \neq y \rightarrow \exists p \exists q (p \neq q \wedge C(p, x, y) \wedge C(q, x, y)))$, where $C(p, x, y)$ means that path p connects endpoint x to endpoint y

e) $\forall x ((\forall u\, K(x, u)) \leftrightarrow x = \text{SysAdm})$, where $K(x, y)$ means that person x knows the password of user y

20. a) $\forall x \forall y ((x < 0) \wedge (y < 0) \rightarrow (xy > 0))$ **b)** $\forall x \forall y ((x > 0) \wedge (y > 0) \rightarrow ((x + y)/2 > 0))$

c) What does "necessarily" mean in this context? The best explanation is to assert that a certain universal implication is not true. So we have $\neg \forall x \forall y ((x < 0) \wedge (y < 0) \rightarrow (x - y < 0))$. Note that we do not want to put the negation symbol inside (it is not true that the difference of two negative integers is never negative), nor do we want to negate just the conclusion (it is not true that the sum is always nonnegative). We could rewrite our solution by passing the negation inside, obtaining $\exists x \exists y ((x < 0) \wedge (y < 0) \wedge (x - y \geq 0))$.

d) $\forall x \forall y (|x + y| \leq |x| + |y|)$

22. $\exists x \forall a \forall b \forall c ((x > 0) \wedge x \neq a^2 + b^2 + c^2)$, where the universe of discourse consists of all integers

24. a) There exists an additive identity for the real numbers—a number that when added to every number does not change its value.

b) A nonnegative number minus a negative number is positive.

c) The difference of two nonpositive numbers is not necessarily nonpositive.

d) The product of two numbers is nonzero if and only if both factors are nonzero.

26. a) This is false, since $1 + 1 \neq 1 - 1$.   **b)** This is true, since $2 + 0 = 2 - 0$.

c) This is false, since there are many values of y for which $1 + y \neq 1 - y$.

d) This is false, since the equation $x + 2 = x - 2$ has no solution.

e) This is true, since we can take $x = y = 0$.   **f)** This is true, since we can take $y = 0$ for each x.

g) This is true, since we can take $y = 0$.   **h)** This is false, since part **(d)** was false.

i) This is certainly false.

28. a) true (let $y = x^2$)   **b)** false (no such y exists if x is negative)   **c)** true (let $x = 0$)

d) false (the commutative law for addition always holds)   **e)** true (let $y = 1/x$)

f) false (the reciprocal of y depends on y—there is not one x that works for all y)   **g)** true (let $y = 1 - x$)

h) false (this system of equations is inconsistent)

i) false (this system has only one solution; if $x = 0$, for example, then no y satisfies $y = 2 \wedge -y = 1$)

j) true (let $z = (x + y)/2$)

30. We need to use the transformations shown in Table 2 of Section 1.3, replacing $\neg\forall$ by $\exists\neg$, and replacing $\neg\exists$ by $\forall\neg$. In other words, we push all the negation symbols inside the quantifiers, changing the sense of the quantifiers as we do so, because of the equivalences in Table 2 of Section 1.3. In addition, we need to use De Morgan's laws (Section 1.2) to change the negation of a conjunction to the disjunction of the negations and to change the negation of a disjunction to the conjunction of the negations. We also use the fact that $\neg\neg p \equiv p$.

a) $\forall y \forall x \, \neg P(x, y)$ **b)** $\exists x \forall y \, \neg P(x, y)$ **c)** $\forall y (\neg Q(y) \vee \exists x \, R(x, y))$

d) $\forall y (\forall x \, \neg R(x, y) \wedge \exists x \, \neg S(x, y))$ **e)** $\forall y (\exists x \forall z \, \neg T(x, y, z) \wedge \forall x \exists z \, \neg U(x, y, z))$

32. As we push the negation symbol toward the inside, each quantifier it passes must change its type. For logical connectives we either use De Morgan's laws or recall that $\neg(p \to q) \equiv p \wedge \neg q$ (Table 6 in Section 1.2) and that $\neg(p \leftrightarrow q) \equiv \neg p \leftrightarrow q$ (Exercise 19 in Section 1.2).

a)
$$\neg\exists z \forall y \forall x \, T(x, y, z) \equiv \forall z \neg\forall y \forall x \, T(x, y, z)$$
$$\equiv \forall z \exists y \neg\forall x \, T(x, y, z)$$
$$\equiv \forall z \exists y \exists x \, \neg T(x, y, z)$$

b)
$$\neg(\exists x \exists y \, P(x, y) \wedge \forall x \forall y \, Q(x, y)) \equiv \neg\exists x \exists y \, P(x, y) \vee \neg\forall x \forall y \, Q(x, y)$$
$$\equiv \forall x \neg\exists y \, P(x, y) \vee \exists x \neg\forall y \, Q(x, y)$$
$$\equiv \forall x \forall y \, \neg P(x, y) \vee \exists x \exists y \, \neg Q(x, y)$$

c)
$$\neg\exists x \exists y (Q(x, y) \leftrightarrow Q(y, x)) \equiv \forall x \neg\exists y (Q(x, y) \leftrightarrow Q(y, x))$$
$$\equiv \forall x \forall y \neg(Q(x, y) \leftrightarrow Q(y, x))$$
$$\equiv \forall x \forall y (\neg Q(x, y) \leftrightarrow Q(y, x))$$

d)
$$\neg\forall y \exists x \exists z \, (T(x, y, z) \vee Q(x, y)) \equiv \exists y \neg\exists x \exists z \, (T(x, y, z) \vee Q(x, y))$$
$$\equiv \exists y \forall x \neg\exists z \, (T(x, y, z) \vee Q(x, y))$$
$$\equiv \exists y \forall x \forall z \neg(T(x, y, z) \vee Q(x, y))$$
$$\equiv \exists y \forall x \forall z \, (\neg T(x, y, z) \wedge \neg Q(x, y))$$

34. In each case we need to specify some predicates and identify the universe of discourse.

a) Let $L(x, y)$ mean that person x has lost y dollars playing the lottery. The original statement is then $\neg\exists x \exists y (y > 1000 \wedge L(x, y))$. Its negation of course is $\exists x \exists y (y > 1000 \wedge L(x, y))$; someone has lost more than \$1000 playing the lottery.

b) Let $C(x, y)$ mean that person x has chatted with person y. The given statement is $\exists x \exists y (y \neq x \wedge \forall z (z \neq x \to (z = y \leftrightarrow C(x, z))))$. The negation is therefore $\forall x \forall y (y \neq x \to \exists z (z \neq x \wedge \neg(z = y \leftrightarrow C(x, z))))$. In English, everybody in this class has either chatted with no one else or has chatted with two or more others.

c) Let $E(x, y)$ mean that person x has sent e-mail to person y. The given statement is $\neg\exists x \exists y \exists z (y \neq z \wedge x \neq y \wedge x \neq z \wedge \forall w (w \neq x \to (E(x, w) \leftrightarrow (w = y \vee w = z))))$. The negation is obviously $\exists x \exists y \exists z (y \neq z \wedge x \neq y \wedge x \neq z \wedge \forall w (w \neq x \to (E(x, w) \leftrightarrow (w = y \vee w = z))))$. In English, some student in this class has sent e-mail to exactly two other students in this class.

d) Let $S(x, y)$ mean that student x has solved exercise y. The statement is $\exists x \forall y \, S(x, y)$. The negation is $\forall x \exists y \, \neg S(x, y)$. In English, for every student in this class, there is some exercise that he or she has not solved. (One could also interpret the given statement as asserting that for every exercise, there exists a student—perhaps a different one for each exercise—who has solved it. In that case the order of the quantifiers would be reversed. Word order in English sometimes makes for a little ambiguity.)

e) Let $S(x, y)$ mean that student x has solved exercise y, and let $B(y, z)$ mean that exercise y is in section z of the book. The statement is $\neg \exists x \forall z \exists y (B(y, z) \wedge S(x, y))$. The negation is of course $\exists x \forall z \exists y (B(y, z) \wedge S(x, y))$. In English, some student has solved at least one exercise in every section of this book.

36. a) In English, the negation is "Some student in this class does not like mathematics." With the obvious propositional function, this is $\exists x \neg L(x)$.

b) In English, the negation is "Every student in this class has seen a computer." With the obvious propositional function, this is $\forall x S(x)$.

c) In English, the negation is "For every student in this class, there is a mathematics course that this student has not taken." With the obvious propositional function, this is $\forall x \exists c \neg T(x, c)$.

d) As in Exercise 15f, let $P(z, y)$ be "Room z is in building y," and let $Q(x, z)$ be "Student x has been in room z." Then the original statement is $\exists x \forall y \exists z (P(z, y) \wedge Q(x, z))$. To form the negation, we change all the quantifiers and put the negation on the inside, then apply De Morgan's law. The negation is therefore $\forall x \exists y \forall z (\neg P(z, y) \vee \neg Q(x, z))$, which is also equivalent to $\forall x \exists y \forall z (P(z, y) \rightarrow \neg Q(x, z))$. In English, this could be read, "For every student there is a building such that for every room in that building, the student has not been in that room."

38. a) There are many counterexamples. If $x = 2$, then there is no y among the integers such that $2 = 1/y$, since the only solution of this equation is $y = 1/2$. Even if we were working in the universe of real numbers, $x = 0$ would provide a counterexample, since $0 = 1/y$ for no real number y.

b) We can rewrite $y^2 - x < 100$ as $y^2 < 100 + x$. Since squares can never be negative, no such y exists if x is, say, -200. This x provides a counterexample.

c) This is not true, since sixth powers are both squares and cubes. Trivial counterexamples would include $x = y = 0$ and $x = y = 1$, but we can also take something like $x = 27$ and $y = 9$, since $27^2 = 3^6 = 9^3$.

40. The distributive law is just the statement that $x(y+z) = xy + xz$ for all real numbers. Therefore the expression we want is $\forall x \forall y \forall z \, (x(y + z) = xy + xz)$, where the quantifiers are assumed to range over (i.e., the universe of discourse is) the real numbers.

42. This statement says that there is a number that is less than or equal to all squares.

a) This is false, since no matter how small a positive number x we might choose, if we let $y = \sqrt{x/2}$, then $x = 2y^2$, and it will not be true that $x \leq y^2$.

b) This is true, since we can take $x = -1$, for example.

c) This is true, since we can take $x = -1$, for example.

44. We need to show that each of these propositions implies the other. Suppose that $\forall x P(x) \vee \forall x Q(x)$ is true. We want to show that $\forall x \forall y (P(x) \vee Q(y))$ is true. By our hypothesis, one of two things must be true. Either P is universally true, or Q is universally true. In the first case, $\forall x \forall y (P(x) \vee Q(y))$ is true, since the first expression in the disjunction is true, no matter what x and y are; and in the second case, $\forall x \forall y (P(x) \vee Q(y))$ is also true, since now the second expression in the disjunction is true, no matter what x and y are. Next we need to prove the converse. So suppose that $\forall x \forall y (P(x) \vee Q(y))$ is true. We want to show that $\forall x P(x) \vee \forall x Q(x)$ is true. If $\forall x P(x)$ is true, then we are done. Otherwise, $P(x_0)$ must be false for some x_0 in the domain of discourse. For this x_0, then, the hypothesis tells us that $P(x_0) \vee Q(y)$ is true, no matter what y is. Since

$P(x_0)$ is false, it must be the case that $Q(y)$ is true for each y. In other words, $\forall y Q(y)$ is true, or, to change the name of the meaningless quantified variable, $\forall x Q(x)$ is true. This certainly implies that $\forall x P(x) \lor \forall x Q(x)$ is true, as desired.

46. **a)** By Exercises 43 and 44b in Section 1.3, we can simply bring the existential quantifier outside: $\exists x(P(x) \lor Q(x) \lor A)$.

b) By Exercise 44 the expression inside the parentheses is logically equivalent to $\forall x \forall y(P(x) \lor Q(y))$. Applying the negation operation, we obtain $\exists x \exists y \neg(P(x) \lor Q(y))$.

c) First we rewrite this using Table 6 in Section 1.2 as $\exists x Q(x) \lor \neg \exists x P(x)$, which is equivalent to $\exists x Q(x) \lor \forall x \neg P(x)$. To combine the existential and universal statements we use Exercise 45b, obtaining $\forall x \exists y(\neg P(x) \lor Q(y))$, which is in prenex normal form.

48. We just need to translate the words into symbols. We use $y \in S$ to mean that the number y is a member of the set S. (See Section 1.6.)

a) $\forall y(y \in S \to x \geq y)$ **b)** $\forall y(y \in S \to x \geq y) \land \forall z(\forall w(w \in S \to z \geq w) \to x \leq z)$

50. We just need to translate the words into symbols: $\lim_{n \to \infty} a_n = L$ means $\forall \epsilon \exists N \forall n(n > N \to |a_n - L| < \epsilon)$, where n and N range over positive integers and ϵ ranges over positive real numbers.

52. The sequence $\{a_n\}$ is a Cauchy sequence if $\forall \epsilon \exists N \forall m \forall n((m > N \land n > N) \to |a_m - a_n| < \epsilon)$, where ϵ ranges over positive real numbers and the other three variables range over positive integers.

SECTION 1.5   Methods of Proof

2. **a)** We have taken the conjunction of two propositions and asserted one of them. This is, according to Table 1, simplification.

b) We have taken the disjunction of two propositions and the negation of one of them, and asserted the other. This is, according to Table 1, disjunctive syllogism. See Table 1 for the other parts of this exercise as well.

c) modus ponens   **d)** addition   **e)** hypothetical syllogism

4. Let r be the proposition "It rains," let f be the proposition "It is foggy," let s be the proposition "The sailing race will be held," let l be the proposition "The life saving demonstration will go on," and let t be the proposition "The trophy will be awarded." We are given premises $(\neg r \lor \neg f) \to (s \land l)$, $s \to t$, and $\neg t$. We want to conclude r. We set up the proof in two columns, with reasons, as in Example 6. Note that it is valid to replace subexpressions by other expressions logically equivalent to them.

Step	Reason
1. $\neg t$	Hypothesis
2. $s \to t$	Hypothesis
3. $\neg s$	Modus tollens using Steps 1 and 2
4. $(\neg r \lor \neg f) \to (s \land l)$	Hypothesis
5. $(\neg(s \land l)) \to \neg(\neg r \lor \neg f)$	Contrapositive of Step 4
6. $(\neg s \lor \neg l) \to (r \land f)$	De Morgan's law and double negative
7. $\neg s \lor \neg l$	Addition, using Step 3
8. $r \land f$	Modus ponens using Steps 6 and 7
9. r	Simplification using Step 8

6. First we use universal instantiation to conclude from "For all x, if x is a man, then x is not an island" the special case of interest, "If Manhattan is a man, then Manhattan is not an island." Then we form the contrapositive (using also double negative): "If Manhattan is an island, then Manhattan is not a man." Finally we use modus ponens to conclude that Manhattan is not a man. Alternatively, we could apply modus tollens.

8. a) If we use modus tollens starting from the back, then we conclude that I am not sore. Another application of modus tollens then tells us that I did not play hockey.

b) We really can't conclude anything specific here.

c) By universal instantiation, we conclude from the first implication by modus ponens that dragonflies have six legs, and we conclude by modus tollens that spiders are not insects. We could say using existential generalization that, for example, there exists a non-six-legged creature that eats a six-legged creature, and that there exists a non-insect that eats an insect.

d) We can apply universal instantiation to the implication and conclude that if Homer (respectively, Maggie) is a student, then he (she) has an Internet account. Now modus tollens tells us that Homer is not a student. There are no conclusions to be drawn about Maggie.

e) The first implication is that if x is healthy to eat, then x does not taste good. Universal instantiation and modus ponens therefore tell us that tofu does not taste good. The third sentence says that if you eat x, then x tastes good. Therefore the fourth hypothesis already follows (by modus tollens) from the first three. No conclusions can be drawn about cheeseburgers from these statements.

f) By disjunctive syllogism, the first two hypotheses allow us to conclude that I am hallucinating. Therefore by modus ponens we know that I see elephants running down the road.

10. In each case we set up the proof in two columns, with reasons, as in Example 6.

a) Let $c(x)$ be "x is in this class," let $r(x)$ be "x owns a red convertible," and let $t(x)$ be "x has gotten a speeding ticket." We are given premises $c(\text{Linda})$, $r(\text{Linda})$, $\forall x(r(x) \rightarrow t(x))$, and we want to conclude $\exists x(c(x) \land t(x))$.

Step	Reason
1. $\forall x(r(x) \rightarrow t(x))$	Hypothesis
2. $r(\text{Linda}) \rightarrow t(\text{Linda})$	Universal instantiation using Step 1
3. $r(\text{Linda})$	Hypothesis
4. $t(\text{Linda})$	Modus ponens using Steps 2 and 3
5. $c(\text{Linda})$	Hypothesis
6. $c(\text{Linda}) \land t(\text{Linda})$	Conjunction using Steps 4 and 5
7. $\exists x(c(x) \land t(x))$	Existential generalization using Step 6

b) Let $r(x)$ be "r is one of the five roommates listed," let $d(x)$ be "x has taken a course in discrete mathematics," and let $a(x)$ be "x can take a course in algorithms." We are given premises $\forall x(r(x) \rightarrow d(x))$ and $\forall x(d(x) \rightarrow a(x))$, and we want to conclude $\forall x(r(x) \rightarrow a(x))$. In what follows y represents an arbitrary person.

Step	Reason
1. $\forall x(r(x) \rightarrow d(x))$	Hypothesis
2. $r(y) \rightarrow d(y)$	Universal instantiation using Step 1
3. $\forall x(d(x) \rightarrow a(x))$	Hypothesis
4. $d(y) \rightarrow a(y)$	Universal instantiation using Step 3
5. $r(y) \rightarrow a(y)$	Hypothetical syllogism using Steps 2 and 4
6. $\forall x(r(x) \rightarrow a(x))$	Universal generalization using Step 5

c) Let $s(x)$ be "x is a movie produced by Sayles," let $c(x)$ be "x is a movie about coal miners," and let $w(x)$ be "movie x is wonderful." We are given premises $\forall x(s(x) \rightarrow w(x))$ and $\exists x(s(x) \land c(x))$, and we want to conclude $\exists x(c(x) \wedge w(x))$. In our proof, y represents an unspecified particular movie.

Step	Reason
1. $\exists x(s(x) \wedge c(x))$	Hypothesis
2. $s(y) \wedge c(y)$	Existential instantiation using Step 1
3. $s(y)$	Simplification using Step 2
4. $\forall x(s(x) \rightarrow w(x))$	Hypothesis
5. $s(y) \rightarrow w(y)$	Universal instantiation using Step 4
6. $w(y)$	Modus ponens using Steps 3 and 5
7. $c(y)$	Simplification using Step 2
8. $w(y) \wedge c(y)$	Conjunction using Steps 6 and 7
9. $\exists x(c(x) \wedge w(x))$	Existential generalization using Step 8

d) Let $c(x)$ be "x is in this class," let $f(x)$ be "x has been to France," and let $l(x)$ be "x has visited the Louvre." We are given premises $\exists x(c(x) \wedge f(x))$, $\forall x(f(x) \rightarrow l(x))$, and we want to conclude $\exists x(c(x) \wedge l(x))$. In our proof, y represents an unspecified particular person.

Step	Reason
1. $\exists x(c(x) \wedge f(x))$	Hypothesis
2. $c(y) \wedge f(y)$	Existential instantiation using Step 1
3. $f(y)$	Simplification using Step 2
4. $c(y)$	Simplification using Step 2
5. $\forall x(f(x) \rightarrow l(x))$	Hypothesis
6. $f(y) \rightarrow l(y)$	Universal instantiation using Step 5
7. $l(y)$	Modus ponens using Steps 3 and 6
8. $c(y) \wedge l(y)$	Conjunction using Steps 4 and 7
9. $\exists x(c(x) \wedge l(x))$	Existential generalization using Step 8

12. a) This is correct, using universal instantiation and modus tollens.

   b) This is not correct. After applying universal instantiation, it contains the fallacy of denying the hypothesis.

   c) After applying universal instantiation, it contains the fallacy of affirming the conclusion.

   d) This is correct, using universal instantiation and modus ponens.

14. a) This is not valid, because the converse of an implication does not follow from the implication (it's the fallacy of affirming the conclusion).

   b) This argument is valid, using universal instantiation and modus ponens.

16. We know that *some* s exists that makes $S(s, \text{Max})$ true, but we cannot conclude that Max is one such s. Therefore this first step is invalid.

18. We need to prove the proposition "If 1 is a positive integer, then $1^2 \geq 1$." The conclusion is the true statement $1 \geq 1$. Therefore the implication is true. This is an example of a trivial proof, since we merely showed that the conclusion was true.

20. We need to prove the following assertion for an arbitrary integer n: "If n is even, then n^2 is even." In each case, we will use the fact that being an even number means being 2 times some integer.

   a) Suppose that n is even. Then $n = 2k$ for some integer k. Therefore $n^2 = (2k)^2 = 4k^2 = 2(2k^2)$. Since we have written n^2 as 2 times an integer, we conclude that n^2 is even.

   b) Suppose that n^2 is not even. In other words, suppose that n^2 is odd. By the theorem proved in Example 19, we conclude that n is odd, hence not even. Since we have proved that the hypothesis is false under the assumption that the conclusion is false, we have given an indirect proof of the implication. (This is really a cheat, of course, since the proof in Example 19 was an indirect proof, based on the direct implication we proved in part (**a**).)

c) Assume that n is even but n^2 is odd. By the theorem proved in Example 19, this latter assumption implies that n is odd. This contradicts our assumption that n is even. Since we have derived a contradiction, the theorem is proved. (The same comment applies as in part (**b**).)

22. a) We must prove the contrapositive: If n is odd, then $3n + 2$ is odd. Assume that n is odd. Then we can write $n = 2k + 1$ for some integer k. Then $3n + 2 = 3(2k + 1) + 2 = 6k + 5 = 2(3k + 2) + 1$. Thus $3n + 2$ is two times some integer plus 1, so it is odd.

b) Suppose that $3n + 2$ is even and that n is odd. Since $3n + 2$ is even, so is $3n$. If we add subtract an odd number from an even number, we get an odd number, so $3n - n = 2n$ is odd. But this is obviously not true. Therefore our supposition was wrong, and the proof by contradiction is complete.

24. An odd number is one of the form $2n + 1$, where n is an integer. We are given two odd numbers, say $2a + 1$ and $2b + 1$. Their product is $(2a + 1)(2b + 1) = 4ab + 2a + 2b + 1 = 2(2ab + a + b) + 1$. This last expression shows that the product is odd, since it is of the form $2n + 1$, with $n = 2ab + a + b$.

26. A rational number is a number that can be written in the form x/y where x and y are integers and $y \neq 0$. Suppose that we have two rational numbers, say a/b and c/d. Then their product is, by the usual rules for multiplication of fractions, $(ac)/(bd)$. Note that both the numerator and the denominator are integers, and that $bd \neq 0$ since b and d were both nonzero. Therefore the product is, by definition, a rational number.

28. This is true. Suppose that a/b is a nonzero rational number and that x is an irrational number. We must prove that the product xa/b is also irrational. We give a proof by contradiction. Suppose that xa/b were rational. Since $a/b \neq 0$, we know that $a \neq 0$, so b/a is also a rational number. Let us multiply this rational number b/a by the assumed rational number xa/b. By Exercise 26, the product is rational. But the product is $(b/a)(xa/b) = x$, which is irrational by hypothesis. This is a contradiction, so in fact xa/b must be irrational, as desired.

30. If x is rational and not zero, then by definition we can write $x = p/q$, where p and q are nonzero integers. Since $1/x$ is then q/p and $p \neq 0$, we can conclude that $1/x$ is rational.

32. We give a proof by contradiction. If there were at most two days falling in the same month, then we could have at most $2 \cdot 12 = 24$ days, since there are 12 months. Since we have chosen 25 days, at least three of them must fall in the same month.

34. There are three main cases, depending on which of the three numbers is smallest. If a is smallest (or tied for smallest), then clearly $a \leq \min(b, c)$, and so the left-hand side equals a. On the other hand, for the right-hand side we have $\min(a, c) = a$ as well. In the second case, b is smallest (or tied for smallest). The same reasoning shows us that the right-hand side equals b; and the left-hand side is $\min(a, b) = b$ as well. In the final case, in which c is smallest (or tied for smallest), the left-hand side is $\min(a, c) = c$, whereas the right-hand side is clearly also c. Since one of the three has to be smallest we have taken care of all the cases.

36. Without loss of generality we can assume that n is nonnegative, since the square of an integer and the square of its negative are the same. Following the hint, we divide an arbitrary positive integer n by 10, obtaining a quotient k and remainder l, whence $n = 10k + l$, and l is an integer between 0 and 9, inclusive. Then we compute n^2 in each of these ten cases. We get the following values.

$$(10k + 0)^2 = 100k^2 = 100k^2 + 0$$
$$(10k + 1)^2 = 100k^2 + 20k + 1$$
$$(10k + 2)^2 = 100k^2 + 40k + 4$$
$$(10k + 3)^2 = 100k^2 + 60k + 9$$
$$(10k + 4)^2 = 100k^2 + 80k + 16$$
$$(10k + 5)^2 = 100k^2 + 100k + 25$$
$$(10k + 6)^2 = 100k^2 + 120k + 36$$
$$(10k + 7)^2 = 100k^2 + 140k + 49$$
$$(10k + 8)^2 = 100k^2 + 160k + 64$$
$$(10k + 9)^2 = 100k^2 + 180k + 81$$

Since each coefficient of k^2 and of k is a multiple of 10, the corresponding term has no effect on the ones digit of the answer. Therefore the ones digits are 0, 1, 4, 9, 6, 5, 6, 9, 4, 1, respectively, so it is always a 0, 1, 4, 5, 6, or 9.

38. We need to prove two things, since this is an "if and only if" statement. First let us prove directly that if n is even then $7n + 4$ is even. Since n is even, it can be written as $2k$ for some integer k. Then $7n + 4 = 14k + 4 = 2(7k + 2)$. This is 2 times an integer, so it is even, as desired. Next we give an indirect proof that if $7n + 4$ is even then n is even. So suppose that n is not even, i.e., that n is odd. Then n can be written as $2k + 1$ for some integer k. Thus $7n + 4 = 14k + 11 = 2(7k + 5) + 1$. This is 1 more than 2 times an integer, so it is odd. That completes the indirect proof.

40. There are two things to prove. For the "if" part, there are two cases. If $m = n$, then of course $m^2 = n^2$; if $m = -n$, then $m^2 = (-n)^2 = (-1)^2 n^2 = n^2$. For the "only if" part, we suppose that $m^2 = n^2$. Putting everything on the left and factoring, we have $(m + n)(m - n) = 0$. Now the only way that a product of two numbers can be zero is if one of them is zero. Therefore we conclude that either $m + n = 0$ (in which case $m = -n$), or else $m - n = 0$ (in which case $m = n$), and our proof is complete.

42. We write these in symbols: $a < b$, $(a + b)/2 > a$, and $(a + b)/2 < b$. The latter two are equivalent to $a + b > 2a$ and $a + b < 2b$, respectively, and these are in turn equivalent to $b > a$ and $a < b$, respectively. It is now clear that all three statements are equivalent.

44. We give direct proofs that (i) implies (ii), that (ii) implies (iii), and that (iii) implies (i). That will suffice. For the first, suppose that $x = p/q$ where p and q are integers with $q \neq 0$. Then $x/2 = p/(2q)$, and this is rational, since p and $2q$ are integers with $2q \neq 0$. For the second, suppose that $x/2 = p/q$ where p and q are integers with $q \neq 0$. Then $x = (2p)/q$, so $3x - 1 = (6p)/q - 1 = (6p - q)/q$ and this is rational, since $6p - q$ and q are integers with $q \neq 0$. For the last, suppose that $3x - 1 = p/q$ where p and q are integers with $q \neq 0$. Then $x = (p/q + 1)/3 = (p + q)/(3q)$, and this is rational, since $p + q$ and $3q$ are integers with $3q \neq 0$.

46. No. This line of reasoning shows that *if* $\sqrt{2x^2 - 1} = x$, then we must have $x = 1$ or $x = -1$. These are therefore the only possible solutions, but we have no guarantee that they *are* solutions, since not all of our steps were reversible (in particular, squaring both sides). Therefore we *must* substitute these values back into the original equation to determine whether they do indeed satisfy it.

48. The number 1 has this property, since the only positive integer not exceeding 1 is 1 itself, and therefore the sum is 1. This is a constructive proof.

50. The only perfect squares that differ by 1 are 0 and 1. Therefore these two consecutive integers cannot both be perfect squares. This is a nonconstructive proof—we do not know which of them meets the requirement. (In fact, a computer algebra system will tell us that neither of them is a perfect square.)

52. Of these three numbers, at least two must have the same sign (both positive or both negative), since there are only two signs. (It is conceivable that some of them are zero, but we view zero as positive for the purposes of this problem.) The product of two with the same sign is nonnegative. This was a nonconstructive proof, since we have not identified which product is nonnegative. (In fact, a computer algebra system will tell us that all three are positive, so all three products are positive.)

54. We know from algebra that the following equations are equivalent: $ax + b = c$, $ax = c - b$. $x = (c - b)/a$. This shows, constructively, what the unique solution of the given equation is.

56. Given r, let a be the closest integer to r less than r, and let b be the closest integer to r greater than r. In the notation introduced in Section 1.8, $a = \lfloor r \rfloor$ and $b = \lceil r \rceil$. In fact, $b = a + 1$. Clearly the distance between r and any integer other than a or b is greater than 1 so cannot be less than $1/2$. Furthermore, since r is irrational, it cannot be exactly half-way between a and b, so exactly one of $r - a < 1/2$ and $b - r < 1/2$ holds.

58. Given x, let n be the greatest integer less than or equal to x, and let $\epsilon = x - n$. In the notation introduced in Section 1.8, $n = \lfloor x \rfloor$. Clearly $0 \le \epsilon < 1$, and ϵ is unique for this n. Any other choice of n would cause the required ϵ to be less than 0 or greater than or equal to 1, so n is unique as well.

60. Let a be "Allen is a good boy"; let h be "Hillary is a good girl"; let d be "David is happy." Then our assumptions are $\neg a \lor h$ and $a \lor d$. Using resolution gives us $h \lor d$, as desired.

62. We apply resolution to give the tautology $(p \lor \mathbf{F}) \land (\neg p \lor \mathbf{F}) \to (\mathbf{F} \lor \mathbf{F})$. The left-hand side is equivalent to $p \land \neg p$, since $p \lor \mathbf{F}$ is equivalent to p, and $\neg p \lor \mathbf{F}$ is equivalent to $\neg p$. The right-hand side is equivalent to $\mathbf{F}$. Since the implication is true, and the conclusion is false, it follows that the hypothesis, $p \land \neg p$, is false, as desired.

64. An assertion like this one is implicitly universally quantified—it means that *for all* rational numbers a and b, a^b is rational. To disprove such a statement it suffices to provide one counterexample. Take $a = 2$ and $b = 1/2$. Then $a^b = 2^{1/2} = \sqrt{2}$, and we know from Example 21 that $\sqrt{2}$ is not rational.

66. The only implications not shown directly are $p_1 \leftrightarrow p_2$, $p_2 \leftrightarrow p_4$, and $p_3 \leftrightarrow p_4$. But these each follow with one or more intermediate steps: $p_1 \leftrightarrow p_2$, since $p_1 \leftrightarrow p_3$ and $p_3 \leftrightarrow p_2$; $p_2 \leftrightarrow p_4$, since $p_2 \leftrightarrow p_1$ (just established) and $p_1 \leftrightarrow p_4$; and $p_3 \leftrightarrow p_4$, since $p_3 \leftrightarrow p_1$ and $p_1 \leftrightarrow p_4$.

68. One way to prove an existential assertion is to exhibit the item whose existence is being asserted. Such a constructive proof is easy here. We simply lay four dominos end-to-end to form a row of length eight squares, and then use eight of these rows to cover the board. It is not hard to see that this construction generalizes to any $m \times n$ board as long as at least one of m and n is even. If m and n are both odd, then the board contains an odd number of squares (since mn is odd), and so cannot be covered with pieces covering two squares each.

70. Let us use the following letters to stand for the relevant propositions: d for "logic is difficult"; s for "many students like logic"; and e for "mathematics is easy." Then the assumptions are $d \lor \neg s$ and $e \to \neg d$. Note that the first of these is equivalent to $s \to d$, since both forms are false if and only if s is true and d is false.

In addition, let us note that the second assumption is equivalent to its contrapositive, $d \to \neg e$. And finally, by combining these two implications, we see that $s \to \neg e$ also follows from our assumptions.

a) Here we are asked whether we can conclude that $s \to \neg e$. As we noted above, the answer is yes, this conclusion is valid.

b) The question concerns $\neg e \to \neg s$. This is equivalent to its contrapositive, $s \to e$. That doesn't seem to follow from our assumptions, so let's find a case in which the assumptions hold but this implication does not. This implication fails in the case in which s is true and e is false. If we take d to be true as well, then both of our assumptions are true. Therefore this conclusion is not valid.

c) The issue is $\neg e \lor d$, which is equivalent to the implication $e \to d$. This does *not* follow from our assumptions. If we take d to be false, e to be true, and s to be false, then this proposition is false but our assumptions are true.

d) The issue is $\neg d \lor \neg e$, which is equivalent to the implication $d \to \neg e$. We noted above that this validly follows from our assumptions.

e) This sentence says $\neg s \to (\neg e \lor \neg d)$. The only case in which this is false is when s is false and both e and d are true. But in this case, our assumption $e \to \neg d$ is also violated. Therefore, in all cases in which the assumptions hold, this statement holds as well, so it *is* a valid conclusion.

72. Suppose that we look at the ten groups of integers in three consecutive locations around the circle (first-second-third, second-third-fourth, ..., eighth-ninth-tenth, ninth-tenth-first, and tenth-first-second). Since each number from 1 to 10 gets used three times in these groups, the sum of the sums of the ten groups must equal three times the sum of the numbers from 1 to 10, namely $3 \cdot 55 = 165$. Therefore the average sum is $165/10 = 16.5$. By Exercise 71, at least one of the sums must be greater than or equal to 16.5, and since the sums are whole numbers, this means that at least one of the sums must be greater than or equal to 17.

74. We show that each of these is equivalent to the statement (v) n is odd, say $n = 2k+1$. Example 14 showed that (v) implies (i), and Example 19 showed that (i) implies (v). For (v) $\to$ (ii) we see that $1 - n = 1 - (2k+1) = 2(-k)$ is even. Conversely, if n were even, say $n = 2m$, then we would have $1 - n = 1 - 2m = 2(-m) + 1$, so $1 - n$ would be odd, and this completes the indirect proof that (ii) $\to$ (v). For (v) $\to$ (iii), we see that $n^3 = (2k+1)^3 = 8k^3 + 12k^2 + 6k + 1 = 2(4k^3 + 6k^2 + 3k) + 1$ is odd. Conversely, if n were even, say $n = 2m$, then we would have $n^3 = 2(4m^3)$, so n^3 would be even, and this completes the indirect proof that (iii) $\to$ (v). Finally, for (v) $\to$ (iv), we see that $n^2 + 1 = (2k+1)^2 + 1 = 4k^2 + 4k + 2 = 2(2k^2 + 2k + 1)$ is even. Conversely, if n were even, say $n = 2m$, then we would have $n^2 + 1 = 2(2m^2) + 1$, so $n^2 + 1$ would be odd, and this completes the indirect proof that (iv) $\to$ (v).

76. We will give an argument establishing the conclusion. We want to show that all hummingbirds are small. Let Tweety be an arbitrary hummingbird. We must show that Tweety is small. The first premise implies that if Tweety is a hummingbird, then Tweety is richly colored. Therefore by modus ponens we can conclude that Tweety is richly colored. The third premise implies that if Tweety does not live on honey, then Tweety is not richly colored. Therefore by modus tollens we can now conclude that Tweety does live on honey. Finally, the second premise implies that if Tweety is a large bird, then Tweety does not live on honey. Therefore again by modus tollens we can now conclude that Tweety is not a large bird, i.e., that Tweety is small, as desired.

SECTION 1.6   Sets

2. There are of course an infinite number of correct answers.

   a) $\{\, 3n \mid n = 0, 1, 2, 3, 4 \,\}$ or $\{\, x \mid x$ is a multiple of $3 \wedge 0 \le x \le 12 \,\}$.

   b) $\{\, x \mid -3 \le x \le 3 \,\}$, where we are assuming that the universe of discourse is the set of integers.

   c) $\{\, x \mid x$ is a letter of the word *monopoly* other than l or $y \,\}$.

4. Each of the sets is a subset of itself. Aside from that, the only relations are $B \subseteq A$ and $C \subseteq D$.

6. **a)** Since the set contains only integers and $\{2\}$ is a set, not an integer, $\{2\}$ is not an element.

   b) Since the set contains only integers and $\{2\}$ is a set, not an integer, $\{2\}$ is not an element.

   c) The set has two elements. One of them is patently $\{2\}$.

   d) The set has two elements. One of them is patently $\{2\}$.

   e) The set has two elements. One of them is patently $\{2\}$.

   f) The set has only one element, $\{\{2\}\}$; since this is not the same as $\{2\}$ (the former is a set containing a set, whereas the latter is a set containing a number), $\{2\}$ is not an element of $\{\{\{2\}\}\}$.

8. **a)** true   **b)** true   **c)** false—see part **(a)**   **d)** true

   e) true—the one element in the set on the left is an element of the set on the right, and the sets are not equal

   f) true—similar to part **(e)**   **g)** false—the two sets are equal

10. We put the subsets inside the supersets. Thus the answer is as shown.

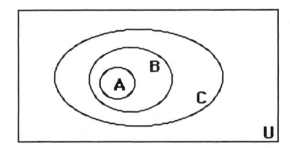

12. Since the empty set is a subset of every set, we just need to take a set B that contains $\emptyset$ as an element. Thus we can let $A = \emptyset$ and $B = \{\emptyset\}$ as the simplest example.

14. The cardinality of a set is the number of elements it has.

   a) The empty set has no elements, so its cardinality is 0.

   b) This set has one element (the empty set), so its cardinality is 1.

   c) This set has two elements, so its cardinality is 2.

   d) This set has three elements, so its cardinality is 3.

16. The union of all the sets in the power set of a set X must be exactly X. In other words, we can recover X from its power set, uniquely. Therefore the answer is yes.

18. **a)** The power set of every set includes at least the empty set, so the power set cannot be empty. Thus $\emptyset$ is not the power set of any set.

   b) This is the power set of $\{a\}$.

   c) This set has three elements. Since 3 is not a power of 2, this set cannot be the power set of any set.

   d) This is the power set of $\{a, b\}$.

20. By definition it is the set of all ordered pairs (c, p) such that c is a course and p is a professor.

22. We can conclude that $A = \emptyset$ or $B = \emptyset$. To prove this, suppose that neither A nor B were empty. Then there would be elements $a \in A$ and $b \in B$. This would give at last one element, namely (a, b), in $A \times B$, so $A \times B$ would not be the empty set. This contradiction shows that either A or B (or both, it goes without saying) is empty.

24. In each case the answer is a set of 3-tuples.

    a) $\{(a, x, 0), (a, x, 1), (a, y, 0), (a, y, 1), (b, x, 0), (b, x, 1), (b, y, 0), (b, y, 1), (c, x, 0), (c, x, 1), (c, y, 0), (c, y, 1)\}$

    b) $\{(0, x, a), (0, x, b), (0, x, c), (0, y, a), (0, y, b), (0, y, c), (1, x, a), (1, x, b), (1, x, c), (1, y, a), (1, y, b), (1, y, c)\}$

    c) $\{(0, a, x), (0, a, y), (0, b, x), (0, b, y), (0, c, x), (0, c, y), (1, a, x), (1, a, y), (1, b, x), (1, b, y), (1, c, x), (1, c, y)\}$

    d) $\{(x, x, x), (x, x, y), (x, y, x), (x, y, y), (y, x, x), (y, x, y), (y, y, x), (y, y, y)\}$

26. Suppose $A \neq B$ and neither A nor B is empty. We must prove that $A \times B \neq B \times A$. Since $A \neq B$, either we can find an element x that is in A but not B, or vice versa. The two cases are similar, so without loss of generality, let us assume that x is in A but not B. Also, since B is not empty, there is some element $y \in B$. Then (x, y) is in $A \times B$ by definition, but it is not in $B \times A$ since $x \notin B$. Therefore $A \times B \neq B \times A$.

28. **a)** There is a real number whose cube is -1. This is true, since $x = -1$ is a solution.

    b) There is an integer such that the number obtained by adding 1 to it is greater than the integer. This is true—in fact, every integer satisfies this statement.

    c) For every integer, the number obtained by subtracting 1 is again an integer. This is true.

    d) The square of every integer is an integer. This is true.

30. **a)** If $S \in S$, then by the defining condition for S we conclude that $S \notin S$, a contradiction.

    b) If $S \notin S$, then by the defining condition for S we conclude that it is not the case that $S \notin S$ (otherwise S would be an element of S), again a contradiction.

SECTION 1.7   Set Operations

2. **a)** $A \cap B$ **b)** $A \cap \overline{B}$, which is the same as $A - B$ **c)** $A \cup B$ **d)** $\overline{A} \cup \overline{B}$

4. Note that $A \subseteq B$.

    a) $\{a, b, c, d, e, f, g, h\} = B$ **b)** $\{a, b, c, d, e\} = A$

    c) There are no elements in A that are not in B, so the answer is $\emptyset$.   **d)** $\{f, g, h\}$

6. **a)** $A \cup \emptyset = \{x \mid x \in A \vee x \in \emptyset\} = \{x \mid x \in A \vee \mathbf{F}\} = \{x \mid x \in A\} = A$

    b) $A \cap \emptyset = \{x \mid x \in A \wedge x \in \emptyset\} = \{x \mid x \in A \wedge \mathbf{F}\} = \{x \mid \mathbf{F}\} = \emptyset$

    c) $A \cup A = \{x \mid x \in A \vee x \in A\} = \{x \mid x \in A\} = A$

    d) $A \cap A = \{x \mid x \in A \wedge x \in A\} = \{x \mid x \in A\} = A$

    e) $A - \emptyset = \{x \mid x \in A \wedge x \notin \emptyset\} = \{x \mid x \in A \wedge \mathbf{T}\} = \{x \mid x \in A\} = A$

    f) $A \cup U = \{x \mid x \in A \vee x \in U\} = \{x \mid x \in A \vee \mathbf{T}\} = \{x \mid \mathbf{T}\} = U$

    g) $A \cap U = \{x \mid x \in A \wedge x \in U\} = \{x \mid x \in A \wedge \mathbf{T}\} = \{x \mid x \in A\} = A$

    h) $\emptyset - A = \{x \mid x \in \emptyset \wedge x \notin A\} = \{x \mid \mathbf{F} \wedge x \notin A\} = \{x \mid \mathbf{F}\} = \emptyset$

8. We will show that these two sets are equal by showing that each is a subset of the other. Suppose $x \in A \cup (A \cap B)$. Then $x \in A$ or $x \in A \cap B$ by the definition of union. In the former case, we have $x \in A$, and in the latter case we have $x \in A$ and $x \in B$ by the definition of intersection; thus in any event, $x \in A$, so we have proved that the left-hand side is a subset of the right-hand side. Conversely, let $x \in A$. Then by the definition of union, $x \in A \cup (A \cap B)$ as well. Thus we have shown that the right-hand side is a subset of the left-hand side.

10. Since $A = (A - B) \cup (A \cap B)$, we conclude that $A = \{1, 5, 7, 8\} \cup \{3, 6, 9\} = \{1, 3, 5, 6, 7, 8, 9\}$. Similarly $B = (B - A) \cup (A \cap B) = \{2, 10\} \cup \{3, 6, 9\} = \{2, 3, 6, 9, 10\}$.

12. **a)** If x is in $A \cap B$, then perforce it is in A (by definition of intersection).
    b) If x is in A, then perforce it is in $A \cup B$ (by definition of union).
    c) If x is in $A - B$, then perforce it is in A (by definition of difference).
    d) If $x \in A$ then $x \notin B - A$. Therefore there can be no elements in $A \cap (B - A)$, so $A \cap (B - A) = \emptyset$.
    e) The left-hand side consists precisely of those things that are either elements of A or else elements of B but not A, in other words, things that are elements of either A or B (or, of course, both). This is precisely the definition of the right-hand side.

14. **a)** Suppose that $x \in A \cup B$. Then either $x \in A$ or $x \in B$. In either case, certainly $x \in A \cup B \cup C$. This establishes the desired inclusion.
    b) Suppose that $x \in A \cap B \cap C$. Then x is in all three of these sets. In particular, it is in both A and B and therefore in $A \cap B$, as desired.
    c) Suppose that $x \in (A - B) - C$. Then x is in $A - B$ but not in C. Since $x \in A - B$, we know that $x \in A$ (we also know that $x \notin B$, but that won't be used here). Since we have established that $x \in A$ but $x \notin C$, we have proved that $x \in A - C$.
    d) To show that the set given on the left-hand side is empty, it suffices to assume that x is some element in that set and derive a contradiction, thereby showing that no such x exists. So suppose that $x \in (A - C) \cap (C - B)$. Then $x \in A - C$ and $x \in C - B$. The first of these statements implies by definition that $x \notin C$, while the second implies that $x \in C$. This is impossible, so our proof by contradiction is complete.
    e) To establish the equality, we need to prove inclusion in both directions. To prove that $(B - A) \cup (C - A) \subseteq (B \cup C) - A$, suppose that $x \in (B - A) \cup (C - A)$. Then either $x \in (B - A)$ or $x \in (C - A)$. Without loss of generality, assume the former (the proof in the latter case is exactly parallel.) Then $x \in B$ and $x \notin A$. From the first of these assertions, it follows that $x \in B \cup C$. Thus we can conclude that $x \in (B \cup C) - A$, as desired. For the converse, that is, to show that $(B \cup C) - A \subseteq (B - A) \cup (C - A)$, suppose that $x \in (B \cup C) - A$. This means that $x \in (B \cup C)$ and $x \notin A$. The first of these assertions tells us that either $x \in B$ or $x \in C$. Thus either $x \in B - A$ or $x \in C - A$. In either case, $x \in (B - A) \cup (C - A)$. (An alternative proof could be given by using Venn diagrams, showing that both sides represent the same region.)

16. That $A \subseteq (A \cap B) \cup (A \cap \overline{B})$ follows from the fact that every element $x \in A$ is an element of either $A \cap B$ (if $x \in B$) or $A \cap \overline{B}$ (if $x \notin B$). On the other hand, if $x \in (A \cap B) \cup (A \cap \overline{B})$, then either $x \in A \cap B$ or $x \in A \cap \overline{B}$. In either case, $x \in A$ by the definition of intersection.

18. First suppose x is in the left-hand side. Then x must be in A but in neither B nor C. Thus $x \in A - C$, but $x \notin B - C$, so x is in the right-hand side. Next suppose that x is in the right-hand side. Thus x must be in $A - C$ and not in $B - C$. The first of these implies that $x \in A$ and $x \notin C$. But now it must also be the case that $x \notin B$, since otherwise we would have $x \in B - C$. Thus we have shown that x is in A but in neither B nor C, which implies that x is in the left-hand side.

20. The set is shaded in each case.

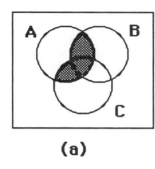 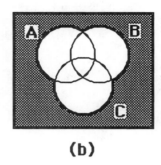 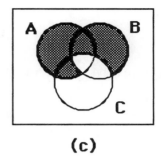

(a)   **(b)**   **(c)**

22. a) We cannot conclude that $A = B$. For instance, if A and B are both subsets of C, then this equation will always hold, and A need not equal B.

b) We cannot conclude that $A = B$; let $C = \emptyset$, for example.

24. This is the set of elements in exactly one of these sets, namely $\{2,5\}$.

26. The figure is as shown; we shade that portion of A that is not in B and that portion of B that is not in A.

28. There are precisely two ways that an item can be in either A or B but not both. It can be in A but not B (which is equivalent to saying that it is in $A - B$), or it can be in B but not A (which is equivalent to saying that it is in $B - A$). Thus an element is in $A \oplus B$ if and only if it is in $(A - B) \cup (B - A)$.

30. a) This is clear from the symmetry (between A and B) in the definition of symmetric difference.

b) We prove two things. To show that $A \subseteq (A \oplus B) \oplus B$, suppose $x \in A$. If $x \in B$, then $x \notin A \oplus B$, so x is an element of the right-hand side. On the other hand if $x \notin B$, then $x \in A \oplus B$, so again x is in the right-hand side. Conversely, suppose x is an element of the right-hand side. There are two cases. If $x \notin B$, then necessarily $x \in A \oplus B$, whence $x \in A$. If $x \in B$, then necessarily $x \notin A \oplus B$, and the only way for that to happen (since $x \in B$) is for x to be in A.

32. This is an identity; each side consists of those things that are in an odd number of the sets A, B, and C.

34. This is an identity; each side consists of those things that are in an odd number of the sets A, B, C, and D.

36. To count the elements of $A \cup B \cup C$ we proceed as follows. First we count the elements in each of the sets and add. This certainly gives us all the elements in the union, but we have overcounted. Each element in $A \cap B$, $A \cap C$, and $B \cap C$ has been counted twice. Therefore we subtract the cardinalities of these intersections to make up for the overcount. Finally, we have compensated a bit too much, since the elements of $A \cap B \cap C$ have now been counted three times and subtracted three times. We adjust by adding back the cardinality of $A \cap B \cap C$.

38. We note that these sets are increasing, that is, $A_1 \subseteq A_2 \subseteq A_3 \subseteq \cdots$. Therefore, the union of any collection of these sets is just the one with the largest subscript, and the intersection is just the one with the smallest subscript.

    a) $A_n = \{\ldots, -2, -1, 0, 1, \ldots, n\}$ **b)** $A_1 = \{\ldots, -2, -1, 0, 1\}$

40. a) 00 1110 0000   **b)** 10 1001 0001   **c)** 01 1100 1110

42. a) No elements are included, so this is the empty set.

    b) All elements are included, so this is the universal set.

44. The bit string for the symmetric difference is obtained by taking the bitwise exclusive *OR* of the two bit strings for the two sets, since we want to include those elements that are in one set or the other but not both.

46. We can take the bitwise *OR* (for union) or *AND* (for intersection) of all the bit strings for these sets.

48. The successor set has one more element than the original set, namely the original set itself. Therefore the answer is $n + 1$.

50. a) If the departments share the equipment, then the maximum number of each type is all that is required, so we want to take the union of the multisets, $A \cup B$.

    b) Both departments will use the minimum number of each type, so we want to take the intersection of the multisets, $A \cap B$.

    c) This will be the difference $B - A$ of the multisets.

    d) If no sharing is allowed, then the university needs to purchase a quantity of each type of equipment that is the sum of the quantities used by the departments; this is the sum of the multisets, $A + B$.

52. Taking the maximum for each person, we have $S \cup T = \{0.6 \text{ Alice}, 0.9 \text{ Brian}, 0.4 \text{ Fred}, 0.9 \text{ Oscar}, 0.7 \text{ Rita}\}$.

SECTION 1.8   Functions

  2. a) This is not a function because the rule is not well-defined. We do not know whether $f(3) = 3$ or $f(3) = -3$. For a function, it cannot be both at the same time.

    b) This is a function. For all integers n, $\sqrt{n^2 + 1}$ is a well-defined real number.

    c) This is not a function with domain $\mathbf{Z}$, since for $n = 2$ (and also for $n = -2$) the value of $f(n)$ is not defined by the given rule. In other words, $f(2)$ and $f(-2)$ are not specified since division by 0 makes no sense.

  4. a) The domain is the set of nonnegative integers, and the range is the set of digits (0 through 9).

    b) The domain is the set of positive integers, and the range is the set of integers greater than 1.

    c) The domain is the set of all bit strings, and the range is the set of nonnegative integers.

    d) The domain is the set of all bit strings, and the range is the set of nonnegative integers (a bit string can have length 0).

6. a) The domain is $\mathbf{Z}^+ \times \mathbf{Z}^+$ and the range is $\mathbf{Z}^+$.

b) Since the largest decimal digit of a strictly positive integer cannot be 0, we have domain $\mathbf{Z}^+$ and range $\{1, 2, 3, 4, 5, 6, 7, 8, 9\}$.

c) The domain is the set of all bit strings. If we view this difference as being a signed difference (number of 1's minus number of 0's), then the range is $\mathbf{Z}$. If we view it as the absolute value of this quantity, then the range is $\mathbf{N}$.

d) The domain is given as $\mathbf{Z}^+$. Clearly the range is $\mathbf{Z}^+$ as well.

e) The domain is the set of bit strings. The range is the set of strings of 1's, i.e., $\{\lambda, 1, 11, 111, \ldots\}$, where λ is the empty string (containing no symbols).

8. We simply round up or down in each case.

a) 1   **b)** 2   **c)** -1 **d)** 0   **e)** 3   **f)** -2 **g)** $\lfloor \frac{1}{2} + 1 \rfloor = \lfloor \frac{3}{2} \rfloor = 1$

h) $\lceil 0 + 1 + \frac{1}{2} \rceil = \lceil \frac{3}{2} \rceil = 2$

10. a) This is one-to-one.   **b)** This is not one-to-one, since b is the image of both a and b.

c) This is not one-to-one, since d is the image of both a and d.

12. a) This is one-to-one, since if $n_1 - 1 = n_2 - 1$, then $n_1 = n_2$.

b) This is not one-to-one, since, for example, $f(3) = f(-3) = 10$.

c) This is one-to-one, since if $n_1^3 = n_2^3$, then $n_1 = n_2$ (take the cube root of each side).

d) This is not one-to-one, since, for example, $f(3) = f(4) = 2$.

14. a) This is clearly onto, since $f(0, -n) = n$ for every integer n.

b) This is not onto, since, for example, 2 is not in the range. To see this, if $m^2 - n^2 = (m - n)(m + n) = 2$, then m and n must have same parity (both even or both odd). In either case, both $m - n$ and $m + n$ are then even, so this expression is divisible by 4 and hence cannot equal 2.

c) This is clearly onto, since $f(0, n - 1) = n$ for every integer n.

d) This is onto. To achieve negative values we set $m = 0$, and to achieve nonnegative values we set $n = 0$.

e) This is not onto, for the same reason as in part (**b**). In fact, the range here is clearly a subset of the range in that part.

16. a) $f(n) = n + 17$ **b)** $f(n) = \lceil n/2 \rceil$

c) We let $f(n) = n - 1$ for even values of n, and $f(n) = n + 1$ for odd values of n. Thus we have $f(1) = 2$, $f(2) = 1$, $f(3) = 4$, $f(4) = 3$, and so on. Note that this is just one function, even though its definition used two formulas, depending on the the parity of n.

d) $f(n) = 17$

18. If we can find an inverse, the function is a bijection. Otherwise we must explain why the function is not on-to-one or not onto.

a) This is a bijection since the inverse function is $f^{-1}(x) = (4 - x)/3$.

b) This is not one-to-one since $f(17) = f(-17)$, for instance. It is also not onto, since the range is the interval $(-\infty, 7]$. For example, 42548 is not in the range.

c) This function is a bijection, but not from $\mathbf{R}$ to $\mathbf{R}$. To see that the domain and range are not $\mathbf{R}$, note that $x = -2$ is not in the domain, and $x = 1$ is not in the range. On the other hand, f is a bijection from $\mathbf{R} - \{-2\}$ to $\mathbf{R} - \{1\}$, since its inverse is $f^{-1}(x) = (1 - 2x)/(x - 1)$.

d) It is clear that this continuous function is increasing throughout its entire domain ($\mathbf{R}$) and it takes on both arbitrarily large values and arbitrarily small (large negative) ones. So it is a bijection. Its inverse is clearly $f^{-1}(x) = \sqrt[5]{x - 1}$.

20. The key here is that larger denominators make smaller fractions, and smaller denominators make larger fractions. We have two things to prove, since this is an "if and only if" statement. First, suppose that f is strictly increasing. This means that $f(x) < f(y)$ whenever $x < y$. To show that g is strictly decreasing, suppose that $x < y$. Then $g(x) = 1/f(x) > 1/f(y) = g(y)$. Conversely, suppose that g is strictly decreasing. This means that $g(x) > g(y)$ whenever $x < y$. To show that f is strictly increasing, suppose that $x < y$. Then $f(x) = 1/g(x) < 1/g(y) = f(y)$.

22. In all parts, we simply need to compute the values $f(-1)$, $f(0)$, $f(2)$, $f(4)$, and $f(7)$ and collect the values into a set.

  a) $\{1\}$ (all five values are the same)   **b)** $\{-1, 1, 5, 8, 15\}$ **c)** $\{0, 1, 2\}$ **d)** $\{0, 1, 5, 16\}$

24. a) the set of even integers   **b)** the set of positive even integers   **c)** the set of real numbers

26. To clarify the setting, suppose that $g : A \to B$ and $f : B \to C$, so that $f \circ g : A \to C$. We will prove that if $f \circ g$ is one-to-one, then g is also one-to-one, so not only is the answer to the question "yes," but part of the hypothesis is not even needed. Suppose that g were not one-to-one. By definition this means that there are distinct elements a_1 and a_2 in A such that $g(a_1) = g(a_2)$. Then certainly $f(g(a_1)) = f(g(a_2))$, which is the same statement as $(f \circ g)(a_1) = (f \circ g)(a_2)$. By definition this means that $f \circ g$ is not one-to-one, and our proof is complete.

28. We have $(f \circ g)(x) = f(g(x)) = f(x + 2) = (x + 2)^2 + 1 = x^2 + 4x + 5$, whereas $(g \circ f)(x) = g(x^2 + 1) = x^2 + 1 + 2 = x^2 + 3$. Note that they are not equal.

30. Forming the compositions we have $(f \circ g)(x) = acx + ad + b$ and $(g \circ f)(x) = cax + cb + d$. These are equal if and only if $ad + b = cb + d$. In other words, equality holds for all 4-tuples (a, b, c, d) for which $ad + b = cb + d$.

32. a) This really has two parts. First suppose that b is in $f(S \cup T)$. Thus $b = f(a)$ for some $a \in S \cup T$. Either $a \in S$, in which case $b \in f(S)$, or $a \in T$, in which case $b \in f(T)$. Thus in either case $b \in f(S) \cup f(T)$. This shows that $f(S \cup T) \subseteq f(S) \cup f(T)$. Conversely, suppose $b \in f(S) \cup f(T)$. Then either $b \in f(S)$ or $b \in f(T)$. This means either that $b = f(a)$ for some $a \in S$ or that $b = f(a)$ for some $a \in T$. In either case, $b = f(a)$ for some $a \in S \cup T$, so $b \in f(S \cup T)$. This shows that $f(S) \cup f(T) \subseteq f(S \cup T)$, and our proof is complete.
  b) Suppose $b \in f(S \cap T)$. Then $b = f(a)$ for some $a \in S \cap T$. This implies that $a \in S$ and $a \in T$, so we have $b \in f(S)$ and $b \in f(T)$. Therefore $b \in f(S) \cap f(T)$, as desired.

34. a) The answer is the set of all solutions to $x^2 = 1$, namely $\{1, -1\}$.
  b) In order for x^2 to be strictly between 0 and 1, we need x to be either strictly between 0 and 1 or strictly between -1 and 0. Therefore the answer is $\{x \mid -1 < x < 0 \lor 0 < x < 1\}$.
  c) In order for x^2 to be greater than 4, we need either $x > 2$ or $x < -2$. Therefore the answer is $\{x \mid x > 2 \lor x < -2\}$.

36. a) We need to prove two things. First suppose $x \in f^{-1}(S \cup T)$. This means that $f(x) \in S \cup T$. Therefore either $f(x) \in S$ or $f(x) \in T$. In the first case $x \in f^{-1}(S)$, and in the second case $x \in f^{-1}(T)$. In either case, then, $x \in f^{-1}(S) \cup f^{-1}(T)$. Thus we have shown that $f^{-1}(S \cup T) \subseteq f^{-1}(S) \cup f^{-1}(T)$. Conversely, suppose that $x \in f^{-1}(S) \cup f^{-1}(T)$. Then either $x \in f^{-1}(S)$ or $x \in f^{-1}(T)$, so either $f(x) \in S$ or $f(x) \in T$. Thus we know that $f(x) \in S \cup T$, so by definition $x \in f^{-1}(S \cup T)$. This shows that $f^{-1}(S) \cup f^{-1}(T) \subseteq f^{-1}(S \cup T)$, as desired.
  b) This is similar to part (a). We have $x \in f^{-1}(S \cap T)$ if and only if $f(x) \in S \cap T$, if and only if $f(x) \in S$ and $f(x) \in T$, if and only if $x \in f^{-1}(S)$ and $x \in f^{-1}(T)$, if and only if $x \in f^{-1}(S) \cap f^{-1}(T)$.

38. There are three cases. Define the "fractional part" of x to be $f(x) = x - \lfloor x \rfloor$. Clearly $f(x)$ is always between 0 and 1 (inclusive at 0, exclusive at 1), and $x = \lfloor x \rfloor + f(x)$. If $f(x)$ is less than $\frac{1}{2}$, then $x + \frac{1}{2}$ will have a value slightly less than $\lfloor x \rfloor + 1$, so when we round down, we get $\lfloor x \rfloor$. In other words, in this case $\lfloor x + \frac{1}{2} \rfloor = \lfloor x \rfloor$, and indeed that is the integer closest to x. If $f(x)$ is greater than $\frac{1}{2}$, then $x + \frac{1}{2}$ will have a value slightly greater than $\lfloor x \rfloor + 1$, so when we round down, we get $\lfloor x \rfloor + 1$. In other words, in this case $\lfloor x + \frac{1}{2} \rfloor = \lfloor x \rfloor + 1$, and indeed that is the integer closest to x in this case. Finally, if the fractional part is exactly $\frac{1}{2}$, then x is midway between two integers, and $\lfloor x + \frac{1}{2} \rfloor = \lfloor x \rfloor + 1$, which is the larger of these two integers.

40. If x is not an integer, then $\lceil x \rceil$ is the integer just larger than x, and $\lfloor x \rfloor$ is the integer just smaller than x. Clearly they differ by 1. If x is an integer, then $\lceil x \rceil - \lfloor x \rfloor = x - x = 0$.

42. Write $x = n - \epsilon$, where n is an integer and $0 \le \epsilon < 1$; thus $\lceil x \rceil = n$. Then $\lceil x + m \rceil = \lceil n - \epsilon + m \rceil = n + m = \lceil x \rceil + m$. Alternatively, we could proceed along the lines of the proof of property 4a of Table 1, shown in the text.

44. **a)** The "if" direction is trivial, since $x \le \lceil x \rceil$. For the other direction, suppose that $x \le n$. Since n is an integer no smaller than x, and $\lceil x \rceil$ is by definition the smallest such integer, clearly $\lceil x \rceil \le n$.
   b) The "if" direction is trivial, since $\lfloor x \rfloor \le x$. For the other direction, suppose that $n \le x$. Since n is an integer not exceeding x, and $\lfloor x \rfloor$ is by definition the largest such integer, clearly $n \le \lfloor x \rfloor$.

46. To prove the first equality, write $x = n - \epsilon$, where n is an integer and $0 \le \epsilon < 1$; thus $\lceil x \rceil = n$. Therefore, $\lfloor -x \rfloor = \lfloor -n + \epsilon \rfloor = -n = -\lceil x \rceil$. The second equality is proved in the same manner, writing $x = n + \epsilon$, where n is an integer and $0 \le \epsilon < 1$. This time $\lfloor x \rfloor = n$, and $\lceil -x \rceil = \lceil -n - \epsilon \rceil = -n = -\lfloor x \rfloor$.

48. In some sense this question is its own answer—the number of integers between a and b, inclusive, is the number of integers between a and b, inclusive. Presumably we seek an expression involving a, b, and the floor and/or ceiling function to answer this question. If we round a up and round b down to integers, then we will be looking at the smallest and largest integers just inside the range of integers we want to count, respectively. These values are of course $\lceil a \rceil$ and $\lfloor b \rfloor$, respectively. Then the answer is $\lfloor b \rfloor - \lceil a \rceil + 1$ (just think of counting all the integers between these two values, including both ends—if a row of fenceposts one foot apart extends for k feet, then there are $k + 1$ fenceposts). Note that this even works when, for example, $a = 0.3$ and $b = 0.7$.

50. Since a byte is eight bits, all we are asking for in each case is $\lceil n/8 \rceil$, where n is the number of bits.
   a) $\lceil 4/8 \rceil = 1$ **b)** $\lceil 10/8 \rceil = 2$ **c)** $\lceil 500/8 \rceil = 63$ **d)** $\lceil 3000/8 \rceil = 375$

52. From Example 23 we know that one ATM cell is 53 bytes, or $53 \cdot 8 = 424$ bits long. Thus in each case we need to divide the number of bits transmitted in 10 seconds by 424 and round down.
   a) In 10 seconds, this link can transmit $128{,}000 \cdot 10 = 1{,}280{,}000$ bits. Therefore the answer is $\lfloor 1{,}280{,}000/424 \rfloor = 3018$.
   b) In 10 seconds, this link can transmit $300{,}000 \cdot 10 = 3{,}000{,}000$ bits. So the answer is $\lfloor 3{,}000{,}000/424 \rfloor = 7075$.
   c) In 10 seconds, this link can transmit $1{,}000{,}000 \cdot 10 = 10{,}000{,}000$ bits. So the answer is $\lfloor 10{,}000{,}000/424 \rfloor = 23{,}584$.

54. The graph consists of the points $(n, 1 - n^2)$ for all $n \in \mathbf{Z}$. The picture shows part of the graph on the usual coordinate axes.

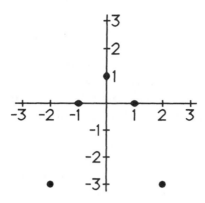

56. The graph is similar to the graph of $f(x) = \lfloor x \rfloor$; the only difference is a change in the scale of the x-axis.

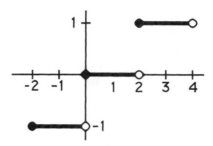

58. The function values for this step function change only at integer values of x, and different things happen for odd x and for even x because of the $x/2$ term. Whatever jump pattern is established on the closed interval $[0, 2]$ must repeat indefinitely in both directions. A thoughtful analysis then yields the following graph.

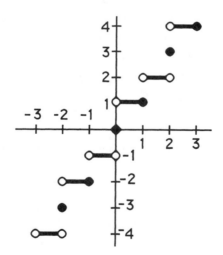

60. a) We can rewrite this as $f(x) = \lceil 3(x - \frac{2}{3}) \rceil$. The graph will therefore look look exactly like the graph of the function $f(x) = \lceil 3x \rceil$, except that the picture will be shifted to the right by $\frac{2}{3}$ unit, since x has been replaced by $x - \frac{2}{3}$. The graph of $f(x) = \lceil 3x \rceil$ is just like the graph shown in Figure 10b, except that the x-axis needs to be rescaled by a factor of 3 (the first jump on the positive x-axis occurs at $x = \frac{1}{3}$ here). Putting this all together yields the following picture. (Alternatively, we can think of this as the graph of $f(x) = \lceil 3x \rceil$ shifted down 2 units, since $\lceil 3x - 2 \rceil = \lceil 3x \rceil - 2$.)

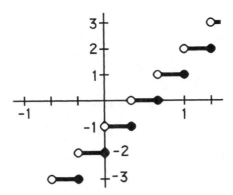

b) The graph will look exactly like the graph shown in Figure 10b, except that the x-axis needs to be rescaled by a factor of 5 (the first jump on the positive x-axis occurs at $x = 5$ here).

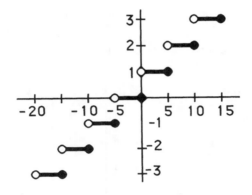

c) Since $\lfloor -1/x \rfloor = -\lceil 1/x \rceil$ (see Exercise 46), the picture is just the picture for Exercise 59d flipped upside down.

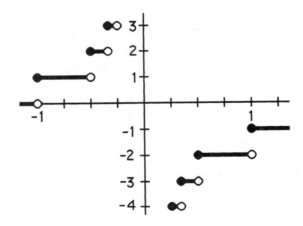

d) The basic shape is the parabola, $y = x^2$. However, because of the greatest integer function, the curve is broken into steps, with jumps at $x = \pm 1, \pm\sqrt{2}, \pm\sqrt{3}, \ldots$. Note the symmetry around the y-axis.

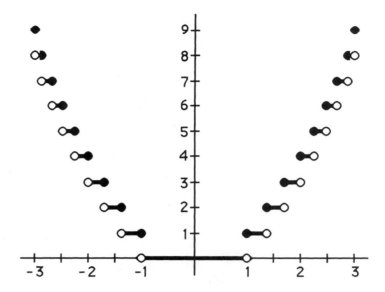

e) The basic shape is the parabola, $y = x^2/4$. However, because of the step functions, the curve is broken into steps. For x an even integer, $f(x) = x^4/4$, since the terms inside the floor and ceiling function symbols are integers. Note how these are isolated point, as in Exercise 59f.

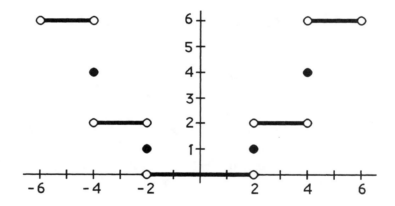

f) When x is an even integer, this is just x. When x is between two even integers, however, this has the value of the odd integer between them. The graph is therefore as shown here.

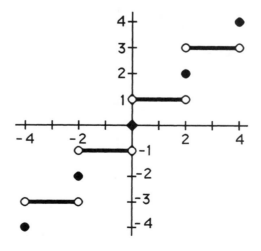

g) Despite the complicated-looking formula, this is not too hard. Note that the expression inside the outer floor function symbols is always going to be an integer plus $\frac{1}{2}$; therefore we can tell exactly what its rounded-down value will be, namely $2\lceil x/2 \rceil$. This is just the graph in Figure 10b, rescaled on both axes.

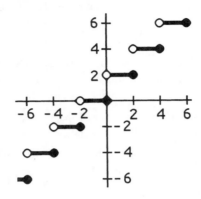

62. This follows immediately from the definition. We want to show that $((f \circ g) \circ (g^{-1} \circ f^{-1}))(z) = z$ for all $z \in Z$ and that $((g^{-1} \circ f^{-1}) \circ (f \circ g))(x) = x$ for all $x \in X$. For the first we have

$$\begin{aligned}
((f \circ g) \circ (g^{-1} \circ f^{-1}))(z) &= (f \circ g)((g^{-1} \circ f^{-1})(z)) \\
&= (f \circ g)(g^{-1}(f^{-1}(z))) \\
&= f(g(g^{-1}(f^{-1}(z)))) \\
&= f(f^{-1}(z)) = z .
\end{aligned}$$

The second equality is similar.

64. If f is one-to-one, then every element of A gets sent to a different element of B. If in addition to the range of A there were another element in B, then $|B|$ would be at least one greater than $|A|$. This cannot happen, so we conclude that f is onto. Conversely, suppose that f is onto, so that every element of B is the image of some element of A. In particular, there is an element of A for each element of B. If two or more elements of A were sent to the same element of B, then $|A|$ would be at least one greater than the $|B|$. This cannot happen, so we conclude that f is one-to-one.

66. a) This is true. Since $\lceil x \rceil$ is already an integer, $\lfloor \lceil x \rceil \rfloor = \lceil x \rceil$.

b) A little experimentation shows that this is not always true. To disprove it we need only produce a counterexample, such as $x = y = \frac{3}{4}$. In this case the left-hand side is $\lfloor 3/2 \rfloor = 1$, while the right-hand side is $0 + 0 = 0$.

c) A little trial and error fails to produce a counterexample, so maybe this is true. We look for a proof. Since we are dividing by 4, let us write $x = 4n + k$, where $0 \le k < 4$. In other words, write x in terms of how much it exceeds the largest multiple of 4 not exceeding it. There are three cases. If $k = 0$, then x is already a multiple of 4, so both sides equal n. If $0 < k \le 2$, then $\lceil x/2 \rceil = 2n + 1$, so the left-hand side is $\lceil n + \frac{1}{2} \rceil = n + 1$. Of course the right-hand side is $n + 1$ as well, so again the two sides agree. Finally, suppose that $2 < k < 4$. Then $\lceil x/2 \rceil = 2n + 2$, and the left-hand side is $\lceil n + 1 \rceil = n + 1$; of course the right-hand side is still $n + 1$, as well. Since we proved that the two sides are equal in all cases, the proof is complete.

d) There are at least two reasons why this is not true. An honest counterexample is a number like $x = 8.5$. Then the left-hand side is 3, whereas the right-hand side is 2. Also, for $-1 < x < 0$, the left-hand side is 0 and the right-hand side is undefined. Of course for $x \le -1$, neither side is defined.

e) This is true. Write $x = n + \epsilon$ and $y = m + \delta$, where n and m are integers and ϵ and δ are nonnegative real numbers less than 1. The left-hand side is $n + m + (n + m)$ or $n + m + (n + m + 1)$, the latter occurring if and only if $\epsilon + \delta \ge 1$. The right-hand side is the sum of two quantities. The first is either $2n$ (if $\epsilon < \frac{1}{2}$)

or $2n + 1$ (if $\epsilon \geq \frac{1}{2}$). The second is either $2m$ (if $\delta < \frac{1}{2}$) or $2m + 1$ (if $\delta \geq \frac{1}{2}$). The only way, then, for the left-hand side to exceed the right-hand side is to have the left-hand side be $2n + 2m + 1$ and the right-hand side be $2n + 2m$. This can occur only if $\epsilon + \delta \geq 1$ while $\epsilon < \frac{1}{2}$ and $\delta < \frac{1}{2}$. But that is an impossibility, since the sum of two numbers less than $\frac{1}{2}$ cannot be as large as 1. Therefore the right-hand side is always at least as large as the left-hand side.

68. A straightforward way to do this problem is to consider the three cases determined by where in the interval between two consecutive integers the real number x lies. Certainly every real number x lies in an interval $[n, n + 1)$ for some integer n; indeed, $n = \lfloor x \rfloor$. (Recall that $[s, t)$ is the notation for the set of real numbers greater than or equal to s and less than t.) If $x \in [n, n + \frac{1}{3})$, then $3x$ lies in the interval $[3n, 3n + 1)$, so $\lfloor 3x \rfloor = 3n$. Moreover in this case $x + \frac{1}{3}$ is still less than $n + 1$, and $x + \frac{2}{3}$ is still less than $n + 1$, so $\lfloor x \rfloor + \lfloor x + \frac{1}{3} \rfloor + \lfloor x + \frac{2}{3} \rfloor = n + n + n = 3n$ as well. For the second case, we assume that $x \in [n + \frac{1}{3}, n + \frac{2}{3})$. This time $3x \in [3n + 1, 3n + 2)$, so $\lfloor 3x \rfloor = 3n + 1$. Moreover in this case $x + \frac{1}{3}$ is in $[n + \frac{2}{3}, n + 1)$, and $x + \frac{2}{3}$ is in $[n + 1, n + \frac{4}{3})$, so $\lfloor x \rfloor + \lfloor x + \frac{1}{3} \rfloor + \lfloor x + \frac{2}{3} \rfloor = n + n + (n + 1) = 3n + 1$ as well. The third case, $x \in [n + \frac{2}{3}, n + 1)$, is similar, with both sides equaling $3n + 2$.

70. a) We merely have to remark that f^* is well-defined by the rule given here. For each $a \in A$, either a is in the domain of definition of f or it is not. If it is, then $f^*(a)$ is the well-defined element $f(a) \in B$, and otherwise $f^*(a) = u$. In either case $f^*(a)$ is a well-defined element of $B \cup \{u\}$.
b) We simply need to set $f^*(a) = u$ for each a not in the domain of definition of f. In part **(a)**, then, $f^*(n) = 1/n$ for $n \neq 0$, and $f^*(0) = u$. In part **(b)** we have a total function already, so $f^*(n) = \lceil n/2 \rceil$ for all $n \in \mathbf{Z}$. In part **(c)** $f^*(m, n) = m/n$ if $n \neq 0$, and $f^*(m, 0) = u$ for all $m \in \mathbf{Z}$. In part **(d)** we have a total function already, so $f^*(m, n) = mn$ for all values of m and n. In part **(e)** the rule only applies if $m > n$, so $f^*(m, n) = m - n$ if $m > n$, and $f^*(m, n) = u$ if $m \leq n$.

SUPPLEMENTARY EXERCISES FOR CHAPTER 1

2. The truth table is as follows.

p	q	r	$p \vee q$	$p \wedge \neg r$	$(p \vee q) \rightarrow (p \wedge \neg r)$
T	T	T	T	F	F
T	T	F	T	T	T
T	F	T	T	F	F
T	F	F	T	T	T
F	T	T	T	F	F
F	T	F	T	F	F
F	F	T	F	F	T
F	F	F	F	F	T

4. a) The converse is "If I drive to work today, then it will rain." The contrapositive is "If I do not drive to work today, then it will not rain." The inverse is "If it does not rain today, then I will not drive to work."
b) The converse is "If $x \geq 0$ then $|x| = x$." The contrapositive is "If $x < 0$ then $|x| \neq x$." The inverse is "If $|x| \neq x$, then $x < 0$."
c) The converse is "If n^2 is greater than 9, then n is greater than 3." The contrapositive is "If n^2 is not greater than 9, then n is not greater than 3." The inverse is "If n is not greater than 3, then n^2 is not greater than 9."

6. Let t be "Sergei takes the job offer"; let b be "Sergei gets a signing bonus"; and let h be "Sergei will receive a higher salary." The given statements are $t \rightarrow b$, $t \rightarrow h$, $b \rightarrow \neg h$, and t. By modus ponens we can conclude b and h from the first two implications, and therefore we can conclude $\neg h$ from the third implication. We now have the contradiction $h \wedge \neg h$, so these statements are inconsistent.

8. Since both knights and knaves claim that they are knights (the former truthfully and the latter deceivingly), we know that A is a knave. But since A's statement must be false, and the first part of the conjunction is true, the second part must be false, so we know that B must be a knave as well. If C were a knight, then B's statement would be true, and knaves must lie, so C must also be a knave. Thus all three are knaves.

10. a) The answer is $\exists x P(x)$ if we do not read any significance into the use of the plural, and $\exists x \exists y (P(x) \wedge P(y) \wedge x \neq y)$ if we do.
b) $\neg \forall x P(x)$, or, equivalently, $\exists x \neg P(x)$ **c)** $\forall y Q(y)$
d) $\forall x P(x)$ (the class has nothing to do with it)   **e)** $\exists y \neg Q(y)$

12. We want to say that for every y, there do not exist four different people each of whom is the grandmother of y. Thus we have $\forall x \neg \exists a \exists b \exists c \exists d (a \neq b \wedge a \neq c \wedge a \neq d \wedge b \neq c \wedge b \neq d \wedge c \neq d \wedge G(a,y) \wedge G(b,y) \wedge G(c,y) \wedge G(d,y))$.

14. Let us assume the hypothesis. This means that there is some x_0 such that $P(x_0, y)$ holds for all y. Then it is certainly true that for all y there exists an x such that $P(x, y)$ is true, since in each case we can take $x = x_0$. Note that the converse is not always a tautology, since the x in $\forall y \exists x P(x, y)$ can depend on y.

16. No. Here is an example. Let $P(x, y)$ be $x > y$, where we are talking about integers. Then for every y there does exist an x such that $x > y$; we could take $x = y + 1$, for example. However, there does not exist an x such that for *every* y, $x > y$; in other words, there is no superlarge integer (if for no other reason than that no integer can be larger than itself).

18. a) It will snow today, but I will not go skiing tomorrow.
b) Some person in this class does not understand mathematical induction.
c) All students in this class like discrete mathematics.
d) There is some mathematics class in which all the students stay awake during lectures.

20. Let $W(r)$ means that room r is painted white. Let $I(r, b)$ mean that room r is in building b. Let $L(b, u)$ mean that building b is on the campus of United States university u. Then the statement is that there is some university u and some building on the campus of u such that every room in b is painted white. In symbols this is $\exists u \exists b (L(b, u) \wedge \forall r (I(r, b) \rightarrow W(r)))$.

22. To say that there are exactly two elements that make the statement true is to say that two elements exist that make the statement true, and that every element that makes the statement true is one of these two elements. More compactly, we can phrase the last part by saying that an element makes the statement true if and only if it is one of these two elements. In symbols this is $\exists x \exists y (x \neq y \wedge \forall z (P(z) \leftrightarrow (z = x \vee z = y)))$. In English we might express the rule as follows. The hypotheses are that $P(x)$ and $P(y)$ are both true, that $x \neq y$, and that every z that satisfies $P(z)$ must be either x or y. The conclusion is that there are exactly two elements that make P true.

24. By universal instantiation we have $P(a) \rightarrow Q(a)$ and $Q(a) \rightarrow R(a)$. By modus tollens we then conclude $\neg Q(a)$, and again by modus tollens we conclude $\neg P(a)$.

26. We give an indirect proof. If x is rational, then $x = p/q$ for some integers p and q with $q \neq 0$. Then $x^3 = p^3/q^3$, and we have expressed x^3 as the quotient of two integers, the second of which is not zero. This by definition means that x^3 is rational, and that completes the indirect proof.

28. Let $m = \lfloor \sqrt{n} \rfloor$. We can see that this is the unique solution in a couple of ways. First, clearly the different choices of m correspond to a partition of $\mathbf{Z}^+$, namely into $\{0\}$, $\{1, 2, 3\}$, $\{4, 5, 6, 7, 8\}$, $\{9, 10, 11, 12, 13, 14, 15\}$, ... So every n is in exactly one of these sets. Alternatively, take the square root of the given inequalities to give $m \leq \sqrt{n} < m + 1$. That m is then the floor of $\sqrt{n}$ (and that m is unique) follows from statement (1a) of Table 1 in Section 1.8.

30. A constructive proof seems indicated. We can look for examples by hand or with a computer program. The smallest ones to be found are $50 = 5^2 + 5^2 = 1^2 + 7^2$ and $65 = 4^2 + 7^2 = 1^2 + 8^2$.

32. We claim that the number 7 is not the sum of at most two squares and a cube. The first two positive squares are 1 and 4, and the first positive cube is 1, and these are the only numbers that could be used in forming the sum. Clearly no sum of three or fewer of these is 7. This counterexample disproves the statement.

34. We are given that $A \subseteq B$. We want to prove that the power set of A is a subset of the power set of B, which means that if $C \subseteq A$ then $C \subseteq B$. But this follows directly from Exercise 11 in Section 1.6.

36. a) Z   b) $\emptyset$ c) O   d) E

38. a) If $x \in A$, then certainly $x \in A \cup B$, so it follows that $x \in A \cap (A \cup B)$. Thus $A \subseteq A \cap (A \cup B)$. Conversely, if $x \in A \cap (A \cup B)$, then necessarily $x \in A$.
   b) This is the dual of part **(a)**. If $x \in A$, then certainly $x \in A \cup (A \cap B)$. Conversely, if $x \in A \cup (A \cap B)$, then either $x \in A$ or $x \in A \cap B$, in which case it also follows that $x \in A$.

40. If $A \subseteq B$, then every element in A is also in B, so clearly $A \cap B = A$. Conversely, if $A \cap B = A$, then every element of A must also be in $A \cap B$, and hence in B. Therefore $A \subseteq B$.

42. This identity is true, so we must show that every element in the left-hand side is also an element in the right-hand side and conversely. Let $x \in (A - B) - C$. Then $x \in A - B$ but $x \notin C$. This means that $x \in A$, but $x \notin B$ and $x \notin C$. Therefore $x \in A - C$, and therefore $x \in (A - C) - B$. The converse is proved in exactly the same way.

44. The inequality follows from the obvious fact that $A \cap B \subseteq A \cup B$. Equality can hold only if there are no elements in either A or B that are not in both A and B, and this can happen only if $A = B$.

46. Since $\overline{A} \cap \overline{B} = \overline{(A \cup B)}$, we are asked to show that $|\overline{(A \cup B)}| = |U| - (|A| + |B| - |A \cap B|)$. This follows immediately from the facts that $|\overline{X}| = |U| - |X|$ (which is clear from the definitions) and (see the discussion following Example 5 in Section 1.7) that $|A \cup B| = |A| + |B| - |A \cap B|$.

48. We showed in Exercise 32b in Section 1.8 that $f(S \cap T) \subseteq f(S) \cap f(T)$. Thus it remains to show the opposite inclusion, assuming that f is one-to-one. Suppose $y \in f(S) \cap f(T)$. Then $y = f(s)$ for some $s \in S$ and $y = f(t)$ for some $t \in T$. Since f is one-to-one, it must be that $s = t$. Thus f is the image of an element that lies in both S and T, so $y \in f(S \cap T)$.

50. If n is even , then $n/2$ is an integer, so $\lceil n/2 \rceil + \lfloor n/2 \rfloor = (n/2) + (n/2) = n$. If n is odd, then $\lceil n/2 \rceil = (n+1)/2$ and $\lfloor n/2 \rfloor = (n - 1)/2$, so again the sum is n.

52. This is certainly true if either x or y is an integer, since then this equation is equivalent to the identity (4b) in Table 1 of Section 1.8. Otherwise, write x and y in terms of their integer and fractional parts: $x = n + \epsilon$ and $y = m + \delta$, where $n = \lfloor x \rfloor$, $0 < \epsilon < 1$, $m = \lfloor y \rfloor$, and $0 < \delta < 1$. If $\delta + \epsilon > 1$, then the equation is true, since both sides equal $m + n + 2$; if $\delta + \epsilon \leq 1$, then the equation is false, since the left-hand side equals $m + n + 1$, but the right-hand side equals $m + n + 2$. To summarize: the equation is true if and only if either at least one of x and y is an integer or the sum of the fractional parts of x and y exceeds 1.

CHAPTER 2
The Fundamentals: Algorithms, the Integers, and Matrices

SECTION 2.1   Algorithms

2. a) This procedure is not finite, since execution of the **while** loop continues forever.

b) This procedure is not effective, because the step $m := 1/n$ cannot be performed when $n = 0$, which will eventually be the case.

c) This procedure lacks definiteness, since the value of i is never set.

d) This procedure lacks definiteness, since the statement does not tell whether x is to be set equal to a or to b.

4. Set the answer to be $-\infty$. For i going from 1 through $n - 1$, compute the difference between the ith and the $(i + 1)^{\text{th}}$ elements in the list. If this is larger than the answer, reset the answer to be this value.

6. We need to go through the list and count the negative entries.

> **procedure** $negatives(a_1, a_2, \ldots, a_n : \text{integers})$
> $k := 0$
> **for** $i := 1$ **to** n
>   **if** $a_i < 0$ **then** $k := k + 1$
> **end** $\{ k$ is the number of negative integers in the list $\}$

8. This is similar to Exercise 7, modified to keep track of the largest even integer we encounter.

> **procedure** $largest\ even\ location(a_1, a_2, \ldots, a_n : \text{integers})$
> $k := 0$
> $largest := -\infty$
> **for** $i := 1$ **to** n
>   **if** $(a_i$ is even and $a_i > largest)$ **then**
>   **begin**
> $k := i$
> $largest := a_i$
>   **end**
> **end** $\{ k$ is the desired location (or 0 if there are no evens) $\}$

10. We assume that if the input $x = 0$, then $n > 0$, since otherwise x^n is not defined. In our procedure, we let $m = |n|$ and compute x^m in the obvious way. Then if n is negative, we replace the answer by its reciprocal.

> **procedure** $power(x : \text{real number}, n : \text{integer})$
> $m := |n|$
> $power := 1$
> **for** $i := 1$ **to** m
> $power := power \cdot x$
> **if** $n < 0$ **then** $power := 1/power$
> $\{ power = x^n \}$

12. Four assignment statements are needed, one for each of the variables and a temporary assignment to get started so that we do not lose one of the original values.

$$temp := x$$
$$x := y$$
$$y := z$$
$$z := temp$$

14. a) With linear search we start at the beginning of the list, and compare 7 successively with 1, 3, 4, 5, 6, 8, 9, and 11. When we come to the end of the list and still have not found 7, we conclude that it is not in the list.

b) We begin the search on the entire list, with $i = 1$ and $j = n = 8$. We set $m := 4$ and compare 7 to the fourth element of the list. Since $7 > 5$, we next restrict the search to the second half of the list, with $i = 5$ and $j = 8$. This time we set $m := 6$ and compare 7 to the sixth element of the list. Since $7 \not> 8$, we next restrict ourselves to the first half of the second half of the list, with $i = 5$ and $j = 6$. This time we set $m := 5$, and compare 7 to the fifth element. Since $7 > 6$, we now restrict ourselves to the portion of the list between $i = 6$ and $j = 6$. Since at this point $i \not< j$, we exit the loop. Since the sixth element of the list is not equal to 7, we conclude that 7 is not in the list.

16. We let *min* be the smallest element found so far. At the end, it is the smallest element, since we update it as necessary as we scan through the list.

> **procedure** *smallest*($a_1, a_2, \ldots, a_n$: natural numbers)
> $min := a_1$
> **for** $i := 2$ **to** n
>   **if** $a_i < min$ **then** $min := a_i$
> { *min* is the smallest integer among the input }

18. This is similar to Exercise 17.

> **procedure** *last smallest*($a_1, a_2, \ldots, a_n$: integers)
> $min := a_1$
> $location := 1$
> **for** $i := 2$ **to** n
>   **if** $min \geq a_i$ **then**
>   **begin**
> $min := a_i$
> $location := i$
>   **end**
> { *location* is the location of the last occurrence of the smallest element in the list }

20. We just combine procedures for finding the largest and smallest elements.

> **procedure** *smallest and largest*($a_1, a_2, \ldots, a_n$: integers)
> $min := a_1$
> $max := a_1$
> **for** $i := 2$ **to** n
> **begin**
>   **if** $a_i < min$ **then** $min := a_i$
>   **if** $a_i > max$ **then** $max := a_i$
> **end**
> { *min* is the smallest integer among the input, and *max* is the largest }

22. We assume that the input is a sequence of symbols, $a_1, a_2, \ldots, a_n$, each of which is either a letter or a blank. We build up the longest word in *word*; its length is *length*. We denote the empty word by λ.

```
procedure longest word(a_1, a_2, ..., a_n : symbols)
maxlength := 0
maxword := λ
i := 1
while i ≤ n
begin
        word := λ
        length := 0
        while a_i ≠ blank and i ≤ n
        begin
                length := length + 1
                word := concatenation of word and a_i
                i := i + 1
        end
        if length > max then
        begin
                maxlength := length
                maxword := word
        end
        i := i + 1
end
```

24. This is similar to Exercise 23. We let the array *hit* keep track of which elements of the codomain B have already been found to be images of elements of the domain A. When we find an element that has already been hit being hit again, we conclude that the function is not one-to-one.

```
procedure one_one(f : function, a_1, a_2, ..., a_n, b_1, b_2, ..., b_m : integers)
for i := 1 to m
        hit(b_i) := 0
one_one := true
for j := 1 to n
        if hit(f(a_j)) = 0 then hit(f(a_j)) := 1
        else one_one := false
```

26. There are two changes. First, we need to test $x = a_m$ (right after the computation of m) and take appropriate action if equality holds (what we do is set i and j both to be m). Second, if $x \not> a_m$, then instead of setting j equal to m, we can set j equal to $m - 1$. The advantages are that this allows the size of the "half" of the list being looked at to shrink slightly faster, and it allows us to stop essentially as soon as we have found the element we are looking for.

28. This could be thought of as just doing two iterations of binary search at once. We compare the sought-after element to the middle element in the still-active portion of the list, and then to the middle element of either the top half or the bottom half. This will restrict the subsequent search to one of four sublists, each about one-quarter the size of the previous list. We need to stop when the list has length three or less and make explicit checks. Here is the pseudocode.

```
procedure tetrary search(x : integer, a_1, a_2, ..., a_n : increasing integers)
i := 1
j := n
while i < j − 2
begin
        l := ⌊(i + j)/4⌋
        m := ⌊(i + j)/2⌋
        u := ⌊3(i + j)/4⌋
```

$$\textbf{if } x > a_m \textbf{ then if } x \le a_u \textbf{ then}$$
$$\qquad\textbf{begin}$$
$$\qquad\qquad i := m + 1$$
$$\qquad\qquad j := u$$
$$\qquad\textbf{end}$$
$$\qquad\textbf{else } i := u + 1$$
$$\textbf{else if } x > a_l \textbf{ then}$$
$$\qquad\textbf{begin}$$
$$\qquad\qquad i := l + 1$$
$$\qquad\qquad j := m$$
$$\qquad\textbf{end}$$
$$\qquad\textbf{else } j := l$$
$$\textbf{end}$$
$$\textbf{if } x = a_i \textbf{ then } location := i$$
$$\textbf{else if } x = a_j \textbf{ then } location := j$$
$$\textbf{else if } x = a_{\lfloor (i+j)/2 \rfloor} \textbf{ then } location := \lfloor (i + j)/2 \rfloor$$
$$\textbf{else } location := 0$$

{ $location$ is the subscript of the term equal to x (0 if not found) }

30. The following algorithm will find all modes in the sequence and put them into a list L. At each point in the execution of this algorithm, $modecount$ is the number of occurrences of the elements found to occur most often so far (the elements in L). Whenever a more frequently occurring element is found (the main inner loop), $modecount$ and L are updated; whenever an element is found with this same count, it is added to L.

procedure *find all modes*($a_1, a_2, \ldots, a_n$: nondecreasing integers)
$modecount := 0$
$i := 1$
while $i \le n$
begin
$\qquad value := a_i$
$\qquad count := 1$
$\qquad$**while** $i \le n$ **and** $a_i = value$
$\qquad$**begin**
$\qquad\qquad count := count + 1$
$\qquad\qquad i := i + 1$
$\qquad$**end**
$\qquad$**if** $count > modecount$ **then**
$\qquad$**begin**
$\qquad\qquad modecount := count$
$\qquad\qquad$ set L to consist just of *value*
$\qquad$**end**
$\qquad$**else if** $count = modecount$ **then** add *value* to L
end
{ L is a list of all the values occurring most often, namely $modecount$ times }

32. The following algorithm will find all terms of a finite sequence of integers that are greater than the sum of all the previous terms. We put them into a list L, but one could just as easily have them printed out, if that were desired. It might be more useful to put the *indices* of these terms into L, rather than the terms themselves (i.e., their values), but we take the former approach for variety. As usual, the empty list is considered to have sum 0, so the first term in the sequence is included in L if and only if it positive.

procedure *find all biggies*($a_1, a_2, \ldots, a_n$: integers)
set L to be the empty list
$sum := 0$
$i := 1$

> **while** $i \leq n$
> **begin**
>> **if** $a_i > sum$ **then** append a_i to L
>> $sum := sum + a_i$
>> $i := i + 1$
> **end**
> { L is a list of all the values that exceed the sum of all the previous terms in the sequence }

34. There are five passes through the list. After one pass the list reads $2, 3, 1, 5, 4, 6$, since the 6 is compared and moved at each stage. During the next pass, the 2 and the 3 are not interchanged, but the 3 and the 1 are, as are the 5 and the 4, yielding $2, 1, 3, 4, 5, 6$. On the third pass, the 2 and the 1 are interchanged, yielding $1, 2, 3, 4, 5, 6$. There are two more passes, but no further interchanges are made, since the list is now in order.

36. The procedure is the same as that given in the solution to Exercise 35. We will exhibit the lists obtained after each step, with all the lists obtained during one pass on the same line.

> $dfkmab, \ dfkmab, \ dfkmab, \ dfkamb, \ dfkabm$
> $dfkabm, \ dfkabm, \ dfakbm, \ dfabkm$
> $dfabkm, \ dafbkm, \ dabfkm$
> $adbfkm, \ abdfkm$
> $abdfkm$

38. We start with $6, 2, 3, 1, 5, 4$. The first step inserts 2 correctly into the sorted list 6, producing $2, 6, 3, 1, 5, 4$. Next 3 is inserted into $2, 6$, and the list reads $2, 3, 6, 1, 5, 4$. Next 1 is inserted into $2, 3, 6$, and the list reads $1, 2, 3, 6, 5, 4$. Next 5 is inserted into $1, 2, 3, 6$, and the list reads $1, 2, 3, 5, 6, 4$. Finally 4 is inserted into $1, 2, 3, 5, 6$, and the list reads $1, 2, 3, 4, 5, 6$. At each insertion, the element to be inserted is compared with the elements already sorted, starting from the beginning, until its correct spot is found, and then the previously sorted elements beyond that spot are each moved one position toward the back of the list.

40. We start with d, f, k, m, a, b. The first step inserts f correctly into the sorted list d, producing no change. Similarly, no change results when k and m are inserted into the sorted lists d, f and d, f, k, respectively. Next a is inserted into d, f, k, m, and the list reads a, d, f, k, m, b. Finally b is inserted into a, d, f, k, m, and the list reads a, b, d, f, k, m. At each insertion, the element to be inserted is compared with the elements already sorted, starting from the beginning, until its correct spot is found, and then the previously sorted elements beyond that spot are each moved one position toward the back of the list.

42. We let $minspot$ be the place at which the minimum remaining element is found. After we find it on the ith pass, we just have to interchange the elements in location $minspot$ and location i.

> **procedure** $selection(a_1, a_2, \ldots, a_n)$
> **for** $i := 1$ **to** $n - 1$
> **begin**
>> $minspot := i$
>> **for** $j := i + 1$ **to** n
>>> **if** $a_j < a_{minspot}$ **then** $minspot := j$
>> interchange $a_{minspot}$ and a_i
> **end** {the list is now in order}

44. We carry out the binary search algorithm given as Algorithm 3 in this section, except that we replace the final check with **if** $x < a_i$ **then** $location := i$ **else** $location := i + 1$.

46. We are counting just the comparisons of the numbers in the list, not any comparisons needed for the book-keeping in the **for** loop. The second element in the list must be compared only with the first (in other words, when $j = 2$ in Algorithm 5, i takes the values 1 before we drop out of the **while** loop). Similarly, the third element must be compared only with the first. We continue in this way, until finally the nth element must be compared only with the first. So the total number of comparisons is $n - 1$. This is the best case for insertion sort in terms of the number of comparisons, but moving the elements to do the insertions requires much more effort.

48. For the insertion sort, one comparison is needed to find the correct location of the 4, one for the 3, four for the 8, one for the 1, four for the 5, and two for the 2. This is a total of 13 comparisons. For the binary insertion sort, one comparison is needed to find the correct location of the 4, two for the 3, two for the 8, three for the 1, three for the 5, and four for the 2. This is a total of 15 comparisons. If the list were long (and not almost in decreasing order to begin with), we would use many fewer comparisons using binary insertion sort. The reason that the answer came out "wrong" here is that the list is so short that the binary search was not efficient.

50. a) This is essentially the same as Algorithm 5, but working from the other end. However, we can do the moving while we do the searching for the correct insertion spot, so the pseudocode has only one section.

> **procedure** *backward insertion sort*$(a_1, a_2, \ldots, a_n : $ real numbers with $n \geq 2)$
> **for** $j := 2$ **to** n
> **begin**
> > $m := a_j$
> > $i := j - 1$
> > **while** $(m < a_i$ and $i > 0)$
> > **begin**
> > > $a_{i+1} := a_i$
> > > $i := i - 1$
> > **end**
> > $a_{i+1} := m$
> **end** $\{a_1, a_2, \ldots, a_n$ are sorted$\}$

b) On the first pass the 2 is compared to the 3 and found to be less, so the 3 moves to the right. We have reached the beginning of the list, so the loop terminates ($i = 0$), and the 2 is inserted, yielding $2, 3, 4, 5, 1, 6$. On the second pass the 4 is compared to the 3, and since $4 > 3$, the **while** loop terminates and nothing changes. Similarly, no changes are made as the 5 is inserted. One the fourth pass, the 1 is compared all the way to the front of the list, with each element moving toward the back of the list as the comparisons go on, and finally the 1 is inserted in its correct position, yielding $1, 2, 3, 4, 5, 6$. The final pass produces no change.
c) Only one comparison is used during each pass, since the condition $m < a_i$ is immediately false. Therefore a total of $n - 1$ comparisons are used.
d) The jth pass requires $j - 1$ comparisons of elements, so the total number of comparisons is $1 + 2 + \cdots + (n - 1) = n(n - 1)/2$.

52. In each case we use as many quarters as we can, then as many dimes to achieve the remaining amount, then as many nickels, then as many pennies.
a) The algorithm uses the maximum number of quarters, three, leaving 12 cents. It then uses the maximum number of dimes (one) and nickels (none), before using two pennies.
b) one quarter, leaving 24 cents, then two dimes, leaving 4 cents, then four pennies
c) three quarters, leaving 24 cents, then two dimes, leaving 4 cents, then four pennies
d) one quarter, leaving 8 cents, then one nickel and three pennies

54. a) The algorithm uses the maximum number of quarters, three, leaving 12 cents. It then uses the maximum number of dimes (one), and then two pennies. The greedy algorithm worked, since we got the same answer as in Exercise 52.

b) one quarter, leaving 24 cents, then two dimes, leaving 4 cents, then four pennies (the greedy algorithm worked, since we got the same answer as in Exercise 52)

c) three quarters, leaving 24 cents, then two dimes, leaving 4 cents, then four pennies (the greedy algorithm worked, since we got the same answer as in Exercise 52)

d) The greedy algorithm would have us use one quarter, leaving 8 cents, then eight pennies, a total of nine coins. However, we could have used three dimes and three pennies, a total of six coins. Thus the greedy algorithm is not correct for this set of coins.

56. One approach is to come up with an example in which using the 12-cent coin before using dimes or nickels would be inefficient. A dime and a nickel together are worth 15 cents, but the greedy algorithm would have us use four coins (a 12-cent coin and three pennies) rather than two. An alternative example would be 29 cents, in which case the greedy algorithm would use a quarter and four pennies, but we could have done better using two 12-cent coins and a nickel.

SECTION 2.2   The Growth of Functions

2. Note that the choices of C and k witnesses are not unique.

a) Yes, since $17x + 11 \le 17x + x = 18x \le 18x^2$ for all $x > 11$. The witnesses are $C = 18$ and $k = 11$.

b) Yes, since $x^2 + 1000 \le x^2 + x^2 = 2x^2$ for all $x > \sqrt{1000}$. The witnesses are $C = 2$ and $k = \sqrt{1000}$.

c) Yes, since $x \log x \le x \cdot x = x^2$ for all x in the domain of the function. (The fact that $\log x < x$ for all x follows from the fact that $x < 2^x$ for all x, which can be seen by looking at the graphs of these two functions.) The witnesses are $C = 1$ and $k = 0$.

d) No. If there were a constant C such that $x^4/2 \le Cx^2$ for sufficiently large x, then we would have $C \ge x^2/2$. This is clearly impossible for a constant to satisfy.

e) No. If 2^x were $O(x^2)$, then the fraction $2^x/x^2$ would have to be bounded above by some constant C. It can be shown that in fact $2^x > x^3$ for all $x \ge 10$ (using mathematical induction—see Section 3.3—or calculus), so $2^x/x^2 \ge x^3/x^2 = x$ for large x, which is certainly not less than or equal to C.

f) Yes, since $\lfloor x \rfloor \lceil x \rceil \le x(x+1) \le x \cdot 2x = 2x^2$ for all $x > 1$. The witnesses are $C = 2$ and $k = 1$.

4. If $x > 5$, then $2^x + 17 \le 2^x + 2^x = 2 \cdot 2^x \le 2 \cdot 3^x$. This shows that $2^x + 17$ is $O(3^x)$ (the witnesses are $C = 2$ and $k = 5$).

6. We can use the following inequalities, valid for all $x > 1$ (note that making the denominator of a fraction smaller makes the fraction larger).

$$\frac{x^3 + 2x}{2x + 1} \le \frac{x^3 + 2x^3}{2x} = \frac{3}{2}x^2$$

This proves the desired statement, with witnesses $k = 1$ and $C = 3/2$.

8. a) Since $x^3 \log x$ is not $O(x^3)$ (because the $\log x$ factor grows without bound as x increases), $n = 3$ is too small. On the other hand, certainly $\log x$ grows more slowly than x, so $2x^2 + x^3 \log x \leq 2x^4 + x^4 = 3x^4$. Therefore $n = 4$ is the answer, with $C = 3$ and $k = 0$.

b) The $(\log x)^4$ is insignificant compared to the x^5 term, so the answer is $n = 5$. Formally we can take $C = 4$ and $k = 1$ as witnesses.

c) For large x, this fraction is fairly close to 1. (This can be seen by dividing numerator and denominator by x^4.) Therefore we can take $n = 0$; in other words, this function is $O(x^0) = O(1)$. Note that $n = -1$ will not do, since a number close to 1 is not less than a constant times n^{-1} for large n. Formally we can write $f(x) \leq 3x^4/x^4 = 3$ for all $x > 1$, so witnesses are $C = 3$ and $k = 1$.

d) This is similar to the previous part, but this time $n = -1$ will do, since for large x, $f(x) \approx 1/x$. Formally we can write $f(x) \leq 6x^3/x^3 = 6$ for all $x > 1$, so witnesses are $C = 6$ and $k = 1$.

10. Since $x^3 \leq x^4$ for all $x > 1$, we know that x^3 is $O(x^4)$ (witnesses $C = 1$ and $k = 1$). On the other hand, if $x^4 \leq Cx^3$, then (dividing by x^3) $x \leq C$. Since this latter condition cannot hold for all large x, no matter what the value of the constant C, we conclude that x^4 is not $O(x^3)$.

12. We showed that $x \log x$ is $O(x^2)$ in Exercise 2c. To show that x^2 is not $O(x \log x)$ it is enough to show that $x^2/(x \log x)$ is unbounded. This is the same as showing that $x/\log x$ is unbounded. First let us note that $\log x < \sqrt{x}$ for all $x > 16$. This can be seen by looking at the graphs of these functions, or by calculus. Therefore the fraction $x/\log x$ is greater than $x/\sqrt{x} = \sqrt{x}$ for all $x > 16$, and this clearly is not bounded.

14. a) No, by an argument similar to Exercise 10.

b) Yes, since $x^3 \leq x^3$ for all x (witnesses $C = 1$, $k = 0$).

c) Yes, since $x^3 \leq x^2 + x^3$ for all x (witnesses $C = 1$, $k = 0$).

d) Yes, since $x^3 \leq x^2 + x^4$ for all x (witnesses $C = 1$, $k = 0$).

e) Yes, since $x^3 \leq 2^x \leq 3^x$ for all $x > 10$ (see Exercise 2e). Thus we have witnesses $C = 1$ and $k = 10$.

f) Yes, since $x^3 \leq 2 \cdot (x^3/2)$ for all x (witnesses $C = 2$, $k = 0$).

16. The given information says that $|f(x)| \leq C|x|$ for all $x > k$, where C and k are particular constants. Let k' be the larger of k and 1. Then since $|x| \leq |x^2|$ for all $x > 1$, we have $|f(x)| \leq C|x^2|$ for all $x > k'$, as desired.

18. $1^k + 2^k + \cdots + n^k \leq n^k + n^k + \cdots + n^k = n \cdot n^k = n^{k+1}$

20. The approach in these problems is to pick out the most rapidly growing term in each sum and discard the rest (including the multiplicative constants).

a) This is $O(n^3 \cdot \log n + \log n \cdot n^3)$, which is the same as $O(n^3 \cdot \log n)$.

b) Since 2^n dominates n^2, and 3^n dominates n^3, this is $O(2^n \cdot 3^n) = O(6^n)$.

c) The dominant terms in the two factors are n^n and $n!$, respectively. Therefore this is $O(n^n n!)$.

22. We can use the following rule of thumb to determine what simple big-Theta function to use: throw away all the lower order terms (those that don't grow as fast as other terms) and all constant coefficients.

a) This function is $\Theta(1)$, so it is not $\Theta(x)$, since 1 (or 10) grows more slowly than x. To be precise, x is not $O(10)$. For the same reason, this function is not $\Omega(x)$.

b) This function is $\Theta(x)$; we can ignore the "$+7$" since it is a lower order term, and we can ignore the coefficient. Of course, since $f(x)$ is $\Theta(x)$, it is also $\Omega(x)$.

c) This function grows faster than x. Therefore $f(x)$ is not $\Theta(x)$ but it is $\Omega(x)$.

d) This function grows more slowly than x. Therefore $f(x)$ is not $\Theta(x)$ or $\Omega(x)$.

e) This function has values that are, for all practical purposes, equal to x (certainly $\lfloor x \rfloor$ is always between $x/2$ and x, for $x > 2$), so it is $\Theta(x)$ and therefore also $\Omega(x)$.

f) As in part **(e)** this function has values that are, for all practical purposes, equal to $x/2$, so it is $\Theta(x)$ and therefore also $\Omega(x)$.

24. a) This follows from the fact that for all $x > 7$, $x \le 3x + 7 \le 4x$.

b) For large x, clearly $x^2 \le 2x^2 + x - 7$. On the other hand, for $x \ge 1$ we have $2x^2 + x - 7 \le 3x^2$.

c) For $x > 2$ we certainly have $\lfloor x + \frac{1}{2} \rfloor \le 2x$ and also $x \le 2\lfloor x + \frac{1}{2} \rfloor$.

d) For $x > 2$, $\log(x^2 + 1) \le \log(2x^2) = 1 + 2\log x \le 3\log x$ (recall that log means $\log_2$). On the other hand, since $x < x^2 + 1$ for all positive x, we have $\log x \le \log(x^2 + 1)$.

e) This follows from the fact that $\log_{10} x = C(\log_2 x)$, where $C = 1/\log_2 10$.

26. We just need to look at the definitions. To say that $f(x)$ is $O(g(x))$ means that there are constants C and k such that $|f(x)| \le C|g(x)|$ for all $x > k$. Note that without loss of generality we may take C and k to be positive. To say that $g(x)$ is $\Omega(f(x))$ is to say that there are positive constants C' and k' such that $|g(x)| \ge C'|f(x)|$ for all $x > k$. These are saying exactly the same thing if we set $C' = 1/C$ and $k' = k$.

28. a) By Exercise 25 we have to show that $3x^2 + x + 1$ is $O(3x^2)$ and that $3x^2$ is $O(3x^2 + x + 1)$. The latter is trivial, since $3x^2 \le 3x^2 + x + 1$ for $x > 0$. The former is almost as trivial, since $3x^2 + x + 1 \le 3x^2 + 3x^2 = 2 \cdot 3x^2$ for all $x > 1$. What we have shown is that $1 \cdot 3x^2 \le 3x^2 + x + 1 \le 2 \cdot 3x^2$ for all $x > 1$; in other words, $C_1 = 1$ and $C_2 = 2$ in Exercise 27.

b) The following picture shows that graph of $3x^2 + x + 1$ falls in the shaded region between the graph of $3x^2$ and the graph of $2 \cdot 3x^2$ for all $x > 1$.

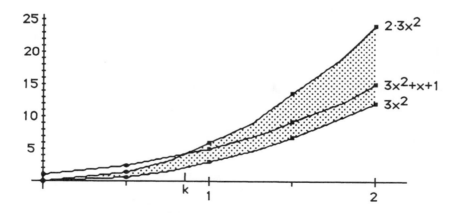

30. Looking at the definition, we see that to say that $f(x)$ is $\Omega(1)$ means that $|f(x)| \ge C$ when $x > k$, for some positive constants k and C. In other words, $f(x)$ keeps at least a certain distance away from 0 for large enough x. For example, $1/x$ is not $\Omega(1)$, since it gets arbitrary close to 0; but $(x - 2)(x - 10)$ is $\Omega(1)$, since $f(x) \ge 9$ for $x > 11$.

32. The nth odd positive integer is $2n - 1$. Thus each of the first n odd positive integers is at most $2n$. Therefore their product is at most $(2n)^n$, so one answer is $O((2n)^n)$. Of course other answers are possible as well.

34. This follows from the fact that $\log_b x$ and $\log_a x$ are the same except for a multiplicative constant, namely $d = \log_b a$. Thus if $f(x) \le C \log_b x$, then $f(x) \le Cd \log_a x$.

36. This does not follow. Let $f(x) = 2x$ and $g(x) = x$. Then $f(x)$ is $O(g(x))$. Now $2^{f(x)} = 2^{2x} = 4^x$, and $2^{g(x)} = 2^x$, and 4^x is not $O(2^x)$. Indeed, $4^x/2^x = 2^x$, so the ratio grows without bound as x grows—it is not bounded by a constant.

38. The definition of "$f(x)$ is $\Theta(g(x))$" is that $f(x)$ is both $O(g(x))$ and $\Omega(g(x))$. That means that there are positive constants C_1, k_1, C_2, and k_2 such that $|f(x)| \leq C_2|g(x)|$ for all $x > k_2$ and $|f(x)| \geq C_1|g(x)|$ for all $x > k_1$. Similarly, we have that there are positive constants C_1', k_1', C_2', and k_2' such that $|g(x)| \leq C_2'|h(x)|$ for all $x > k_2'$ and $|g(x)| \geq C_1'|h(x)|$ for all $x > k_1'$. We can combine these inequalities to obtain $|f(x)| \leq C_2C_2'|h(x)|$ for all $x > \max(k_2, k_2')$ and $|f(x)| \geq C_1C_1'|h(x)|$ for all $x > \max(k_1, k_1')$. This means that $f(x)$ is $\Theta(h(x))$.

40. The definitions tell us that there are positive constants C_1, k_1, C_2, and k_2 such that $|f_1(x)| \leq C_2|g_1(x)|$ for all $x > k_2$ and $|f_1(x)| \geq C_1|g_1(x)|$ for all $x > k_1$, and that there are positive constants C_1', k_1', C_2', and k_2' such that $|f_2(x)| \leq C_2'|g_2(x)|$ for all $x > k_2'$ and $|f_2(x)| \geq C_1'|g_2(x)|$ for all $x > k_1'$. We can multiply these inequalities to obtain $|f_1(x)f_2(x)| \leq C_2C_2'|g_1(x)g_2(x)|$ for all $x > \max(k_2, k_2')$ and $|f_1(x)f_2(x)| \geq C_1C_1'|g_1(x)g_2(x)|$ for all $x > \max(k_1, k_1')$. This means that $f_1(x)f_2(x)$ is $\Theta(g_1(x)g_2(x))$.

42. Typically C will be less than 1. From some point onward to the right $(x > k)$, the graph of $f(x)$ must be above the graph of $g(x)$ after the latter has been scaled down by the factor C. Note that $f(x)$ does not have to be larger than $g(x)$ itself.

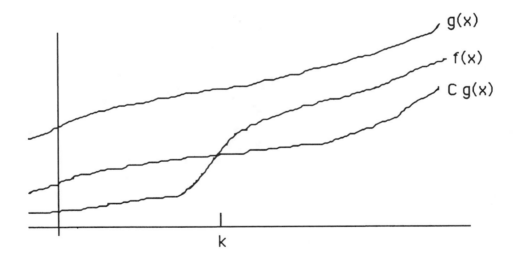

44. We need to show inequalities both ways. First, we show that $|f(x)| \leq Cx^n$ for all $x \geq 1$, as follows, noting that $x^i \leq x^n$ for such values of x whenever $i < n$. We have the following inequalities, where M is the largest of the absolute values of the coefficients and C is $M(n+1)$:

$$\begin{aligned}
|f(x)| &= |a_n x^n + a_{n-1}x^{n-1} + \cdots + a_1 x + a_0| \\
&\leq |a_n|x^n + |a_{n-1}|x^{n-1} + \cdots + |a_1|x + |a_0| \\
&\leq |a_n|x^n + |a_{n-1}|x^n + \cdots + |a_1|x^n + |a_0|x^n \\
&\leq Mx^n + Mx^n + \cdots + Mx^n + Mx^n = Cx^n
\end{aligned}$$

For the other direction, which is a little messier, let k be chosen larger than 1 and larger than $2nm/|a_n|$, where m is the largest of the absolute values of the a_i's for $i < n$. Then each a_{n-i}/x^i will be smaller than

$|a_n|/2n$ in absolute value for all $x > k$. Now we have for all $x > k$,

$$|f(x)| = |a_n x^n + a_{n-1}x^{n-1} + \cdots + a_1 x + a_0|$$
$$= x^n \left| a_n + \frac{a_{n-1}}{x} + \cdots + \frac{a_1}{x^{n-1}} + \frac{a_0}{x^n} \right|$$
$$\geq x^n |a_n/2|,$$

as desired.

46. We just make the analogous change in the definition of big-Omega that was made in the definition of big-O: there exist positive constants C, k_1, and k_2 such that $|f(x,y)| \geq C|g(x,y)|$ for all $x > k_1$ and $y > k_2$.

48. For all values of x and y greater than 1, each term of the given expression is greater than $x^3 y^3$, so the entire expression is greater than $x^3 y^3$. In other words, we take $C = k_1 = k_2 = 1$ in the definition given in Exercise 46.

50. For all positive values of x and y, we know that $\lceil xy \rceil \geq xy$ by definition (since the ceiling function value cannot be less than the argument). Thus $\lceil xy \rceil$ is $\Omega(xy)$ from the definition, taking $C = 1$ and $k_1 = k_2 = 0$. In fact, $\lceil xy \rceil$ is also $O(xy)$ (and therefore $\Theta(xy)$); this is easy to see since $\lceil xy \rceil \leq (x+1)(y+1) \leq (2x)(2y) = 4xy$ for all x and y greater than 1.

52. a) Under the hypotheses,

$$\lim_{x \to \infty} \frac{cf(x)}{g(x)} = c \lim_{x \to \infty} \frac{f(x)}{g(x)} = c \cdot 0 = 0.$$

b) Under the hypotheses,

$$\lim_{x \to \infty} \frac{f_1(x) + f_2(x)}{g(x)} = \lim_{x \to \infty} \frac{f_1(x)}{g(x)} + \lim_{x \to \infty} \frac{f_2(x)}{g(x)} = 0 + 0 = 0.$$

54. The behaviors of f and g alone are not really at issue; what is important is whether $f(x)/g(x)$ approaches 0 as $x \to \infty$. Thus, as shown in the picture, it might happen that the graphs of f and g rise, but f increases enough more rapidly than g so that the ratio gets small. In the picture, we see that $f(x)/g(x)$ is asymptotic to the x-axis.

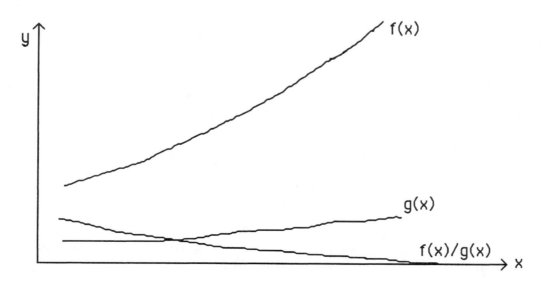

56. No. Let $f(x) = x$ and $g(x) = x^2$. Then clearly $f(x)$ is $o(g(x))$, but the ratio of the logs of the absolute values is the constant 2, and 2 does not approach 0. Therefore it is not the case in this example that $\log|f(x)|$ is $o(\log|g(x)|)$.

58. This follows from the fact that the limit of $f(x)/g(x)$ is 0 in this case, as can be most easily seen by dividing numerator and denominator by x^n (the numerator then is bounded and the absolute value of the denominator grows without bound as $x \to \infty$).

60. Since $f(x) = 1/x$ is a decreasing function which has the value $1/x$ at $x = j$, it is clear that $1/j < 1/x$ throughout the interval from $j - 1$ to j. Summing over all the intervals for $j = 2, 3, \ldots, n$, and noting that the definite integral is the area under the curve, we obtain the inequality in the hint. Therefore

$$H_n = 1 + \sum_{j=2}^{n} \frac{1}{j} < 1 + \int_1^n \frac{1}{x}\,dx = 1 + \ln n = 1 + C\log n \le 2C\log n$$

for $n > 2$, where $C = \log e$. (See Section 3.2 for this summation notation.)

62. Clearly $n! \le n^n$ for all $n \ge 1$. Therefore $\log(n!) \le \log(n^n) = n\log n$. Thus $\log(n!)$ is $O(n\log n)$.

SECTION 2.3   Complexity of Algorithms

2. We can sort the first four elements (which we assume are distinct integers) by the comparisons shown. (After the first three steps, the smallest element is definitely in the first position; after the next two steps, the next smallest element is in the second position.) Since only six comparisons are used, regardless of the length of the list, this algorithm has complexity $O(1)$.

> **procedure** *sort four*$(a_1, a_2, \ldots, a_n$: distinct integers)
> **if** $a_4 < a_3$ **then** interchange a_4 and a_3
> **if** $a_3 < a_2$ **then** interchange a_3 and a_2
> **if** $a_2 < a_1$ **then** interchange a_2 and a_1
> **if** $a_4 < a_3$ **then** interchange a_4 and a_3
> **if** $a_3 < a_2$ **then** interchange a_3 and a_2
> **if** $a_4 < a_3$ **then** interchange a_4 and a_3

4. If we successively square k times, then we have computed x^{2^k}. Thus we can compute x^{2^k} with only k multiplications, rather than the $2^k - 1$ multiplications that the naive algorithm would require, so this method is much more efficient.

6. a) By the way that $S - 1$ is defined, it is clear that $S \wedge (S - 1)$ is the same as S except that the rightmost one bit has been changed to a zero. Thus we add 1 to *count* for every one bit (since we stop as soon as $S = 0$, i.e., as soon as S consists of just zero bits).
b) Obviously the number of bitwise *AND* operations is equal to the final value of *count*, i.e., the number of one bits in S.

8. a) Initially $y := 3$. For $i = 1$ we set y to $3 \cdot 2 + 1 = 7$. For $i = 2$ we set y to $7 \cdot 2 + 1 = 15$, and we are done.
b) There is one multiplication and one addition for each of the n passes through the loop, so there are n multiplications and n additions in all.

10. We are asked to compute $(2n^2 + 2^n) \cdot 10^{-9}$ for each of these values of n. When appropriate, we change the units from seconds to some larger unit of time.
   a) 1.224×10^{-6} seconds   **b)** approximately 1.05×10^{-3} seconds
   c) approximately 1.13×10^6 seconds, which is about 13 days (nonstop)
   d) approximately 1.27×10^{21} seconds, which is about 4×10^{13} years (nonstop)

12. a) The number of comparisons does not depend on the values of a_1 through a_n. Exactly $2n - 1$ comparisons are used, as was determined in Example 1. In other words, the best case performance is $O(n)$.
   b) In the best case $x = a_1$. We saw in Example 4 that three comparisons are used in that case. The best case performance, then, is $O(1)$.
   c) It is hard to give an exact answer, since it depends on the binary representation of the number n, among other things. In any case, the best case performance is really not much different from the worst case performance, namely $O(\log n)$, since the list is essentially cut in half at each iteration, and the algorithm does not stop until the list has only one element left in it.

14. a) In order to find the maximum element of a list of n elements, we need to make at least $n - 1$ comparisons, one to rule out each of the other elements. Since Algorithm 1 in Section 2.1 used just this number (not counting bookkeeping), it is optimal.
   b) Linear search is not optimal, since we found that binary search was more efficient. This assumes that we can be given the list already sorted into increasing order.

16. We will count comparisons of elements in the list to x. (This ignores comparisons of subscripts, but since we are only interested in a big-O analysis, no harm is done.) Furthermore, we will assume that the number of elements in the list is a power of 4, say $n = 4^k$. Just as in the case of binary search, we need to determine the maximum number of times the **while** loop is iterated. Each pass through the loop cuts the number of elements still being considered (those whose subscripts are from i to j) by a factor of 4. Therefore after k iterations, the active portion of the list will have length 1; that is, we will have $i = j$. The loop terminates at this point. Now each iteration of the loop requires two comparisons in the worst case (one with a_m and one with either a_l or a_u). Three more comparisons are needed at the end. Therefore the number of comparisons is $2k + 3$, which is $O(k)$. But $k = \log_4 n$, which is $O(\log n)$ since logarithms to different bases differ only by multiplicative constants, so the time complexity of this algorithm (in all cases, not just the worst case) is $O(\log n)$.

18. The algorithm we gave for finding all the modes essentially just goes through the list once, doing a little bookkeeping at each step. In particular, between any two successive executions of the statement $i := i + 1$ there are at most about eight operations (such as comparing *count* with *modecount*, or reinitializing *value*). Therefore at most about $8n$ steps are done in all, so the time complexity in all cases is $O(n)$.

20. The algorithm we gave is clearly of linear time complexity, i.e., $O(n)$, since we were able to keep updating the sum of previous terms, rather than recomputing it each time. This applies in all cases, not just the worst case.

22. The algorithm read through the list once and did a bounded amount of work on each term. Looked at another way, only a bounded amount of work was done between increments of j in the algorithm given in the solution. Thus the complexity is $O(n)$.

24. It takes $n - 1$ comparisons to find the least element in the list, then $n - 2$ comparisons to find the least element among the remaining elements, and so on. Thus the total number of comparisons is $(n-1)+(n-2)+\cdots+2+1 = n(n-1)/2$, which is $O(n^2)$.

26. Each iteration (determining whether we can use a coin of a given denomination) takes a bounded amount of time, and there are at most n iterations, since each iteration decreases the number of cents remaining. Therefore there are $O(n)$ comparisons.

28. a) The bubble sort algorithm uses about $n^2/2$ comparisons for a list of length n, and $(2n)^2/2 = 2n^2$ comparisons for a list of length $2n$. Therefore the number of comparisons goes up by a factor of 4.

b) The analysis is the same as for bubble sort.

c) The analysis is the same as for bubble sort.

d) The binary insertion sort algorithm uses about $Cn \log n$ comparisons for a list of length n, where C is a constant. Therefore it uses about $C \cdot 2n \log 2n = C \cdot 2n \log 2 + C \cdot 2n \log n = C \cdot 2n + C \cdot 2n \log n$ comparisons for a list of length $2n$. Therefore the number of comparisons increases by about a factor of 2 (for large n, the first term is small compared to the second and can be ignored).

SECTION 2.4   The Integers and Division

2. a) $1 \mid a$ since $a = 1 \cdot a$.   **b)** $a \mid 0$ since $0 = a \cdot 0$.

4. Suppose $a \mid b$, so that $b = at$ for some t, and $b \mid c$, so that $c = bs$ for some s. Then substituting the first equation into the second, we obtain $c = (at)s = a(ts)$. This means that $a \mid c$, as desired.

6. Under the hypotheses, we have $c = as$ and $d = bt$ for some s and t. Multiplying we obtain $cd = ab(st)$, which means that $ab \mid cd$, as desired.

8. The numbers 19, 101, 107, and 113 are prime, as we can verify by trial division. The numbers $27 = 3^3$ and $93 = 3 \cdot 31$ are not prime.

10. In each case we can carry out the arithmetic on a calculator.

a) Since $8 \cdot 5 = 40$ and $44 - 40 = 4$, we have quotient $44 \ \mathbf{div} \ 8 = 5$ and remainder $44 \ \mathbf{mod} \ 8 = 4$.

b) Since $21 \cdot 37 = 777$, we have quotient $777 \ \mathbf{div} \ 21 = 37$ and remainder $777 \ \mathbf{mod} \ 21 = 0$.

c) As above, we can compute $123 \ \mathbf{div} \ 19 = 6$ and $123 \ \mathbf{mod} \ 19 = 9$. However, since the dividend is negative and the remainder is nonzero, the quotient is $-(6+1) = -7$ and the remainder is $19 - 9 = 10$. To check that $-123 \ \mathbf{div} \ 19 = -7$ and $-123 \ \mathbf{mod} \ 19 = 10$, we note that $-123 = (-7)(19) + 10$.

d) Since $1 \ \mathbf{div} \ 23 = 0$ and $1 \ \mathbf{mod} \ 23 = 1$, we have $-1 \ \mathbf{div} \ 23 = -1$ and $-1 \ \mathbf{mod} \ 23 = 22$.

e) Since $2002 \ \mathbf{div} \ 87 = 23$ and $2002 \ \mathbf{mod} \ 87 = 1$, we have $-2002 \ \mathbf{div} \ 87 = -24$ and $2002 \ \mathbf{mod} \ 87 = 86$.

f) Clearly $0 \ \mathbf{div} \ 17 = 0$ and $0 \ \mathbf{mod} \ 17 = 0$.

g) We have $1234567 \ \mathbf{div} \ 1001 = 1233$ and $1234567 \ \mathbf{mod} \ 1001 = 334$.

h) Since $100 \ \mathbf{div} \ 101 = 0$ and $100 \ \mathbf{mod} \ 101 = 100$, we have $-100 \ \mathbf{div} \ 101 = -1$ and $-100 \ \mathbf{mod} \ 101 = 1$.

12. We obtain the answers by trial division. The factorizations are $39 = 3 \cdot 13$, $81 = 3^4$, $101 = 101$ (prime), $143 = 11 \cdot 13$, $289 = 17^2$, and $899 = 29 \cdot 31$.

14. A zero appears at the end of a number for every factor of 10 $(= 2 \cdot 5)$ the number has. Now 100! certainly has more factors of 2 than it has factors of 5, so the number of factors of 10 it has is the same as the number of factors of 5. Each of the twenty numbers 5, 10, 15, ..., 100 contributes a factor of 5 to 100!, and in addition the four numbers 25, 50, 75, and 100 contribute one more factor of 5. Therefore there are 24 factors of 5 in 100!, so 100! ends in exactly 24 zeros.

16. We must find, by inspection with mental arithmetic, the greatest common divisors of the numbers from 1 to 11 with 12, and list those whose gcd is 1. These are 1, 5, 7, and 11. There are so few since 12 had many factors—in particular, both 2 and 3.

18. Since these numbers are small, the easiest approach is to find the prime factorization of each number and look for any common prime factors.
   a) Since $21 = 3 \cdot 7$, $34 = 2 \cdot 17$, and $55 = 5 \cdot 11$, these are pairwise relatively prime.
   b) Since $85 = 5 \cdot 17$, these are not pairwise relatively prime.
   c) Since $25 = 5^2$, 41 is prime, $49 = 7^2$, and $64 = 2^6$, these are pairwise relatively prime.
   d) Since 17, 19, and 23 are prime and $18 = 2 \cdot 3^2$, these are pairwise relatively prime.

20. a) Since $6 = 1 + 2 + 3$, and these three summands are the only proper divisors of 6, we conclude that 6 is perfect. Similarly $28 = 1 + 2 + 4 + 7 + 14$.
   b) We need to find all the proper divisors of $2^{p-1}(2^p - 1)$. Certainly all the numbers $1, 2, 4, 8, \ldots, 2^{p-1}$ are proper divisors, and their sum is $2^p - 1$ (this is a geometric series). Also each of these divisors times $2^p - 1$ is also a divisor, and all but the last is proper. Again adding up this geometric series we find a sum of $(2^p - 1)(2^{p-1} - 1)$. There are no other other proper divisors. Therefore the sum of all the divisors is $(2^p - 1) + (2^p - 1)(2^{p-1} - 1) = (2^p - 1)(1 + 2^{p-1} - 1) = (2^p - 1)2^{p-1}$, which is our original number. Therefore this number is perfect.

22. Assume that $a \equiv b \pmod{m}$. This means that $m \mid a - b$, say $a - b = mc$, so that $a = b + mc$. Now let us compute $a \bmod m$. We know that $b = qm + r$ for some nonnegative r less than m (namely, $r = b \bmod m$). Therefore we can write $a = qm + r + mc = (q + c)m + r$. By definition this means that r must also equal $a \bmod m$. That is what we wanted to prove.

24. We need to find a factor if there is one, or else check all possible prime divisors up to the square root of the given number to verify that there is no nontrivial divisor.
   a) $2^7 - 1 = 127$. Division by 2, 3, 5, 7, and 11 shows that these are not factors. Since $\sqrt{127} < 13$, we are done; 127 is prime.
   b) $2^9 - 1 = 511 = 7 \cdot 73$, so this number is not prime.
   c) $2^{11} - 1 = 2047 = 23 \cdot 89$, so this number is not prime.
   d) $2^{13} - 1 = 8191$. Division by 2, 3, 5, 7, 11, 13, 17, 19, 23, 29, 31, 37, 41, 43, 47, 53, 59, 61, 67, 71, 73, 79, 83, and 89 (phew!) shows that these are not factors. Since $\sqrt{8191} < 97$, we are done; 8191 is prime.

26. Certainly if n is prime, then all the integers from 1 to $n - 1$ are less than or equal to n and relatively prime to n, but no others are, so $\phi(n) = n - 1$. Conversely, suppose that n is not prime. If $n = 1$, then we have $\phi(1) = 1 \neq 1 - 1$. If $n > 1$, then $n = ab$ with $1 < a < n$ and $1 < b < n$. Note that neither a nor b is relatively prime to n. Therefore the number of positive integers less than or equal to n and relatively prime to n is at most $n - 3$ (since a, b, and n are not in this collection), so $\phi(n) \neq n - 1$.

28. We form the greatest common divisors by finding the minimum exponent for each prime factor.
   a) $2^2 \cdot 3^3 \cdot 5^2$ **b)** $2 \cdot 3 \cdot 11$ **c)** 17   **d)** 1   **e)** 5   **f)** $2 \cdot 3 \cdot 5 \cdot 7$

30. We form the least common multiples by finding the maximum exponent for each prime factor.
   a) $2^5 \cdot 3^3 \cdot 5^5$ **b)** $2^{11} \cdot 3^9 \cdot 5 \cdot 7 \cdot 11 \cdot 13 \cdot 17^{14}$ **c)** 17^{17} **d)** $2^2 \cdot 5^3 \cdot 7 \cdot 13$
   e) undefined (0 is not a positive integer)   **f)** $2 \cdot 3 \cdot 5 \cdot 7$

32. We have $1000 = 2^3 \cdot 5^3$ and $625 = 5^4$, so $\gcd(1000, 625) = 5^3 = 125$, and $\text{lcm}(1000, 625) = 2^3 \cdot 5^4 = 5000$. As expected, $125 \cdot 5000 = 625000 = 1000 \cdot 625$.

34. By Theorem 6 we have $a = dq + r$ with $0 \leq r < d$. Dividing the equation by d we obtain $a/d = q + (r/d)$, with $0 \leq (r/d) < 1$. Thus by definition it is clear that q is $\lfloor a/d \rfloor$. The original equation shows, of course, that $r = a - dq$, proving the second of the original statements.

36. In each case we just apply the division algorithm (carry out the division) to obtain the quotient and remainder, as in elementary school. However, if the dividend is negative, we must make sure to make the remainder positive, which may involve a quotient 1 less than might be expected.

    a) Since $-17 = 2 \cdot (-9) + 1$, the remainder is 1. That is, $-17 \bmod 2 = 1$. Note that we do not write $-17 = 2 \cdot (-8) - 1$, so $-17 \bmod 2 \neq -1$.

    b) Since $144 = 7 \cdot 20 + 4$, the remainder is 4. That is, $144 \bmod 7 = 4$.

    c) Since $-101 = 13 \cdot (-8) + 3$, the remainder is 3. That is, $-101 \bmod 13 = 3$. Note that we do not write $-101 = 13 \cdot (-7) - 10$; we can't have $-101 \bmod 13 = -10$, because $a \bmod b$ is always nonnegative.

    d) Since $199 = 19 \cdot 10 + 9$, the remainder is 9. That is, $199 \bmod 19 = 9$.

38. Among the infinite set of correct answers are 4, 16, -8, 1204, and -7016360.

40. By Exercise 41 we know that the product of the greatest common divisor and the least common multiple of two numbers is the product of the two numbers. Therefore the answer is $(2^7 \cdot 3^8 \cdot 5^2 \cdot 7^{11})/(2^3 \cdot 3^4 \cdot 5) = 2^4 \cdot 3^4 \cdot 5 \cdot 7^{11}$.

42. From $a \equiv b \pmod{m}$ we know that $b = a + sm$ for some integer s. Similarly, $d = c + tm$. Subtracting, we have $b - d = (a - c) + (s - t)m$, which means that $a - c \equiv b - d \pmod{m}$.

44. From $a \equiv b \pmod{m}$ we know that $b = a + sm$ for some integer s. Multiplying by c we have $bc = ac + s(mc)$, which means that $ac \equiv bc \pmod{mc}$.

46. From $a \equiv b \pmod{m}$ we know that $b = a + sm$ for some integer s. Now if d is a common divisor of a and m, then it divides the right-hand side of this equation, so it also divides b. We can rewrite the equation as $a = b - sm$, and then by similar reasoning, we see that every common divisor of b and m is also a divisor of a. This shows that the set of common divisors of a and m is equal to the set of common divisors of b and m, so certainly $\gcd(a, m) = \gcd(b, m)$.

48. In each case we need to compute $k \bmod 101$ by dividing by 101 and finding the remainders. This can be done with a calculator that keeps 13 digits of accuracy internally. Just divide the number by 101, subtract off the integer part of the answer, and multiply the fraction that remains by 101. The result will be almost exactly an integer, and that integer is the answer.

    a) 58   **b)** 60   **c)** 52   **d)** 3

50. We just calculate using the formula. We are given $x_0 = 3$. Then $x_1 = (4 \cdot 3 + 1) \bmod 7 = 13 \bmod 7 = 6$; $x_2 = (4 \cdot 6 + 1) \bmod 7 = 25 \bmod 7 = 4$; $x_3 = (4 \cdot 4 + 1) \bmod 7 = 17 \bmod 7 = 3$. At this point the sequence must continue to repeat 3, 6, 4, 3, 6, 4, ... forever.

52. We assume that the input to this procedure consists of a modulus ($m \geq 2$), a multiplier (a), an increment (c), a seed (x_0), and the number (n) of pseudorandom numbers desired. The output will be the sequence $\{x_i\}$.

> **procedure** *pseudorandom*$(m, a, c, x_0, n :$ nonnegative integers)
> **for** $i := 1$ **to** n
> $\quad x_i := (ax_{i-1} + c) \bmod m$

54. We just need to "subtract 3" from each letter. For example, E goes down to B, and B goes down to Y.
   a) BLUE JEANS   **b)** TEST TODAY   **c)** EAT DIM SUM

56. We know that $1 \cdot 0 + 2 \cdot 2 + 3 \cdot 0 + 4 \cdot 1 + 5 \cdot 5 + 6 \cdot 7 + 7 \cdot Q + 8 \cdot 8 + 9 \cdot 9 + 10 \cdot 1 \equiv 0 \pmod{11}$. This simplifies to $230 + 7Q \equiv 0 \pmod{11}$. We subtract 230 from both sides and simplify to $7Q \equiv 1 \pmod{11}$, since $231 = 11 \cdot 21$. It is now a simple matter to use trial and error (or the methods to be introduced in Section 2.6) to find that $Q = 8$ (since $56 \equiv 1 \pmod{11}$).

58. The number of (positive) factors that a positive integer n has can be determined from the prime factorization of n. If we write this prime factorization as $n = p_1^{e_1} p_2^{e_2} \cdots p_r^{e_r}$, then there are $(e_1 + 1)(e_2 + 1) \cdots (e_r + 1)$ different factors. This follows from the ideas in Chapter 4. Specifically, in choosing a factor we can choose $0, 1, 2, \ldots, e_1$ of the p_1 factors, a total of $e_1 + 1$ choices; for each of these there are $e_2 + 1$ choices as to how many p_2 factors to include, and so on. If we don't want to go through the analysis using the ideas given below, we could simply compute the number of factors for each n, starting at 1 (perhaps using a computer program), and thereby obtain the answers by "brute force."
   a) If an integer is to have exactly three different factors (we assume "positive factors" is intended here), then n must be the square of a prime number; that is the only way to make $(e_1 + 1)(e_2 + 1) \cdots (e_r + 1) = 3$. The smallest prime number is 2. So the smallest positive integer with exactly three factors is $2^2 = 4$.
   b) This time we want $(e_1 + 1)(e_2 + 1) \cdots (e_r + 1) = 4$. We can do this with $r = 1$ and $e_1 = 3$, or with $r = 2$ and $e_1 = e_2 = 1$. The smallest numbers obtainable in these ways are $2^3 = 8$ and $2 \cdot 3 = 6$, respectively. So the smallest number with four factors is 6.
   c) This time we want $(e_1 + 1)(e_2 + 1) \cdots (e_r + 1) = 5$. We can do this only with $r = 1$ and $e_1 = 4$, so the smallest such number is $2^4 = 16$.
   d) This time we want $(e_1 + 1)(e_2 + 1) \cdots (e_r + 1) = 6$. We can do this with $r = 1$ and $e_1 = 5$, or with $r = 2$ and $e_1 = 2$ and $e_2 = 1$. The smallest numbers obtainable in these ways are $2^5 = 32$ and $2^2 \cdot 3 = 12$, respectively. So the smallest number with six factors is 12.
   e) This time we want $(e_1 + 1)(e_2 + 1) \cdots (e_r + 1) = 10$. We can do this with $r = 1$ and $e_1 = 9$, or with $r = 2$ and $e_1 = 4$ and $e_2 = 1$. The smallest numbers obtainable in these ways are $2^9 = 512$ and $2^4 \cdot 3 = 48$, respectively. So the smallest number with ten factors is 48.

60. Obviously there are no definitive answers to these problems, but we present below a reasonable and satisfying rule for forming the sequence in each case.
   a) All the entries are primes. In fact, the nth term is the smallest prime number greater than or equal to n.
   b) Here we see that the sequence jumps at the prime locations. We can state this succinctly by saying that the nth term is the number of prime numbers not exceeding n.
   c) There are 0s in the prime locations and 1s elsewhere. In other words, the nth term of the sequence is 0 if n is a prime number and 1 otherwise.
   d) This sequence is actually important in number theory. The nth term is -1 if n is prime, 0 if n has a repeated prime factor (for example, $12 = 2^2 \cdot 3$, so 2 is a repeated prime factor of 12 and therefore the twelfth term is 0), and 1 otherwise (if n is not prime but is square-free).
   e) The nth term is 0 if n has two or more distinct prime factors, and is 1 otherwise. In other words the nth term is 1 if n is a power of a prime number.
   f) The nth term is the square of the nth prime.

SECTION 2.5   Integers and Algorithms

2. To convert from decimal to binary, we successively divide by 2. We write down the remainders so obtained from right to left; that is the binary representation of the given number.

a) Since $321/2$ is 160 with a remainder of 1, the rightmost digit is 1. Then since $160/2$ is 80 with a remainder of 0, the second digit from the right is 0. We continue in this manner, obtaining successive quotients of 40, 20, 10, 5, 2, 1, and 0, and remainders of 0, 0, 0, 0, 1, 0, and 1. Putting all these remainders in order from right to left we obtain $(1\,0100\,0001)_2$ as the binary representation. We could, as a check, expand this binary numeral: $2^0 + 2^6 + 2^8 = 1 + 64 + 256 = 321$.

b) We could carry out the same process as in part **(a)**. Alternatively, we might notice that $1023 = 1024 - 1 = 2^{10} - 1$. Therefore the binary representation is 1 less than $(100\,0000\,0000)_2$, which is clearly $(11\,1111\,1111)_2$.

c) If we carry out the divisions by 2, the quotients are 50316, 25158, 12579, 6289, 3144, 1572, 786, 393, 196, 98, 49, 24, 12, 6, 3, 1, and 0, with remainders of 0, 0, 0, 1, 1, 0, 0, 0, 1, 0, 0, 1, 0, 0, 0, 1, and 1. Putting the remainders in order from right to left we have $(1\,1000\,1001\,0001\,1000)_2$.

4. a) $1 + 2 + 8 + 16 = 27$ **b)** $1 + 4 + 16 + 32 + 128 + 512 = 693$

c) $2 + 4 + 8 + 16 + 32 + 128 + 256 + 512 = 958$

d) $1 + 2 + 4 + 8 + 16 + 1024 + 2048 + 4096 + 8192 + 16384 = 31775$

6. Following Example 6, we simply write the binary equivalents of each digit. Since $(A)_{16} = (1010)_2$, $(B)_{16} = (1011)_2$, $(C)_{16} = (1100)_2$, $(D)_{16} = (1101)_2$, $(E)_{16} = (1110)_2$, and $(F)_{16} = (1111)_2$, we have $(BADFACED)_{16} = (1011101011011111101011001110101)_2$. Following the convention shown in Exercise 3 of grouping binary digits by fours, we can write this in a more readable form as 1011 1010 1101 1111 1010 1100 1110 1101.

8. We follow the method stated in Example 6.

a) 1111 0111 becomes F7   **b)** 1010 1010 1010 becomes AAA   **c)** 111 0111 0111 0111 becomes 7777

10. Following Example 6, we simply write the hexadecimal equivalents of each group of four binary digits. Note that we group from the right, so the left-most group, which is just 1, becomes 0001. Thus we have $(0001\,1000\,0110\,0011)_2 = (1863)_{16}$.

12. Let $(\ldots h_1 h_1 h_0)_{16}$ be the hexadecimal expansion of a positive integer. The value of that integer is, therefore, $h_0 + h_1 \cdot 16 + h_2 \cdot 16^2 + \cdots = h_0 + h_1 \cdot 2^4 + h_2 \cdot 2^8 + \cdots$. If we replace each hexadecimal digit h_i by its binary expansion $(b_{i3} b_{i2} b_{i1} b_{i0})_2$, then $h_i = b_{i0} + 2b_{i1} + 4b_{i2} + 8b_{i3}$. Therefore the value of the entire number is $b_{00} + 2b_{01} + 4b_{02} + 8b_{03} + (b_{10} + 2b_{11} + 4b_{12} + 8b_{13}) \cdot 2^4 + (b_{20} + 2b_{21} + 4b_{22} + 8b_{23}) \cdot 2^8 + \cdots = b_{00} + 2b_{01} + 4b_{02} + 8b_{03} + 2^4 b_{10} + 2^5 b_{11} + 2^6 b_{12} + 2^7 b_{13} + 2^8 b_{20} + 2^9 b_{21} + 2^{10} b_{22} + 2^{11} b_{23} + \cdots$, which is the value of the binary expansion $(\ldots b_{23} b_{22} b_{21} b_{20} b_{13} b_{12} b_{11} b_{10} b_{03} b_{02} b_{01} b_{00})_2$.

14. This is exactly the same as what we can do with hexadecimal expansion, replacing groups of four with groups of three. Specifically, convert each octal digit into its 3-digit binary equivalent. For example, $(306)_8 = (011\,000\,110)_2$.

16. Since we have procedures for converting both octal and hexadecimal to and from binary (Example 6 and Exercises 13–15), to convert from hexadecimal to octal, we first convert from hexadecimal to binary and then convert from binary to octal.

18. We work through binary in each case; see Exercises 16 and 17. Thus

$$(12345670)_8 = (001\,010\,011\,100\,101\,110\,111\,000)_2 = (0010\,1001\,1100\,1011\,1011\,1000)_2 = (29CBB8)_{16}$$

and
$$(\text{ABB093BABBA})_{16} = (1010\ 1011\ 1011\ 0000\ 1001\ 0011\ 1011\ 1010\ 1011\ 1011\ 1010)_2$$
$$= (010\ 101\ 011\ 101\ 100\ 001\ 001\ 001\ 110\ 111\ 010\ 101\ 110\ 111\ 010)_2$$
$$= (253541116725672)_8.$$

20. In effect this algorithm computes powers $123 \bmod 101$, $123^2 \bmod 101$, $123^4 \bmod 101$, $123^8 \bmod 101$, $123^{16} \bmod 101$, ..., and then multiplies (modulo 101) the required values. Since $1001 = (1111101001)_2$, we need to multiply together $123 \bmod 101$, $123^8 \bmod 101$, $123^{32} \bmod 101$, $123^{64} \bmod 101$, $123^{128} \bmod 101$, $123^{256} \bmod 101$, and $123^{512} \bmod 101$, reducing modulo 101 at each step. We compute by repeatedly squaring: $123 \bmod 101 = 22$, $123^2 \bmod 101 = 22^2 \bmod 101 = 484 \bmod 101 = 80$, $123^4 \bmod 101 = 80^2 \bmod 101 = 6400 \bmod 101 = 37$, $123^8 \bmod 101 = 37^2 \bmod 101 = 1369 \bmod 101 = 56$, $123^{16} \bmod 101 = 56^2 \bmod 101 = 3136 \bmod 101 = 5$, $123^{32} \bmod 101 = 5^2 \bmod 101 = 25$, $123^{64} \bmod 101 = 25^2 \bmod 101 = 625 \bmod 101 = 19$, $123^{128} \bmod 101 = 19^2 \bmod 101 = 361 \bmod 101 = 58$, $123^{256} \bmod 101 = 58^2 \bmod 101 = 3364 \bmod 101 = 31$, and $123^{512} \bmod 101 = 31^2 \bmod 101 = 961 \bmod 101 = 52$. Thus our final answer will be the product of 22, 56, 25, 19, 58, 31, and 52. We compute these one at a time modulo 101: $22 \cdot 56$ is 20, $20 \cdot 25$ is 96, $96 \cdot 19$ is 6, $6 \cdot 58$ is 45, $45 \cdot 31$ is 82, and finally $82 \cdot 52$ is 22. So $123^{1001} \bmod 101 = 22$.

22. To apply the Euclidean algorithm, we divide the larger number by the smaller, replace the larger by the smaller and the smaller by the remainder of this division, and repeat this process until the remainder is 0. At that point, the smaller number is the greatest common divisor.
   a) $\gcd(1,5) = \gcd(1,0) = 1$ **b)** $\gcd(100,101) = \gcd(100,1) = \gcd(1,0) = 1$
   c) $\gcd(123,277) = \gcd(123,31) = \gcd(31,30) = \gcd(30,1) = \gcd(1,0) = 1$
   d) $\gcd(1529,14039) = \gcd(1529,278) = \gcd(278,139) = \gcd(139,0) = 139$
   e) $\gcd(1529,14038) = \gcd(1529,277) = \gcd(277,144) = \gcd(144,133) = \gcd(133,11) = \gcd(11,1) = \gcd(1,0)$ $= 1$
   f) $\gcd(11111,111111) = \gcd(11111,1) = \gcd(1,0) = 1$

24. We need to divide successively by 55, 34, 21, 13, 8, 5, 3, 2, and 1, so 9 divisions are required.

26. **a)** $5 = 9 - 3 - 1$ **b)** $13 = 9 + 3 + 1$ **c)** $37 = 27 + 9 + 1$ **d)** $79 = 81 - 3 + 1$

28. The key fact here is that $10 \equiv -1 \pmod{11}$, and so $10^k \equiv (-1)^k \pmod{11}$. Thus 10^k is congruent to 1 if k is even and to -1 if k is odd. Let the decimal expansion of the integer a be given by $(a_{n-1}a_{n-2}\ldots a_3a_2a_1a_0)_{10}$. Thus $a = 10^{n-1}a_{n-1} + 10^{n-2}a_{n-2} + \cdots + 10a_1 + a_0$. Since $10^k \equiv (-1)^k \pmod{11}$, we have $a \equiv \pm a_{n-1} \mp a_{n-2} + \cdots - a_3 + a_2 - a_1 + a_0 \pmod{11}$, where signs alternate and depend on the parity of n. Therefore $a \equiv 0 \pmod{11}$ if and only if $(a_0 + a_2 + a_4 + \cdots) - (a_1 + a_3 + a_5 + \cdots)$, which we obtain by collecting the odd and even indexed terms, is congruent to $0 \pmod{11}$. Since being divisible by 11 is the same as being congruent to $0 \pmod{11}$, we have proved that a positive integer is divisible by 11 if and only if the sum of its decimal digits in even-numbered positions minus the sum of its decimal digits in odd-numbered positions is divisible by 11.

30. **a)** Since the binary representation of 22 is 10110, the six bit one's complement representation is 010110.
   b) Since the binary representation of 31 is 11111, the six bit one's complement representation is 011111.
   c) Since the binary representation of 7 is 111, we complement 000111 to obtain 111000 as the one's complement representation of -7.
   d) Since the binary representation of 19 is 10011, we complement 010011 to obtain 101100 as the one's complement representation of -19.

32. Every 1 is changed to a 0, and every 0 is changed to a 1.

34. We just combine the two ideas in Exercises 32 and 33: to form $a - b$, we compute $a + (-b)$, using Exercise 32 to find $-b$ and Exercise 33 to find the sum.

36. Following the definition, we find the two's complement expansion of a positive number simply by representing it in binary, using six bits; and we find the two's complement expansion of a negative number $-x$ by representing $2^5 - x$ in binary using five bits and preceding it with a 1.
   a) Since 22 is positive, and its binary expansion is 10110, the answer is 010110.
   b) Since 31 is positive, and its binary expansion is 11111, the answer is 011111.
   c) Since -7 is negative, we first find the 5-bit binary expansion of $2^5 - 7 = 25$, namely 11001, and precede it by a 1, obtaining 111001.
   d) Since -19 is negative, we first find the 5-bit binary expansion of $2^5 - 19 = 13$, namely 01101, and precede it by a 1, obtaining 101101.

38. We can experiment a bit to find a convenient algorithm. We saw in Exercise 36 that the expansion of -7 is 111001, while of course the expansion of 7 is 000111. Apparently to find the expansion of $-m$ from that of m we complement each bit and then add 1, working in base 2. Similarly, the expansion of -8 is 111000, whereas the expansion of 8 is 001000; again $110111 + 1 = 111000$. At the extremes (using six bits) we have 1 represented by 000001, so -1 is represented by $111110 + 1 = 111111$; and 31 is represented by 011111, so -31 is represented by $100000 + 1 = 100001$.

40. We just combine the two ideas in Exercises 38 and 39: to form $a - b$, we compute $a + (-b)$, using Exercise 38 to find $-b$ and Exercise 39 to find the sum.

42. If the number is positive (i.e., the left-most bit is 0), then the expansions are the same. If the number is negative (i.e., the left-most bit is 1), then we take the one's complement representation and add 1, working in base 2. For example, the one's complement representation of -19 using six bits is, from Exercise 30, 101100. Adding 1 we obtain 101101, which is the two's complement representation of -19 using six bits, from Exercise 36.

44. We obtain these expansions from the top down. For example in part (**e**) we compute that $7! > 1000$ but $6! \leq 1000$, so the highest factorial appearing is $6! = 720$. We use the division algorithm to find the quotient and remainder when 1000 is divided by 720, namely 1 and 280, respectively. Therefore the expansion begins $1 \cdot 6!$ and continues with the expansion of 280, which we find in the same manner.
   a) $2 = 2!$ **b)** $7 = 3! + 1!$ **c)** $19 = 3 \cdot 3! + 1!$ **d)** $87 = 3 \cdot 4! + 2 \cdot 3! + 2! + 1!$
   e) $1000 = 6! + 2 \cdot 5! + 4! + 2 \cdot 3! + 2 \cdot 2!$ **f)** $1000000 = 2 \cdot 9! + 6 \cdot 8! + 6 \cdot 7! + 2 \cdot 6! + 5 \cdot 5! + 4! + 2 \cdot 3! + 2 \cdot 2!$

46. The algorithm is essentially the same as the usual grade-school algorithm for adding. We add from right to left, one column at a time, carrying to the next column if necessary. A carry out of the column representing $i!$ is needed whenever the sum obtained for that column is greater than i, in which case we subtract $i + 1$ from that digit and carry 1 into the next column (since $(i + 1)! = (i + 1) \cdot i!$).

48. The partial products are 11100 and 1110000, namely 1110 shifted one place and three places to the left. We add these two numbers, obtaining 10001100.

50. Subtraction is really just like addition, so the number of bit operations should be comparable, namely $O(n)$. More specifically, if we analyze the algorithm for Exercise 49, we see that the loop is executed n times, and only a few operations are performed during each pass.

52. In the worst case, each bit of a has to be compared to each bit of b, so $O(n)$ comparisons are needed. An exact analysis of the procedure given in the solution to Exercise 51 shows that $n + 1$ comparisons of bits are needed in the worst case, assuming that the logical "and" condition in the **while** loop is evaluated efficiently from left to right (so that a_0 is not compared to b_0 there).

54. A multiplication modulo m consists of multiplying two integers, each at most $\log m$ bits long (since they are less than m), followed by a division by m, which is also $\log m$ bits long. Thus this takes $(\log m)^2$ bit operations by Example 10 and the analysis of Algorithm 4 mentioned in the text. This is what goes on inside the loop of Algorithm 5. The loop is iterated $\log n$ times. Therefore the total number of bit operations is $O((\log m)^2 \log n)$.

SECTION 2.6   Applications of Number Theory

2. a) In order to find the coefficients s and t such that $9s + 11t = \gcd(9, 11)$, we carry out the steps of the Euclidean algorithm.

$$11 = 9 + 2$$
$$9 = 4 \cdot 2 + 1$$

Then we work up from the bottom, expressing the greatest common divisor (which we have just seen to be 1) in terms of the numbers involved in the algorithm, namely 11, 9, and 2. In particular, the last equation tells us that $1 = 9 - 4 \cdot 2$, so that we have expressed the gcd as a linear combination of 9 and 2. But now the first equation tells us that $2 = 11 - 9$; we plug this into our previous equation and obtain

$$1 = 9 - 4 \cdot (11 - 9) = 5 \cdot 9 - 4 \cdot 11.$$

Thus we have expressed 1 as a linear combination (with integer coefficients) of 9 and 11, namely $\gcd(9, 11) = 5 \cdot 9 - 4 \cdot 11$.

b) Again, we carry out the Euclidean algorithm. Since $44 = 33 + 11$, and $11 \mid 33$, we know that $\gcd(33, 44) = 11$. From the equation shown here, we can immediately write $11 = (-1) \cdot 33 + 44$.

c) The calculation of the greatest common divisor takes several steps:

$$78 = 2 \cdot 35 + 8$$
$$35 = 4 \cdot 8 + 3$$
$$8 = 2 \cdot 3 + 2$$
$$3 = 2 + 1$$

Then we need to work our way back up, successively plugging in for the remainders determined in this calculation:

$$1 = 3 - 2$$
$$= 3 - (8 - 2 \cdot 3) = 3 \cdot 3 - 8$$
$$= 3 \cdot (35 - 4 \cdot 8) - 8 = 3 \cdot 35 - 13 \cdot 8$$
$$= 3 \cdot 35 - 13 \cdot (78 - 2 \cdot 35) = 29 \cdot 35 - 13 \cdot 78$$

d) Here are the two calculations—down to the gcd using the Euclidean algorithm, and then back up by substitution until we have expressed the gcd as the desired linear combination of the original numbers.

$$55 = 2 \cdot 21 + 13$$
$$21 = 13 + 8$$
$$13 = 8 + 5$$
$$8 = 5 + 3$$
$$5 = 3 + 2$$
$$3 = 2 + 1$$

Thus the greatest common divisor is 1.

$$\begin{aligned}
1 &= 3 - 2 \\
&= 3 - (5 - 3) = 2 \cdot 3 - 5 \\
&= 2 \cdot (8 - 5) - 5 = 2 \cdot 8 - 3 \cdot 5 \\
&= 2 \cdot 8 - 3 \cdot (13 - 8) = 5 \cdot 8 - 3 \cdot 13 \\
&= 5 \cdot (21 - 13) - 3 \cdot 13 = 5 \cdot 21 - 8 \cdot 13 \\
&= 5 \cdot 21 - 8 \cdot (55 - 2 \cdot 21) = 21 \cdot 21 - 8 \cdot 55
\end{aligned}$$

e) We compute the greatest common divisor in one step: $203 = 2 \cdot 101 + 1$. Therefore we have $1 = (-2) \cdot 101 + 203$.

f) We compute the greatest common divisor using the Euclidean algorithm:

$$\begin{aligned}
323 &= 2 \cdot 124 + 75 \\
124 &= 75 + 49 \\
75 &= 49 + 26 \\
49 &= 26 + 23 \\
26 &= 23 + 3 \\
23 &= 7 \cdot 3 + 2 \\
3 &= 2 + 1
\end{aligned}$$

Thus the greatest common divisor is 1.

$$\begin{aligned}
1 &= 3 - 2 \\
&= 3 - (23 - 7 \cdot 3) = 8 \cdot 3 - 23 \\
&= 8 \cdot (26 - 23) - 23 = 8 \cdot 26 - 9 \cdot 23 \\
&= 8 \cdot 26 - 9 \cdot (49 - 26) = 17 \cdot 26 - 9 \cdot 49 \\
&= 17 \cdot (75 - 49) - 9 \cdot 49 = 17 \cdot 75 - 26 \cdot 49 \\
&= 17 \cdot 75 - 26 \cdot (124 - 75) = 43 \cdot 75 - 26 \cdot 124 \\
&= 43 \cdot (323 - 2 \cdot 124) - 26 \cdot 124 = 43 \cdot 323 - 112 \cdot 124
\end{aligned}$$

g) Here are the two calculations—down to the gcd using the Euclidean algorithm, and then back up by substitution until we have expressed the gcd as the desired linear combination of the original numbers.

$$\begin{aligned}
2339 &= 2002 + 337 \\
2002 &= 5 \cdot 337 + 317 \\
337 &= 317 + 20 \\
317 &= 15 \cdot 20 + 17 \\
20 &= 17 + 3 \\
17 &= 5 \cdot 3 + 2 \\
3 &= 2 + 1
\end{aligned}$$

Thus the greatest common divisor is 1.

$$
\begin{aligned}
1 &= 3 - 2 \\
&= 3 - (17 - 5 \cdot 3) = 6 \cdot 3 - 17 \\
&= 6 \cdot (20 - 17) - 17 = 6 \cdot 20 - 7 \cdot 17 \\
&= 6 \cdot 20 - 7 \cdot (317 - 15 \cdot 20) = 111 \cdot 20 - 7 \cdot 317 \\
&= 111 \cdot (337 - 317) - 7 \cdot 317 = 111 \cdot 337 - 118 \cdot 317 \\
&= 111 \cdot 337 - 118 \cdot (2002 - 5 \cdot 337) = 701 \cdot 337 - 118 \cdot 2002 \\
&= 701 \cdot (2339 - 2002) - 118 \cdot 2002 = 701 \cdot 2339 - 819 \cdot 2002
\end{aligned}
$$

h) The procedure is the same:

$$
\begin{aligned}
4669 &= 3457 + 1212 \\
3457 &= 2 \cdot 1212 + 1033 \\
1212 &= 1033 + 179 \\
1033 &= 5 \cdot 179 + 138 \\
179 &= 138 + 41 \\
138 &= 3 \cdot 41 + 15 \\
41 &= 2 \cdot 15 + 11 \\
15 &= 11 + 4 \\
11 &= 2 \cdot 4 + 3 \\
4 &= 3 + 1
\end{aligned}
$$

Thus the greatest common divisor is 1.

$$
\begin{aligned}
1 &= 4 - 3 \\
&= 4 - (11 - 2 \cdot 4) = 3 \cdot 4 - 11 \\
&= 3 \cdot (15 - 11) - 11 = 3 \cdot 15 - 4 \cdot 11 \\
&= 3 \cdot 15 - 4 \cdot (41 - 2 \cdot 15) = 11 \cdot 15 - 4 \cdot 41 \\
&= 11 \cdot (138 - 3 \cdot 41) - 4 \cdot 41 = 11 \cdot 138 - 37 \cdot 41 \\
&= 11 \cdot 138 - 37 \cdot (179 - 138) = 48 \cdot 138 - 37 \cdot 179 \\
&= 48 \cdot (1033 - 5 \cdot 179) - 37 \cdot 179 = 48 \cdot 1033 - 277 \cdot 179 \\
&= 48 \cdot 1033 - 277 \cdot (1212 - 1033) = 325 \cdot 1033 - 277 \cdot 1212 \\
&= 325 \cdot (3457 - 2 \cdot 1212) - 277 \cdot 1212 = 325 \cdot 3457 - 927 \cdot 1212 \\
&= 325 \cdot 3457 - 927 \cdot (4669 - 3457) = 1252 \cdot 3457 - 927 \cdot 4669
\end{aligned}
$$

i) The procedure is the same:

$$
\begin{aligned}
13422 &= 10001 + 3421 \\
10001 &= 2 \cdot 3421 + 3159 \\
3421 &= 3159 + 262 \\
3159 &= 12 \cdot 262 + 15 \\
262 &= 17 \cdot 15 + 7 \\
15 &= 2 \cdot 7 + 1
\end{aligned}
$$

Thus the greatest common divisor is 1.

$$1 = 15 - 2 \cdot 7$$
$$= 15 - 2 \cdot (262 - 17 \cdot 15) = 35 \cdot 15 - 2 \cdot 262$$
$$= 35 \cdot (3159 - 12 \cdot 262) - 2 \cdot 262 = 35 \cdot 3159 - 422 \cdot 262$$
$$= 35 \cdot 3159 - 422 \cdot (3421 - 3159) = 457 \cdot 3159 - 422 \cdot 3421$$
$$= 457 \cdot (10001 - 2 \cdot 3421) - 422 \cdot 3421 = 457 \cdot 10001 - 1336 \cdot 3421$$
$$= 457 \cdot 10001 - 1336 \cdot (13422 - 10001) = 1793 \cdot 10001 - 1336 \cdot 13422$$

4. We need to show that $13 \cdot 937 \equiv 1 \pmod{2436}$, or in other words, that $13 \cdot 937 - 1 = 12180$ is divisible by 2436. A calculator shows that it is, since $12180 = 2436 \cdot 5$.

6. We need to find a number x such that $2x \bmod 17 = 1$. This can be done by inspection, since we immediately notice that $2 \cdot 9 = 18$, and $18 \bmod 17 = 1$. If we did not notice this so quickly, then we could have used the technique shown below for Exercise 8.

8. We need to find s and t such that $144s + 233t = 1$. Then clearly s will be the desired inverse, since $144s \equiv 1 \pmod{233}$ (i.e., $144s - 1 = -233t$ is divisible by 233). To do so, we proceed as in Exercise 2. First we go through the Euclidean algorithm computation that $\gcd(144, 233) = 1$:

$$233 = 144 + 89$$
$$144 = 89 + 55$$
$$89 = 55 + 34$$
$$55 = 34 + 21$$
$$34 = 21 + 13$$
$$21 = 13 + 8$$
$$13 = 8 + 5$$
$$8 = 5 + 3$$
$$5 = 3 + 2$$
$$3 = 2 + 1$$

Then we reverse our steps and write 1 as the desired linear combination:

$$1 = 3 - 2$$
$$= 3 - (5 - 3) = 2 \cdot 3 - 5$$
$$= 2 \cdot (8 - 5) - 5 = 2 \cdot 8 - 3 \cdot 5$$
$$= 2 \cdot 8 - 3 \cdot (13 - 8) = 5 \cdot 8 - 3 \cdot 13$$
$$= 5 \cdot (21 - 13) - 3 \cdot 13 = 5 \cdot 21 - 8 \cdot 13$$
$$= 5 \cdot 21 - 8 \cdot (34 - 21) = 13 \cdot 21 - 8 \cdot 34$$
$$= 13 \cdot (55 - 34) - 8 \cdot 34 = 13 \cdot 55 - 21 \cdot 34$$
$$= 13 \cdot 55 - 21 \cdot (89 - 55) = 34 \cdot 55 - 21 \cdot 89$$
$$= 34 \cdot (144 - 89) - 21 \cdot 89 = 34 \cdot 144 - 55 \cdot 89$$
$$= 34 \cdot 144 - 55 \cdot (233 - 144) = 89 \cdot 144 - 55 \cdot 233$$

Thus $s = 89$, so an inverse of 144 modulo 233 is 89, since $144 \cdot 89 = 12816 \equiv 1 \pmod{233}$.

10. If x is an inverse of a modulo m, then by definition $ax - 1 = tm$ for some integer t. If a and m in this equation both have a common divisor greater than 1, then 1 must also have this same common divisor, since $1 = ax - tm$. This is absurd, since the only positive divisor of 1 is 1. Therefore no such x exists.

12. We know from Exercise 6 that 9 is an inverse of 2 modulo 17. Therefore if we multiply both sides of this equation by 9 we will get $x \equiv 9 \cdot 7 \pmod{17}$. Since 63 **mod** $17 = 12$, the solutions are all integers congruent to 12 modulo 17, such as 12, 29, and -5. We can check, for example, that $2 \cdot 12 = 24 \equiv 7 \pmod{17}$.

14. a) We can search for inverses using the technique shown in Exercise 8. With a little work (or trial and error, which is actually faster in this case), we find that $2 \cdot 6 \equiv 1 \pmod{11}$, $3 \cdot 4 \equiv 1 \pmod{11}$, $5 \cdot 9 \equiv 1 \pmod{11}$, and $7 \cdot 8 \equiv 1 \pmod{11}$. Actually, the problem does not ask us to show these pairs explicitly, only to show that they exist. The general argument given in Exercise 16 shows this.
b) In this specific case we can compute $10! = 1 \cdot 2 \cdot 3 \cdot 4 \cdot 5 \cdot 6 \cdot 7 \cdot 8 \cdot 9 \cdot 10 = 1 \cdot (2 \cdot 6) \cdot (3 \cdot 4) \cdot (5 \cdot 9) \cdot (7 \cdot 8) \cdot 10 \equiv 1 \cdot 1 \cdot 1 \cdot 1 \cdot 10 = 10 \equiv -1 \pmod{11}$. Alternatively, we can use the proof in Exercise 16.

16. a) Every positive integer less than p has an inverse modulo p, and by Exercise 9 this inverse is unique among positive integers less than p. This follows from Theorem 3, since every number less than p must be relatively prime to p (because p is prime it has no smaller divisors). We can group each positive integer less than p with its inverse. The only issue is whether some numbers are their own inverses, in which case this grouping does not produce pairs. By Exercise 15 only 1 and -1 (which is the same as $p - 1$ modulo p) are their own inverses. Therefore all the other positive integers less than p can be grouped into pairs consisting of inverses of each other, and there are clearly $(p - 1 - 2)/2 = (p - 3)/2$ such pairs.
b) When we compute $(p - 1)!$, we can write the product by grouping the pairs of inverses modulo p. Each such pair produces the product 1 modulo p, so modulo p the entire product is the same as the product of the only unpaired elements, namely $1 \cdot (p - 1) = p - 1$. Since this equals -1 modulo p, our proof is complete.
c) By the contrapositive of what we have just proved, we can conclude that if $(n - 1)! \not\equiv -1 \pmod{n}$ then n is not prime.

18. Since 3, 4, and 5 are pairwise relatively prime, we can use the Chinese Remainder Theorem. The answer will be unique modulo $3 \cdot 4 \cdot 5 = 60$. Using the notation in the text, we have $a_1 = 2$, $m_1 = 3$, $a_2 = 1$, $m_2 = 4$, $a_3 = 3$, $m_3 = 5$, $m = 60$, $M_1 = 60/3 = 20$, $M_2 = 60/4 = 15$, $M_3 = 60/5 = 12$. Then we need to find inverses y_i of M_i modulo m_i for $i = 1, 2, 3$. This can be done by inspection (trial and error), since the moduli here are so small, or systematically using the Euclidean algorithm (as in Example 3); we find that $y_1 = 2$, $y_2 = 3$, and $y_3 = 3$. Thus our solution is $x = 2 \cdot 20 \cdot 2 + 1 \cdot 15 \cdot 3 + 3 \cdot 12 \cdot 3 = 233 \equiv 53 \pmod{60}$. So the solutions are all integers of the form $53 + 60k$, where k is an integer.

20. We cannot apply the Chinese Remainder Theorem directly, since the moduli are not pairwise relatively prime. However, we can, using the Chinese Remainder Theorem, translate these congruences into a set of congruences that together are equivalent to the given congruence. Since we want $x \equiv 5 \pmod{6}$, we must have $x \equiv 5 \equiv 1 \pmod{2}$ and $x \equiv 5 \equiv 2 \pmod{3}$. Similarly, from the second congruence we must have $x \equiv 1 \pmod{2}$ and $x \equiv 3 \pmod{5}$; and from the third congruence we must have $x \equiv 2 \pmod{3}$ and $x \equiv 3 \pmod{5}$. Since these six statements are consistent, we see that our system is equivalent to the system $x \equiv 1 \pmod{2}$, $x \equiv 2 \pmod{3}$, $x \equiv 3 \pmod{5}$. These can be solved using the Chinese Remainder Theorem (see Exercise 19 or Example 6) to yield $x \equiv 23 \pmod{30}$. Therefore the solutions are all integers of the form $23 + 30k$, where k is an integer.

22. This is just a restatement of the Chinese Remainder Theorem. Given any such a we can certainly compute a **mod** m_1, a **mod** m_2, ..., a **mod** m_n to represent it. The Chinese Remainder Theorem says that there is only one nonnegative integer less than m yielding each n-tuple, so the representation is unique.

24. We follow the hint and suppose that there are two solutions to the set of congruences. Thus suppose that $x \equiv a_i \pmod{m_i}$ and $y \equiv a_i \pmod{m_i}$ for each i. We want to show that these solutions are the same modulo m; this will guarantee that there is only one nonnegative solution less than m. The assumption certainly implies that $x \equiv y \pmod{m_i}$ for each i. But then Exercise 23 tells us that $x \equiv y \pmod{m}$, as desired.

26. We are asked to solve $x \equiv 0 \pmod 5$ and $x \equiv 1 \pmod 3$. We know from the Chinese Remainder Theorem that there is a unique answer modulo 15. It is probably quickest just to look for it by dividing each multiple of 5 by 3, and we see immediately that $x = 10$ satisfies the condition. Thus the solutions are all integers congruent to 10 modulo 15. If the numbers involved were larger, then we could use the technique implicit in the proof of Theorem 4 (see Exercise 39).

28. a) By Fermat's Little Theorem we know that $3^4 \equiv 1 \pmod 5$; therefore $3^{300} = (3^4)^{75} \equiv 1^{75} \equiv 1 \pmod 5$, and so $3^{302} = 3^2 \cdot 3^{300} \equiv 9 \cdot 1 = 9 \pmod 5$, so $3^{302} \bmod 5 = 4$. Similarly, $3^6 \equiv 1 \pmod 7$; therefore $3^{300} = (3^6)^{50} \equiv 1 \pmod 5$, and so $3^{302} = 3^2 \cdot 3^{300} \equiv 9 \pmod 7$, so $3^{302} \bmod 7 = 2$. Finally, $3^{10} \equiv 1 \pmod{11}$; therefore $3^{300} = (3^{10})^{30} \equiv 1 \pmod{11}$, and so $3^{302} = 3^2 \cdot 3^{300} \equiv 9 \pmod{11}$, so $3^{302} \bmod 11 = 9$.

b) Since 3^{302} is congruent to 9 modulo 5, 7, and 11, it is also congruent to 9 modulo 385. (This was a particularly trivial application of the Chinese Remainder Theorem.)

30. Let $x_k = b^{(n-1)/2^k} = b^{2^{s-k}t}$, for $k = 0, 1, 2, \ldots, s$. Because n is prime and $n \nmid b$, Fermat's Little Theorem tells us that $x_0 = b^{n-1} \equiv 1 \pmod n$. By Exercise 15, because $x_1^2 = (b^{(n-1)/2})^2 = x_0 \equiv 1 \pmod n$, either $x_1 \equiv -1 \pmod n$ or $x_1 \equiv 1 \pmod n$. If $x_1 \equiv 1 \pmod n$, because $x_2^2 = x_1 \equiv 1 \pmod n$, either $x_2 \equiv -1 \pmod n$ or $x_2 \equiv 1 \pmod n$. In general, if we have found that $x_0 \equiv x_1 \equiv x_2 \equiv \cdots \equiv x_k \equiv 1 \pmod n$, with $k < s$, then, because $x_{k+1}^2 = x_k \equiv 1 \pmod n$, we know that either $x_{k+1} \equiv -1 \pmod n$ or $x_{k+1} \equiv 1 \pmod n$. Continuing this procedure for $k = 1, 2, \ldots, s$, we find that either $x_s = b^t \equiv 1 \pmod n$, or $x_k \equiv -1 \pmod n$ for some integer k with $0 \leq k \leq s$. Hence, n passes Miller's test for the base b.

32. This follows from Exercise 35, taking $m = 1$. Alternatively, we can argue directly as follows. Factor $1729 = 7 \cdot 13 \cdot 19$. We must show that this number meets the definition of Carmichael number, namely that $b^{1728} \equiv 1 \pmod{1729}$ for all b relatively prime to 1729. Note that if $\gcd(b, 1729) = 1$, then $\gcd(b, 7) = \gcd(b, 13) = \gcd(b, 19) = 1$. Using Fermat's Little Theorem we find that $b^6 \equiv 1 \pmod 7$, $b^{12} \equiv 1 \pmod{13}$, and $b^{18} \equiv 1 \pmod{19}$. It follows that $b^{1728} = (b^6)^{288} \equiv 1 \pmod 7$, $b^{1728} = (b^{12})^{144} \equiv 1 \pmod{13}$, and $b^{1728} = (b^{18})^{96} \equiv 1 \pmod{19}$. By Exercise 23 (or the Chinese Remainder Theorem) it follows that $b^{1728} \equiv 1 \pmod{1729}$, as desired.

34. Let b be a positive integer with $\gcd(b, n) = 1$. The $\gcd(b, p_j) = 1$ for $j = 1, 2, \ldots, k$, and hence, by Fermat's Little Theorem, $b^{p_j - 1} \equiv 1 \pmod{p_j}$ for $j = 1, 2, \ldots, k$. Because $p_j - 1 \mid n - 1$, there are integers t_j with $t_j(p_j - 1) = n - 1$. Hence for each j we know that $b^{n-1} = b^{(p_j-1)t_j} = (b^{(p_j-1)})^{t_j} \equiv 1 \pmod{p_j}$. Therefore $b^{n-1} \equiv 1 \pmod n$, as desired.

36. We could use the technique shown in the proof of Theorem 4 to solve each part, or use the approach in our solution to Exercise 26, but since there are so many to do here, it is simpler just to write out all the representations of 0 through 27 and find those given in each part. This task is easily done, since the pattern is clear:

$0 = (0,0)$	$7 = (3,0)$	$14 = (2,0)$	$21 = (1,0)$
$1 = (1,1)$	$8 = (0,1)$	$15 = (3,1)$	$22 = (2,1)$
$2 = (2,2)$	$9 = (1,2)$	$16 = (0,2)$	$23 = (3,2)$
$3 = (3,3)$	$10 = (2,3)$	$17 = (1,3)$	$24 = (0,3)$

$$4 = (0,4) \qquad 11 = (3,4) \qquad 18 = (2,4) \qquad 25 = (1,4)$$
$$5 = (1,5) \qquad 12 = (0,5) \qquad 19 = (3,5) \qquad 26 = (2,5)$$
$$6 = (2,6) \qquad 13 = (1,6) \qquad 20 = (0,6) \qquad 27 = (3,6)$$

Now we can read off the answers.

a) 0   **b)** 21   **c)** 1   **d)** 22   **e)** 2   **f)** 24   **g)** 14   **h)** 19   **i)** 27

38. To add 4 and 7 we first find that 4 is represented by $(1,4)$ and that 7 is represented by $(1,2)$. Adding coordinate-wise, we see that the sum is represented by $(1+1,4+2) = (2,6) = (2,1)$; we are working modulo 5 in the second coordinate. Then we find $(2,1)$ in the table and see that it represents 11. Therefore we conclude that $4+7 = 11$. Note that we can only compute answers less than $3 \cdot 5 = 15$ using this method.

40. The statement we are asked to prove involves the result of dividing $2^a - 1$ by $2^b - 1$. Let us actually carry out that division algebraically—long division of these expressions. The leading term in the quotient is 2^{a-b} (as long as $a \geq b$), with a remainder at that point of $2^{a-b} - 1$. If now $a - b \geq b$ then the next step in the long division produces the next summand in the quotient, 2^{a-2b}, with a remainder at this stage of $2^{a-2b} - 1$. This process of long division continues until the remainder at some stage is less than the divisor, i.e., $2^{a-kb} - 1 < 2^a - 1$. But then the remainder is $2^{a-kb} - 1$, and clearly $a - kb$ is exactly $a \bmod b$. This completes the proof.

42. By Exercise 41, $2^a - 1$ and $2^b - 1$ are relatively prime precisely when $2^{\gcd(a,b)} - 1 = 1$, which happens if and only if $\gcd(a,b) = 1$. Thus it is enough to check here that 35, 34, 33, 31, 29, and 23 are relatively prime. This is clear, since the prime factorizations are, respectively, 35, $2 \cdot 17$, $3 \cdot 11$, 31, 29, and 23.

44. To decide whether $2^{13} - 1 = 8191$ is prime, we need only look for a prime factor not exceeding $\sqrt{8191} \approx 90.5$. By Exercise 43 every such prime divisor must be of the form $26k + 1$. The only candidates are therefore 53 and 79. We easily check that neither is a divisor, and so we conclude that 8191 is prime.

We can take the same approach for $2^{23} - 1 = 8{,}388{,}607$, but we might worry that there will be far too many potential divisors to test, since we must go as far as 2896. By Exercise 43 every prime divisor of $2^{23} - 1$ must be of the form $46k + 1$. The first candidate divisor is therefore 47. Luckily $47 \mid 8{,}388{,}607$, so we conclude that it is not prime.

46. Translating the letters into numbers we have 0019 1900 0210. Thus we need to compute $C = P^{13} \bmod 2537$ for $P = 19$, $P = 1900$, and $P = 210$. The results of these calculations, done by fast modular multiplication or a computer algebra system are 2299, 1317, and 2117, respectively. Thus the encrypted message is 2299 1317 2117.

48. We take $a = 356$ and $b = 252$ to avoid a needless first step. When we apply the Euclidean algorithm we obtain the following quotients and remainders: $q_1 = 1$, $r_2 = 104$, $q_2 = 2$, $r_3 = 44$, $q_3 = 2$, $r_4 = 16$, $q_4 = 2$, $r_5 = 12$, $q_5 = 1$, $r_6 = 4$, $q_6 = 3$. Note that $n = 6$. Thus we compute the successive s's and t's as follows, using the given recurrences:

$$s_2 = s_0 - q_1 s_1 = 1 - 1 \cdot 0 = 1, \qquad\qquad t_2 = t_0 - q_1 t_1 = 0 - 1 \cdot 1 = -1$$
$$s_3 = s_1 - q_2 s_2 = 0 - 2 \cdot 1 = -2, \qquad\qquad t_3 = t_1 - q_2 t_2 = 1 - 2 \cdot (-1) = 3$$
$$s_4 = s_2 - q_3 s_3 = 1 - 2 \cdot (-2) = 5, \qquad\qquad t_4 = t_2 - q_3 t_3 = -1 - 2 \cdot 3 = -7$$
$$s_5 = s_3 - q_4 s_4 = -2 - 2 \cdot 5 = -12, \qquad\qquad t_5 = t_3 - q_4 t_4 = 3 - 2 \cdot (-7) = 17$$
$$s_6 = s_4 - q_5 s_5 = 5 - 1 \cdot (-12) = 17, \qquad\qquad t_6 = t_4 - q_5 t_5 = -7 - 1 \cdot 17 = -24$$

Thus we have $s_6 a + t_6 b = 17 \cdot 356 + (-24) \cdot 252 = 4$, which is $\gcd(356, 252)$.

50. We take $a = 100001$ and $b = 1001$ to avoid a needless first step. When we apply the Euclidean algorithm we obtain the following quotients and remainders: $q_1 = 99$, $r_2 = 902$, $q_2 = 1$, $r_3 = 99$, $q_3 = 9$, $r_4 = 11$, $q_4 = 9$. Note that $n = 4$. Thus we compute the successive s's and t's as follows, using the given recurrences:

$$s_2 = s_0 - q_1 s_1 = 1 - 99 \cdot 0 = 1, \qquad\qquad t_2 = t_0 - q_1 t_1 = 0 - 99 \cdot 1 = -99$$
$$s_3 = s_1 - q_2 s_2 = 0 - 1 \cdot 1 = -1, \qquad\qquad t_3 = t_1 - q_2 t_2 = 1 - 1 \cdot (-99) = 100$$
$$s_4 = s_2 - q_3 s_3 = 1 - 9 \cdot (-1) = 10, \qquad\qquad t_4 = t_2 - q_3 t_3 = -99 - 9 \cdot 100 = -999$$

Thus we have $s_4 a + t_4 b = 10 \cdot 100001 + (-999) \cdot 1001 = 11$, which is $\gcd(100001, 1001)$.

52. We square the first five positive integers and reduce modulo 11, obtaining 1, 4, 9, 5, 3. The squares of the next five are necessarily the same set of numbers modulo 11, since $(-x)^2 = x^2$, so we are done. Therefore the quadratic residues modulo 11 are all integers congruent to 1, 3, 4, 5, or 9 modulo 11.

54. Consider the list $x^2 \bmod p$ as x runs from 1 to $p - 1$ inclusive. This gives us $p - 1$ numbers between 1 and $p - 1$ inclusive. By Exercise 53 every a that appears in this list appears exactly twice. Therefore exactly half of the $p - 1$ numbers must appear in the list (i.e., be quadratic residues).

56. First assume that $\left(\frac{a}{p}\right) = 1$. Then the congruence $x^2 \equiv a \pmod{p}$ has a solution, say $x = s$. By Fermat's Little Theorem $a^{(p-1)/2} = (s^2)^{(p-1)/2} = s^{p-1} \equiv 1 \pmod{p}$, as desired. Next consider the case $\left(\frac{a}{p}\right) = -1$. Then the congruence $x^2 \equiv a \pmod{p}$ has no solution. Let i be an integer between 1 and $p - 1$, inclusive. By Theorem 3, i has an inverse i' modulo p, and therefore there is an integer j, namely $i'a$, such that $ij \equiv a \pmod{p}$. Furthermore, since the congruence $x^2 \equiv a \pmod{p}$ has no solution, $j \neq i$. Thus we can group the integers from 1 to $p - 1$ into $(p - 1)/2$ pairs each with the product a. Multiplying these pairs together, we find that $(p - 1)! \equiv a^{(p-1)/2} \pmod{p}$. But now Wilson's Theorem (see Exercise 16) tells us that this latter value is -1, again as desired.

58. If $p \equiv 1 \pmod{4}$, then $(p - 1)/2$ is even, so the right-hand side of the equivalence in Exercise 56 with $a = -1$ is $+1$, that is, -1 is a quadratic residue. Conversely, if $p \equiv 3 \pmod{4}$, then $(p - 1)/2$ is odd, so the right-hand side of the equivalence in Exercise 56 with $a = -1$ is -1, that is, -1 is not a quadratic residue.

60. We follow the hint. Working modulo 3, we want to solve $x^2 \equiv 16 \equiv 1$. It is easy to see that there are exactly two solutions modulo 3, namely $x = 1$ and $x = 2$. Similarly we find the solutions $x = 1$ and $x = 4$ to $x^2 \equiv 16 \equiv 1 \pmod{5}$; and the solutions $x = 3$ and $x = 4$ to $x^2 \equiv 16 \equiv 1 \pmod{7}$. Therefore we want to find values of x modulo $3 \cdot 5 \cdot 7 = 105$ such that $x \equiv 1$ or 2 (mod 3), $x \equiv 1$ or 4 (mod 5) and $x \equiv 3$ or 4 (mod 7). We can do this by applying the Chinese Remainder Theorem (as in Example 6) eight times, for the eight combinations of these values. For example, to solve $x \equiv 1 \pmod{3}$, $x \equiv 1 \pmod{5}$, and $x \equiv 3 \pmod{7}$, we find that $m = 105$, $M_1 = 35$, $M_2 = 21$, $M_3 = 15$, $y_1 = 2$, $y_2 = 1$, $y_3 = 1$, so $x \equiv 1 \cdot 35 \cdot 2 + 1 \cdot 21 \cdot 1 + 3 \cdot 15 \cdot 1 = 136 \equiv 31 \pmod{105}$. Doing the similar calculation with the other seven possibilities yields the other solutions modulo 105: $x = 4$, $x = 11$, $x = 46$, $x = 59$, $x = 74$, $x = 94$ and $x = 101$.

SECTION 2.7   Matrices

2. We just add entry by entry.

a) $\begin{bmatrix} 0 & 3 & 9 \\ 1 & 4 & -1 \\ 2 & -5 & -3 \end{bmatrix}$

b) $\begin{bmatrix} -4 & 9 & 2 & 10 \\ -4 & -5 & 4 & 0 \end{bmatrix}$

4. To multiply matrices $\mathbf{A}$ and $\mathbf{B}$, we compute the $(i,j)^{\text{th}}$ entry of the product $\mathbf{AB}$ by adding all the products of elements from the ith row of $\mathbf{A}$ with the corresponding element in the jth column of $\mathbf{B}$, that is $\sum_{k=1}^{n} a_{ik}b_{kj}$. (See Section 3.2 for this summation notation.) This can only be done, of course, when the number of columns of $\mathbf{A}$ equals the number of rows of $\mathbf{B}$ (called n in the formula shown here).

a) $\begin{bmatrix} -1 & 1 & 0 \\ 0 & 1 & -1 \\ 1 & -2 & 1 \end{bmatrix}$

b) $\begin{bmatrix} 4 & -1 & -7 & 6 \\ -7 & -5 & 8 & 5 \\ 4 & 0 & 7 & 3 \end{bmatrix}$

c) $\begin{bmatrix} 2 & 0 & -3 \\ 24 & -7 & 20 \\ -10 & 4 & -17 \end{bmatrix}$ *wrong* $\begin{bmatrix} 4 & {}^{-4}-1 \\ 13{}^{29} & 2 \\ 0 & {}_{24}-3 \end{bmatrix}$

6. First note that $\mathbf{A}$ must be a 3×3 matrix in order for the sizes to work out as shown. If we name the elements of $\mathbf{A}$ in the usual way as $[a_{ij}]$, then the given equation is really nine equations in the nine unknowns a_{ij}, obtained simply by writing down what the matrix multiplication on the left means:

$$1 \cdot a_{11} + 3 \cdot a_{21} + 2 \cdot a_{31} = 7$$
$$1 \cdot a_{12} + 3 \cdot a_{22} + 2 \cdot a_{32} = 1$$
$$1 \cdot a_{13} + 3 \cdot a_{23} + 2 \cdot a_{33} = 3$$
$$2 \cdot a_{11} + 1 \cdot a_{21} + 1 \cdot a_{31} = 1$$
$$2 \cdot a_{12} + 1 \cdot a_{22} + 1 \cdot a_{32} = 0$$
$$2 \cdot a_{13} + 1 \cdot a_{23} + 1 \cdot a_{33} = 3$$
$$4 \cdot a_{11} + 0 \cdot a_{21} + 3 \cdot a_{31} = -1$$
$$4 \cdot a_{12} + 0 \cdot a_{22} + 3 \cdot a_{32} = -3$$
$$4 \cdot a_{13} + 0 \cdot a_{23} + 3 \cdot a_{33} = 7$$

This is really not as bad as it looks, since each variable only appears in three equations. For example, the first, fourth, and seventh equations are a system of three equations in the three variables a_{11}, a_{21}, and a_{31}. We can solve them using standard algebraic techniques to obtain $a_{11} = -1$, $a_{21} = 2$ and $a_{31} = 1$. By similar reasoning we also obtain $a_{12} = 0$, $a_{22} = 1$ and $a_{32} = -1$; and $a_{13} = 1$, $a_{23} = 0$ and $a_{33} = 1$. Thus our answer is

$$\mathbf{A} = \begin{bmatrix} -1 & 0 & 1 \\ 2 & 1 & 0 \\ 1 & -1 & 1 \end{bmatrix}.$$

As a check we can carry out the matrix multiplication and verify that we obtain the given right-hand side.

8. Since the entries of $\mathbf{A} + \mathbf{B}$ are $a_{ij} + b_{ij}$ and the entries of $\mathbf{B} + \mathbf{A}$ are $b_{ij} + a_{ij}$, that $\mathbf{A} + \mathbf{B} = \mathbf{B} + \mathbf{A}$ follows from the commutativity of addition of real numbers.

10. a) This product is a 3×5 matrix.
   b) This is not defined since the number of columns of $\mathbf{B}$ does not equal the number of rows of $\mathbf{A}$.
   c) This product is a 3×4 matrix.
   d) This is not defined since the number of columns of $\mathbf{C}$ does not equal the number of rows of $\mathbf{A}$.
   e) This is not defined since the number of columns of $\mathbf{B}$ does not equal the number of rows of $\mathbf{C}$.
   f) This product is a 4×5 matrix.

12. We use the definition of matrix addition and multiplication. All summations here are from 1 to k. (See Section 3.2 for this summation notation.)

    a) $(\mathbf{A} + \mathbf{B})\mathbf{C} = \left[\sum(a_{iq} + b_{iq})c_{qj}\right] = \left[\sum a_{iq}c_{qj} + \sum b_{iq}c_{qj}\right] = \mathbf{AC} + \mathbf{BC}$

    b) $\mathbf{C}(\mathbf{A} + \mathbf{B}) = \left[\sum c_{iq}(a_{qj} + b_{qj})\right] = \left[\sum c_{iq}a_{qj} + \sum c_{iq}b_{qj}\right] = \mathbf{CA} + \mathbf{CB}$

14. Let $\mathbf{A}$ and $\mathbf{B}$ be two diagonal $n \times n$ matrices. Let $\mathbf{C} = [c_{ij}]$ be the product $\mathbf{AB}$. From the definition of matrix multiplication, $c_{ij} = \sum a_{iq}b_{qj}$. (See Section 3.2 for this summation notation.) Now all the terms a_{iq} in this expression are zero except for $q = i$, so $c_{ij} = a_{ii}b_{ij}$. But $b_{ij} = 0$ unless $i = j$, so the only nonzero entries of $\mathbf{C}$ are the diagonal entries $c_{ii} = a_{ii}b_{ii}$.

16. The $(i, j)^{\text{th}}$ entry of $(\mathbf{A}^t)^t$ is the $(j, i)^{\text{th}}$ entry of $\mathbf{A}^t$, which is the $(i, j)^{\text{th}}$ entry of $\mathbf{A}$.

18. We need to multiply these two matrices together in both directions and check that both products are $\mathbf{I}_3$. Indeed, they are.

20. **a)** Using Exercise 19, noting that $ad - bc = -5$, we write down the inverse immediately:
$$\begin{bmatrix} -3/5 & 2/5 \\ 1/5 & 1/5 \end{bmatrix}.$$

    b) We multiply to obtain $\mathbf{A}^2 = \begin{bmatrix} 3 & 4 \\ 2 & 11 \end{bmatrix}$ and then $\mathbf{A}^3 = \begin{bmatrix} 1 & 18 \\ 9 & 37 \end{bmatrix}$.

    c) We multiply to obtain $(\mathbf{A}^{-1})^2 = \begin{bmatrix} 11/25 & -4/25 \\ -2/25 & 3/25 \end{bmatrix}$ and then $(\mathbf{A}^{-1})^3 = \begin{bmatrix} -37/125 & 18/125 \\ 9/125 & -1/125 \end{bmatrix}$.

    d) Applying the method of Exercise 19 for obtaining inverses to the answer in part **(b)**, we obtain the answer in part **(c)**. Therefore $(\mathbf{A}^3)^{-1} = (\mathbf{A}^{-1})^3$.

22. A matrix is symmetric if and only if it equals its transpose. So let us compute the transpose of $\mathbf{AA}^t$ and see if we get this matrix back. Using Exercise 17b and then Exercise 16, we have $(\mathbf{AA}^t)^t = ((\mathbf{A}^t)^t)\mathbf{A}^t = \mathbf{AA}^t$, as desired.

24. **a)** If we compute the product as $\mathbf{A}_1(\mathbf{A}_2\mathbf{A}_3)$, then by the result of Exercise 23 it will take $50 \cdot 10 \cdot 40$ multiplications for the first product and then $20 \cdot 50 \cdot 40$ for the second. This is a total of 60,000 multiplications. If we compute the product as $(\mathbf{A}_1\mathbf{A}_2)\mathbf{A}_3$, then it will take $20 \cdot 50 \cdot 10$ multiplications for the first product and then $20 \cdot 10 \cdot 40$ for the second. This is a total of 18,000 multiplications. Therefore the second method is more efficient.

    b) If we compute the product as $\mathbf{A}_1(\mathbf{A}_2\mathbf{A}_3)$, then by the result of Exercise 23 it will take $5 \cdot 50 \cdot 1$ multiplications for the first product and then $10 \cdot 5 \cdot 1$ for the second. This is a total of 300 multiplications. If we compute the product as $(\mathbf{A}_1\mathbf{A}_2)\mathbf{A}_3$, then it will take $10 \cdot 5 \cdot 50$ multiplications for the first product and then $10 \cdot 50 \cdot 1$ for the second. This is a total of 1000 multiplications. Therefore the first method is more efficient.

26. **a)** We simply note that under the given definitions of $\mathbf{A}$, $\mathbf{X}$, and $\mathbf{B}$, the definition of matrix multiplication is exactly the system of equations shown.

    b) The given system is the matrix equation $\mathbf{AX} = \mathbf{B}$. If $\mathbf{A}$ is invertible with inverse $\mathbf{A}^{-1}$, then we can multiply both sides of this equation by $\mathbf{A}^{-1}$ to obtain $\mathbf{A}^{-1}\mathbf{AX} = \mathbf{A}^{-1}\mathbf{B}$. The left-hand side simplifies to $\mathbf{IX}$, however, by the definition of inverse, and this is simply $\mathbf{X}$. Thus the given system is equivalent to the system $\mathbf{X} = \mathbf{A}^{-1}\mathbf{B}$, which obviously tells us exactly what $\mathbf{X}$ is (and therefore what all the values x_i are).

28. We follow the definitions.

    a) $\begin{bmatrix} 1 & 1 \\ 1 & 1 \end{bmatrix}$ **b)** $\begin{bmatrix} 0 & 1 \\ 0 & 0 \end{bmatrix}$ **c)** $\begin{bmatrix} 1 & 1 \\ 1 & 0 \end{bmatrix}$

30. We follow the definition and obtain $\begin{bmatrix} 1 & 0 \\ 1 & 1 \\ 1 & 1 \end{bmatrix}$.

32. a) $\mathbf{A} \vee \mathbf{A} = [a_{ij} \vee a_{ij}] = [a_{ij}] = \mathbf{A}$ **b)** $\mathbf{A} \wedge \mathbf{A} = [a_{ij} \wedge a_{ij}] = [a_{ij}] = \mathbf{A}$

34. a) $(\mathbf{A} \vee \mathbf{B}) \vee \mathbf{C} = [(a_{ij} \vee b_{ij}) \vee c_{ij}] = [a_{ij} \vee (b_{ij} \vee c_{ij})] = \mathbf{A} \vee (\mathbf{B} \vee \mathbf{C})$

b) This is identical to part **(a)**, with $\wedge$ replacing $\vee$.

36. Since the ith row of $\mathbf{I}$ consists of all 0's except for a 1 in the $(i, i)^{\text{th}}$ position, we have $\mathbf{I} \odot \mathbf{A} = [(0 \wedge a_{1j}) \vee \cdots \vee (1 \wedge a_{ij}) \vee \cdots \vee (0 \wedge a_{nj})] = [a_{ij}] = \mathbf{A}$. Similarly, since the jth column of $\mathbf{I}$ consists of all 0's except for a 1 in the $(j, j)^{\text{th}}$ position, we have $\mathbf{A} \odot \mathbf{I} = [(a_{i1} \wedge 0) \vee \cdots \vee (a_{ij} \wedge 1) \vee \cdots \vee (a_{in} \wedge 0)] = [a_{ij}] = \mathbf{A}$.

SUPPLEMENTARY EXERCISES FOR CHAPTER 2

2. a) We need to keep track of the first and second largest elements as we go along, updating as we look at the elements in the list.

```
procedure toptwo(a₁, a₂, ..., aₙ : integers)
largest := a₁
second := −∞
for i := 2 to n
begin
        if aᵢ > second then second := aᵢ
        if aᵢ > largest then
        begin
                second := largest
                largest := aᵢ
        end
end
```

b) The loop is executed $n - 1$ times, and there are 2 comparisons per iteration. Therefore (ignoring bookkeeping) there are $2n - 2$ comparisons.

4. a) Since the list is in order, all the occurrences appear consecutively. Thus the output of our algorithm will be a pair of numbers, *first* and *last*, which give the first location and the last location of occurrences of x, respectively. All the numbers between *first* and *last* are also locations of appearances of x. If there are no appearances of x, we set *first* equal to 0 to indicate this fact.

```
procedure all(x, a₁, a₂, ..., aₙ : integers, with a₁ ≥ a₂ ≥ ··· ≥ aₙ)
i := 1
while i ≤ n and aᵢ < x
        i := i + 1
if i = n + 1 then first := 0
else if aᵢ > x then first := 0
else
begin
        first := i
        i := i + 1
        while i ≤ n and aᵢ = x
                i := i + 1
        last := i − 1
end
```

b) The number of comparisons depends on the data. Roughly speaking, in the worst case we have to go all the way through the list. This requires that x be compared with each of the elements, a total of n comparisons (not including bookkeeping). The situation is really a bit more complicated than this, but in any case the answer is $O(n)$.

6. **a)** We follow the instructions given. If n is odd then we start the loop at $i = 2$, and if n is even then we start the loop at $i = 3$. Within the loop, we compare the next two elements to see which is larger and which is smaller. The larger is possibly the new maximum, and the smaller is possibly the new minimum.

   b)   **procedure** *clever smallest and largest*$(a_1, a_2, \ldots, a_n :$ integers$)$
   if n is odd **then**
   begin
   > $min := a_1$
   > $max := a_1$

   end
   else if $a_1 < a_2$ **then**
   begin
   > $min := a_1$
   > $max := a_2$

   end
   else
   begin
   > $min := a_2$
   > $max := a_1$

   end
   if n is odd **then** $i := 2$ **else** $i := 3$
   while $i < n$
   begin
   >   **if** $a_i < a_{i+1}$ **then**
   >   **begin**
   >   > $smaller := a_i$
   >   > $bigger := a_{i+1}$
   >
   >   **end**
   >   **else**
   >   **begin**
   >   > $smaller := a_{i+1}$
   >   > $bigger := a_i$
   >
   >   **end**
   >   **if** $smaller < min$ **then** $min := smaller$
   >   **if** $bigger > max$ **then** $max := bigger$
   > $i := i + 2$

   end { min is the smallest integer among the input, and max is the largest}

   c) If n is even, then pairs of elements are compared (first with second, third with fourth, and so on), which accounts for $n/2$ comparisons, and there are an additional $2((n/2) - 1) = n - 2$ comparisons to determine whether to update min and max. This gives a total of $(3n - 4)/2$ comparisons. If n is odd, then there are $(n - 1)/2$ pairs to compare and $2((n - 1)/2) = n - 1$ comparisons for the updates, for a total of $(3n - 3)/2$. Note that in either case, this total is $\lceil 3n/2 \rceil - 2$ (see Exercise 7).

8. The naive approach would be to keep track of the largest element found so far and the second largest element found so far. Each new element is compared against the largest, and if it is smaller also compared against the second largest, and the "best-so-far" values are updated if necessary. This would require about $2n$ comparisons in all. We can do it more efficiently by taking Exercise 6 as a hint. If n is odd, set l to be the first element in the list, and set s to be $-\infty$. If n is even, set l to be the larger of the first two elements and s to be the smaller. At each stage, l will be the largest element seen so far, and s the second largest. Now consider the remaining elements two by two. Compare them and set a to be the larger and b the smaller. Compare a with

l. If $a > l$, then a will be the new largest element seen so far, and the second largest element will be either l or b; compare them to find out which. If $a < l$, then l is still the largest element, and we can compare a and s to determine the second largest. Thus it takes only three comparisons for every pair of elements, rather than the four needed with the naive approach. The counting of comparisons is exactly the same as in Exercise 6: $\lceil 3n/2 \rceil - 2$.

10. We start with the solution to Exercise 37 in Section 2.1 and modify it to alternately examine the list from the front and from the back. The variables *front* and *back* will show what portion of the list still needs work. (After the kth pass from front to back, we know that the final k elements are in their correct positions, and after the kth pass from back to front, we know that the first k elements are in their correct positions.) The outer **if** statement takes care of changing directions each pass.

> **procedure** *shakersort*$(a_1, \ldots, a_n)$
> *front* := 1
> *back* := n
> *still_interchanging* := **true**
> **while** *front* < *back* and *still_interchanging*
>   **if** $n + back + front$ is odd **then**
>   **begin** {process from front to back}
>   *still_interchanging* := **false**
>   **for** j := *front* **to** *back* $- 1$
>   **if** $a_j > a_{j+1}$ **then**
>   **begin**
>   *still_interchanging* := **true**
>   interchange a_j and a_{j+1}
>   **end**
>   *back* := *back* $- 1$
>   **end**
>   **else** {process from back to front}
>   **begin**
>   *still_interchanging* := **false**
>   **for** j := *back* **down to** *front* $+ 1$
>   **if** $a_{j-1} > a_j$ **then**
>   **begin**
>   *still_interchanging* := **true**
>   interchange a_{j-1} and a_j
>   **end**
>   *front* := *front* $+ 1$
> **end** { $a_1, \ldots, a_n$ is in nondecreasing order}

12. Lists that are already in close to the correct order will have few items out of place. One pass through the shaker sort will then have a good chance of moving these items to their correct positions. If we are lucky, significantly fewer than $n - 1$ passes through the list will be needed.

14. Since $8x^3 + 12x + 100 \log x \le 8x^3 + 12x^3 + 100x^3 = 120x^3$ for all $x > 1$, the conclusion follows by definition.

16. This is a sum of n things, each of which is no larger than $2n^2$. Therefore the sum is $O(2n^3)$, or more simply, $O(n^3)$. This is the "best" possible answer.

18. Let us look at the ratio $n^n/n!$. We can write this as

$$\frac{n}{n} \cdot \frac{n}{n-1} \cdot \frac{n}{n-2} \cdots \frac{n}{2} \cdot \frac{n}{1}.$$

Each factor is greater than or equal to 1, and the last factor is n. Therefore the ratio is greater than or equal to n. In particular, it cannot be bounded above by a constant C. Therefore the defining condition for n^n being $O(n!)$ cannot be met.

20. Let $q = \left\lceil \dfrac{a}{d} - \dfrac{1}{2} \right\rceil$ and $r = a - dq$. Then we have forced $a = dq + r$, so it remains to prove that $-d/2 < r \le d/2$.

Now since $q - 1 < \dfrac{a}{d} - \dfrac{1}{2} \le q$, we have (by multiplying through by d and adding $d/2$) $dq - \dfrac{d}{2} < a \le dq + \dfrac{d}{2}$, so $-\dfrac{d}{2} < a - dq \le \dfrac{d}{2}$, as desired.

22. There is one zero at the end of this number for every factor of 2 in all of the numbers from 1 to 100. We count them as follows. All the even numbers have a factor of 2, and there are $100/2 = 50$ of these. All the multiples of 4 have another factor of 2, and there are $100/4 = 25$ of these. All the multiples of 8 have another factor of 2, and there are $\lfloor 100/8 \rfloor = 12$ of these, and so on. Thus the answer is $50 + 25 + 12 + 6 + 3 + 1 = 97$.

24. We need to divide successively by 233, 144, 89, 55, 34, 21, 13, 8, 5, 3, 2, and 1, a total of 12 divisions.

26. a) The first statement is clear. For the second, if a and b are both even, then certainly 2 is a factor of their greatest common divisor, and the complementary factor must be the greatest common divisor of the numbers obtained by dividing out this 2. For the third statement, if a is even and b is odd, then the factor of 2 in a will not appear in the greatest common divisor, so we can ignore it. Finally, the last statement follows from Lemma 1 in Section 2.5, taking $q = 1$ (despite the notation, nothing in Lemma 1 required q to be the quotient).

b) All the steps involved in implementing part **(a)** as an algorithm require only comparisons, subtractions, and divisions of even numbers by 2. Since division by 2 is a shift of one bit to the right, only the operations mentioned here are used. (Note that the algorithm needs two more reductions: if a is odd and b is even, then $\gcd(a, b) = \gcd(a, b/2)$, and if $a < b$, then interchange a and b.)

c) We show the operation of the algorithm as a string of equalities; each equation is one step.

$$\gcd(1202, 4848) = \gcd(4848, 1202) = 2\gcd(2424, 601) = 2\gcd(1212, 601) = 2\gcd(606, 601)$$
$$= 2\gcd(303, 601) = 2\gcd(601, 303) = 2\gcd(298, 303) = 2\gcd(303, 298)$$
$$= 2\gcd(303, 149) = 2\gcd(154, 149) = 2\gcd(77, 149) = 2\gcd(149, 77)$$
$$= 2\gcd(72, 77) = 2\gcd(77, 72) = 2\gcd(77, 36) = 2\gcd(77, 18)$$
$$= 2\gcd(77, 9) = 2\gcd(68, 9) = 2\gcd(34, 9) = 2\gcd(17, 9)$$
$$= 2\gcd(8, 9) = 2\gcd(9, 8) = 2\gcd(9, 4) = 2\gcd(9, 2)$$
$$= 2\gcd(9, 1) = 2\gcd(8, 1) = 2\gcd(4, 1) = 2\gcd(2, 1)$$
$$= 2\gcd(1, 1) = 2$$

28. a) Each week consists of seven days. Therefore to find how many (whole) weeks there are in n days, we need to see how many 7's there are in n. That is exactly what n **div** 7 tells us.

b) Each day consists of 24 hours. Therefore to find how many (whole) days there are in n hours, we need to see how many 24's there are in n. That is exactly what n **div** 24 tells us.

30. We need to arrange that every pair of the four numbers has a factor in common. There are six such pairs, so let us use the first six prime numbers as the common factors. Call the numbers a, b, c, and d. We will give a and b a common factor of 2; a and c a common factor of 3; a and d a common factor of 5; b and c a common factor of 7; b and d a common factor of 11; and c and d a common factor of 13. The simplest way to accomplish this is to let $a = 2 \cdot 3 \cdot 5 = 30$; $b = 2 \cdot 7 \cdot 11 = 154$; $c = 3 \cdot 7 \cdot 13 = 273$; and $d = 5 \cdot 11 \cdot 13 = 715$. The numbers are mutually relatively prime, since no number is a factor of all of them (indeed, each prime is a factor of only two of them). Many other examples are possible, of course.

32. If $x \equiv 3 \pmod 9$, then $x = 3 + 9t$ for some integer t. In particular this equation tells us that $3 \mid x$. On the other hand the first congruence says that $x = 2 + 6s = 2 + 3 \cdot (2s)$ for some integer s, which implies that the remainder when x is divided by 3 is 2. Obviously these two conclusions are inconsistent, so there is no simultaneous solution to the two congruences.

34. a) There are two things to prove here. First suppose that $\gcd(m_1, m_2) \mid a_1 - a_2$; say $a_1 - a_2 = k \cdot \gcd(m_1, m_2)$. By Theorem 1 in Section 2.6 there are integers s and t such that $\gcd(m_1, m_2) = sm_1 + tm_2$. Multiplying both sides by k and substituting into our first equation we have $a_1 - a_2 = ksm_1 + ktm_2$, which can be rewritten as $a_1 - ksm_1 = a_2 + ktm_2$. This common value is clearly congruent to a_1 modulo m_1 and congruent to a_2 modulo m_2, so it is a solution to the given system. Conversely, suppose that there is a solution x to the system. Then $x = a_1 + sm_1 = a_2 + tm_2$ for some integers s and t. This says that $a_1 - a_2 = tm_2 - sm_1$. But $\gcd(m_1, m_2)$ divides both m_1 and m_2 and therefore divides the right-hand side of this last equation. Therefore it also divides the left-hand side, $a_1 - a_2$, as desired.

b) We follow the idea sketched in Exercises 23 and 24 of Section 2.6. First we show that if $a \equiv b \pmod{m_1}$ and $a \equiv b \pmod{m_2}$, then $a \equiv b \pmod{\operatorname{lcm}(m_1, m_2)}$. The first hypothesis says that $m_1 \mid a - b$; the second says that $m_2 \mid a - b$. Therefore $a - b$ is a common multiple of m_1 and m_2. If $a - b$ were not also a multiple of $\operatorname{lcm}(m_1, m_2)$, then $(a - b) \bmod \operatorname{lcm}(m_1, m_2)$ would be a common multiple as well, contradicting the definition of $\operatorname{lcm}(m_1, m_2)$. Therefore $a - b$ is a multiple of $\operatorname{lcm}(m_1, m_2)$, i.e., $a \equiv b \pmod{\operatorname{lcm}(m_1, m_2)}$. Now suppose that there were two solutions to the given system of congruences. By what we have just proved, since these two solutions are congruent modulo m_1 (since they are both congruent to a_1) and congruent modulo m_2 (since they are both congruent to a_2), they must be congruent to each other modulo $\operatorname{lcm}(m_1, m_2)$. That is precisely what we wanted to prove.

36. Since $\mathbf{A}$ is the matrix defined by $a_{ii} = c$ and $a_{ij} = 0$ for $i \neq j$, it is easy to see from the definition of multiplication that $\mathbf{AB}$ and $\mathbf{BA}$ are both the same as $\mathbf{B}$ except that every entry has been multiplied by c. Therefore these two matrices are equal.

38. We just use Algorithm 1 in Section 2.7, where $\mathbf{A}$ and $\mathbf{B}$ are now $n \times n$ upper triangular matrices, by replacing m by n in line 1, and having q iterate only from i to j, rather than from 1 to k. (Actually even more efficiency is possible if we store only the nonzero portion of the matrices—see solution to Exercise 39.)

40. See the solution to Exercise 39. Looking at the nested loops, we see that the number of multiplications is given by the following expression: $[1 + 2 + \cdots + n] + [1 + 2 + \cdots (n-1)] + \cdots + [1]$. To simplify this, we need some results from Section 3.3, namely Example 8, which says that the sum of the first k positive integers is $k(k+1)/2$, and Exercise 15, which says that the sum $1 \cdot 2 + 2 \cdot 3 + 3 \cdot 4 + \cdots + k(k+1) = k(k+1)(k+1)/3$. Doing the algebra, we obtain $n(n+1)(n+2)/6$ as the total number of multiplications.

42. There are five ways to parenthesize the calculation $\mathbf{ABCD}$, namely as $(\mathbf{AB})(\mathbf{CD})$, as $((\mathbf{AB})\mathbf{C})\mathbf{D}$, as $(\mathbf{A}(\mathbf{BC}))\mathbf{D}$, as $\mathbf{A}((\mathbf{BC})\mathbf{D})$, and as $\mathbf{A}(\mathbf{B}(\mathbf{CD}))$. We can compute the number of multiplications for each and compare. These numbers are (in thousands) 108, 117, 80, 44, and 81. Thus the most efficient method is the fourth, using 44,000 multiplications.

44. The greedy algorithm in this case will produce the base c expansion for the number of cents required (except that for amounts greater than or equal to c^{k+1}, the c^k coins must be used rather than nonexistent c^i coins for

$i > k$). Since such expansions are unique if each digit (other than the digit in the c^k place) is less than c, the only other ways to make change would involve using c or more coins of a given denomination, and this would obviously not be minimal, since c coins of denomination c^i could be replaced by one coin of denomination c^{i+1}.

46. As we see from Exercise 45, at most n questions (guesses) are needed. Furthermore, at least this many yes/no questions are needed as well, since if we asked fewer questions, then by the pigeonhole principle, two numbers would produce the same set of answers and we would be unable to guess the number accurately. Thus the complexity is n questions. (The case $n = 0$ is not included, since in that case no questions are needed.) We are assuming throughout this exercise and the previous one that the inclusive sense of "between" was intended.

CHAPTER 3
Mathematical Reasoning, Induction, and Recursion

SECTION 3.1   Proof Strategy

2. Write $n = 2k + 1$ for some integer k. Then $n^2 = (2k+1)^2 = 4k^2 + 4k + 1 = 4k(k+1) + 1$. Since either k or $k+1$ is even, $4k(k+1)$ is a multiple of 8. Therefore $n^2 - 1$ is a multiple of 8, so $n^2 \equiv 1 \pmod{8}$.

4. If $|y| \geq 2$, then $2x^2 + 5y^2 \geq 2x^2 + 20 \geq 20$, so the only possible values of y to try are 0 and ± 1. In the former case we would be looking for solutions to $2x^2 = 14$ and in the latter case to $2x^2 = 9$. Clearly there are no integer solutions to these equations, so there are no solutions to the original equation.

6. If there were integer solutions to this equation, then by definition we would have $x^2 \equiv 3 \pmod{4}$. But this impossible, because the square of an even number is congruent to 0 modulo 4 (since $(2k)^2 = 4k^2$), and the square of an odd number is congruent to 1 modulo 4 (since $(2k+1)^2 = 4(k^2+k)+1$).

8. If there were integer solutions to this equation, then by definition we would have $x^2 \equiv 2 \pmod{5}$. However we easily compute (as in Exercise 2) that the square of an integer of the form $5k$ is congruent to 0 modulo 5; the square of an integer of the form $5k+1$ is congruent to 1 modulo 5; the square of an integer of the form $5k+2$ is congruent to 4 modulo 5; the square of an integer of the form $5k+3$ is congruent to 4 modulo 5; and the square of an integer of the form $5k+4$ is congruent to 1 modulo 5. (See also Exercise 20.) This is a contradiction, so no solutions exist.

10. Following the hint, we let $x = m^2 - n^2$, $y = 2mn$, and $z = m^2 + n^2$. Then $x^2 + y^2 = (m^2 - n^2)^2 + (2mn)^2 = m^4 - 2m^2n^2 + n^4 + 4m^2n^2 = m^4 + 2m^2n^2 + n^4 = (m^2 + n^2)^2 = z^2$. Thus we have found infinitely many solutions, since m and n can be arbitrarily large.

12. If $a = 5$ and $b = 8$, then the quadratic mean is $\sqrt{(5^2 + 8^2)/2} \approx 6.67$, and the arithmetic mean is $(5+8)/2 = 6.5$. If $a = 10$ and $b = 100$, then the quadratic mean is $\sqrt{(10^2 + 100^2)/2} \approx 71.06$, and the arithmetic mean is $(10 + 100)/2 = 55$. We conjecture that the quadratic mean of a and b is always greater than their arithmetic mean if a and b are distinct positive real numbers (clearly if $a = b$ then both means are this common value). So we want to verify the inequality $\sqrt{(a^2 + b^2)/2} > (a + b)/2$. Squaring both sides (this is legal because everything in sight is positive) and multiplying by 4 gives us the equivalent inequality $2a^2 + 2b^2 > a^2 + 2ab + b^2$, which is in turn equivalent to $(a - b)^2 > 0$ after putting everything on the left-hand side and factoring. This is clearly always true, and our proof is complete.

14. If we were to end up with nine 0's, then in the step before this we must have had either nine 0's or nine 1's, since each adjacent pair of bits must have been equal and therefore all the bits must have been the same. Thus if we are to start with something other than nine 0's and yet end up with nine 0's, we must have had nine 1's at some point. But in the step before that each adjacent pair of bits must have been different; in other words, they must have alternated 0, 1, 0, 1, and so on. This is impossible with an odd number of bits. This contradiction shows that we can never get nine 0's.

16. This proposition is false. We need only find one counterexample. If we let $n = 3$, then $2^n + 1 = 9$, which is not prime.

18. We give a proof by contradiction. Suppose that n is not a perfect square but that $\sqrt{n}$ is a rational number, say a/b, with a and b integers. Then $nb^2 = a^2$. Consider the prime factorizations of the two sides of this equation, which must be identical by the Fundamental Theorem of Arithmetic (Theorem 2 in Section 2.4). On the right-hand side, every prime factor appears to an even power, because of the square. On the left-hand side, since n is not a perfect square, not every prime factor of n appears to an even power, but every prime factor of b does; therefore at least one prime factor of the left-hand side appears to an odd power. This is impossible. Therefore $\sqrt{n}$ is not rational.

20. We give a proof by cases. There are four possible remainders when an integer n not divisible by 5 is divided by 5, namely 1, 2, 3, and 4. Thus we can write $n = 5k + 1$, or $n = 5k + 2$, or $n = 5k + 3$, or $n = 5k + 4$. We will show that in each case the remainder when n^2 is divided by 5 is either 1 or 4.

First suppose that $n = 5k + 1$. Then $n^2 = (5k + 1)^2 = 25k^2 + 10k + 1 = 5(5k^2 + 2k) + 1$. Therefore we see that the remainder when n^2 is divided by 5 is 1. Next suppose that $n = 5k + 2$. This time $n^2 = 5(5k^2 + 4k) + 4$, so the remainder when n^2 is divided by 5 is 4. For the third case we have $n^2 = (5k + 3)^2 = 25k^2 + 30k + 9 = 5(5k^2 + 6k + 1) + 4$, so again the remainder is 4. Finally, in the last case we have $n^2 = (5k + 4)^2 = 5(5k^2 + 8k + 3) + 1$, so the remainder is 1.

22. This is false, since $2^2 - 1 = 3$ is not composite. It is true, however, that $n^2 - 1$ is composite whenever n is a positive integer greater than 2. To prove this, we can factor $n^2 - 1$ as $(n + 1)(n - 1)$. If n is a positive integer greater than 2, then both $n + 1$ and $n - 1$ are positive integers greater than 1, so we have written $n^2 - 1$ as a nontrivial product, making it composite by definition.

24. This is false, since the left-hand side can be as large as or larger than m, while the right-hand side cannot. For example, let $m = 5$, $a = 3$, and $b = 4$. Then the left-hand side is $3 + 4 = 7$, whereas the right-hand side is $7 \bmod 5 = 2$. It is true, however, that $(a \bmod m + b \bmod m) \bmod m = (a + b) \bmod m$, since each side is the remainder obtained when $a + b$ is divided by m.

26. This is false. In fact, for $n \geq 4$, there are never n consecutive odd integers that are all primes. To see this, we note that among any three consecutive odd numbers, exactly one will be divisible by 3. Indeed, as we count through the odd numbers, the remainders modulo 3 go 1, 0, 2, 1, 0, 2, and so on. No number divisible by 3 is prime except for 3 itself, so the only case in which even three consecutive odd numbers can all be prime is the sequence $3, 5, 7$. Thus it never happens that four consecutive odd numbers are all prime.

28. We need only find a prime number n such that $n + 2$ is not prime. The smallest examples are $n = 2$ and $n = 7$.

30. One key step in the proof was that the product of numbers of the form $4k + 1$ is again of that form. Unfortunately, the similar statement that the product of numbers of the form $4k + 3$ is again of the form $4k + 3$ is false (e.g., $7 \cdot 11 = 77 = 4 \cdot 19 + 1$). In more detail, trying to produce an analogous proof that there are infinitely many primes of the form $4k + 1$ would lead us to look at $Q = 4q_1 q_2 \cdots q_n + 1$. This number could have all of its prime factors of the form $4k + 3$, and so we would have no contradiction to assuming that we had listed all the primes of the form $4k + 1$.

32. The values of the floor and ceiling function will depend on whether their arguments are integral or not. So there seem to be two cases here. First let us suppose that n is even. Then $n/2$ is an integer, and $n^2/4$

is also an integer, so the equation is a simple algebraic fact. The second case is harder. Suppose that n is odd, say $n = 2k + 1$. Then $n/2 = k + \frac{1}{2}$. Therefore the left-hand side gives us $k(k + 1) = k^2 + k$, since we have to round down for the first factor and round up for the second. What about the right-hand side? $n^2 = (2k + 1)^2 = 4k^2 + 4k + 1$, so $n^2/4 = k^2 + k + \frac{1}{4}$. Therefore the floor function gives us $k^2 + k$, and the proof is completed.

34. If x is an integer, then of course the two sides are identical. So suppose that $x = k + \epsilon$, where k is an integer and ϵ is a real number with $0 < \epsilon < 1$. Then the values of the left-hand side, which is $\lfloor (k + n)/m \rfloor$, and the right-hand side, which is $\lfloor (k + n + \epsilon)/m \rfloor$, are the same, since adding a number strictly between 0 and 1 to the numerator of a fraction whose numerator and denominator are integers cannot cause the fraction to reach the next higher integer value (the numerator cannot reach the next multiple of m).

36. First note that since both a and b must be greater than 1, the sequences $\lfloor ka \rfloor$ and $\lfloor kb \rfloor$ do not list any positive integer twice. The issue is whether any positive integer is listed in both sequences, or whether some positive integer is omitted altogether. Let $N(x, n)$ denote the number of positive integers in the set $\{\, \lfloor kx \rfloor \mid k$ is a positive integer $\}$ that are less than or equal to n. Then it is enough to prove that $N(a, n) + N(b, n) = n$ for all positive integers n. (That way no positive integer could be left out or appear twice when we consider all the numbers $\lfloor ka \rfloor$ and $\lfloor kb \rfloor$.) Now $N(a, n)$ is the number of positive integers k for which $\lfloor ka \rfloor \le n$, which is just the number of positive integers k for which $ka < n + 1$, since a is irrational, and this is clearly $\lfloor (n + 1)/a \rfloor$. We have a similar result for b. Let $f(x)$ denote the fractional part of x (i.e., $f(x) = x - \lfloor x \rfloor$). Then we have

$$N(a, n) + N(b, n) = \left\lfloor \frac{n + 1}{a} \right\rfloor + \left\lfloor \frac{n + 1}{b} \right\rfloor = \frac{n + 1}{a} - f\left(\frac{n + 1}{a}\right) + \frac{n + 1}{b} - f\left(\frac{n + 1}{b}\right).$$

But the sum of the first and third terms of the right-hand side here is $n + 1$, since we are given that $(1/a) + (1/b) = 1$. The second and fourth terms are each fractions strictly between 0 and 1, and the entire expression is an integer, so they must sum to 1. Therefore the displayed value is $n + 1 - 1 = n$, as desired.

38. We can give a nice indirect proof here, by showing that if n is not prime, then the sum of its divisors is not $n + 1$. There are two cases. If $n = 1$, then the sum of the divisors is $1 \ne 1 + 1$. Otherwise n is composite, so can be written as $n = ab$, where both a and b are divisors of n different from 1 and from n (although it might happen that $a = b$). Then n has at least the three distinct divisors 1, a, and n, and their sum is clearly not equal to $n + 1$. This completes the indirect proof. One should also observe that the converse of this statement is also true: if n is prime, then the sum of its divisors is $n + 1$ (since its only divisors are 1 and itself).

40. If every positive even integer can be written as the difference of two consecutive primes in infinitely many ways, then 2 can be written as the difference of two consecutive primes in infinitely many ways. This says that the difference of consecutive primes is 2 infinitely often, which says that there are infinitely many twin primes.

42. a) $16 \to 8 \to 4 \to 2 \to 1$
    b) $11 \to 34 \to 17 \to 52 \to 26 \to 13 \to 40 \to 20 \to 10 \to 5 \to 16 \to 8 \to 4 \to 2 \to 1$
    c) $35 \to 106 \to 53 \to 160 \to 80 \to 40 \to 20 \to 10 \to 5 \to 16 \to 8 \to 4 \to 2 \to 1$
    d) $113 \to 340 \to 170 \to 85 \to 256 \to 128 \to 64 \to 32 \to 16 \to 8 \to 4 \to 2 \to 1$

44. Let s_1, s_2, ..., s_m be all the divisors of s, and let t_1, t_2, ..., t_n be all the divisors of t. Then the product of the sums is

$$(s_1 + s_2 + \cdots + s_m)(t_1 + t_2 + \cdots + t_n) = \sum_{i=1}^{m} \sum_{j=1}^{n} s_i t_j.$$

(See Section 3.2 for summation notation.) The right-hand side of this equation, however, is the sum of all the divisors of st, since each divisor of st can be written uniquely as the divisor of s times a divisor of t (because s and t are relatively prime).

46. For a proof, refer to a standard number theory textbook, such as pages 239–240 of *Elementary Number Theory and Its Applications*, fourth edition, by Kenneth H. Rosen (Addison-Wesley, 2000).

48. This problem appeared in the Putnam exam in 1948, and this solution, which requires calculus, is adapted from *The William Lowell Putnam Mathematical Competition, Problems and Solutions: 1938–1964* by A. M. Gleason, R. E. Greenwood, and L. M. Kelly (The Mathematical Association of America, 1980). The graph of the square root function is concave down, and so the average of the function values at two points is less than the function value at the average of those two points. So we have

$$\frac{\sqrt{x} + \sqrt{x+1}}{2} < \sqrt{x + \frac{1}{2}}$$

for all $x \geq 0$. Therefore $\sqrt{x} + \sqrt{x+1} < \sqrt{4x+2}$ and this proves that $\lfloor \sqrt{x} + \sqrt{x+1} \rfloor \leq \lfloor \sqrt{4x+2} \rfloor$ since the floor function is nondecreasing, which is half of what we need to show. Now suppose that for some positive integer n we had $\lfloor \sqrt{n} + \sqrt{n+1} \rfloor < \lfloor \sqrt{4n+2} \rfloor$. Let $p = \lfloor \sqrt{4n+2} \rfloor$. Then

$$\sqrt{n} + \sqrt{n+1} < p \leq \sqrt{4n+2}.$$

Square all three sides to get

$$2n + 1 + 2\sqrt{n(n+1)} < p^2 \leq 4n + 2.$$

whence

$$2\sqrt{n(n+1)} < p^2 - 2n - 1 \leq 2n + 1.$$

Square again to give

$$4n(n+1) < (p^2 - 2n - 1)^2 \leq 4n^2 + 4n + 1.$$

Now the outer numbers here are consecutive integers, and the middle number is also an integer, so $(p^2 - 2n - 1)^2 = (2n+1)^2$, and hence $p^2 = 4n + 2$. But this is impossible, because squares are congruent to 0 or 1, modulo 2, not 2. This contradiction completes the proof.

50. The decision problem has no input. The answer is either always yes or always no, depending on whether or not the specific program with its specific input halts or not. In the former case, the decision procedure is "say yes," and in the latter case it is "say no."

SECTION 3.2   Sequences and Summations

2. In each case we just plug $n = 8$ into the formula.
   a) $2^{8-1} = 128$ **b)** 7   **c)** $1 + (-1)^8 = 0$ **d)** $-(-2)^8 = -256$

4. a) $a_0 = (-2)^0 = 1$, $a_1 = (-2)^1 = -2$, $a_2 = (-2)^2 = 4$, $a_3 = (-2)^3 = -8$
   b) $a_0 = a_1 = a_2 = a_3 = 3$
   c) $a_0 = 7 + 4^0 = 8$, $a_1 = 7 + 4^1 = 11$, $a_2 = 7 + 4^2 = 23$, $a_3 = 7 + 4^3 = 71$
   d) $a_0 = 2^0 + (-2)^0 = 2$, $a_1 = 2^1 + (-2)^1 = 0$, $a_2 = 2^2 + (-2)^2 = 8$, $a_3 = 2^3 + (-2)^3 = 0$

6. These are easy to compute by hand, calculator, or computer.

a) 10, 7, 4, 1, −2, −5, −8, −11, −14, −17

b) We can use the formula in Table 2, or we can just keep adding to the previous term ($1+2 = 3$, $3+3 = 6$, $6 + 4 = 10$, and so on): 1, 3, 6, 10, 15, 21, 28, 36, 45, 55. These are called the triangular numbers.

c) 1, 5, 19, 65, 211, 665, 2059, 6305, 19171, 58025

d) 1, 1, 1, 2, 2, 2, 2, 2, 3, 3 (there will be $2k + 1$ copies of k)   **e)** 1, 2, 3, 5, 8, 13, 21, 34, 55, 89

f) The largest number whose binary expansion has n bits is $(11\ldots1)_2$, which is $2^n - 1$. So the sequence is 1, 3, 7, 15, 31, 63, 127, 255, 511, 1023.

g) 1, 2, 2, 4, 8, 11, 33, 37, 148, 153   **h)** 1, 2, 2, 2, 2, 3, 3, 3, 3, 3

8. One rule could be that each term is 2 greater than the previous term; the sequence would be 3, 5, 7, 9, 11, 13, …. . Another rule could be that the nth term is the nth odd prime; the sequence would be 3, 5, 7, 11, 13, 17, …. . Actually, we could choose any number we want for the fourth term (say 12) and find a third degree polynomial whose value at n would be the nth term; in this case we need to solve for A, B, C, and D in the equations $y = Ax^3 + Bx^2 + Cx + D$ where $(1,3)$, $(2,5)$, $(3,7)$, $(4,12)$ have been plugged in for x and y. Doing so yields $(x^3 - 6x^2 + 15x - 4)/2$. With this formula, the sequence is 3, 5, 7, 12, 23, 43, 75, 122, 187, 273. Obviously many other answers are possible.

10. a) The first term is 3, and the nth term is obtained by adding $2n - 1$ to the previous term. In other words, we successively add 3, then 5, then 7, and so on. Alternatively, we see that the nth term is $n^2 + 2$; we can see this by inspection if we happen to notice how close each term is to a perfect square, or we can fit a quadratic polynomial to the data.

b) This is an arithmetic sequence whose first term is 7 and whose difference is 4. Thus the nth term is $7 + 4(n - 1) = 4n + 3$.

c) The nth term is clearly the binary expansion of n.

d) The sequence consists of one 1, followed by three 3s, followed by five 5s, and so on, with the number of copies of the next value increasing by 2 each time, and the values themselves following the rule that the first two values are 1 and 2 and each subsequent value is the sum of the previous two values. Obviously other answers are possible as well.

e) If we stare at this sequence long enough and compare it with Table 1, then we notice that the nth term is $3^n - 1$.

f) We notice that each term evenly divides the next, and the multipliers are successively 3, 5, 7, 9, 11, and so on. That must be the intended pattern.

g) The sequence consists of one 1, followed by two 0s, then three 1s, four 0s, five 1s, and so on, alternating between 0s and 1s and having one more item in each group than in the previous group.

h) It doesn't take long to notice that each term is the square of its predecessor.

12. Let us ask ourselves which is the last term in the sequence whose value is k? Clearly it is $1 + 2 + 3 + \cdots + k$, which equals $k(k + 1)/2$. We can rephrase this by saying that $a_n \le k$ if and only if $k(k + 1)/2 \ge n$. Thus, to find k as a function of n, we must find the smallest k such that $k(k + 1)/2 \ge n$. This is equivalent to $k^2 + k - 2n \ge 0$. By the quadratic formula, this tells us that k has to be at least $(-1 + \sqrt{1 + 8n})/2$. Therefore we have $k = \lceil(-1 + \sqrt{1 + 8n})/2\rceil = \left\lceil -\frac{1}{2} + \sqrt{2n + \frac{1}{4}} \right\rceil$. By Exercise 39 in Section 1.8, this is the same as the integer closest to $\sqrt{2n + \frac{1}{4}}$, where we choose the smaller of the two closest integers if $\sqrt{2n + \frac{1}{4}}$ is a half integer. The desired answer is $\lfloor \sqrt{2n} + \frac{1}{2} \rfloor$, which by Exercise 38 in Section 1.8 is the integer closest to $\sqrt{2n}$ (note that $\sqrt{2n}$ can never be a half integer). To see that these are the same, note that it can never happen that $\sqrt{2n} \le m + \frac{1}{2}$ while $\sqrt{2n + \frac{1}{4}} > m + \frac{1}{2}$ for some positive integer m, since this would imply that

$2n \le m^2 + m + \frac{1}{4}$ and $2n > m^2 + m$, an impossibility. Therefore the integer closest to $\sqrt{2n}$ and the (smaller) integer closest to $\sqrt{2n + \frac{1}{4}}$ are the same, and we are done.

14. a) $1 + 3 + 5 + 7 = 16$ **b)** $1^2 + 3^2 + 5^2 + 7^2 = 84$
  c) $(1/1) + (1/3) + (1/5) + (1/7) = 176/105$ **d)** $1 + 1 + 1 + 1 = 4$

16. a) The terms of this sequence alternate between 2 (if j is even) and 0 (if j is odd). Thus the sum is $2 + 0 + 2 + 0 + 2 + 0 + 2 + 0 + 2 = 10$.
  b) We can break this into two parts and compute $\left(\sum_{j=0}^{8} 3^j\right) - \left(\sum_{j=0}^{8} 2^j\right)$. Each summation can be computed from the formula for the sum of a geometric progression. Thus the answer is

$$\frac{3^9 - 1}{3 - 1} - \frac{2^9 - 1}{2 - 1} = 9841 - 511 = 9330.$$

  c) As in part **(b)** we can break this into two parts and compute $\left(\sum_{j=0}^{8} 2 \cdot 3^j\right) + \left(\sum_{j=0}^{8} 3 \cdot 2^j\right)$. Each summation can be computed from the formula for the sum of a geometric progression. Thus the answer is

$$\frac{2 \cdot 3^9 - 2}{3 - 1} + \frac{3 \cdot 2^9 - 3}{2 - 1} = 19682 + 1533 = 21215.$$

  d) This could be worked as in part **(b)**, but it is easier to note that the sum telescopes (see Exercise 19). Each power of 2 cancels except for the -2^0 when $j = 0$ and the 2^9 when $j = 8$. Therefore the answer is $2^9 - 2^0 = 511$. (Alternatively, note that $2^{j+1} - 2^j = 2^j$.)

18. We will just write out the sums explicitly in each case.
  a) $(1 - 1) + (1 - 2) + (2 - 1) + (2 - 2) + (3 - 1) + (3 - 2) = 3$
  b) $(0+0) + (0+2) + (0+4) + (3+0) + (3+2) + (3+4) + (6+0) + (6+2) + (6+4) + (9+0) + (9+2) + (9+4) = 78$
  c) $(0 + 1 + 2) + (0 + 1 + 2) + (0 + 1 + 2) = 9$
  d) $(0 + 0 + 0 + 0) + (0 + 1 + 8 + 27) + (0 + 4 + 32 + 108) = 180$

20. We use the suggestion (simple algebra shows that this is indeed an identity) and note that all the terms in the summation cancel out except for the $1/k$ when $k = 1$ and the $1/(k + 1)$ when $k = n$:

$$\sum_{k=1}^{n} \frac{1}{k(k + 1)} = \sum_{k=1}^{n} \left(\frac{1}{k} - \frac{1}{k + 1}\right) = \frac{1}{1} - \frac{1}{n + 1} = \frac{n}{n + 1}$$

22. First we note that $k^3 - (k - 1)^3 = 3k^2 - 3k + 1$. Then we sum this equation for all values of k from 1 to n. On the left, because of telescoping, we have just n^3; on the right we have

$$3\sum_{k=1}^{n} k^2 - 3\sum_{k=1}^{n} k + \sum_{k=1}^{n} 1 = 3\sum_{k=1}^{n} k^2 - \frac{3n(n + 1)}{2} + n.$$

Equating the two sides and solving for $\sum_{k=1}^{n} k^2$, we obtain the desired formula.

$$\sum_{k=1}^{n} k^2 = \frac{1}{3}\left(n^3 + \frac{3n(n + 1)}{2} - n\right)$$
$$= \frac{n}{3}\left(\frac{2n^2 + 3n + 3 - 2}{2}\right)$$
$$= \frac{n}{3}\left(\frac{2n^2 + 3n + 1}{2}\right) = \frac{n(n + 1)(2n + 1)}{6}$$

24. This exercise is like Example 15. From Table 2 we know that $\sum_{k=1}^{200} k^3 = 200^2 \cdot 201^2/4 = 404{,}010{,}000$, and $\sum_{k=1}^{98} k^3 = 98^2 \cdot 99^2/4 = 23{,}532{,}201$. Therefore the desired sum is $404{,}010{,}000 - 23{,}532{,}201 = 380{,}477{,}799$.

86 Chapter 3   Mathematical Reasoning, Induction, and Recursion

26. If we write down the first few terms of this sum we notice a pattern. It starts $(1+1+1+1+1+1+1)+(2+2+2+2+2+2+2+2+2+2+2+2+2+2+2+2+2+2+2)+(3+3+3+3+\cdots+3)+\cdots$. There are seven 1s, then 19 2s, then 37 3s, and so on; in general, the number of i's is $(i+1)^3 - i^3 = 3i^2 + 3i + 1$. So we need to sum $i(3i^2 + 3i + 1)$ for an appropriate range of values for i. We must find this range. It gets a little messy at the end if m is such that the sequence stops before a complete range of the last value is present. Let $n = \lfloor \sqrt[3]{m} \rfloor - 1$. Then there are $n+1$ blocks, and $(n+1)^3 - 1$ is where the next-to-last block ends. The sum of those complete blocks is $\sum_{i=1}^{n} i(3i^2 + 3i + 1) = \sum_{i=1}^{n} 3i^3 + 3i^2 + i = n(3n+4)(n+1)^2/4$ (using Table 2 and algebra). The remaining terms in our summation all have the value $n+1$ and the number of them present is $m - ((n+1)^3 - 1)$. Our final answer is therefore $n(3n+4)(n+1)^2/4 + (n+1)(m - (n+1)^3 + 1)$, where, once again, $n = \lfloor \sqrt[3]{m} \rfloor - 1$.

28. $n! = \prod_{i=1}^{n} i$

30. $(0!)(1!)(2!)(3!)(4!) = 1 \cdot 1 \cdot 2 \cdot 6 \cdot 24 = 288$

32. a) This is countable. The integers in the set are ± 1, ± 2, ± 4, ± 5, ± 7, and so on. We can list these numbers in the order 1, -1, 2, -2, 4, -4, 5, -5, 7, -7, $\ldots$, thereby establishing the desired correspondence. In other words, the correspondence is given by $1 \leftrightarrow 1$, $2 \leftrightarrow -1$, $3 \leftrightarrow 2$, $4 \leftrightarrow -2$, $5 \leftrightarrow 4$, and so on.
b) This is similar to part **(a)**; we can simply list the elements of the set in order of increasing absolute value, listing each positive term before its corresponding negative: 5, -5, 10, -10, 15, -15, 20, -20, 25, -25, 30, -30, 40, -40, 45, -45, 50, -50, $\ldots$.
c) This is countable but a little tricky. We can arrange the numbers in a 2-dimensional table as follows:

$.\overline{1}$	$.1$	$.11$	$.111$	$.1111$	$.11111$	$.111111$	$\ldots$
$1.\overline{1}$	1	1.1	1.11	1.111	1.1111	1.11111	$\ldots$
$11.\overline{1}$	11	11.1	11.11	11.111	11.1111	11.11111	$\ldots$
$111.\overline{1}$	111	111.1	111.11	111.111	111.1111	111.11111	$\ldots$
$\vdots$	$\vdots$	$\vdots$	$\vdots$	$\vdots$	$\vdots$	$\vdots$	

Thus we have shown that our set is the countable union of countable sets (each of the countable sets is one row of this table). Therefore by Exercise 37, the entire set is countable.
d) This set is not countable. We can prove it by the same diagonalization argument as was used to prove that the set of all reals is uncountable in Example 20. All we need to do is choose $d_i = 1$ when $d_{ii} = 9$ and choose $d_i = 9$ when $d_{ii} = 1$ or d_{ii} is blank (if the decimal expansion is finite).

34. If a set A is countable, then we can list its elements, a_1, a_2, $\ldots$, a_n, $\ldots$ (possibly ending after a finite number of terms). Every subset of A consists of some (or none or all) of the items in this sequence, and we can list them in the same order in which they appear in the sequence. This gives us a sequence (again, infinite or finite) listing all the elements of the subset. Thus the subset is also countable.

36. Let A and B be the two given countable sets, and let us list their elements as a_1, a_2, $\ldots$, a_n, $\ldots$ and b_1, b_2, $\ldots$, b_n, $\ldots$. Then we can list the elements of their union as a_1, b_1, a_2, b_2, $\ldots$, except that we do not list any element that has already appeared in this list (in case $A \cap B \neq \varnothing$), and if one or both of the original lists stops (in case A or B is finite), then of course we do not list nonexistent terms. Since we have displayed $A \cup B$ as a list, we conclude that it is countable.

38. Exercise 71 in Section 1.8 gave a one-to-one correspondence between $\mathbf{Z}^+ \times \mathbf{Z}^+$ and $\mathbf{Z}^+$. Since $\mathbf{Z}^+$ is countable, so is $\mathbf{Z}^+ \times \mathbf{Z}^+$.

40. There are at most two real solutions of each quadratic equation, so the number of solutions is countable as long as the number of triples (a, b, c), with a, b, and c integers, is countable. But this follows from Exercise 37 in the following way. There are a countable number of pairs (b, c), since for each b (and there are countably many b's) there are only a countable number of pairs with that b as its first coordinate. Now for each a (and there are countably many a's) there are only a countable number of triples with that a as its first coordinate (since we just showed that there are only a countable number of pairs (b, c)). Thus again by Exercise 37 there are only countably many triples.

42. We know from Example 20 that the set of real numbers between 0 and 1 is uncountable. Let us associate to each real number in this range (including 0 but excluding 1) a function from the set of positive integers to the set $\{0, 1, 2, 3, 4, 5, 6, 7, 8, 9\}$ as follows: If x is a real number whose decimal representation is $0.d_1 d_2 d_3 \ldots$ (with ambiguity resolved by forbidding the decimal to end with an infinite string of 9's), then we associate to x the function whose rule is given by $f(n) = d_n$. Clearly this is a one-to-one function from the set of real numbers between 0 and 1 and a subset of the set of all functions from the set of positive integers to the set $\{0, 1, 2, 3, 4, 5, 6, 7, 8, 9\}$. Two different real numbers must have different decimal representations, so the corresponding functions are different. (A few functions are left out, because of forbidding representations such as $0.239999\ldots$.) Since the set of real numbers between 0 and 1 is uncountable, the subset of functions we have associated with them must be uncountable. But the set of all such functions has at least this cardinality, so it, too, must be uncountable (by Exercise 35).

44. Define the function f as suggested from the positive rational numbers to the positive integers. This is a one-to-one function, because if we are given the value of $f(p/q)$, we can immediately recover p and q uniquely by writing $f(p/q)$ in base eleven and noting what appears to the left of the one and only A in the expansion and what appears to the right (and interpret these as numerals in base ten). Thus we have a one-to-one correspondence between the set of positive rational numbers and an infinite subset of the natural numbers, which is countable; therefore the set of positive rational numbers is countable.

SECTION 3.3 Mathematical Induction

Important note about notation for proofs by mathematical induction: *In performing the inductive step, it really does not matter what letter we use. We see in the text the proof of $P(k) \rightarrow P(k+1)$; but it would be just as valid to prove $P(n) \rightarrow P(n+1)$, since the k in the first case and the n in the second case are just dummy variables. We will use both notations in this Guide; in particular, we will use k for the first few exercises but often use n afterwards.*

2. The proof is given in the solution to Exercise 1.

4. The proposition to be proved is $P(n)$:

$$2 - 2 \cdot 7 + 2 \cdot 7^2 - \cdots + 2 \cdot (-7)^n = \frac{1 - (-7)^{n+1}}{4}.$$

In order to prove this for all integers $n \geq 0$, we first prove the base case $P(0)$ and then prove the inductive step, that $P(k)$ implies $P(k+1)$. Now in $P(0)$, the left-hand side has just one term, namely 2, and the right-hand side is $(1 - (-7)^1)/4 = 8/4 = 2$. Since $2 = 2$, we have verified that $P(0)$ is true. For the inductive step, we *assume* that $P(k)$ is true (i.e., the displayed equation above), and derive from it the truth of $P(k+1)$, which is the equation

$$2 - 2 \cdot 7 + 2 \cdot 7^2 - \cdots + 2 \cdot (-7)^k + 2 \cdot (-7)^{k+1} = \frac{1 - (-7)^{(k+1)+1}}{4}.$$

To prove an equation like this, it is usually best to start with the more complicated side and manipulate it until we arrive at the other side. In this case we start on the left. Note that all but the last term constitute precisely the left-hand side of $P(k)$, and therefore by the inductive hypothesis, we can replace it by the right-hand side of $P(k)$. The rest is algebra:

$$
\begin{aligned}
[2 - 2 \cdot 7 + 2 \cdot 7^2 - \cdots + 2 \cdot (-7)^k] + 2 \cdot (-7)^{k+1} &= \frac{1 - (-7)^{k+1}}{4} + 2 \cdot (-7)^{k+1} \\
&= \frac{1 - (-7)^{k+1} + 8 \cdot (-7)^{k+1}}{4} \\
&= \frac{1 + 7 \cdot (-7)^{k+1}}{4} \\
&= \frac{1 - (-7) \cdot (-7)^{k+1}}{4} \\
&= \frac{1 - (-7)^{(k+1)+1}}{4}.
\end{aligned}
$$

6. By looking at the first few sums, we guess that the sum is $n/(n+1)$. We prove this by induction. It is clear for $n = 1$, since there is just one term, $1/2$. Suppose that

$$
\frac{1}{1 \cdot 2} + \frac{1}{2 \cdot 3} + \cdots + \frac{1}{k(k+1)} = \frac{k}{k+1}.
$$

We want to show that

$$
\left[\frac{1}{1 \cdot 2} + \frac{1}{2 \cdot 3} + \cdots + \frac{1}{k(k+1)} \right] + \frac{1}{(k+1)(k+2)} = \frac{k+1}{k+2}.
$$

Starting from the left, we replace the quantity in brackets by $k/(k+1)$ (by the inductive hypothesis), and then do the algebra

$$
\frac{k}{k+1} + \frac{1}{(k+1)(k+2)} = \frac{k^2 + 2k + 1}{(k+1)(k+2)} = \frac{k+1}{k+2},
$$

yielding the desired expression.

8. We proceed by induction. The base case is true, since $1^3 = [1 \cdot (1+1)/2]^2$. We assume the inductive hypothesis, that

$$
1^3 + 2^3 + \cdots + k^3 = \left(\frac{k(k+1)}{2} \right)^2,
$$

and try to prove that

$$
[1^3 + 2^3 + \cdots + k^3] + (k+1)^3 = \left(\frac{(k+1)(k+2)}{2} \right)^2.
$$

Replacing the quantity in brackets on the left-hand side by what it equals by virtue of the inductive hypothesis, we have

$$
\left(\frac{k(k+1)}{2} \right)^2 + (k+1)^3 = (k+1)^2 \left(\frac{k^2}{4} + k + 1 \right) = (k+1)^2 \left(\frac{k^2 + 4k + 4}{4} \right) = \left(\frac{(k+1)(k+2)}{2} \right)^2,
$$

as desired.

10. The base case is clear, since $1 \cdot 1! = 2! - 1$. Assuming the inductive hypothesis, we then have

$$
\begin{aligned}
1 \cdot 1! + 2 \cdot 2! + \cdots + k \cdot k! + (k+1) \cdot (k+1)! &= (k+1)! - 1 + (k+1) \cdot (k+1)! \\
&= (k+1)!(1 + k + 1) - 1 = (k+2)! - 1,
\end{aligned}
$$

as desired.

12. The base case is $n = 7$, and indeed $3^7 < 7!$, since $2187 < 5040$. Assume the statement for k. Then $3^{k+1} = 3 \cdot 3^k < (k+1) \cdot 3^k < (k+1) \cdot k! = (k+1)!$, the statement for $k+1$.

14. The base case is $n = 2$, and indeed $2! < 2^2$. Assume the inductive hypothesis. Then $(k+1)! = (k+1)k! < (k+1)k^k < (k+1)(k+1)^k = (k+1)^{k+1}$.

16. The base case reduces to $6 = 6$. Assuming the inductive hypothesis we have

$$1 \cdot 2 \cdot 3 + 2 \cdot 3 \cdot 4 + \cdots + k(k+1)(k+2) + (k+1)(k+2)(k+3)$$
$$= \frac{k(k+1)(k+2)(k+3)}{4} + (k+1)(k+2)(k+3)$$
$$= (k+1)(k+2)(k+3)\left(\frac{k}{4} + 1\right)$$
$$= \frac{(k+1)(k+2)(k+3)(k+4)}{4}.$$

18. The base case, $n = 2$, is the true statement that $5/4$ is less than $6/4$. Assume the inductive hypothesis. Then we have

$$1 + \frac{1}{4} + \cdots + \frac{1}{k^2} + \frac{1}{(k+1)^2} < 2 - \frac{1}{k} + \frac{1}{(k+1)^2}$$
$$= 2 - \left(\frac{1}{k} - \frac{1}{(k+1)^2}\right)$$
$$= 2 - \left(\frac{k^2 + 2k + 1 - k}{k(k+1)^2}\right)$$
$$= 2 - \frac{k^2 + k}{k(k+1)^2} - \frac{1}{k(k+1)^2}$$
$$= 2 - \frac{1}{k+1} - \frac{1}{k(k+1)^2} < 2 - \frac{1}{k+1}.$$

20. The statement is true for the base case, $n = 0$, since $3 \mid 0$. Suppose that $3 \mid (k^3 + 2k)$. We must show that $3 \mid ((k+1)^3 + 2(k+1))$. If we expand the expression in question, we obtain $k^3 + 3k^2 + 3k + 1 + 2k + 2 = (k^3 + 2k) + 3(k^2 + k + 1)$. By the inductive hypothesis, 3 divides $k^3 + 2k$, and certainly 3 divides $3(k^2 + k + 1)$, so 3 divides their sum, and we are done.

22. The statement is true for the base case, $n = 0$, since $6 \mid 0$. Suppose that $6 \mid (n^3 - n)$. We must show that $6 \mid ((n+1)^3 - (n+1))$. If we expand the expression in question, we obtain $n^3 + 3n^2 + 3n + 1 - n - 1 = (n^3 - n) + 3n(n+1)$. By the inductive hypothesis, 6 divides the first term, $n^3 - n$. Furthermore clearly 3 divides the second term, and the second term is also even, since one of n and $n+1$ is even; therefore 6 divides the second term as well. This tells us that 6 divides the given expression, as desired. (Note that here we have, as promised, used n as the dummy variable in the inductive step, rather than k.)

24. The base case is $n = 4$ (the smallest integer greater than 3). We check that $4^2 - 7 \cdot 4 + 12 = 0$ is nonnegative. Next suppose that $n^2 - 7n + 12 \geq 0$; we must show that $(n+1)^2 - 7(n+1) + 12 \geq 0$. Expanding the left-hand side, we obtain $n^2 + 2n + 1 - 7n - 7 + 12 = (n^2 - 7n + 12) + (2n - 6)$. The first of the parenthesized expressions is nonnegative by the inductive hypothesis; the second is clearly also nonnegative by the assumption that n is at least 4. Therefore their sum is nonnegative, and the inductive step is complete.

26. This proof will be similar to the proof in Example 7. The base case is clear, since for $n = 3$, the set has exactly one subset containing exactly three elements, and $3(3-1)(3-2)/6 = 1$. Assume the inductive hypothesis, that a set with n elements has $n(n-1)(n-2)/6$ subsets with exactly three elements; we want to prove that a set S with $n+1$ elements has $(n+1)n(n-1)/6$ subsets with exactly three elements. Fix an element a in S, and let T be the set of elements of S other than a. There are two varieties of subsets of S containing exactly three elements. First there are those that do not contain a. These are precisely the three-element subsets of T, and by the inductive hypothesis, there are $n(n-1)(n-2)/6$ of them. Second, there are those that contain a together with two elements of T. Therefore there are just as many of these subsets as there are two-element subsets of T. By Exercise 25, there are exactly $n(n-1)/2$ such subsets of T; therefore there are also $n(n-1)/2$ three-element subsets of S containing a. Thus the total number of subsets of S containing exactly three elements is $(n(n-1)(n-2)/6)+n(n-1)/2$, which simplifies algebraically to $(n+1)n(n-1)/6$, as desired.

28. A little computation convinces us that the answer is that $n^2 \leq n!$ for $n = 0$, 1, and all $n \geq 4$. (Clearly the inequality does not hold for $n = 2$ or $n = 3$.) We will prove by mathematical induction that the inequality holds for all $n \geq 4$. The base case is clear, since $16 \leq 24$. Now suppose that $n^2 \leq n!$ for a given $n \geq 4$. We must show that $(n+1)^2 \leq (n+1)!$. Expanding the left-hand side, applying the inductive hypothesis, and then invoking some valid bounds shows this:

$$n^2 + 2n + 1 \leq n! + 2n + 1$$
$$\leq n! + 2n + n = n! + 3n$$
$$\leq n! + n \cdot n \leq n! + n \cdot n!$$
$$= (n+1)n! = (n+1)!$$

30. The base case is clear, since $1/2 \leq 1/2$. We assume the inductive hypothesis (the inequality shown in the exercise) and want to prove the similar inequality for $n+1$. We proceed as follows, using the trick of writing $1/(2(n+1))$ in terms of $1/(2n)$ so that we can invoke the inductive hypothesis:

$$\frac{1}{2(n+1)} = \frac{1}{2n} \cdot \frac{2n}{2(n+1)}$$
$$\leq \frac{1 \cdot 3 \cdot 5 \cdots (2n-1))}{2 \cdot 4 \cdots 2n} \cdot \frac{2n}{2(n+1)}$$
$$\leq \frac{1 \cdot 3 \cdot 5 \cdots (2n-1))}{2 \cdot 4 \cdots 2n} \cdot \frac{2n+1}{2(n+1)}$$
$$= \frac{1 \cdot 3 \cdot 5 \cdots (2n-1) \cdot (2n+1)}{2 \cdot 4 \cdots 2n \cdot 2(n+1)}$$

32. The answer is that we can form all multiples of 5 cents greater than or equal to 20 cents, as well as 10 cents. (The fact that 5 cents and 15 cents cannot be obtained is clear.) To prove this by induction, we check the base case, that 20 cents can be formed (with two dimes). Next assume the inductive hypothesis, that we can form $5k$ cents (where $k \geq 4$); we need to show how to obtain $5(k+1) = 5k+5$ cents. If a quarter is used to form $5k$ cents, then we can replace it by three dimes, increasing the amount of money by the desired 5 cents. On the other hand, if a quarter is not used, then at least two dimes must be used (since $5k \geq 20$), so we can replace two dimes by a quarter, again increasing the amount of money by the desired 5 cents.

34. We claim that it takes exactly $n-1$ breaks to separate a bar (or any connected piece of a bar obtained by horizontal or vertical breaks) into n pieces. We use strong induction. If $n = 1$, this is trivially true (one piece, no breaks). Assume the strong inductive hypothesis, that the statement is true for breaking into k or fewer pieces, and consider the task of obtaining $k+1$ pieces. We must show that it takes exactly k breaks. The process must start with a break, leaving two smaller pieces. We can view the rest of the process as breaking one of these pieces into $i+1$ pieces and breaking the other piece into $k-i$ pieces, for some i between 0 and $k-1$, inclusive. By the inductive hypothesis it will take exactly i breaks to handle the first piece and $k-i-1$ breaks to handle the second piece. Therefore the total number of breaks will be $1 + i + (k-i-1) = k$, as desired.

36. We proceed by induction. The base case is true, since $1 \cdot 2^1 = (1-1)2^{1+1} + 2$. We assume the inductive hypothesis, that

$$\sum_{k=1}^{n} k \cdot 2^k = (n-1)2^{n+1} + 2\,,$$

and try to prove that

$$\sum_{k=1}^{n+1} k \cdot 2^k = n \cdot 2^{n+2} + 2\,.$$

Splitting the left-hand side into its first n terms followed by its last term and invoking the inductive hypothesis, we have

$$\sum_{k=1}^{n+1} k \cdot 2^k = \left(\sum_{k=1}^{n} k \cdot 2^k\right) + (n+1)2^{n+1} = (n-1)2^{n+1} + 2 + (n+1)2^{n+1} = 2n \cdot 2^{n+1} + 2 = n \cdot 2^{n+2} + 2\,,$$

as desired.

38. The base case is $n = 1$. If we are given a set of two elements from $\{1, 2\}$, then indeed one of them divides the other. Assume the inductive hypothesis, and consider a set A of $n + 2$ elements from $\{1, 2, \ldots, 2n, 2n + 1, 2n + 2\}$. We must show that at least one of these elements divides another. If as many as $n+1$ of the elements of A are less than $2n + 1$, then the desired conclusion follows immediately from the inductive hypothesis. Therefore we can assume that both $2n + 1$ and $2n + 2$ are in A, together with n smaller elements. If $n + 1$ is one of these smaller elements, then we are done, since $n + 1 \mid 2n + 2$. So we can assume that $n + 1 \notin A$. Now apply the inductive hypothesis to $B = A - \{2n + 1, 2n + 2\} \cup \{n + 1\}$. Since B is a collection of $n + 1$ numbers from $\{1, 2, \ldots, 2n\}$, the inductive hypothesis guarantees that one element of B divides another. If $n + 1$ is not one of these two numbers, then we are done. So we can assume that $n + 1$ is one of these two numbers. Certainly $n + 1$ can't be the divisor, since its smallest multiple is too big to be in B, so there is some $k \in B$ that divides $n + 1$. But now k and $2n + 2$ are numbers in A, with k dividing $n + 2$, and we are done. An alternative proof of this theorem is given in Example 11 of Section 4.2.

40. We prove this using strong induction. It is clearly true for $n = 1$, because no splits are performed, so the sum computed is 0, which equals $n(n - 1)/2$ when $n = 1$. Assume the strong inductive hypothesis, and suppose that our first splitting is into piles of i stones and $n - i$ stones, where i is a positive integer less than n. This gives a product $i(n - i)$. The rest of the products will be obtained from splitting the piles thus formed, and so by the inductive hypothesis, the sum of the products will be $i(i - 1)/2 + (n - i)(n - i - 1)/2$. So we must show that

$$i(n - i) + \frac{i(i - 1)}{2} + \frac{(n - i)(n - i - 1)}{2} = \frac{n(n - 1)}{2}$$

no matter what i is. This follows by elementary algebra, and our proof is complete.

42. There is nothing to prove in the base case, $n = 1$, since $\mathbf{A} = \mathbf{A}$. For the inductive step we just invoke the inductive hypothesis and the definition of matrix multiplication:

$$\mathbf{A}^{n+1} = \mathbf{A}\mathbf{A}^n = \begin{bmatrix} a & 0 \\ 0 & b \end{bmatrix} \begin{bmatrix} a^n & 0 \\ 0 & b^n \end{bmatrix}$$

$$= \begin{bmatrix} a \cdot a^n + 0 \cdot 0 & a \cdot 0 + 0 \cdot b^n \\ 0 \cdot a^n + b \cdot 0 & 0 \cdot 0 + b \cdot b^n \end{bmatrix} = \begin{bmatrix} a^{n+1} & 0 \\ 0 & b^{n+1} \end{bmatrix}$$

44. We prove this by induction on k. The base case $k = 0$ is the trivial statement that $1 \equiv 1 \pmod{m}$. Suppose that the statement is true for k. We must show it for $k + 1$. So let $a \equiv b \pmod{m}$. By the inductive hypothesis we know that $a^k \equiv b^k \pmod{m}$. Then we apply Theorem 10 from Section 2.4 to conclude that $a \cdot a^k \equiv b \cdot b^k \pmod{m}$, which by definition says that $a^{k+1} \equiv b^{k+1} \pmod{m}$, as desired.

46. These are really easier to do directly than by induction.

a) Suppose that $x \in \bigcup\limits_{k=1}^{n} A_k$. Then $x \in A_k$ for some k. Since $A_k \subseteq B_k$, we know that $x \in B_k$. Therefore by definition, $x \in \bigcup\limits_{k=1}^{n} B_k$, as desired.

b) Suppose that $x \in \bigcap\limits_{k=1}^{n} A_k$. Then $x \in A_k$ for all k. Since $A_k \subseteq B_k$, we know that $x \in B_k$ for all k. Therefore by definition, $x \in \bigcap\limits_{k=1}^{n} B_k$, as desired.

48. This is identical to Exercise 47, with $\vee$ replacing $\cup$, $\wedge$ replacing $\cap$, and $\neg$ replacing complementation. The base case is trivial, since it merely says that $\neg p_1$ is equivalent to itself. Assuming the inductive hypothesis, we look at $\neg(p_1 \vee p_2 \vee \cdots \vee p_n \vee p_{n+1})$. By De Morgan's law (grouping all but the last term together) this is the same $\neg(p_1 \vee p_2 \vee \cdots \vee p_n) \wedge \neg p_{n+1}$. But by the inductive hypothesis, this equals, $\neg p_1 \wedge \neg p_2 \wedge \cdots \wedge \neg p_n \wedge \neg p_{n+1}$, as desired.

50. When $n = 1$ the left-hand side is 1, and the right-hand side is $(1 + \frac{1}{2})^2/2 = 9/8$. Thus the basis step was wrong.

52. The mistake is in applying the inductive hypothesis to look at $\max(x - 1, y - 1)$, because even though x and y are positive integers, $x - 1$ and $y - 1$ need not be (one or both could be 0). In fact, that is what happens if we let $x = 1$ and $y = 2$ when $k = 1$.

54. The flaw comes in the inductive step, where we are implicitly assuming that $n \geq 1$ in order to talk about a^{n-1} in the denominator (otherwise the exponent is not a nonnegative integer, so we cannot apply the inductive hypothesis). We checked the base case only for $n = 0$, so we are not justified in assuming that $n \geq 1$ when we try to prove the statement for $n + 1$ in the inductive step. Indeed, it is precisely at $n = 1$ that the proposition breaks down.

56. Suppose that a statement $\forall n P(n)$ has been proved by this method. Let S be the set of counterexamples to P, i.e., let $S = \{ n \mid \neg P(n) \}$. We will show that $S = \emptyset$. If $S \neq \emptyset$, then let n be the minimum element of S (which exists by the well-ordering property). Clearly $n \neq 1$ and $n \neq 2$, by the base cases of our proof method. But since n is the least element of S and $n \geq 3$, we know that $P(n - 1)$ and $P(n - 2)$ are true. Therefore by the inductive step of our proof method, we know that $P(n)$ is also true. This contradicts the choice of n. Therefore $S = \emptyset$, as desired.

58. The statement is true for $n = 1$, since $H_1 = 1 = 2 \cdot 1 - 1$. Assume the inductive hypothesis, that the statement is true for n. Then on the one hand we have

$$H_1 + H_2 + \cdots + H_n + H_{n+1} = (n + 1)H_n - n + H_{n+1}$$
$$= (n + 1)H_n - n + H_n + \frac{1}{n + 1}$$
$$= (n + 2)H_n - n + \frac{1}{n + 1},$$

and on the other hand

$$(n+2)H_{n+1} - (n+1) = (n+2)\left(H_n + \frac{1}{n+1}\right) - (n+1)$$

$$= (n+2)H_n + \frac{n+2}{n+1} - (n+1)$$

$$= (n+2)H_n + 1 + \frac{1}{n+1} - n - 1$$

$$= (n+2)H_n - n + \frac{1}{n+1}.$$

That these two expressions are equal was precisely what we had to prove.

60. The statement is true for $n = 1$, since 1 line separates the plane into 2 regions, and $(1^2 + 1 + 2)/2 = 2$. Assume the inductive hypothesis, that n lines of the given type separate the plane into $(n^2 + n + 2)/2$ regions. Consider an arrangement of $n + 1$ lines. Remove the last line. Then there are $(n^2 + n + 2)/2$ regions by the inductive hypothesis. Now we put the last line back in, drawing it slowly, and see what happens to the regions. As we come in "from infinity," the line separates one infinite region into two (one on each side of it); this separation is complete as soon as the line hits one of the first n lines. Then, as we continue drawing from this first point of intersection to the second, the line again separates one region into two. We continue in this way. Every time we come to another point of intersection between the line we are drawing and the figure already present, we lop off another additional region. Furthermore, once we leave the last point of intersection and draw our line off to infinity again, we separate another region into two. Therefore the number of additional regions we formed is equal to the number of points of intersection plus one. Now there are n points of intersection, since our line must intersect each of the other lines in a distinct point (this is where the geometric assumptions get used). Therefore this arrangement has $n + 1$ more points of intersection than the arrangement of n lines, namely $((n^2 + n + 2)/2) + (n + 1)$, which, after a bit of algebra, reduces to $((n+1)^2 + (n+1) + 2)/2$, exactly as desired.

62. It is not easy to stumble upon the trick needed in the inductive step in this exercise, so do not feel bad if you did not find it. The form is straightforward. For the base case ($n = 1$), we simply observe that $4^{1+1} + 5^{2 \cdot 1 - 1} = 16 + 5 = 21$, which is divisible by 21. Then we assume the inductive hypothesis, that $4^{n+1} + 5^{2n-1}$ is divisible for 21, and let us look at the expression when $n + 1$ is plugged in for n. We want somehow to manipulate it so that the expression for n appears. We have

$$4^{(n+1)+1} + 5^{2(n+1)-1} = 4 \cdot 4^{n+1} + 25 \cdot 5^{2n-1}$$

$$= 4 \cdot 4^{n+1} + (4 + 21) \cdot 5^{2n-1}$$

$$= 4(4^{n+1} + 5^{2n-1}) + 21 \cdot 5^{2n-1}.$$

Looking at the last line, we see that the expression in parentheses is divisible by 21 by the inductive hypothesis, and obviously the second term is divisible by 21, so the entire quantity is divisible by 21, as desired.

64. Suppose that this equation has a solution in positive integers. We will show that it must have a smaller solution, which would lead to infinite descent and a contradiction. If $8x^4 + 4y^4 + 2z^4 = w^4$, then the left-hand side is even, so w must be even. Write $w = 2a$ and we have $8x^4 + 4y^4 + 2z^4 = 16a^4$. Divide by 2 to yield $4x^4 + 2y^4 + z^4 = 8a^4$. Now since all the terms other than z^4 are even, z must be even as well. Write $z = 2b$, substitute, and divide by 2 again to obtain $2x^4 + y^4 + 8b^4 = 4a^4$. By similar reasoning we now have $y = 2c$ and $x^4 + 8c^4 + 4b^4 = 2a^4$; and one more application yields $x = 2d$ and $8d^4 + 4c^4 + 2b^4 = a^4$. This last equation is the same as we started with, with the solution (d, c, b, a) smaller than the solution (x, y, z, w), and our proof by infinite descent is complete.

66. a) That S is nonempty is trivial, since letting $s = 1$ and $t = 1$ gives $a + b$, which is certainly a positive integer in S.

b) The Well Ordering Property asserts that every nonempty set of positive integers has a least element. Since we just showed that S is a nonempty set of positive integers, it has a least element, which we will call c.

c) If d is a divisor of a and of b, then it is also a divisor of as and bt, and hence of their sum. Since c is such a sum, d is a divisor of c.

d) This is the hard part. By symmetry it is enough to show one of these, say that $c \mid a$. Assume (for a proof by contradiction) that $c \nmid a$. Then by the Division Algorithm (Section 2.4), we can write $a = qc + r$, where $0 < r < c$. Now $c = as + bt$ (for appropriate choices of s and t), since $c \in S$, so we can compute that $r = a - qc = a - q(as + bt) = a(1 - qs) + b(-qt)$. This expresses the positive integer r as a linear combination with integer coefficients of a and b and hence tells us that $r \in S$. But since $r < c$, this contradicts the choice of c. Therefore our assumption that $c \nmid a$ is wrong, and $c \mid a$, as desired.

e) We claim that the c found in this exercise is the greatest common divisor of a and b. Certainly by part **(d)** it is a common divisor of a and b. On the other hand, part **(c)** tells us that every common divisor of a and b is a divisor of (and therefore no greater than) c. Thus c is a greatest common divisor of a and b. Of course the greatest common divisor is unique, since one cannot have two numbers, each of which is greater than the other.

68. The upper left 4×4 quarter of the figure given in the solution to Exercise 69 gives such a tiling.

70. a) Every $3 \times 2k$ board can be covered in an obvious way: put two pieces together to form a 3×2 rectangle, then lay the rectangles edge to edge. In particular, for all $n \geq 1$ the 3×2^n rectangle can be covered.

b) This is similar to part **(a)**. For all $k \geq 1$ it is easy to cover the $6 \times 2k$ board, using two coverings of the $3 \times 2k$ board from part **(a)**, laid side by side.

c) A little trial and error shows that the $3^1 \times 3^1$ board cannot be covered. Therefore not all such boards can be covered.

d) All boards of this shape can be covered for $n \geq 1$, using reasoning similar to parts **(a)** and **(b)**.

72. This is too complicated to discuss here. For a solution, see the article by I. P. Chu and R. Johnsonbaugh, "Tiling Deficient Boards with Trominoes," *Mathematics Magazine* **59** (1986) 34–40.

74. In order to explain this argument, we label the squares in the 5×5 chessboard 11, 12, ..., 15, 21, ..., 25, ..., 51, ..., 55, where the first digit stands for the row number and the second digit stands for the column number. Also, in order to talk about the L-shaped tile, think of it positioned to look like the letter L; then we call the square on top the head, the square in the lower right the tail, and the square in the corner the corner. We claim that the board with square 12 removed cannot be tiled. First note that in order to cover square 11, the position of one piece is fixed. Next we consider how to cover square 13. There are three possibilities. If we put a head there, then we are forced to put the corner of another piece in square 15. If we put a corner there, then we are forced to put the tail of another piece in 15, and if we put a tail there, then square 15 cannot be covered at all. So we conclude that squares 13, 14, 15, 23, 24, and 25 will have to be covered by two more pieces. By symmetry, the same argument shows that two more pieces must cover squares 31, 41, 51, 32, 42, and 52. This much has been forced, and now we are left with the 3×3 square in the lower left part of the chessboard to cover with three more pieces. If we put a corner in 33, then we immediately run into an impasse in trying to cover 53 and 35. If we put a head in 33, then 53 cannot be covered; and if we put a tail in 33, then 35 cannot be covered. So we have reached a contradiction, and the desired covering does not exist.

76. Let $Q(n)$ be $P(n+k-1)$. Thus $Q(1)$ is $P(b)$, $Q(2)$ is $P(b+1)$, and so on. Therefore the statement that $P(n)$ is true for $n = b, b+1, b+2, \ldots$ is the same as the statement that $Q(m)$ is true for all positive integers m.

We are given that $P(b)$ is true (i.e., that $Q(1)$ is true), and that $P(k) \rightarrow P(k+1)$ for all $k \geq b$ (i.e., that $Q(m) \rightarrow Q(m+1)$ for all positive integers m). Therefore by the principle of mathematical induction, $Q(m)$ is true for all m, as desired.

78. If $x < y$ then $y - x$ is a positive real number, and its reciprocal $1/(y-x)$ is a positive real number, so we can choose a positive integer $A > 1/(y-x)$. (Technically this is the Archimedean property of the real numbers.) Now look at $\lfloor x \rfloor + (j/A)$ for positive integers j. Each of these is a rational number. Choose j to be the least positive integer such that this number is greater than x. Such a j exists by the well-ordering principle, since clearly if j is large enough, then $\lfloor x \rfloor + (j/A)$ exceeds x. (Note that $j = 0$ results in a value not greater than x.) So we have $r = \lfloor x \rfloor + (j/A) > x$ but $\lfloor x \rfloor + ((j-1)/A) = r - (1/A) \leq x$. From this last inequality, substituting $y - x$ for $1/A$ (which only makes the left-hand side smaller) we have $r - (y-x) < x$, whence $r < y$, as desired.

SECTION 3.4   Recursive Definitions and Structural Induction

2. **a)** $f(1) = -2f(0) = -2 \cdot 3 = -6$, $f(2) = -2f(1) = -2 \cdot (-6) = 12$, $f(3) = -2f(2) = -2 \cdot 12 = -24$, $f(4) = -2f(3) = -2 \cdot (-24) = 48$, $f(5) = -2f(4) = -2 \cdot 48 = -96$
   b) $f(1) = 3f(0) + 7 = 3 \cdot 3 + 7 = 16$, $f(2) = 3f(1) + 7 = 3 \cdot 16 + 7 = 55$, $f(3) = 3f(2) + 7 = 3 \cdot 55 + 7 = 172$, $f(4) = 3f(3) + 7 = 3 \cdot 172 + 7 = 523$, $f(5) = 3f(4) + 7 = 3 \cdot 523 + 7 = 1576$
   c) $f(1) = f(0)^2 - 2f(0) - 2 = 3^2 - 2 \cdot 3 - 2 = 1$, $f(2) = f(1)^2 - 2f(1) - 2 = 1^2 - 2 \cdot 1 - 2 = -3$, $f(3) = f(2)^2 - 2f(2) - 2 = (-3)^2 - 2 \cdot (-3) - 2 = 13$, $f(4) = f(3)^2 - 2f(3) - 2 = 13^2 - 2 \cdot 13 - 2 = 141$, $f(5) = f(4)^2 - 2f(4) - 2 = 141^2 - 2 \cdot 141 - 2 = 19{,}597$
   d) First note that $f(1) = 3^{f(0)/3} = 3^{3/3} = 3 = f(0)$. In the same manner, $f(n) = 3$ for all n.

4. **a)** $f(2) = f(1) - f(0) = 1 - 1 = 0$, $f(3) = f(2) - f(1) = 0 - 1 = -1$, $f(4) = f(3) - f(2) = -1 - 0 = -1$, $f(5) = f(4) - f(3) = -1 - 1 = 0$
   b) Clearly $f(n) = 1$ for all n, since $1 \cdot 1 = 1$.
   c) $f(2) = f(1)^2 + f(0)^3 = 1^2 + 1^3 = 2$, $f(3) = f(2)^2 + f(1)^3 = 2^2 + 1^3 = 5$, $f(4) = f(3)^2 + f(2)^3 = 5^2 + 2^3 = 33$, $f(5) = f(4)^2 + f(3)^3 = 33^2 + 5^3 = 1214$
   d) Clearly $f(n) = 1$ for all n, since $1/1 = 1$.

6. **a)** This is valid, since we are provided with the value at $n = 0$, and each subsequent value is determined by the previous one. Since all that changes from one value to the next is the sign, we conjecture that $f(n) = (-1)^n$. This is true for $n = 0$, since $(-1)^0 = 1$. If it is true for $n = k$, then we have $f(k+1) = -f(k+1-1) = -f(k) = -(-1)^k$ by the inductive hypothesis, whence $f(k+1) = (-1)^{k+1}$.
   b) This is valid, since we are provided with the values at $n = 0$, 1, and 2, and each subsequent value is determined by the value that occurred three steps previously. We compute the first several terms of the sequence: 1, 0, 2, 2, 0, 4, 4, 0, 8, ... We conjecture the formula $f(n) = 2^{n/3}$ when $n \equiv 0 \pmod 3$, $f(n) = 0$ when $n \equiv 1 \pmod 3$, $f(n) = 2^{(n+1)/3}$ when $n \equiv 2 \pmod 3$. To prove this, first note that in the basis cases we have $f(0) = 1 = 2^{0/3}$, $f(1) = 0$, and $f(2) = 2 = 2^{(2+1)/3}$. Assume the inductive hypothesis that the formula is valid for smaller inputs. Then for $n \equiv 0 \pmod 3$ we have $f(n) = 2f(n-3) = 2 \cdot 2^{(n-3)/3} = 2 \cdot 2^{n/3} \cdot 2^{-1} = 2^{n/3}$, as desired. For $n \equiv 1 \pmod 3$ we have $f(n) = 2f(n-3) = 2 \cdot 0 = 0$, as desired. And for $n \equiv 2 \pmod 3$ we have $f(n) = 2f(n-3) = 2 \cdot 2^{(n-3+1)/3} = 2 \cdot 2^{(n+1)/3} \cdot 2^{-1} = 2^{(n+1)/3}$, as desired.
   c) This is invalid. We are told that $f(2)$ is defined in terms of $f(3)$, but $f(3)$ has not been defined.
   d) This is invalid, because the value at $n = 1$ is defined in two conflicting ways—first as $f(1) = 1$ and then as $f(1) = 2f(1-1) = 2f(0) = 2 \cdot 0 = 0$.

e) This appears syntactically to be not valid, since we have conflicting instruction for odd $n \geq 3$. On the one hand $f(3) = f(2)$, but on the other hand $f(3) = 2f(1)$. However, we notice that $f(1) = f(0) = 2$ and $f(2) = 2f(0) = 4$, so these apparently conflicting rules tell us that $f(3) = 4$ on the one hand and $f(3) = 2 \cdot 2 = 4$ on the other hand. Thus we got the same answer either way. Let us show that in fact this definition is valid because the rules coincide.

We compute the first several terms of the sequence: 2, 2, 4, 4, 8, 8, ... We conjecture the formula $f(n) = 2^{\lceil (n+1)/2 \rceil}$. To prove this inductively, note first that $f(0) = 2 = 2^{\lceil (0+1)/2 \rceil}$. For larger values we have for n odd using the first part of the recursive step that $f(n) = f(n-1) = 2^{\lceil (n-1+1)/2 \rceil} = 2^{\lceil n/2 \rceil} = 2^{\lceil (n+1)/2 \rceil}$, since $n/2$ is not an integer. For $n \geq 2$, whether even or odd, using the second part of the recursive step we have $f(n) = 2f(n-2) = 2 \cdot 2^{\lceil (n-2+1)/2 \rceil} = 2 \cdot 2^{\lceil (n+1)/2 \rceil - 1} = 2 \cdot 2^{\lceil (n+1)/2 \rceil} \cdot 2^{-1} = 2^{\lceil (n+1)/2 \rceil}$, as desired.

8. Many answers are possible.

a) Each term is 4 more than the term before it. We can therefore define the sequence by $a_1 = 2$ and $a_{n+1} = a_n + 4$ for all $n \geq 1$.

b) We note that the terms alternate: 0, 2, 0, 2, and so on. Thus we could define the sequence by $a_1 = 0$, $a_2 = 2$, and $a_n = a_{n-2}$ for all $n \geq 3$.

c) The sequence starts out 2, 6, 12, 20, 30, and so on. The differences between successive terms are 4, 6, 8, 10, and so on. Thus the nth term is $2n$ greater than the term preceding it; in symbols: $a_n = a_{n-1} + 2n$. Together with the initial condition $a_1 = 2$, this defines the sequence recursively.

d) The sequence starts out 1, 4, 9, 16, 25, and so on. The differences between successive terms are 3, 5, 7, 9, and so on—the odd numbers. Thus the nth term is $2n - 1$ greater than the term preceding it; in symbols: $a_n = a_{n-1} + 2n - 1$. Together with the initial condition $a_1 = 1$, this defines the sequence recursively.

10. The base case is that $S_m(0) = m$. The recursive part is that $S_m(n+1)$ is the successor of $S_m(n)$ (i.e., the integer that follows $S_m(n)$, namely $S_m(n) + 1$).

12. The base case $n = 1$ is clear, since $f_1^2 = f_1 f_2 = 1$. Assume the inductive hypothesis. Then $f_1^2 + f_2^2 + \cdots + f_n^2 + f_{n+1}^2 = f_n f_{n+1} + f_{n+1}^2 = f_{n+1}(f_n + f_{n+1}) = f_{n+1} f_{n+2}$, as desired.

14. The base case $n = 1$ is clear, since $f_2 f_0 - f_1^2 = 1 \cdot 0 - 1^2 = -1 = (-1)^1$. Assume the inductive hypothesis. Then we have

$$\begin{aligned}
f_{n+2} f_n - f_{n+1}^2 &= (f_{n+1} + f_n)f_n - f_{n+1}^2 \\
&= f_{n+1} f_n + f_n^2 - f_{n+1}^2 \\
&= -f_{n+1}(f_{n+1} - f_n) + f_n^2 \\
&= -f_{n+1} f_{n-1} + f_n^2 \\
&= -(f_{n+1} f_{n-1} - f_n^2) \\
&= -(-1)^n = (-1)^{n+1}.
\end{aligned}$$

16. The base case $n = 1$ is clear, since $f_0 - f_1 + f_2 = 0 - 1 + 1 = 0$, and $f_1 - 1 = 0$ as well. Assume the inductive hypothesis. Then we have (substituting using the defining relation for the Fibonacci sequence where appropriate)

$$\begin{aligned}
f_0 - f_1 + f_2 - \cdots - f_{2n-1} + f_{2n} - f_{2n+1} + f_{2n+2} &= f_{2n-1} - 1 - f_{2n+1} + f_{2n+2} \\
&= f_{2n-1} - 1 + f_{2n} \\
&= f_{2n+1} - 1 \\
&= f_{2(n+1)-1} - 1.
\end{aligned}$$

18. We prove this by induction on n. Clearly $\mathbf{A}^1 = \mathbf{A} = \begin{bmatrix} f_2 & f_1 \\ f_1 & f_0 \end{bmatrix}$. Assume the inductive hypothesis. Then

$$\mathbf{A}^{n+1} = \mathbf{A}\mathbf{A}^n = \begin{bmatrix} 1 & 1 \\ 1 & 0 \end{bmatrix} \begin{bmatrix} f_{n+1} & f_n \\ f_n & f_{n-1} \end{bmatrix} = \begin{bmatrix} f_{n+1} + f_n & f_n + f_{n-1} \\ f_{n+1} & f_n \end{bmatrix} = \begin{bmatrix} f_{n+2} & f_{n+1} \\ f_{n+1} & f_n \end{bmatrix},$$

as desired.

20. The max or min of one number is itself; $\max(a_1, a_2) = a_1$ if $a_1 \geq a_2$ and a_2 if $a_1 < a_2$, whereas $\min(a_1, a_2) = a_2$ if $a_1 \geq a_2$ and a_1 if $a_1 < a_2$; and for $n \geq 2$,

$$\max(a_1, a_2, \ldots, a_{n+1}) = \max(\max(a_1, a_2, \ldots, a_n), a_{n+1})$$

and

$$\min(a_1, a_2, \ldots, a_{n+1}) = \min(\min(a_1, a_2, \ldots, a_n), a_{n+1}).$$

22. Clearly only positive integers can be in S, since 1 is a positive integer, and the sum of two positive integers is again a positive integer. To see that all positive integers are in S, we proceed by induction. Obviously $1 \in S$. Assuming that $n \in S$, we get that $n + 1$ is in S by applying the recursive part of the definition with $s = n$ and $t = 1$. Thus S is precisely the set of positive integers.

24. a) Odd integers are obtained from other odd integers by adding 2. Thus we can define this set S as follows: $1 \in S$; and if $n \in S$, then $n + 2 \in S$.

b) Powers of 3 are obtained from other powers of 3 by multiplying by 3. Thus we can define this set S as follows: $3 \in S$ (this is 3^1, the power of 3 using the smallest positive integer exponent); and if $n \in S$, then $3n \in S$.

c) There are several ways to do this. One that is suggested by Horner's method is as follows. We will assume that the variable for these polynomials is the letter x. All integers are in S (this base case gives us all the constant polynomials); if $p(x) \in S$ and n is any integer, then $xp(x) + n$ is in S. Another method constructs the polynomials term by term. Its base case is to let 0 be in S; and its inductive step is to say that if $p(x) \in S$, c is an integer, and n is a nonnegative integer, then $p(x) + cx^n$ is in S.

26. a) If we apply each of the recursive step rules to the only element given in the basis step, we see that $(2, 3)$ and $(3, 2)$ are in S. If we apply the recursive step to these we add $(4, 6)$, $(5, 5)$, and $(6, 4)$. The next round gives us $(6, 9)$, $(7, 8)$, $(8, 7)$, and $(9, 6)$. A fourth set of applications adds $(8, 12)$, $(9, 11)$, $(10, 10)$, $(11, 9)$, and $(12, 8)$; and a fifth set of applications adds $(10, 15)$, $(11, 14)$, $(12, 13)$, $(13, 12)$, $(14, 11)$, and $(15, 10)$.

b) Let $P(n)$ be the statement that $5 \mid a + b$ whenever $(a, b) \in S$ is obtained by n applications of the recursive step. For the basis step, $P(0)$ is true, since the only element of S obtained with no applications of the recursive step is $(0, 0)$, and indeed $5 \mid 0 + 0$. Assume the strong inductive hypothesis that $5 \mid a + b$ whenever $(a, b) \in S$ is obtained by k or fewer applications of the recursive step, and consider an element obtained with $k + 1$ applications of the recursive step. Since the final application of the recursive step to an element (a, b) must be applied to an element obtained with fewer applications of the recursive step, we know that $5 \mid a + b$. So we just need to check that this inequality implies $5 \mid a + 2 + b + 3$ and $5 \mid a + 3 + b + 2$. But this is clear, since each is equivalent to $5 \mid a + b + 5$, and 5 divides both $a + b$ and 5.

c) This holds for the basis step, since $5 \mid 0 + 0$. If this holds for (a, b), then it also holds for the elements obtained from (a, b) in the recursive step by the same argument as in part **(b)**.

28. a) The simplest elements of S are $(1, 2)$ and $(2, 1)$. That is the basis step. To get new elements of S from old ones, we need to maintain the parity of the sum, so we either increase the first coordinate by 2, increase the second coordinate by 2, or increase each coordinate by 1. Thus our recursive step is that if $(a, b) \in S$, then $(a + 2, b) \in S$, $(a, b + 2) \in S$, and $(a + 1, b + 1) \in S$.

b) The statement here is that b is a multiple of a. One approach is to have an infinite number of base cases to take care of the fact that every element is a multiple of itself. So we have $(n, n) \in S$ for all $n \in \mathbf{Z}^+$. If one objects to having an infinite number of base cases, then we can start with $(1, 1) \in S$ and a recursive rule that if $(a, a) \in S$, then $(a + 1, a + 1) \in S$. Larger multiples of a can be obtained by adding a to a known multiple of a, so our recursive step is that if $(a, b) \in S$, then $(a, a + b) \in S$.

c) The smallest pairs in which the sum of the coordinates is a multiple of 3 are $(1, 2)$ and $(2, 1)$. So our basis step is $(1, 2) \in S$ and $(2, 1) \in S$. If we start with a point for which the sum of the coordinates is a multiple of 3 and want to maintain this divisibility condition, then we can add 3 to the first coordinate, or add 3 to the second coordinate, or add 1 to the one of the coordinates and 2 to the other. Thus our recursive step is that if $(a, b) \in S$, then $(a + 3, b) \in S$, $(a, b + 3) \in S$, $(a + 1, b + 2) \in S$, and $(a + 2, b + 1) \in S$.

30. Since we are concerned only with the substrings 01 and 10, all we care about are the changes from 0 to 1 or 1 to 0 as we move from left to right through the string. For example, we view 0011110110100 as a block of 0's followed by a block of 1's followed by a block of 0's followed by a block of 1's followed by a block of 0's followed by a block of 1's followed by a block of 0's. There is one occurrence of 01 or 10 at the start of each block other than the first, and the occurrences alternate between 01 and 10. If the string has an odd number of blocks (or the string is empty), then there will be an equal number of 01's and 10's. If the string has an even number of blocks, then the string will have one more 01 than 10 if the first block is 0's, and one more 10 than 01 if the first block is 1's. (One could also give an inductive proof, based on the length of the string, but a stronger statement is needed: that if the string ends in a 1 then 01 occurs at most one more time than 10, but that if the string ends in a 0, then 01 occurs at most as often as 10.)

32. **a)** $ones(\lambda) = 0$ and $ones(wx) = x + ones(w)$, where w is a bit string and x is a bit (viewed as an integer when being added)

b) The basis step is when $t = \lambda$, in which case we have $ones(s\lambda) = ones(s) = ones(s) + 0 = ones(s) + ones(\lambda)$. For the inductive step, write $t = wx$, where w is a bit string and x is a bit. Then we have $ones(s(wx)) = ones((sw)x) = x + ones(sw)$ by the recursive definition, which is $x + ones(s) + ones(w)$ by the inductive hypothesis, which is $ones(s) + (x + ones(w))$ by commutativity and associativity of addition, which finally equals $ones(s) + ones(wx)$ by the recursive definition.

34. **a)** 1010   **b)** 1 1011   **c)** 1110 1001 0001

36. We induct on w_2. The base case is $(w_1\lambda)^R = w_1^R = \lambda w_1^R = \lambda^R w_1^R$. For the inductive step, assume that $w_2 = w_3 x$, where w_3 is a string of length one less than the length of w_2, and x is a symbol (the last symbol of w_2). Then we have $(w_1 w_2)^R = (w_1 w_3 x)^R = x(w_1 w_3)^R$ (by the recursive definition given in the solution to Exercise 35). This in turn equals $x w_3^R w_1^R$ by the inductive hypothesis, which is $(w_3 x)^R w_1^R$ (again by the definition). Finally, this equals $w_2^R w_1^R$, as desired.

38. There are two types of palindromes, so we need two base cases, namely λ is a palindrome, and x is a palindrome for every symbol x. The recursive step is that if α is a palindrome and x is a symbol, then $x\alpha x$ is a palindrome.

40. The key fact here is that if a bit string of length greater than 1 has more 0's than 1's, then either it is the concatenation of two such strings, or else it is the concatenation of two such strings with one 1 inserted either before the first, between them, or after the last. This can be proved by looking at the running count of the excess of 0's over 1's as we read the string from left to right. Therefore one recursive definition is that 0 is in the set, and if x and y are in the set, then so are xy, $1xy$, $x1y$, and $xy1$.

42. Recall from Exercise 37 the recursive definition of the ith power of a string. We also will use the result of Exercise 36 and the following lemma: $w^{i+1} = w^i w$ for all $i \geq 0$, which is clear (or can be proved by induction on i, using the associativity of concatenation).

Now to prove that $(w^R)^i = (w^i)^R$, we use induction on i. It is clear for $i = 0$, since $(w^R)^0 = \lambda = \lambda^R = (w^i)^R$. Assuming the inductive hypothesis, we have $(w^R)^{i+1} = w^R (w^R)^i = w^R (w^i)^R = (w^i w)^R = (w^{i+1})^R$, as desired.

44. For the basis step we have the tree consisting of just the root, so there is one leaf and there are no internal vertices, and $l(T) = i(T) + 1$ holds. For the recursive step, assume that this relationship holds for T_1 and T_2, and consider the tree with a new root, whose children are the roots of T_1 and T_2. The new root is an internal vertex of T, and every internal vertex in T_1 or T_2 is an internal vertex of T, so $i(T) = i(T_1) + i(T_2) + 1$. Similarly, the leaves of T_1 and T_2 are the leaves of T, so $l(T) = l(T_1) + l(T_2)$. Thus we have $l(T) = l(T_1) + l(T_2) = i(T_1) + 1 + i(T_2) + 1$ by the inductive hypothesis, which equals $(i(T_1) + i(T_2) + 1) + 1 = i(T) + 1$, as desired.

46. The basis step requires that we show that this formula holds when $(m, n) = (1, 1)$. The induction step requires that we show that if the formula holds for all pairs smaller than (m, n) in the lexicographic ordering of $\mathbf{Z}^+ \times \mathbf{Z}^+$, then it also holds for (m, n). For the basis step we have $a_{1,1} = 5 = 2(1+1) + 1$. For the inductive step, assume that $a_{m',n'} = 2(m' + n') + 1$ whenever (m', n') is less than (m, n) in the lexicographic ordering of $\mathbf{Z}^+ \times \mathbf{Z}^+$. By the recursive definition, if $n = 1$ then $a_{m,n} = a_{m-1,n} + 2$; since $(m-1, n)$ is smaller than (m, n), the induction hypothesis tells us that $a_{m-1,n} = 2(m-1+n) + 1$, so $a_{m,n} = 2(m-1+n) + 1 + 2 = 2(m+n) + 1$, as desired. Now suppose that $n > 1$, so $a_{m,n} = a_{m,n-1} + 2$. Again we have $a_{m,n-1} = 2(m + n - 1) + 1$, so $a_{m,n} = 2(m + n - 1) + 1 + 2 = 2(m + n) + 1$, and the proof is complete.

48. a) $A(1, 0) = 0$ by the second line of the definition.
   b) $A(0, 1) = 2$ by the first line of the definition.
   c) $A(1, 1) = 2$ by the third line of the definition.
   d) $A(2, 2) = A(1, A(2, 1)) = A(1, 2) = A(0, A(1, 1)) = A(0, 2) = 4$

50. We prove this by induction on n. It is clear for $n = 1$, since $A(1, 1) = 2 = 2^1$. Assume that $A(1, n) = 2^n$. Then $A(1, n+1) = A(0, A(1, n)) = A(0, 2^n) = 2 \cdot 2^n = 2^{n+1}$, as desired.

52. This is impossible to compute, if by compute we mean write down a nice numeral for the answer. As explained in the solution to Exercise 51, one can show by induction that $A(2, n)$ is equal to $2^{2^{\cdot^{\cdot^2}}}$, with n 2's in the tower. To compute $A(3, 4)$ we use the definition to write $A(3, 4) = A(2, A(3, 3))$. We saw in the solution to Exercise 51, however, that $A(3, 3) = 65536$, so $A(3, 4) = A(2, 65536)$. Thus $A(3, 4)$ is a tower of 2's with 65536 2's in the tower. There is no nicer way to write or describe this number—it is too big.

54. We use a double induction here, inducting first on m and then on n. The outside base case is $m = 0$ (with n arbitrary). Then $A(m, n) = 2n$ for all n. Also $A(m+1, n) = 2n$ for $n = 0$ and $n = 1$, and $2n \geq 2n$ in those cases; and $A(m+1, n) = 2^n$ for all $n > 1$ (by Exercise 50), and in those cases $2^n \geq 2n$ as well. Now we assume the inductive hypothesis, that $A(m+1, t) \geq A(m, t)$ for all t. We will show by induction on n that $A(m+2, n) \geq A(m+1, n)$. For $n = 0$ this reduces to $0 \geq 0$, and for $n = 1$ it reduces to $2 \geq 2$. Assume the inner inductive hypothesis, that $A(m+2, n) \geq A(m+1, n)$. Then

$$A(m+2, n+1) = A(m+1, A(m+2, n))$$
$$\geq A(m+1, A(m+1, n)) \quad \text{(using the inductive hypothesis and Exercise 53)}$$
$$\geq A(m, A(m+1, n)) \quad \text{(by the inductive hypothesis on } m\text{)}$$
$$= A(m+1, n+1).$$

56. Let $P(n)$ be the statement "F is well-defined at n." Then $P(0)$ is true, since $F(0)$ is specified. Assume that $P(n)$ is true. Then F is also well-defined at $n+1$, since $F(n+1)$ is given in terms of $F(n)$. Therefore by mathematical induction, $P(n)$ is true for all n, i.e., F is well-defined as a function on the set of all nonnegative integers.

58. **a)** This would be a proper definition if the recursive part were stated to hold for $n \geq 2$. As it stands, however, $F(1)$ is ambiguous, and $F(0)$ is undefined.

b) This definition makes no sense as it stands; $F(3)$ is not defined, since $F(0)$ isn't. Also, $F(2)$ is ambiguous.

c) For $n = 3$, the recursive part makes no sense, since we would have to know $F(3/2)$. Also, $F(2)$ is ambiguous.

d) The definition is ambiguous about $n = 1$, since both the second clause and the third clause seem to apply. This would be a valid definition if the third clause applied only to odd $n \geq 3$.

e) We note that $F(1)$ is defined explicitly, $F(2)$ is defined in terms of $F(1)$, $F(4)$ is defined in terms of $F(2)$, and $F(3)$ is defined in terms of $F(8)$, which is defined in terms of $F(4)$. So far, so good. However, let us see what the definition says to do with $F(5)$:

$$F(5) = F(14) = 1 + F(7) = 1 + F(20) = 1 + 1 + F(10) = 1 + 1 + 1 + F(5).$$

This not only leaves us begging the question as to what $F(5)$ is, but is a contradiction, since $0 \neq 3$. (If we replace "$3n - 1$" by "$3n + 1$" in this problem, then it is an unsolved problem—the Collatz conjecture—as to whether F is well-defined; see Example 13 in Section 3.1.)

60. In each case we will apply the definition. Note that $\log^{(1)} n = \log n$ (for $n > 0$). Similarly, $\log^{(2)} n = \log(\log n)$ as long as it is defined (which is when $n > 1$), $\log^{(3)} n = \log(\log(\log n))$ as long as it is defined (which is when $n > 2$), and so on. Normally the parentheses are understood and omitted.

a) $\log^{(2)} 16 = \log\log 16 = \log 4 = 2$, since $2^4 = 16$ and $2^2 = 4$

b) $\log^{(3)} 256 = \log\log\log 256 = \log\log 8 = \log 3 \approx 1.585$

c) $\log^{(3)} 2^{65536} = \log\log\log 2^{65536} = \log\log 65536 = \log 16 = 4$

d) $\log^{(4)} 2^{2^{65536}} = \log\log\log\log 2^{2^{65536}} = \log\log\log 2^{65536} = 4$ by part **(c)**

62. Note that $\log^{(1)} 2 = 1$, $\log^{(2)} 2^2 = 1$, $\log^{(3)} 2^{2^2} = 1$, $\log^{(4)} 2^{2^{2^2}} = 1$, and so on. In general $\log^{(k)} n = 1$ when n is a tower of k 2s; once n exceeds a tower of k 2s, $\log^{(k)} n > 1$. Therefore the largest n such that $\log^* n = k$ is a tower of k 2s. Here $k = 5$, so the answer is $2^{2^{2^{2^2}}} = 2^{65536}$. This number overflows most calculators. In order to determine the number of decimal digits it has, we recall that the number of decimal digits of a positive integer x is $\lfloor \log_{10} x \rfloor + 1$. Therefore the number of decimal digits of 2^{65536} is $\lfloor \log_{10} 2^{65536} \rfloor + 1 = \lfloor 65536 \log_{10} 2 \rfloor + 1 = 19{,}729$.

64. Each application of the function f divides its argument by 2. Therefore iterating this function k times (which is what $f^{(k)}$ does) has the effect of dividing by 2^k. Therefore $f^{(k)}(n) = n/2^k$. Now $f_1^*(n)$ is the smallest k such that $f^{(k)}(n) \leq 1$, that is, $n/2^k \leq 1$. Solving this for k easily yields $k \geq \log n$, where logarithm is taken to the base 2. Thus $f_1^*(n) = \lceil \log n \rceil$ (we need to take the ceiling function because k must be an integer).

SECTION 3.5   Recursive Algorithms

2. The sum of the first n positive integers is the sum of the first $n-1$ positive integers plus n. This trivial observation leads to the recursive algorithm shown here.

> **procedure** *sum of first*(n : positive integer)
> **if** $n = 1$ **then** *sum of first*(n) := 1
> **else** *sum of first*(n) := *sum of first*($n - 1$) + n

4. The recursive algorithm works by comparing the last element with the maximum of all but the last. We assume that the input is given as a sequence.

> **procedure** *max*($a_1, a_2, \ldots, a_n$: integers)
> **if** $n = 1$ **then** *max*($a_1, a_2, \ldots, a_n$) := a_1
> **else**
> **begin**
> $m := max(a_1, a_2, \ldots, a_{n-1})$
>   **if** $m > a_n$ **then** *max*($a_1, a_2, \ldots, a_n$) := m
>   **else** *max*($a_1, a_2, \ldots, a_n$) := a_n
> **end**

6. This is the inefficient method.

> **procedure** *power*(x, n, m : positive integers)
> **if** $n = 1$ **then** *power*(x, n, m) := x **mod** m
> **else** *power*(x, n, m) := $(x \cdot power(x, n - 1, m))$ **mod** m

8. This is actually quite subtle. The recursive algorithm will need to keep track not only of what the mode actually is, but also of how often the mode appears. We will describe this algorithm in words, rather than in pseudocode. The input is a list $a_1, a_2, \ldots, a_n$ of integers. Call this list L. If $n = 1$ (the base case), then the output is that the mode is a_1 and it appears 1 time. For the recursive case ($n > 1$), form a new list L' by deleting from L the term a_n and all terms in L equal to a_n. Let k be the number of terms deleted. If $k = n$ (in other words, if L' is the empty list), then the output is that the mode is a_n and it appears n times. Otherwise, apply the algorithm recursively to L', obtaining a mode m, which appears t times. Now if $t \geq k$, then the output is that the mode is m and it appears t times; otherwise the output is that the mode is a_n and it appears k times.

10. The sum of the first one positive integer is 1, and that is the answer the recursive algorithm gives when $n = 1$, so the basis step is correct. Now assume that the algorithm works correctly for $n = k$. If $n = k + 1$, then the **else** clause of the algorithm is executed, and $k + 1$ is added to the (assumed correct) sum of the first k positive integers. Thus the algorithm correctly finds the sum of the first $k + 1$ positive integers.

12. Our induction is on the value of y. When $y = 0$, the product $xy = 0$, and the algorithm correctly returns that value. Assume that the algorithm works correctly for smaller values of y, and consider its performance on y. If y is even (and necessarily at least 2), then the algorithm computes 2 times the product of x and $y/2$. Since it does the product correctly (by the inductive hypothesis), this equals $2(x \cdot y/2)$, which equals xy by the commutativity and associativity of multiplication. Similarly, when y is odd, the algorithm computes 2 times the product of x and $(y - 1)/2$ and then adds x. Since it does the product correctly (by the inductive hypothesis), this equals $2(x \cdot (y - 1)/2) + x$, which equals $xy - x + x = xy$, again by the rules of algebra.

14. The largest in a list of one integer is that one integer, and that is the answer the recursive algorithm gives when $n = 1$, so the basis step is correct. Now assume that the algorithm works correctly for $n = k$. If $n = k + 1$, then the **else** clause of the algorithm is executed. First, by the inductive hypothesis, the algorithm correctly sets m to be the largest among the first k integers in the list. Next it returns as the answer either that value or the $(k + 1)$st element, whichever is larger. This is clearly the largest element in the entire list. Thus the algorithm correctly finds the maximum of a given list of integers.

16. We use the hint.

procedure *twopower*(n : positive integer, a : real number)
if $n = 1$ **then** *twopower*(n, a) := a^2
else *twopower*(n, a) := *twopower*($n - 1, a$)^2

18. We use the idea in Exercise 16, together with the fact that $a^n = (a^{n/2})^2$ if n is even, and $a^n = a \cdot (a^{(n-1)/2})^2$ if n is odd, to obtain the following recursive algorithm. In essence we are using the binary expansion of n implicitly.

procedure *fastpower*(n : positive integer, a : real number)
if $n = 1$ **then** *fastpower*(n, a) := a
else if n is even **then** *fastpower*(n, a) := *fastpower*($n/2, a$)^2
else *fastpower*(n, a) := $a \cdot$ *fastpower*(($n - 1$)/2, a)^2

20. To compute f_7, Algorithm 8 requires $f_8 - 1 = 20$ additions, and Algorithm 9 requires $7 - 1 = 6$ additions.

22. This is essentially just Algorithm 9, with a different operation and different initial conditions.

procedure *iterative*(n : nonnegative integer)
if $n = 0$ **then** $y := 1$
else
begin
    $x := 1$
    $y := 2$
    for $i := 1$ **to** $n - 1$
    begin
        $z := x \cdot y$
        $x := y$
        $y := z$
    end
end
{ y is the nth term of the sequence}

24. This is very similar to the recursive procedure for computing the Fibonacci numbers. Note that we can combine the three base cases (stopping rules) into one.

procedure *sequence*(n : nonnegative integer)
if $n < 3$ **then** *sequence*(n) := $n + 1$
else *sequence*(n) := *sequence*($n - 1$) + *sequence*($n - 2$) + *sequence*($n - 3$)

26. The iterative algorithm is much more efficient here. If we compute with the recursive algorithm, we end up computing the small values (early terms in the sequence) over and over and over again (try it for $n = 5$).

28. We obtain the answer by computing $P(m, m)$, where P is the following procedure, which we obtain simply by copying the recursive definition from Exercise 47 in Section 3.4 into an algorithm.

procedure $P(m, n$: positive integers)
if $m = 1$ **then** $P(m, n) := 1$
else if $n = 1$ **then** $P(m, n) := 1$
else if $m < n$ **then** $P(m, n) := P(m, m)$
else if $m = n$ **then** $P(m, n) := 1 + P(m, m - 1)$
else $P(m, n) := P(m, n - 1) + P(m - n, n)$

30. The following algorithm is clearly correct.

> **procedure** *power*(w : bit string, i : nonnegative integer)
> **if** $i = 0$ **then** *power*(w, i) := λ
> **else** *power*(w, i) := w concatenated with *power*($w, i - 1$)

32. The procedure is the same as that given in the solution to Example 8. We will show the tree and inverted tree that indicate how the sequence is taken apart and put back together.

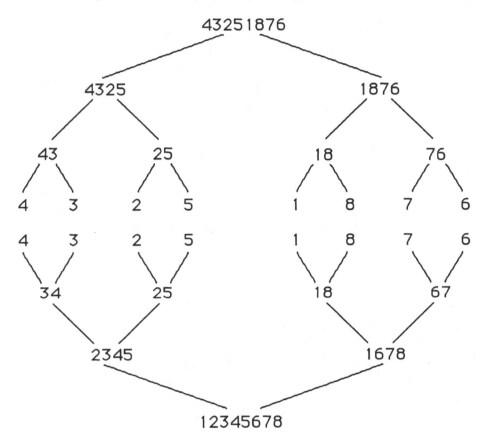

34. From the analysis given before the statement of Lemma 1, it follows that the number of comparisons is $m + n - r$, where the lists have m and n elements, respectively, and r is the number of elements remaining in one list at the point the other list is exhausted. In this exercise $m = n = 5$, so the answer is always $10 - r$.

a) The answer is $10 - 1 = 9$, since the second list has only 1 element when the first list has been emptied.

b) The answer is $10 - 5 = 5$, since the second list has 5 elements when the first list has been emptied.

c) The answer is $10 - 2 = 8$, since the second list has 2 elements when the first list has been emptied.

36. In each case we need to show that a certain number of comparisons is necessary in the worst case, and then we need to give an algorithm that does the merging with this many comparisons.

a) There are 5 possible outcomes (the element of the first list can be greater than 0, 1, 2, 3, or 4 elements of the second list). Therefore by decision tree theory (see Section 9.2), at least $\lceil \log 5 \rceil = 3$ comparisons are needed. We can achieve this with a binary search: first compare the element of the first list to the second element of the second, and then at most two comparisons are needed to find the correct place for this element.

b) Algorithm 11 merges the lists with 5 comparisons. We must show that 5 are needed in the worst case. Naively applying decision tree theory does not help, since $\lceil \log 15 \rceil = 4$ (there are $C(5 + 2 - 1, 2) = 15$ ways to choose the places among the second list for the elements of the first list to go). Instead, suppose that the lists are a_1, a_2 and b_1, b_2, b_3, b_4, in order. Then without loss of generality assume that the first comparison is

a_1 against b_i. If $i \geq 2$ and $a_1 < b_i$, then there are at least 9 outcomes still possible, requiring $\lceil \log 9 \rceil = 4$ more comparisons. If $i = 1$ and $a_1 > b_1$, then there are 10 outcomes, again requiring 4 more comparisons.

c) There are $C(5 + 3 - 1, 3) = 35$ outcomes, so at least $\lceil \log 35 \rceil = 6$ comparisons are needed. On the other hand Algorithm 11 uses only 6 comparisons.

d) There are $C(5 + 4 - 1, 4) = 70$ outcomes, so at least $\lceil \log 70 \rceil = 7$ comparisons are needed. On the other hand Algorithm 11 uses only 7 comparisons.

38. On the first pass, we separate the list into two lists, the first being all the elements less than 3 (namely 1 and 2), and the second being all the elements greater than 3, namely $5, 7, 8, 9, 4, 6$ (in that order). As soon as each of these two lists is sorted (recursively) by quick sort, we are done. We show the entire process in the following sequence of list. The numbers in parentheses are the numbers that are correctly placed by the algorithm on the current level of recursion, and the brackets are those elements that were correctly placed previously. Five levels of recursion are required. $12(3)578946$, $(1)2[3]4(5)7896$, $[1](2)[3](4)[5]6(7)89$, $[1][2][3][4][5](6)[7](8)9$, $[1][2][3][4][5][6][7][8](9)$

40. In practice, this algorithm is coded differently from what we show here, requiring more comparisons but being more efficient because the data structures are simpler (and the sorting is done in place). We denote the list $a_1, a_2, \ldots, a_n$ by a, with similar notations for the other lists. Also, rather than putting a_1 at the end of the first sublist, we put it between the two sublists and do not have to deal with it in either sublist.

> **procedure** $quick(a_1, a_2, \ldots, a_n)$
> $b :=$ the empty list
> $c :=$ the empty list
> $temp := a_1$
> **for** $i := 2$ **to** n
>   **if** $a_i < a_1$ **then** adjoin a_i to the end of list b
>   **else** adjoin a_i to the end of list c
> $\{\text{notation: } m = \text{length}(b) \text{ and } k = \text{length}(c)\}$
> **if** $m \neq 0$ **then** $quick(b_1, b_2, \ldots, b_m)$
> **if** $k \neq 0$ **then** $quick(c_1, c_2, \ldots, c_k)$
> $\{\text{now put the sorted lists back into } a\}$
> **for** $i := 1$ **to** m
> $a_i := b_i$
> $a_{m+1} := temp$
> **for** $i := 1$ **to** k
> $a_{m+i+1} := c_i$
> $\{\text{the list } a \text{ is now sorted}\}$

42. In the best case, the initial split will require 3 comparisons and result in sublists of length 1 and 2 still to be sorted. These require 0 and 1 comparisons, respectively, and the list has been sorted. Therefore the answer is $3 + 0 + 1 = 4$.

44. For $n = 5$ we compute that $\log 5! \approx 6.9$ and $(5 \log 5)/4 \approx 2.9$, so the inequality holds (it actually holds for all $n > 1$). Therefore we can assume that $n \geq 6$. Since $n!$ is the product of all the integers from n down to 1, we certainly have $n! > n(n-1)(n-2) \cdots \lceil n/2 \rceil$ (since at least the term 2 is missing). Note that there are more than $n/2$ terms in this product, and each term is at least as big as $n/2$. Therefore the product is greater than $(n/2)^{(n/2)}$. Taking the log of both sides of the inequality, we have

$$\log n! > \log \left(\frac{n}{2}\right)^{n/2} = \frac{n}{2} \log \frac{n}{2} = \frac{n}{2}(\log n - 1) > (n \log n)/4,$$

since $n > 4$ implies $\log n - 1 > (\log n)/2$.

SECTION 3.6   Program Correctness

2. There are two cases. If $x \geq 0$ initially, then nothing is executed, so $x \geq 0$ at the end. If $x < 0$ initially, then x is set equal to 0, so $x = 0$ at the end; hence again $x \geq 0$ at the end.

4. There are three cases. If $x < y$ initially, then *min* is set equal to x, so $(x \leq y \land min = x)$ is true. If $x = y$ initially, then *min* is set equal to y (which equals x), so again $(x \leq y \land min = x)$ is true. Finally, if $x > y$ initially, then *min* is set equal to y, so $(x > y \land min = y)$ is true. Hence in all cases the disjunction $(x \leq y \land min = x) \lor (x > y \land min = y)$ is true.

6. There are three cases. If $x < 0$, then y is set equal to $-2|x|/x = (-2)(-x)/x = 2$. If $x > 0$, then y is set equal to $2|x|/x = 2x/x = 2$. If $x = 0$, then y is set equal to 2. Hence in all cases $y = 2$ at the termination of this program.

8. We prove that Algorithm 9 in Section 3.5 is correct. It is clearly correct if $n = 0$ or $n = 1$, so we assume that $n \geq 2$. Then the program terminates when the **for** loop terminates, so we concentrate our attention on that loop. Before the loop begins, we have $x = 0$ and $y = 1$. Let the loop invariant p be "$(x = f_{i-1} \land y = f_i) \lor (i$ is undefined $\land x = f_0 \land y = f_1)$." This is true at the beginning of the loop, since i is undefined and $f_0 = 0$ and $f_1 = 1$. What we must show now is $p \land (1 \leq i < n)\{S\}p$. If $p \land (1 \leq i < n)$, then $x = f_{i-1}$ and $y = f_i$. Hence z becomes f_{i+1} by the definition of the Fibonacci sequence. Now x becomes y, namely f_i, and y becomes z, namely f_{i+1}, and i is incremented. Hence for this new (defined) i, $x = f_{i-1}$ and $y = f_i$, as desired. We therefore conclude that upon termination $x = f_{i-1} \land y = f_i \land i = n$; hence $y = f_n$, as desired.

10. We must show that if p_0 is true before S is executed, then q is true afterwards. Suppose that p_0 is true before S is executed. By the given implication, we know that p_1 is also true. Therefore, since $p_1\{S\}q$, we conclude that q is true after S is executed, as desired.

12. Suppose that the initial assertion is true before the program begins, so that a and d are positive integers. Consider the following loop invariant p: "$a = dq + r$ and $r \geq 0$." This is true before the loop starts, since the equation then states $a = d \cdot 0 + a$, and we are told that a (which equals r at this point) is a positive integer, hence greater than or equal to 0. Now we must show that if p is true and $r \geq d$ before some pass through the loop, then it remains true after the pass. Certainly we still have $r \geq 0$, since all that happened to r was the subtraction of d, and $r \geq d$ to begin this pass. Furthermore, let q' denote the new value of q and r' the new value of r. Then $dq' + r' = d(q + 1) + (r - d) = dq + d + r - d = dq + r = a$, as desired. Furthermore, the loop terminates eventually, since one cannot repeated subtract the positive integer d from the positive integer r without r eventually becoming less than d. When the loop terminates, the loop invariant p must still be true, and the condition $r \geq d$ must be false—i.e., $r < d$ must be true. But this is precisely the desired final assertion.

SUPPLEMENTARY EXERCISES FOR CHAPTER 3

2. a) By algebra we can factor $a^n + 1$ when n is odd into $(a+1)(a^{n-1} - a^{n-2} + a^{n-3} - \cdots + a^2 - a + 1)$. This will be a nontrivial factorization of the integer $a^n + 1$ when $n > 1$ and $a > 1$, since in this case $1 < a + 1 < a^n + 1$. Thus our conjecture is that under the stated conditions, $a^n + 1$ is composite. (There are other cases in which $a^n + 1$ is composite as well, such as $a = 2$ and $n = 32$, but our conjecture is not able to handle these. This is related to the notion of Fermat primes.) Actually we can extend our conjecture to cover all $n > 2$ having an odd prime factor, since $a^{st} = (a^s)^t$.

b) The proof is given in the first two sentences of part **(a)**.

4. This follows from Exercise 18 in Section 3.1, since 5 is not a perfect square.

6. There are four cases, determined by the remainder when n is divided by 5. We omit the intermediate algebra. In the first case, we have $n = 5k + 1$. Then $n^2 - 1 = 5(5k^2 + 2k)$, so $n^4 - 1 = (n^2 - 1)(n^2 + 1) = 5(5k^2 + 2k)(n^2 + 1)$ and hence $n^4 - 1$ is divisible by 5. In the second case, $n = 5k + 2$, so we get $n^4 - 1 = 5(125k^4 + 200k^3 + 120k^2 + 32k + 3)$, again as desired. The third case is similar, with $n = 5k + 3$ and $n^4 - 1 = 5(125k^4 + 300k^3 + 270k^2 + 108k + 16)$. The fourth case, $n = 5k + 4$, is similar to the first, and $n^4 - 1 = 5(5k^2 + 8k + 3)(n^2 + 1)$.

8. a) $1, 2, 3, 4, 6, 8, 11, 13, 16, 18, 26, 28, 36, 38, 47, 48, 53, 57, 62, 69$

b) Suppose there were only a finite set of Ulam numbers, say $u_1 < u_2 < \cdots < u_n$. Then it is clear that $u_{n-1} + u_n$ can be written uniquely as the sum of two distinct Ulam numbers, so this is an Ulam number larger than u_n, a contradiction. Therefore there are an infinite number of Ulam numbers.

10. The proposition is true for $n = 1$, since $1^3 + 3^3 = 28 = 1(1+1)^2(2 \cdot 1^2 + 4 \cdot 1 + 1)$. Assume the inductive hypothesis. Then

$$1^3 + 3^3 + \cdots + (2n+1)^3 + (2n+3)^3 = (n+1)^2(2n^2 + 4n + 1) + (2n+3)^3$$
$$= 2n^4 + 8n^3 + 11n^2 + 6n + 1 + 8n^3 + 36n^2 + 54n + 27$$
$$= 2n^4 + 16n^3 + 47n^2 + 60n + 28$$
$$= (n+2)^2(2n^2 + 8n + 7)$$
$$= (n+2)^2(2(n+1)^2 + 4(n+1) + 1).$$

12. Our proof is by induction, it being trivial for $n = 1$, since $1/3 = 1/3$. Under the inductive hypothesis

$$\frac{1}{1 \cdot 3} + \cdots + \frac{1}{(2n-1)(2n+1)} + \frac{1}{(2n+1)(2n+3)} = \frac{n}{2n+1} + \frac{1}{(2n+1)(2n+3)}$$
$$= \frac{1}{2n+1}\left(n + \frac{1}{2n+3}\right)$$
$$= \frac{1}{2n+1}\left(\frac{2n^2 + 3n + 1}{2n+3}\right)$$
$$= \frac{1}{2n+1}\left(\frac{(2n+1)(n+1)}{2n+3}\right) = \frac{n+1}{2n+3},$$

as desired.

14. We prove this statement by induction. The base case is $n = 5$, and indeed $5^2 + 5 = 30 < 32 = 2^5$. Assuming the inductive hypothesis, we have $(n+1)^2 + (n+1) = n^2 + 3n + 2 < n^2 + 4n < n^2 + n^2 = 2n^2 < 2(n^2 + n)$, which is less than $2 \cdot 2^n$ by the inductive hypothesis, and this equals 2^{n+1}, as desired.

16. We can let $N = 16$. We prove that $n^4 < 2^n$ for all $n > N$. The base case is $n = 17$, when $17^4 = 83521 < 131072 = 2^{17}$. Assuming the inductive hypothesis, we have $(n+1)^4 = n^4 + 4n^3 + 6n^2 + 4n + 1 < n^4 + 4n^3 + 6n^3 + 4n^3 + 2n^3 = n^4 + 16n^3 < n^4 + n^4 = 2n^4$, which is less than $2 \cdot 2^n$ by the inductive hypothesis, and this equals 2^{n+1}, as desired.

18. If $n = 0$ (base case), then the expression equals $0 + 1 + 8 = 9$, which is divisible by 9. Assume that $n^3 + (n+1)^3 + (n+2)^3$ is divisible by 9. We must show that $(n+1)^3 + (n+2)^3 + (n+3)^3$ is also divisible by 9. The difference of these two expressions is $(n+3)^3 - n^3 = 9n^2 + 27n + 27 = 9(n^2 + 3n + 3)$, a multiple of 9. Therefore since the first expression is divisible by 9, so is the second.

20. The two parts are nearly identical, so we do only part **(a)**. Part **(b)** is proved in the same way, substituting multiplication for addition throughout. The base case is the tautology that if $a_1 \equiv b_1 \pmod{m}$, then $a_1 \equiv b_1 \pmod{m}$. Assume the inductive hypothesis. This tells us that $\sum_{j=1}^{n} a_j \equiv \sum_{j=1}^{n} b_j \pmod{m}$. Combining this fact with the fact that $a_{n+1} \equiv b_{n+1} \pmod{m}$, we obtain the desired congruence, $\sum_{j=1}^{n+1} a_j \equiv \sum_{j=1}^{n+1} b_j \pmod{m}$ from Theorem 10 in Section 2.4.

22. After some computation we conjecture that $n + 6 < (n^2 - 8n)/16$ for all $n \geq 28$. (We find that it is not true for smaller values of n.) For the basis case we have $28 + 6 = 34$ and $(28^2 - 8 \cdot 28)/16 = 35$, so the statement is true. Assume that the statement is true for $n = k$. Then since $k > 27$ we have

$$\frac{(k+1)^2 - 8(k+1)}{16} = \frac{k^2 - 8k}{16} + \frac{2k - 7}{16} > k + 6 + \frac{2k - 7}{16} \quad \text{by the inductive hypothesis}$$

$$> k + 6 + \frac{2 \cdot 27 - 7}{16} > k + 6 + 2.9 > (k+1) + 6,$$

as desired.

24. When $n = 1$, we are looking for the derivative of $g(x) = e^{cx}$, which is ce^{cx} by the chain rule, so the statement is true for $n = 1$. Assume that the statement is true for $n = k$, that is, the kth derivative is given by $g^{(k)} = c^k e^{cx}$. Differentiating by the chain rule again (and remembering that c^k is constant) gives us the $(k+1)$st derivative: $g^{(k+1)} = c \cdot c^k e^{cx} = c^{k+1} e^{cx}$, as desired.

26. We look at the first few Fibonacci numbers to see if there is a pattern (all congruences are modulo 3): $f_0 = 0$, $f_1 = 1$, $f_2 = 1$, $f_3 = 2$, $f_4 = 3 \equiv 0$, $f_5 = 5 \equiv 2$, $f_6 = 8 \equiv 2$, $f_7 = 13 \equiv 1$, $f_8 = 21 \equiv 0$, $f_9 = 34 \equiv 1$. We may not see a pattern yet, but note that f_8 and f_9 are the same, modulo 3, as f_0 and f_1. Therefore the sequence must continue to repeat from this point, since the recursive definition gives f_n just in terms of n_{n-1} and f_{n-2}. In particular, $f_{10} \equiv f_2 = 1$, $f_{11} \equiv f_3 = 2$, and so on. Since the pattern has period 8, we can formulate our conjecture as follows:

$$f_n \equiv 0 \pmod{3} \text{ if } n \equiv 0 \text{ or } 4 \pmod{8}$$
$$f_n \equiv 1 \pmod{3} \text{ if } n \equiv 1, 2, \text{ or } 7 \pmod{8}$$
$$f_n \equiv 2 \pmod{3} \text{ if } n \equiv 3, 5, \text{ or } 6 \pmod{8}$$

To prove this by mathematical induction is tedious. There are two base cases, $n = 0$ and $n = 1$. The conjecture is certainly true in each of them, since $0 \equiv 0 \pmod{8}$ and $f_0 \equiv 0 \pmod{3}$, and $1 \equiv 1 \pmod{8}$ and $f_0 \equiv 1 \pmod{3}$. So we assume the inductive hypothesis and consider a given $n + 1$. There are eight cases to consider, depending on the value of $(n+1) \bmod 8$. We will carry out one of them; the other seven cases are similar. If $n + 1 \equiv 5 \pmod{8}$, for example, then $n - 1$ and n are congruent to 3 and 4 modulo 8, respectively. By the inductive hypothesis, $f_{n-1} \equiv 2 \pmod{3}$ and $f_n \equiv 0 \pmod{3}$. Therefore f_{n+1}, which is the sum of these two numbers, is equivalent to $2 + 0$, or 2, modulo 3, as desired.

28. There are two base cases: for $n = 0$ we have $f_0 + f_2 = 0 + 1 = 1 = l_1$, and $f_1 + f_3 = 1 + 2 = 3 = l_2$, as desired. Assume the inductive hypothesis, that $f_k + f_{k+2} = l_{k+1}$ for all $k \leq n$ (we are using strong induction here). Then $f_{n+1} + f_{n+3} = f_n + f_{n-1} + f_{n+2} + f_{n+1} = (f_n + f_{n+2}) + (f_{n-1} + f_{n+1}) = l_{n+1} + l_n$ by the inductive hypothesis (with $k = n$ and $k = n - 1$). This last expression equals $l_{n+2} = l_{(n+1)+1}$, however, by the definition of the Lucas numbers, as desired.

30. We follow the hint. Starting with the trivial identity

$$\frac{m+n-1}{n} = \frac{m-1}{n} + 1$$

and multiplying both sides by

$$\frac{m(m+1)\cdots(m+n-2)}{(n-1)!}$$

we obtain the identity given in the hint:

$$\frac{m(m+1)\cdots(m+n-1)}{n!} = \frac{(m-1)m(m+1)\cdots(m+n-2)}{n!} + \frac{m(m+1)\cdots(m+n-2)}{(n-1)!}$$

Now we want to show that the product of any n consecutive positive integers is divisible by $n!$. We prove this by induction on n. The case $n = 1$ is clear, since every integer is divisible by $1!$. Assume the inductive hypothesis, that the statement is true for $n - 1$. To prove the statement for n, now, we will give a proof using induction on the starting point of the sequence of n consecutive positive integers. Call this starting point m. The base case, $m = 1$, is again clear, since the product of the first n positive integers *is* $n!$. Assume the inductive hypothesis that the statement is true for $m - 1$. Note that we have two inductive hypotheses active here: the statement is true for $n - 1$, and the statement is true also for $m - 1$ and n. We are trying to prove the statement true for m and n. At this point we simply stare at the identity given above. The first term on the right-hand side is an integer by the inductive hypothesis about $m - 1$ and n. The second term on the right-hand side is an integer by the inductive hypothesis about $n - 1$. Therefore the expression is an integer. But the statement that the left-hand side is an integer is precisely what we wanted—that the product of the n positive integers starting with m is divisible by $n!$.

32. The algebra gets very messy here, but the ideas are not advanced. We will use the following standard trigonometric identity, which is proved using the standard formulas for the sine and cosine of sums and differences:

$$\cos A \sin B = \frac{\sin(A+B) - \sin(A-B)}{2}$$

The proof of the identity in this exercise is by induction, of course. The base case, $n = 1$, is the true statement that

$$\cos x = \frac{\cos x \sin(x/2)}{\sin(x/2)}.$$

Assume the inductive hypothesis:

$$\sum_{j=1}^{n} \cos jx = \frac{\cos((n+1)x/2)\sin(nx/2)}{\sin(x/2)}$$

Now it is clear that the inductive step is equivalent to showing that adding the $(n+1)^{\text{th}}$ term in the sum to the expression on the right-hand side of the last displayed equation yields the same expression with $n + 1$ substituted for n. In other words, we must show that

$$\cos(n+1)x + \frac{\cos((n+1)x/2)\sin(nx/2)}{\sin(x/2)} = \frac{\cos((n+2)x/2)\sin((n+1)x/2)}{\sin(x/2)},$$

which can be rewritten without fractions as

$$\sin(x/2)\cos(n+1)x + \cos((n+1)x/2)\sin(nx/2) = \cos((n+2)x/2)\sin((n+1)x/2).$$

But this follows after a little calculation using the trigonometric identity displayed at the beginning of this solution, since both sides equal

$$\frac{\sin((2n+3)x/2) - \sin(x/2)}{2}.$$

34. We compute a few terms to get a feel for what is going on: $x_1 = \sqrt{6} \approx 2.45$, $x_2 = \sqrt{\sqrt{6}+6} \approx 2.91$, $x_3 \approx 2.98$, and so on. The values seem to be approaching 3 from below in an increasing manner.

    a) Clearly $x_0 < x_1$. Assume that $x_{k-1} < x_k$. Then $x_k = \sqrt{x_{k-1}+6} < \sqrt{x_k+6} = x_{k+1}$, and the inductive step is proved.

    b) Since $\sqrt{6} < \sqrt{9} = 3$, the basis step is proved. Assume that $x_k < 3$. Then $x_{k+1} = \sqrt{x_k+6} < \sqrt{3+6} = 3$, and the inductive step is proved.

    c) By a result from mathematical analysis, an increasing bounded sequence converges to a limit. If we call this limit L, then we must have $L = \sqrt{L+6}$, by letting $n \to \infty$ in the defining equation. Solving this equation for L yields $L = 3$. (The root $L = -2$ is extraneous, since L is positive.)

36. (It will be helpful for the reader to draw a diagram to help in following this proof.) We use induction on n, the number of cities, the result being trivial if $n = 1$ or $n = 2$. Assume the inductive hypothesis and suppose that we have a country with $k+1$ cities, labeled c_1 through c_{k+1}. Remove c_{k+1} and apply the inductive hypothesis to find a city c that can be reached either directly or with one intermediate stop from each of the other cities among c_1 through c_k. If the one-way road leads from c_{k+1} to c, then we are done, so we can assume that the road leads from c to c_{k+1}. If there are any one-way roads from c_{k+1} to a city with a one-way road to c, then we are also done, so we can assume that each road between c_{k+1} and a city with a one-way road to c leads from such a city to c_{k+1}. Thus c and all the cities with a one-way road to c have a direct road to c_{k+1}. All the remaining cities must have a one-way road from them to a city with a one-way road to c (that was part of the definition of c), and so they have paths of length 2 to c_{k+1}, via some such city. Therefore c_{k+1} satisfies the conditions of the problem, and the proof is complete.

38. We have to assume from the statement of the problem that all the cars get are equally efficient in terms of miles per gallon. We proceed by induction on n, the number of cars in the group. If $n = 1$, then the one car has enough fuel to complete the lap. Assume the inductive hypothesis that the statement is true for a group of k cars, and suppose we have a group of $k+1$ cars. It helps to think of the cars as stationary, not moving yet. We claim that at least one car c in the group has enough fuel to reach the next car in the group. If this were not so, then the total amount of fuel in all the cars combined would not cover the full lap (think of each car as traveling as far as it can on its own fuel). So now pretend that the car d just ahead of car c is not present, and instead the fuel in that car is in c's tank. By the inductive hypothesis (we still have the same total amount of fuel), some car in this situation can complete a lap by obtaining fuel from other cars as it travels around the track. Then this same car can complete the lap in the actual situation, because if and when it needs to move from the location of car c to the location of the car d, the amount of fuel it has available without d's fuel that we are pretending c already has will be sufficient for it to reach d, at which time this extra fuel becomes available (because this car made it to c's location and car c has enough fuel to reach d's location).

40. **a)** The basis step is to prove the statement that this algorithm terminates for all fractions of the form $1/q$. Since this fraction is already a unit fraction, there is nothing more to prove.

    b) For the inductive step, assume that the algorithm terminates for all proper positive fractions with numerators smaller than p, suppose that we are starting with the proper positive fraction p/q, and suppose that the algorithm selects $1/n$ as the first step in the algorithm. Note that necessarily $n > 1$. Therefore we can write $p/q = p'/q' + 1/n$. If $p/q = 1/n$, we are done, so assume that $p/q > 1/n$. By finding a common denominator and subtracting, we see that we can take $p' = np - q$ and $q' = nq$. We claim that $p' < p$, which algebraically is easily seen to be equivalent to $p/q < 1/(n-1)$, and this is true by the choice of n such that $1/n$ is the largest unit fraction not exceeding p/q. Therefore by the inductive hypothesis we can write p'/q' as the sum of distinct unit fractions with increasing denominators, and thereby have written p/q as the sum of unit fractions. The only thing left to check is that $p'/q' < 1/n$, so that the algorithm will not try to choose $1/n$ again for p'/q'. But if this were not the case, then $p/q \geq 2/n$, and combining this with the inequality $p/q < 1/(n-1)$ given above, we would have $2/n < 1/(n-1)$, which would mean that $n = 1$, a contradiction.

42. What we really need to show is that the definition "terminates" for every n. It is conceivable that trying to apply the definition gets us into some kind of infinite loop, using the second line; we need to show that this is not the case. We will give a very strange kind of proof by mathematical induction. First, following the hint, we will show that the definition tells us that $M(n) = 91$ for all positive integers $n \leq 101$. We do this by backwards induction, starting with $n = 101$ and going down toward $n = 1$. There are 11 base cases: $n = 101, 100, 99, \ldots, 91$. The first line of the definition tells us immediately that $M(101) = 101 - 10 = 91$. To compute $M(100)$ we have

$$M(100) = M(M(100 + 11)) = M(M(111))$$
$$= M(111 - 10) = M(101) = 91.$$

The last equality came from the fact that we had already computed $M(101)$. Similarly,

$$M(99) = M(M(99 + 11)) = M(M(110))$$
$$= M(110 - 10) = M(100) = 91,$$

and so on down to

$$M(91) = M(M(91 + 11)) = M(M(102))$$
$$= M(102 - 10) = M(92) = 91.$$

In each case the final equality comes from the previously computed value. Now assume the inductive hypothesis, that $M(k) = 91$ for all k from $n + 1$ through 101 (i.e., if $n + 1 \leq k \leq 101$); we must prove that $M(n) = 91$, where n is some fixed positive integer less than 91. To compute $M(n)$, we have

$$M(n) = M(M(n + 11)) = M(91) = 91$$

where the next to last equality comes from the fact that $n + 11$ is between $n + 1$ and 101. Thus we have proved that $M(n) = 91$ for all $n \leq 101$. The first line of the definition takes care of values of n greater than 101, so the entire function is well-defined.

44. Let $P(n)$ be the statement that exactly $n - 1$ moves are required to assemble a puzzle with n pieces. Now $P(1)$ is trivially true. Assume that $P(k)$ is true for all $k < n$, and consider a puzzle with n pieces. The final move must be the joining of two blocks, of size k and $n - k$ for some integer k, $1 \leq k \leq n - 1$. By the inductive hypothesis, it required $k - 1$ moves to construct the one block, and $n - k - 1$ moves to construct the other. Therefore $1 + (k - 1) + (n - k - 1) = n - 1$ moves are required in all, so $P(n)$ is true.

46. This problem is similar to and uses the result of Exercise 60 in Section 3.3. The lemma we need is that if there are n planes meeting the stated conditions, then adding one more plane, which intersects the original figure in the manner described, results in the addition of $(n^2 + n + 2)/2$ new regions. The reason for this is that the pattern formed on the new plane by all the lines of intersection of this plane with the planes already present has, by Exercise 60 in Section 3.3, $(n^2 + n + 2)/2$ regions; and each of these two-dimensional regions separates the three-dimensional region through which it passes into two three-dimensional regions. Therefore the proof

by induction of the present exercise reduces to noting that one plane separates space into $(1^3 + 5 \cdot 1 + 6)/6 = 2$ regions, and verifying the algebraic identity

$$\frac{n^3 + 5n + 6}{6} + \frac{n^2 + n + 2}{2} = \frac{(n+1)^3 + 5(n+1) + 6}{6}.$$

48. a) This set is not well ordered, since the set itself has no least element (the negative integers get smaller and smaller).

b) This set is well ordered—the problem inherent in part **(a)** is not present here because the entire set has -99 as its least element. Every subset also has a least element.

c) This set is not well ordered. The entire set, for example, has no least element, since the numbers of the form $1/n$ for n a positive integer get smaller and smaller.

d) This set is well ordered. The situation is analogous to part **(b)**.

50. The strong induction principle clearly implies ordinary induction, for if one has shown that $P(k) \to P(k+1)$, then it automatically follows that $[P(1) \wedge \cdots \wedge P(k)] \to P(k+1)$; in other words, strong induction can always be invoked whenever ordinary induction is used.

Conversely, suppose that $P(n)$ is a statement that one can prove using strong induction. Let $Q(n)$ be $P(1) \wedge \cdots \wedge P(n)$. Clearly $\forall n P(n)$ is logically equivalent to $\forall n Q(n)$. We show how $\forall n Q(n)$ can be proved using ordinary induction. First, $Q(1)$ is true because $Q(1) = P(1)$ and $P(1)$ is true by the base case for the proof of $\forall n P(n)$ by strong induction. Now suppose that $Q(k)$ is true, i.e., $P(1) \wedge \cdots \wedge P(k)$ is true. By the proof of $\forall n P(n)$ by strong induction it follow that $P(k+1)$ is true. But $Q(k) \wedge P(k+1)$ is just $Q(k+1)$. Thus we have proved $\forall n Q(n)$ by ordinary induction.

52. In the preamble to Exercise 48 in Section 2.6 an algorithm was described for writing the greatest common divisor of two positive integers as a linear combination of these two integer (see also Theorem 1 in that section). We can use that algorithm, together with the result of Exercise 51, to solve this problem. For $n = 1$ there is nothing to do, since $a_1 = a_1$, and we already have an algorithm for $n = 2$. For $n > 2$, we can write $\gcd(a_{n-1}, a_n)$ as a linear combination of a_{n-1} and a_n, say as

$$\gcd(a_{n-1}, a_n) = c_{n-1} a_{n-1} + c_n a_n.$$

Then we apply the algorithm recursively to the numbers $a_1, a_2, \ldots, a_{n-2}, \gcd(a_{n-1}, a_n)$. This gives us the following equation:

$$\gcd(a_1, a_2, \ldots, a_{n-2}, \gcd(a_{n-1}, a_n)) = c_1 a_1 + c_2 a_2 + \cdots + c_{n-2} a_{n-2} + Q \cdot \gcd(a_{n-1}, a_n)$$

Plugging in from the previous display, we have the desired linear combination:

$$\gcd(a_1, a_2, \ldots, a_n) = \gcd(a_1, a_2, \ldots, a_{n-2}, \gcd(a_{n-1}, a_n))$$
$$= c_1 a_1 + c_2 a_2 + \cdots + c_{n-2} a_{n-2} + Q(c_{n-1} a_{n-1} + c_n a_n)$$
$$= c_1 a_1 + c_2 a_2 + \cdots + c_{n-2} a_{n-2} + Q c_{n-1} a_{n-1} + Q c_n a_n$$

54. The following definition works. The empty string is in the set, and if x and y are in the set, then so are xy, $1x00$, $00x1$, and $0x1y0$. One way to see this is to think of graphing, for a string in this set, the quantity (number of 0's) $- 2 \cdot$ (number of 1's) as a function of the position in the string. This graph must start and end at the horizontal axis. If it contains another point on the axis, then we can split the string into xy where x and y are both in the set. If the graph stays above the axis, then the string must be of the form $00x1$, and if it stays below the axis, then it must be of the form $1x00$. The only other case is that in which the graph crosses the axis at a 1 in the string, without landing on the axis. In this case, the string must look like $0x1y0$.

56. a) The set contains three strings of length 3, and each of them gives us four more strings of length 6, using the fourth through seventh rules, except that there is a bit of overlap, so that in fact there are only 13 strings in all. The strings are abc, bac, acb, $abcabc$, $ababcc$, $aabcbc$, $abcbac$, $abbacc$, $abacbc$, $bacabc$, $abcacb$, $aacbbc$, and $acbabc$.

b) We prove this by induction on the length of the string. The base case is vacuously true, since there are no strings in the set of length 0 (and it is trivially true anyway, since 0 is a multiple of 3). Assume the inductive hypothesis that the statement is true for shorter strings, and let y be a string in S. If $y \in S$ by one of the first three rules, then y has length 3. If $y \in S$ by one of the last four rules, then the length of y is equal to 3 plus the length of x. By the inductive hypothesis, the length of x is a multiple of 3, so the length of y is also a multiple of 3.

58. By applying the recursive rules we get the following list: $((()))$, $(()())$, $()()()$, $()(())$, $(())()$.

60. We use induction on the length of the string x of balanced parentheses. If $x = \lambda$, then the statement is true since $0 = 0$. Otherwise $x = (a)$ or $x = ab$, where a and b are shorter balanced strings of parentheses. In the first case, the number of parentheses of each type in x is one more than the corresponding number in a, so by the inductive hypothesis these numbers are equal. In the second case, the number of parentheses of each type in x is the sum of the corresponding numbers in a and b, so again by the inductive hypothesis these numbers are equal.

62. We prove the "only if" part by induction on the length of the balanced string w. If $w = \lambda$, then there is nothing to prove. If $w = (x)$, then we have by the inductive hypothesis that $N(x) = 0$ and that $N(a) \geq 0$ if a is a prefix of x. Then $N(w) = 1 + 0 + (-1) = 0$; and $N(b) \geq 1 \geq 0$ if b is a nonempty prefix of w, since $b = (a$. If $w = xy$, then we have by the inductive hypothesis that $N(x) = N(y) = 0$; and $N(a) \geq 0$ if a is a prefix of x or y. Then $N(w) = 0 + 0 = 0$; and $N(b) \geq 0$ if b is a prefix of w, since either b is a prefix of x or $b = xa$ where a is a prefix of y.

We also prove the "if" part by induction on the length of the string w. Suppose that w satisfies the condition. If $w = \lambda$, then $w \in B$. Otherwise w must begin with a parenthesis, and it must be a left parenthesis, since otherwise the prefix of length 1 would give us $N()) = -1$. Now there are two cases: either $w = ab$, where $N(a) = N(b) = 0$ and $a \neq \lambda \neq b$, or not. If so, then a and b are balanced strings of parentheses by the inductive hypothesis (noting that prefixes of a are prefixes of w, and prefixes of b are a followed by prefixes of w), so w is balanced by the recursive definition of the set of balanced strings. In the other case, $N(u) \geq 1$ for all nonempty prefixes u of w, other than w itself. Thus w must end with a right parenthesis to make $N(w) = 0$. So $w = (x)$, and $N(x) = 0$. Furthermore $N(u) \geq 0$ for every prefix u of x, since if $N(u)$ dipped to -1, then $N((u) = 0$ and we would be in the first case. Therefore by the inductive hypothesis x is balanced, and so by the definition of balanced strings w is balanced, as desired.

64. We copy the definition into an algorithm.

> **procedure** $gcd(a, b :$ nonnegative integers, not both zero)
> **if** $a > b$ **then** $gcd(a, b) := gcd(b, a)$
> **else if** $a = 0$ **then** $gcd(a, b) := b$
> **else if** a and b are even **then** $gcd(a, b) := 2 \cdot gcd(a/2, b/2)$
> **else if** a is even and b is odd **then** $gcd(a, b) := gcd(a/2, b)$
> **else** $gcd(a, b) := gcd(a, b - a)$

66. To prove that a recursive program is correct, we need to check that it works correctly for the base case, and that it works correctly for the inductive step under the inductive assumption that it works correctly on its recursive call. To apply this rule of inference to Algorithm 6 in Section 3.5, we reason as follows. The base case is $n = 1$. In that case the **then** clause is executed, and not the **else** clause, and so the procedure gives the correct value, namely 1. Now assume that the procedure works correctly for $n - 1$, and we want to show that it gives the correct value for the input n, where $n > 1$. In this case, the **else** clause is executed, and not the **then** clause, so the procedure gives us n times whatever the procedure gives for input $n - 1$. By the inductive hypothesis, we know that this latter value is $(n - 1)!$. Therefore the procedure gives $n \cdot (n - 1)!$, which by definition is equal to $n!$, exactly as we wished.

68. We apply the definition:

$$a(0) = 0$$
$$a(1) = 1 - a(a(0)) = 1 - a(0) = 1 - 0 = 1$$
$$a(2) = 2 - a(a(1)) = 2 - a(1) = 2 - 1 = 1$$
$$a(3) = 3 - a(a(2)) = 3 - a(1) = 3 - 1 = 2$$
$$a(4) = 4 - a(a(3)) = 4 - a(2) = 4 - 1 = 3$$
$$a(5) = 5 - a(a(4)) = 5 - a(3) = 5 - 2 = 3$$
$$a(6) = 6 - a(a(5)) = 6 - a(3) = 6 - 2 = 4$$
$$a(7) = 7 - a(a(6)) = 7 - a(4) = 7 - 3 = 4$$
$$a(8) = 8 - a(a(7)) = 8 - a(4) = 8 - 3 = 5$$
$$a(9) = 9 - a(a(8)) = 9 - a(5) = 9 - 3 = 6$$

70. We follow the hint. First note that by algebra, $\mu^2 = 1 - \mu$, and that $\mu \approx 0.618$. Therefore we have $(\mu n - \lfloor \mu n \rfloor) + (\mu^2 n - \lfloor \mu^2 n \rfloor) = \mu n - \lfloor \mu n \rfloor + (1 - \mu)n - \lfloor (1 - \mu)n \rfloor = \mu n - \lfloor \mu n \rfloor + n - \mu n - \lfloor n - \mu n \rfloor = \mu n - \lfloor \mu n \rfloor + n - \mu n - n - \lfloor -\mu n \rfloor = -\lfloor \mu n \rfloor - (-\lceil \mu n \rceil) = -\lfloor \mu n \rfloor + \lceil \mu n \rceil = 1$, since μn is irrational and therefore not an integer. (We used here some of the properties of the floor and ceiling function from Table 1 in Section 1.8.) Next, continuing with the hint, suppose that $0 \le \alpha < 1 - \mu$, and consider $\lfloor (1 + \mu)(1 - \alpha) \rfloor + \lfloor \alpha + \mu \rfloor$. The second floor term is 0, since $\alpha < 1 - \mu$. The product $(1 + \mu)(1 - \alpha)$ is greater than $(1 + \mu)\mu = \mu + \mu^2 = 1$ and less than $(1 + 1 - \alpha)(1 - \alpha) < 2 \cdot 1 = 2$, so the whole sum equals 1, as desired. For the other case, suppose that $1 - \mu < \alpha < 1$, and again consider $\lfloor (1 + \mu)(1 - \alpha) \rfloor + \lfloor \alpha + \mu \rfloor$. Here $\alpha + \mu$ is between 1 and 2, and $(1 + \mu)(1 - \alpha) < 1$, so again the sum is 1.

The rest of the proof is pretty messy algebra. Since we already know from Exercise 69 that the function $a(n)$ is well-defined by the recurrence $a(n) = n - a(a(n - 1))$ for all $n \ge 1$ and initial condition $a(0) = 0$, it suffices to prove that $\lfloor (n + 1)\mu \rfloor$ satisfies these equations. It clearly satisfies the second, since $0 < \mu < 1$. Thus we must show that $\lfloor (n + 1)\mu \rfloor = n - \lfloor (\lfloor n\mu \rfloor + 1)\mu \rfloor$ for all $n \ge 1$. Let $\alpha = n\mu - \lfloor n\mu \rfloor$; then $0 \le \alpha < 1$, and $\alpha \ne 1 - \mu$, since μ is irrational. First consider $\lfloor (\lfloor n\mu \rfloor + 1)\mu \rfloor$. It equals $\lfloor \mu(1 + \mu n - \alpha) \rfloor = \lfloor \mu + \mu^2 n - \alpha\mu \rfloor = \lfloor \mu + 1 - \alpha + \lfloor \mu^2 n \rfloor - \alpha\mu \rfloor$ by the first fact proved above. Since $\lfloor \mu^2 n \rfloor$ is an integer, this equals $\lfloor \mu^2 n \rfloor + \lfloor \mu + 1 - \alpha - \alpha\mu \rfloor = \lfloor \mu^2 n \rfloor + \lfloor (1 + \mu)(1 - \alpha) \rfloor = \mu^2 n - 1 + \alpha + \lfloor (1 + \mu)(1 - \alpha) \rfloor$. Next consider $\lfloor (n + 1)\mu \rfloor$. It equals $\lfloor \mu n + \mu \rfloor = \lfloor \lfloor \mu n \rfloor + \alpha + \mu \rfloor = \lfloor \mu n \rfloor + \lfloor \alpha + \mu \rfloor = \mu n - \alpha + \lfloor \alpha + \mu \rfloor$. Putting these together we have $\lfloor (\lfloor n\mu \rfloor + 1)\mu \rfloor + \lfloor (n + 1)\mu \rfloor - n = \mu^2 n - 1 + \alpha + \lfloor (1 + \mu)(1 - \alpha) \rfloor + \mu n - \alpha + \lfloor \alpha + \mu \rfloor - n = (\mu^2 + \mu - 1)n - 1 + \lfloor (1 + \mu)(1 - \alpha) \rfloor + \lfloor \alpha + \mu \rfloor$, which equals $0 - 1 + 1 = 0$ by the definition of μ and the second fact proved above. This is equivalent to what we wanted.

72. a) We apply the definition:

$$a(0) = 0$$
$$a(1) = 1 - a(a(a(0))) = 1 - a(a(0)) = 1 - a(0) = 1 - 0 = 1$$
$$a(2) = 2 - a(a(a(1))) = 2 - a(a(1)) = 2 - a(1) = 2 - 1 = 1$$
$$a(3) = 3 - a(a(a(2))) = 3 - a(a(1)) = 3 - a(1) = 3 - 1 = 2$$
$$a(4) = 4 - a(a(a(3))) = 4 - a(a(2)) = 4 - a(1) = 4 - 1 = 3$$
$$a(5) = 5 - a(a(a(4))) = 5 - a(a(3)) = 5 - a(2) = 5 - 1 = 4$$
$$a(6) = 6 - a(a(a(5))) = 6 - a(a(4)) = 6 - a(3) = 6 - 2 = 4$$
$$a(7) = 7 - a(a(a(6))) = 7 - a(a(4)) = 7 - a(3) = 7 - 2 = 5$$
$$a(8) = 8 - a(a(a(7))) = 8 - a(a(5)) = 8 - a(4) = 8 - 3 = 5$$
$$a(9) = 9 - a(a(a(8))) = 9 - a(a(5)) = 9 - a(4) = 9 - 3 = 6$$

b) We apply the definition:

$$a(0) = 0$$
$$a(1) = 1 - a(a(a(a(0)))) = 1 - a(a(a(0))) = 1 - a(a(0)) = 1 - a(0) = 1 - 0 = 1$$
$$a(2) = 2 - a(a(a(a(1)))) = 2 - a(a(a(1))) = 2 - a(a(1)) = 2 - a(1) = 2 - 1 = 1$$
$$a(3) = 3 - a(a(a(a(2)))) = 3 - a(a(a(1))) = 3 - a(a(1)) = 3 - a(1) = 3 - 1 = 2$$
$$a(4) = 4 - a(a(a(a(3)))) = 4 - a(a(a(2))) = 4 - a(a(1)) = 4 - a(1) = 4 - 1 = 3$$
$$a(5) = 5 - a(a(a(a(4)))) = 5 - a(a(a(3))) = 5 - a(a(2)) = 5 - a(1) = 5 - 1 = 4$$
$$a(6) = 6 - a(a(a(a(5)))) = 6 - a(a(a(4))) = 6 - a(a(3)) = 6 - a(2) = 6 - 1 = 5$$
$$a(7) = 7 - a(a(a(a(6)))) = 7 - a(a(a(5))) = 7 - a(a(4)) = 7 - a(3) = 7 - 2 = 5$$
$$a(8) = 8 - a(a(a(a(7)))) = 8 - a(a(a(5))) = 8 - a(a(4)) = 8 - a(3) = 8 - 2 = 6$$
$$a(9) = 9 - a(a(a(a(8)))) = 9 - a(a(a(6))) = 9 - a(a(5)) = 9 - a(4) = 9 - 3 = 6$$

c) We apply the definition:

$$a(1) = 1$$
$$a(2) = 1$$
$$a(3) = a(3 - a(2)) + a(3 - a(1)) = a(3 - 1) + a(3 - 1) = a(2) + a(2) = 1 + 1 = 2$$
$$a(4) = a(4 - a(3)) + a(4 - a(2)) = a(4 - 2) + a(4 - 1) = a(2) + a(3) = 1 + 2 = 3$$
$$a(5) = a(5 - a(4)) + a(5 - a(3)) = a(5 - 3) + a(5 - 2) = a(2) + a(3) = 1 + 2 = 3$$
$$a(6) = a(6 - a(5)) + a(6 - a(4)) = a(6 - 3) + a(6 - 3) = a(3) + a(3) = 2 + 2 = 4$$
$$a(7) = a(7 - a(6)) + a(7 - a(5)) = a(7 - 4) + a(7 - 3) = a(3) + a(4) = 2 + 3 = 5$$
$$a(8) = a(8 - a(7)) + a(8 - a(6)) = a(8 - 5) + a(8 - 4) = a(3) + a(4) = 2 + 3 = 5$$
$$a(9) = a(9 - a(8)) + a(9 - a(7)) = a(9 - 5) + a(9 - 5) = a(4) + a(4) = 3 + 3 = 6$$
$$a(10) = a(10 - a(9)) + a(10 - a(8)) = a(10 - 6) + a(10 - 5) = a(4) + a(5) = 3 + 3 = 6$$

74. The first term a_1 tells how many 1s there are. If $a_1 \geq 2$, then the sequence would not be nondecreasing, since a 1 would follow this 2. Therefore $a_1 = 1$. This tells us that there is one 1, so the next term must be at least 2. By the same reasoning as before, a_2 can't be 3 or larger, so $a_2 = 2$. This tells us that there are two 2s, and they must all come together since the sequence is nondecreasing. So $a_3 = 2$ as well. But now we know that there are two 3s, and of course they must come next. We continue in this way and obtain the first 20 terms:

$$1, 2, 2, 3, 3, 4, 4, 4, 5, 5, 5, 6, 6, 6, 6, 7, 7, 7, 7, 8$$

76. Suppose that $f(n)$ and $g(n)$ are both in $\mathcal{L}$. Since $g(n) \in \mathcal{L}$ and $0 \in \mathcal{L}$ (by the first condition), $-g(n) = 0 - g(n) \in \mathcal{L}$ (by the first condition). Therefore, again by the third condition, $f(n) - (-g(n)) = f(n) + g(n) \in \mathcal{L}$.

78. A polynomial can be built up from the constant functions and the function $f(n) = n$ by multiplication and addition. The constant functions and the function $f(n) = n$ are in $\mathcal{L}$ by definition, and Exercises 76 and 77 show that the class $\mathcal{L}$ is closed under addition and multiplication. Therefore every polynomial is in $\mathcal{L}$. Note that every polynomial is eventually positive or eventually negative since the highest order term dominates.

80. We just go step by step, using the closure properties in the definition and the previous exercises. Note that all the functions involved here are eventually positive, since $\ln n > 0$ for $n > 1$, and $\ln \ln n > 0$ for $n > e$. Since $n \in \mathcal{L}$, $\ln n \in \mathcal{L}$, and therefore $\ln \ln n \in \mathcal{L}$. Using Exercise 77, we then see that $\ln n \ln \ln n \in \mathcal{L}$. By Exercise 79, this tells us that $\sqrt{\ln n \ln \ln n} \in \mathcal{L}$. Similarly reasoning shows that $\sqrt{n}\sqrt{\ln n \ln \ln n} \in \mathcal{L}$, and so $e^{\sqrt{n}\sqrt{\ln n \ln \ln n}} \in \mathcal{L}$.

116
Chapter 4 Counting

CHAPTER 4
Counting

SECTION 4.1 The Basics of Counting

2. By the product rule there are $27 \cdot 37 = 999$ offices.

4. By the product rule there are $12 \cdot 2 \cdot 3 = 72$ different types of shirt.

6. By the product rule there are $4 \cdot 6 = 24$ routes.

8. There are 26 choices for the first initial, then 25 choices for the second, if no letter is to be repeated, then 24 choices for the third. (We interpret "repeated" broadly, so that a string like RWR, for example, is prohibited, as well as a string like RRW.) Therefore by the product rule the answer is $26 \cdot 25 \cdot 24 = 15{,}600$.

10. We have two choices for each bit, so there are $2^8 = 256$ bit strings.

12. We use the sum rule, adding the number of bit strings of each length up to 6. If we include the empty string, then we get $2^0 + 2^1 + 2^2 + 2^3 + 2^4 + 2^5 + 2^6 = 2^7 - 1 = 127$ (using the formula for the sum of a geometric progression, Section 3.3, Example 5).

14. If $n = 0$, then the empty string—vacuously—satisfies the condition (or does not, depending on how one views it). If $n = 1$, then there is one, namely the string 1. If $n \geq 2$, then such a string is determined by specifying the $n - 2$ bits between the first bit and the last, so there are 2^{n-2} such strings.

16. We can subtract from the number of strings of length 4 of lower case letters the number of strings of length 4 of lower case letters other than x. Thus the answer is $26^4 - 25^4 = 66{,}351$.

18. **a)** Every seventh number is divisible by 7. Therefore there are $\lfloor 999/7 \rfloor = 142$ such numbers. Note that we use the floor function, because the kth multiple of 7 does not occur until the number $7k$ has been reached.
b) For solving this part and the next four parts, we need to use the principle of inclusion–exclusion. Just as in part **(a)**, there are $\lfloor 999/11 \rfloor = 90$ numbers in our range divisible by 11, and there are $\lfloor 999/77 \rfloor = 12$ numbers in our range divisible by both 7 and 11 (the multiples of 77 are the numbers we seek). If we take these 12 numbers away from the 142 numbers divisible by 7, we see that there are 130 numbers in our range divisible by 7 but not 11.
c) As explained in part **(b)**, the answer is 12.
d) By the principle of inclusion–exclusion, the answer, using the data from part **(b)**, is $142 + 90 - 12 = 220$.
e) If we subtract from the answer to part **(d)** the number of numbers divisible by both 7 and 11, we will have the number of numbers divisible by neither of them; so the answer is $220 - 12 = 208$.
f) If we subtract the answer to part **(d)** from the total number of positive integers less than 1000, we will have the number of numbers divisible by exactly one of them; so the answer is $999 - 220 = 779$.
g) If we assume that numbers are written without leading 0s, then we should break the problem down into three cases—one-digit numbers, two-digit numbers and three-digit numbers. Clearly there are 9 one-digit

numbers, and each of them has distinct digits. There are 90 two-digit numbers (10 through 99), and all but 9 of them have distinct digits, so there are 81 two-digit numbers with distinct digits. An alternative way to compute this is to note that the first digit must be 1 through 9 (9 choices), and the second digit must be something different from the first digit (9 choices out of the 10 possible digits), so by the product rule, we get $9 \cdot 9 = 81$ choices in all. This approach also tells us that there are $9 \cdot 9 \cdot 8 = 648$ three-digit numbers with distinct digits (again, work from left to right—in the ones place, only 8 digits are left to choose from). So the final answer is $9 + 81 + 648 = 738$.

h) It turns out to be easier to count the odd numbers with distinct digits and subtract from our answer to part **(g)**, so let us proceed that way. There are 5 odd one-digit numbers. For two-digit numbers, first choose the ones digit (5 choices), then choose the tens digit (8 choices), since neither the ones digit value nor 0 is available); therefore there are 40 such two-digit numbers. (Note that this is not exactly half of 81.) For the three-digit numbers, first choose the ones digit (5 choices), then the hundreds digit (8 choices), then the tens digit (8 choices, giving us 320 in all. So there are $5 + 40 + 320 = 365$ odd numbers with distinct digits. Thus the final answer is $738 - 365 = 373$.

20. It will be useful to note first that there are exactly 9000 numbers in this range.

a) Every ninth number is divisible by 9, so the answer is one ninth of 9000 or 1000.

b) Every other number is even, so the answer is one half of 9000 or 4500.

c) We can reason from left to right. There are 9 choices for the first (left-most) digit (since it cannot be a 0), then 9 choices for the second digit (since it cannot equal the first digit), then, in a similar way, 8 choices for the third digit, and 7 choices for the right-most digit. Therefore there are $9 \cdot 9 \cdot 8 \cdot 7 = 4536$ ways to specify such a number. In other words, there are 4536 such numbers. Note that this coincidentally turns out to be almost exactly half of the numbers in the range.

d) Every third number is divisible by 3, so one third of 9000 or 3000 numbers in this range are divisible by 3. The remaining 6000 are not.

e) For this and the next three parts we need to note first that one fifth of the numbers in this range, or 1800 of them, are divisible by 5, and one seventh of them, or 1286 are divisible by 7. [This last calculation is a little more subtle than we let on, since 9000 is not divisible by 7 (the quotient is 1285.71...). But 1001 is divisible by 7, and $1001 + 1285 \cdot 7 = 9996$, so there are indeed 1286, and not 1285 such multiples. (By contrast, in the range 1002 to 10001, inclusive, which also includes 9000 numbers, there are only 1285 multiples of 7.)] We also need to know how many of these numbers are divisible by both 5 and 7, which means divisible by 35. The answer, by the similar reasoning, is 257, namely those multiples from $29 \cdot 35 = 1015$ to $285 \cdot 35 = 9975$. (One more note: We could also have come up with these numbers more formally, using the ideas in Section 6.5, especially Example 2. We could find the number of multiples less than 10,000 and subtract the number of multiples less than 1000.) Now to the problem at hand. The number of numbers divisible by 5 or 7 is the number of numbers divisible by 5, plus the number of numbers divisible by 7, minus (because of having overcounted) the number of numbers divisible by both. So our answer is $1800 + 1286 - 257 = 2829$.

f) Since we just found that 2829 of these numbers are divisible by either 5 or 7, it follows that the rest of them, $9000 - 2829 = 6171$, are not.

g) We noted in the solution to part **(e)** that 1800 numbers are divisible by 5, and 257 of these are also divisible by 7. Therefore $1800 - 257 = 1543$ numbers in our range are divisible by 5 but not by 7.

h) We found this as part of our solution to part **(e)**, namely 257.

22. a) There are 10 ways to choose the first digit, 9 ways to choose the second, and so on; therefore the answer is $10 \cdot 9 \cdot 8 \cdot 7 = 5040$.

b) There are 10 ways to choose each of the first three digits and 5 ways to choose the last; therefore the answer is $10^3 \cdot 5 = 5000$.

c) There are 4 ways to choose the position that is to be different from 9, and 9 ways to choose the digit to go there. Therefore there are $4 \cdot 9 = 36$ such strings.

24. $10^3 26^3 + 26^3 10^3 = 35,152,000$

26. $26^3 10^3 + 26^4 10^2 = 63,273,600$

28. **a)** By the product rule, the answer is $26^8 = 208,827,064,576$.

b) By the product rule, the answer is $26 \cdot 25 \cdot 24 \cdot 23 \cdot 22 \cdot 21 \cdot 20 \cdot 19 = 62,990,928,000$.

c) This is the same as part **(a)**, except that there are only seven slots to fill, so the answer is $26^7 = 8,031,810,176$.

d) This is similar to **(b)**, except that there is only one choice in the first slot, rather than 26, so the answer is $1 \cdot 25 \cdot 24 \cdot 23 \cdot 22 \cdot 21 \cdot 20 \cdot 19 = 2,422,728,000$.

e) This is the same as part **(c)**, except that there are only six slots to fill, so the answer is $26^6 = 308,915,776$.

f) This is the same as part **(e)**; again there are six slots to fill, so the answer is $26^6 = 308,915,776$.

g) This is the same as part **(f)**, except that there are only four slots to fill, so the answer is $26^4 = 456,976$. We are assuming that the question means that the legal strings are BO????BO, where any letters can fill the middle four slots.

h) By part **(f)**, there are 26^6 strings that start with the letters BO in that order. By the same argument, there are 26^6 strings that end that way. By part **(g)**, there are 26^4 strings that both start and end with the letters BO in that order. Therefore by the inclusion–exclusion principle, the answer is $26^6 + 26^6 - 26^4 = 617,374,576$.

30. In each case the answer is n^{10}, where n is the number of elements in the codomain, since there are n choices for a function value for each of the 10 elements in the domain.

a) $2^{10} = 1024$ **b)** $3^{10} = 59,049$ **c)** $4^{10} = 1,048,576$ **d)** $5^{10} = 9,765,625$

32. There are 2^n such functions, since there is a choice of 2 function values for each element of the domain.

34. By our solution to Exercise 35, the answer is $(n+1)^5$ in each case, where n is the number of elements in the codomain.

a) $2^5 = 32$ **b)** $3^5 = 243$ **c)** $6^5 = 7776$ **d)** $10^5 = 100,000$

36. We know that there are 2^{100} subsets in all. Clearly 101 of them do not have more than one element, namely the empty set and the 100 sets consisting of 1 element. Therefore the answer is $2^{100} - 101 \approx 1.3 \times 10^{30}$.

38. **a)** We first place the bride in any of the 6 positions. Then, from left to right in the remaining positions, we choose the other five people to be in the picture; this can be done in $9 \cdot 8 \cdot 7 \cdot 6 \cdot 5 = 15120$ ways. Therefore the answer is $6 \cdot 15120 = 90,720$.

b) We first place the bride in any of the 6 positions, and then place the groom in any of the 5 remaining positions. Then, from left to right in the remaining positions, we choose the other four people to be in the picture; this can be done in $8 \cdot 7 \cdot 6 \cdot 5 = 1680$ ways. Therefore the answer is $6 \cdot 5 \cdot 1680 = 50,400$.

c) From part **(a)** there are 90720 ways for the bride to be in the picture. There are (from part **(b)**) 50400 ways for both the bride and groom to be in the picture. Therefore there are $90720 - 50400 = 40320$ ways for just the bride to be in the picture. Symmetrically, there are 40320 ways for just the groom to be in the picture. Therefore the answer is $40320 + 40320 = 80,640$.

40. There are 2^5 strings that begin with two 0's (since there are two choices for each of the last five bits). Similarly there are 2^4 strings that end with three 1's. Furthermore, there are 2^2 strings that both begin with two 0's and end with three 1's (since only bits 3 and 4 are free to be chosen). By the inclusion–exclusion principle, there are $2^5 + 2^4 - 2^2 = 44$ such strings in all.

42. First we count the number of bit strings of length 10 that contain five consecutive 0's. We will base the count on where the string of five or more consecutive 0's starts. If it starts in the first bit, then the first five bits are all 0's, but there is free choice for the last five bits; therefore there are $2^5 = 32$ such strings. If it starts in the second bit, then the first bit must be a 1, the next five bits are all 0's, but there is free choice for the last four bits; therefore there are $2^4 = 16$ such strings. If it starts in the third bit, then the second bit must be a 1 but the first bit and the last three bits are arbitrary; therefore there are $2^4 = 16$ such strings. Similarly, there are 16 such strings that have the consecutive 0's starting in each of positions four, five, and six. This gives us a total of $32 + 5 \cdot 16 = 112$ strings that contain five consecutive 0's. Symmetrically, there are 112 strings that contain five consecutive 1's. Clearly there are exactly two strings that contain both (0000011111 and 1111100000). Therefore by the inclusion–exclusion principle, the answer is $112 + 112 - 2 = 222$.

44. This is a straightforward application of the inclusion–exclusion principle: $38 + 23 - 7 = 54$ (we need to subtract the 7 double majors counted twice in the sum).

46. We need to compute the number of variable names of length i for $i = 1, 2, \ldots, 8$, and add. A variable name of length i is specified by choosing a first character, which can be done in 53 ways ($2 \cdot 26$ letters and 1 underscore to choose from), and $i - 1$ other characters, each of which can be done in $53 + 10 = 63$ ways. Therefore the answer is

$$\sum_{i=1}^{8} 52 \cdot 63^{i-1} = 52 \cdot \frac{63^8 - 1}{63 - 1} \approx 2.1 \times 10^{14}.$$

48. We draw the tree, with its root at the top. We show a branch for each of the possibilities 0 and 1, for each bit in order, except that we do not allow three consecutive 0's. Since there are 13 leaves, the answer is 13.

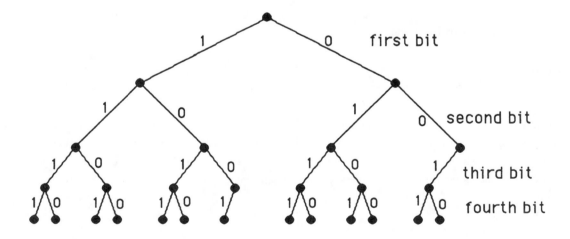

50. The tree is a bit too large to draw in its entirety. We show only half of it, namely the half corresponding to the National League team's having won the first game. By symmetry, the final answer will be twice the number computed with this tree. A branch to the left indicates a win by the National League team; a branch to the right, a win by the American league team. No further branching occurs whenever one team has won four games. Since we see 35 leaves, the answer is 70.

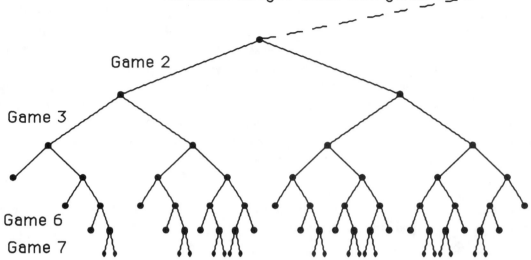

52. a) It is more convenient to branch on bottle size first. Note that there are a different number of branches coming off each of the nodes at the second level. The number of leaves in the tree is 17, which is the answer.

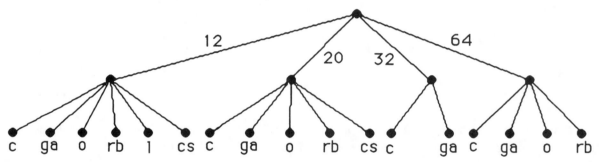

b) We can add the number of different varieties for each of the sizes. The 12-ounce bottle has 6, the 20-ounce bottle has 5, the 32-once bottle has 2, and the 64-ounce bottle has 4. Therefore $6 + 5 + 2 + 4 = 17$ different types of bottles need to be stocked.

54. There are 2^n lines in the truth table, since each of the n propositions can have 2 truth values. Each line can be filled in with T or F, so there are a total of 2^{2^n} possibilities.

56. We want to show that a procedure consisting of m tasks can be done in $n_1 n_2 \cdots n_m$ ways, if the ith task can be done in n_i ways. The product rule stated in the text is the base case, $m = 2$. Assume the inductive hypothesis. Then to do the procedure we have to do each of the first m tasks, which by the inductive hypothesis can be done in $n_1 n_2 \cdots n_m$ ways, and then the $(m + 1)^{\text{th}}$ task, so there are $(n_1 n_2 \cdots n_m) n_{m+1}$ possibilities, as desired.

58. a) The largest value of TOTAL LENGTH is $2^{16} - 1$, since this would be the number represented by a string of 16 1s. So the maximum length of a datagram is 65,535 octets (or bytes).

b) The largest value of HLEN is $2^4 - 1 = 15$, since this would be the number represented by a string of four 1s. So the maximum length of a header is 15 32-bit blocks. Since there are four 8-bit octets (or bytes) in a block, the maximum length of the header is $4 \cdot 15 = 60$ octets.

c) We saw in part **(a)** that the maximum total length is 65,535 octets. If at least 20 of these must be devoted to the header, the data area can be at most 65,515 octets long.

d) There are $2^8 = 256$ different octets, since each bit of an octet can be 0 or 1. In part **(c)** we saw that the data area could be at most 65,515 octets long. So the answer is 256^{65515}, which is a huge number (approximately 7×10^{157775}, according to a computer algebra system).

SECTION 4.2   The Pigeonhole Principle

2. This follows from the pigeonhole principle, with $k = 26$.

4. We assume that the woman does not replace the balls after drawing them.

a) There are two colors: these are the pigeonholes. We want to know the least number of pigeons needed to insure that at least one of the pigeonholes contains three pigeons. By the generalized pigeonhole principle, the answer is 5. If five balls are selected, at least $\lceil 5/2 \rceil = 3$ must have the same color. On the other hand four balls is not enough, because two might be red and two might be blue. Note that the number of balls was irrelevant (assuming that it was at least 5).

b) She needs to select 13 balls in order to insure at least three blue ones. If she does so, then at most 10 of them are red, so at least three are blue. On the other hand, if she selects 12 or fewer balls, then 10 of them could be red, and she might not get her three blue balls. This time the number of balls did matter.

6. There are only d possible remainders when an integer is divided by d, namely 0, 1, ..., $d - 1$. By the pigeonhole principle, if we have $d + 1$ remainders, then at least two must be the same.

8. This is just a restatement of the pigeonhole principle, with $k = |T|$.

10. The midpoint of the segment whose endpoints are (a, b) and (c, d) is $((a + c)/2, (b + d)/2)$. We are concerned only with integer values of the original coordinates. Clearly the coordinates of these fractions will be integers as well if and only if a and c have the same parity (both odd or both even) and b and d have the same parity. Thus what matters in this problem is the parities of the coordinates. There are four possible pairs of parities: (odd, odd), (odd, even), (even, odd), and (even, even). Since we are given five points, the pigeonhole principle guarantees that at least two of them will have the same pair of parities. The midpoint of the segment joining these two points will therefore have integer coordinates.

12. This is similar in spirit to Exercise 10. Working modulo 5 there are 25 pairs: $(0, 0)$, $(0, 1)$, ..., $(4, 4)$. Thus we could have 25 ordered pairs of integers (a, b) such that no two of them were equal when reduced modulo 5. The pigeonhole principle, however, guarantees that if we have 26 such pairs, then at least two of them will have the same coordinates, modulo 5.

14. a) We can group the first ten positive integers into five subsets of two integers each, each subset adding up to 11: $\{1, 10\}$, $\{2, 9\}$, $\{3, 8\}$, $\{4, 7\}$, and $\{5, 6\}$. If we select seven integers from this set, then by the pigeonhole principle at least two of them come from the same subset. Furthermore, if we forget about these two in the same group, then there are five more integers and four groups; again the pigeonhole principle guarantees two integers in the same group. This gives us two pairs of integers, each pair from the same group. In each case these two integers have a sum of 11, as desired.

b) No. The set $\{1, 2, 3, 4, 5, 6\}$ has only 5 and 6 from the same group, so the only pair with sum 11 is 5 and 6.

16. We can apply the pigeonhole principle by grouping the numbers cleverly into pairs (subsets) that add up to 16, namely $\{1, 15\}$, $\{3, 13\}$, $\{5, 11\}$, and $\{7, 9\}$. If we select five numbers from the set $\{1, 3, 5, 7, 9, 11, 13, 15\}$, then at least two of them must fall within the same subset, since there are only four subsets. Two numbers in the same subset are the desired pair that add up to 16. We also need to point out that choosing four numbers is not enough, since we could choose $\{1, 3, 5, 7\}$, and no pair of them add up to more than 12.

18. a) If not, then there would be 4 or fewer male students and 4 or fewer female students, so there would be $4 + 4 = 8$ or fewer students in all, contradicting the assumption that there are 9 students in the class.
 b) If not, then there would be 2 or fewer male students and 6 or fewer female students, so there would be $2 + 6 = 8$ or fewer students in all, contradicting the assumption that there are 9 students in the class.

20. One maximal length increasing sequence is $5, 7, 10, 15, 21$. One maximal length decreasing sequence is $22, 7, 3$. See Exercise 23 for an algorithm.

22. This follows immediately from Theorem 3, with $n = 10$.

24. Let the people be A, B, C, D, and E. Suppose the following pairs are friends: $A-B$, $B-C$, $C-D$, $D-E$, and $E-A$. The other five pairs are enemies. In this example, there are no three mutual friends and no three mutual enemies.

26. Let A be one of the people. She must have either 10 friends or 10 enemies, since if there were 9 or fewer of each, then that would account for at most 18 of the 19 other people. Without loss of generality assume that A has 10 friends. By Exercise 25 there are either 4 mutual enemies among these 10 people, or 3 mutual friends. In the former case we have our desired set of 4 mutual enemies; in the latter case, these 3 people together with A form the desired set of 4 mutual friends.

28. This is clear by symmetry, since we can just interchange the notions of friends and enemies.

30. There are 99,999,999 possible positive salaries less than one million dollars, i.e., from \$0.01 to \$999,999.99. By the pigeonhole principle, if there were more than this many people with positive salaries less than one million dollars, then at least two of them must have the same salary.

32. Let $K(x)$ be the number of other computers that computer x is connected to. The possible values for $K(x)$ are $1, 2, 3, 4, 5$. Since there are 6 computers, the pigeonhole principle guarantees that at least two of the values $K(x)$ are the same, which is what we wanted to prove.

34. This is similar to Example 9. Label the computers C_1 through C_8, and label the printers P_1 through P_4. If we connect C_k to P_k for $k = 1, 2, 3, 4$ and connect each of the computers C_5 through C_8 to *all* the printers, then we have used a total of $4 + 4 \cdot 4 = 20$ cables. Clearly this is sufficient, because if computers C_1 through C_4 need printers, then they can use the printers with the same subscripts, and if any computers with higher subscripts need a printer instead of one or more of these, then they can use the printers that are not being used, since they are connected to all the printers. Now we must show that 19 cables are not enough. Since there are 19 cables and 4 printers, the average number of computers per printer is $19/4$, which is less than 5. Therefore some printer must be connected to fewer than 5 computers (the average of a set of numbers cannot be bigger than each of the numbers in the set). That means it is connected to 4 or fewer computers, so there are at least 4 computers that are not connected to it. If those 4 computers all needed a printer simultaneously, then they would be out of luck, since they are connected to at most the 3 other printers.

36. Let $K(x)$ be the number of other people at the party that person x knows. The possible values for $K(x)$ are $0, 1, \ldots, n - 1$, where $n \geq 2$ is the number of people at the party. We cannot apply the pigeonhole principle directly, since there are n pigeons and n pigeonholes. However, it is impossible for both 0 and $n - 1$ to be in the range of K, since if one person knows everybody else, then nobody can know no one else (we assume that "knowing" is symmetric). Therefore the range of K has at most $n - 1$ elements, whereas the domain has n elements, so K is not one-to-one, precisely what we wanted to prove.

38. a) The solution of Exercise 37, with 24 replaced by 2 and 149 replaced by 127, tells us that the statement is true.

b) The solution of Exercise 37, with 24 replaced by 23 and 149 replaced by 148, tells us that the statement is true.

c) We begin in a manner similar to the solution of Exercise 37. Look at $a_1, a_2, \ldots, a_{75}, a_1 + 25, \ldots, a_{75} + 25$, where a_i is the total number of matches played up through and including hour i. Then $1 \leq a_1 < a_2 < \cdots < a_{75} \leq 125$, and $26 \leq a_1 + 25 < a_2 + 25 < \cdots < a_{75} + 25 \leq 150$. Now either these 150 numbers are precisely all the number from 1 to 150, or else by the pigeonhole principle we get, as in Exercise 37, $a_i = a_j + 25$ for some i and j and we are done. In the former case, however, since each of the numbers $a_i + 25$ is greater than or equal to 26, the numbers $1, 2, \ldots, 25$ must all appear among the a_i's. But since the a_i's are increasing, the only way this can happen is if $a_1 = 1$, $a_2 = 2$, $\ldots$, $a_{25} = 25$. Thus there were exactly 25 matches in the first 25 hours.

d) We need a different approach for this part, an approach, incidentally, that works for many numbers besides 30 in this setting. Let $a_1, a_2, \ldots, a_{75}$ be as before, and note that $1 \leq a_1 < a_2 < \cdots < a_{75} \leq 125$. By the pigeonhole principle two of the numbers among $a_1, a_2, \ldots, a_{31}$ are congruent modulo 30. If they differ by 30, then we have our solution. Otherwise they differ by 60 or more, so $a_{31} \geq 61$. Similarly, among a_{31} through a_{61}, either we find a solution, or two numbers must differ by 60 or more; therefore we can assume that $a_{61} \geq 121$. But this means that $a_{66} \geq 126$, a contradiction.

40. Look at the pigeonholes $\{1000, 1001\}$, $\{1002, 1003\}$, $\{1004, 1005\}$, $\ldots$, $\{1098, 1099\}$. There are clearly 50 sets in this list. By the pigeonhole principle, if we have 51 numbers in the range from 1000 to 1099 inclusive, then at least two of them must come from the same set. These are the desired two consecutive house numbers.

42. Suppose this statement were not true. Then for each i, the ith box contains at most $n_i - 1$ objects. Adding, we have at most $(n_1 - 1) + (n_2 - 1) + \cdots + (n_t - 1) = n_1 + n_2 + \cdots + n_t - t$ objects in all, contradicting the fact that there were $n_1 + n_2 + \cdots + n_t - t + 1$ objects in all. Therefore the statement must be true.

SECTION 4.3   Permutations and Combinations

2. $P(7, 7) = 7! = 5040$

4. There are 10 combinations and 60 permutations. We list them in the following way. Each combination is listed, without punctuation, in increasing order, followed by the five other permutations involving the same numbers, in parentheses, without punctuation.

123 (132 213 231 312 321) 124 (142 214 241 412 421) 125 (152 215 251 512 521)

134 (143 314 341 413 431) 135 (153 315 351 513 531) 145 (154 415 451 514 541)

234 (243 324 342 423 432) 235 (253 325 352 523 532)

245 (254 425 452 524 542) 345 (354 435 453 534 543)

6. a) $C(5,1) = 5$ **b)** $C(5,3) = C(5,2) = 5 \cdot 4/2 = 10$ **c)** $C(8,4) = 8 \cdot 7 \cdot 6 \cdot 5/(4 \cdot 3 \cdot 2) = 70$
d) $C(8,8) = 1$ **e)** $C(8,0) = 1$ **f)** $C(12,6) = 12 \cdot 11 \cdot 10 \cdot 9 \cdot 8 \cdot 7/(6 \cdot 5 \cdot 4 \cdot 3 \cdot 2) = 924$

8. $P(5,5) = 5! = 120$

10. $P(6,6) = 6! = 720$

12. a) To specify a bit string of length 12 that contains exactly three 1's, we simply need to choose the three positions that contain the 1's. There are $C(12,3) = 220$ ways to do that.
b) To contain at most three 1's means to contain three 1's, two 1's, one 1, or no 1's. Reasoning as in part **(a)**, we see that there are $C(12,3) + C(12,2) + C(12,1) + C(12,0) = 220 + 66 + 12 + 1 = 299$ such strings.
c) To contain at least three 1's means to contain three 1's, four 1's, five 1's, six 1's, seven 1's, eight 1's, nine 1's, 10 1's, 11 1's, or 12 1's. We could reason as in part **(b)**, but we would have too many numbers to add. A simpler approach would be to figure out the number of ways not to have at least three 1's (i.e., to have two 1's, one 1, or no 1's) and then subtract that from 2^{12}, the total number of bit strings of length 12. This way we get $4096 - (66 + 12 + 1) = 4017$.
d) To have an equal number of 0's and 1's in this case means to have six 1's. Therefore the answer is $C(12,6) = 924$.

14. $C(99,2) = 99 \cdot 98/2 = 4851$

16. We need to compute $C(10,1) + C(10,3) + C(10,5) + C(10,7) + C(10,9) = 10 + 120 + 252 + 120 + 10 = 512$. (In the next section we will see that there are just as many subsets with an odd number of elements as there are subsets with an even number of elements (Exercise 31 in Section 4.4). Since there are $2^{10} = 1024$ subsets in all, the answer is $1024/2 = 512$, in agreement with our computation.)

18. a) Each flip can be either heads or tails, so there are $2^8 = 256$ possible outcomes.
b) To specify an outcome that has exactly three heads, we simply need to choose the three flips that came up heads. There are $C(8,3) = 56$ such outcomes.
c) To contain at least three heads means to contain three heads, four heads, five heads, six heads, seven heads, or eight heads. Reasoning as in part **(b)**, we see that there are $C(8,3) + C(8,4) + C(8,5) + C(8,6) + C(8,7) + C(8,8) = 56 + 70 + 56 + 28 + 8 + 1 = 219$ such outcomes. We could also subtract from 256 the number of ways to get two of fewer heads, namely $28 + 8 + 1 = 37$. Since $256 - 37 = 219$, we obtain the same answer using this alternative method.
d) To have an equal number of heads and tails in this case means to have four heads. Therefore the answer is $C(8,4) = 70$.

20. a) There are $C(10,3)$ ways to choose the positions for the 0's, and that is the only choice to be made, so the answer is $C(10,3) = 120$.
b) There are more 0's than 1's if there are fewer than five 1's. Using the same reasoning as in part **(a)**, together with the sum rule, we obtain the answer $C(10,0) + C(10,1) + C(10,2) + C(10,3) + C(10,4) = 1 + 10 + 45 + 120 + 210 = 386$. Alternatively, by symmetry, half of all cases in which there are not five 0's have more 0's than 1's; therefore the answer is $(2^{10} - C(10,5)/2 = (1024 - 252)/2 = 386$.
c) We want the number of bit strings with 7, 8, 9, or 10 1's. By the same reasoning as above, there are $C(10,7) + C(10,8) + C(10,9) + C(10,10) = 120 + 45 + 10 + 1 = 176$ such strings.
d) If a string does not have at least three 1's, then it has 0, 1, or 2 1's. There are $C(10,0) + C(10,1) + C(10,2) = 1 + 10 + 45 = 56$ such strings. There are $2^{10} = 1024$ strings in all. Therefore there are $1024 - 56 = 968$ strings with at least three 1's.

22. a) If ED is to be a substring, then we can think of that block of letters as one superletter, and the problem is to count permutations of seven items—the letters A, B, C, F, G, and H, and the superletter ED. Therefore the answer is $P(7,7) = 7! = 5040$.

b) Reasoning as in part **(a)**, we see that the answer is $P(6,6) = 6! = 720$.

c) As in part **(a)**, we glue BA into one item and glue FGH into one item. Therefore we need to permute five items, and there are $P(5,5) = 5! = 120$ ways to do it.

d) This is similar to part **(c)**. Glue AB into one item, glue DE into one item, and glue GH into one item, producing five items, so the answer is $P(5,5) = 5! = 120$.

e) If both CAB and BED are substrings, then $CABED$ has to be a substring. So we are really just permuting four items: $CABED$, F, G, and H. Therefore the answer is $P(4,4) = 4! = 24$.

f) There are no permutations with both of these substrings, since B cannot be followed by both C and F at the same time.

24. First position the women relative to each other. Since there are 10 women, there are $P(10,10)$ ways to do this. This creates 11 slots where a man (but not more than one man) may stand: in front of the first woman, between the first and second women, ..., between the ninth and tenth women, and behind the tenth woman. We need to choose six of these positions, in order, for the first through six man to occupy (order matters, because the men are distinct people). This can be done is $P(11,6)$ ways. Therefore the answer is $P(10,10) \cdot P(11,6) = 10! \cdot 11!/5! = 1{,}207{,}084{,}032{,}000$.

26. a) This is just a matter of choosing 10 players from the group of 13, since we are not told to worry about what positions they play; therefore the answer is $C(13,10) = 286$.

b) This is the same as part **(a)**, except that we need to worry about the order in which the choices are made, since there are 10 distinct positions to be filled. Therefore the answer is $P(13,10) = 13!/3! = 1{,}037{,}836{,}800$.

c) There is only one way to choose the 10 players without choosing a woman, since there are exactly 10 men. Therefore (using part **(a)**) there are $286 - 1 = 285$ ways to choose the players if at least one of them must be a woman.

28. We are just being asked for the number of strings of T's and F's of length 40 with exactly 17 T's. The only choice is which 17 of the 40 positions are to have the T's, so the answer is $C(40,17) \approx 8.9 \times 10^{10}$.

30. a) There are $C(16,5)$ ways to select a committee if there are no restrictions. There are $C(9,5)$ ways to select a committee from just the 9 men. Therefore there are $C(16,5) - C(9,5) = 4368 - 126 = 4242$ committees with at least one woman.

b) There are $C(16,5)$ ways to select a committee if there are no restrictions. There are $C(9,5)$ ways to select a committee from just the 9 men. There are $C(7,5)$ ways to select a committee from just the 7 men. These two possibilities do not overlap, since there are no ways to select a committee containing neither men nor women. Therefore there are $C(16,5) - C(9,5) - C(7,5) = 4368 - 126 - 21 = 4221$ committees with at least one woman and at least one man.

32. a) The only reasonable way to do this is by subtracting from the number of strings with no restrictions the number of strings that do not contain the letter a. The answer is $26^6 - 25^6 = 308915776 - 244140625 = 64{,}775{,}151$.

b) If our string is to contain both of these letters, then we need to subtract from the total number of strings the number that fail to contain one or the other (or both) of these letters. As in part **(a)**, 25^6 strings fail to contain an a; similarly 25^6 fail to contain a b. This is overcounting, however, since 24^6 fail to contain both of these letters. Therefore there are $25^6 + 25^6 - 24^6$ strings that fail to contain at least one of these letters. Therefore the answer is $26^6 - (25^6 + 25^6 - 24^6) = 308915776 - (244140625 + 244140625 - 191102976) = 11{,}737{,}502$.

c) First choose the position for the a; this can be done in 5 ways, since the b must follow it. There are four remaining positions, and these can be filled in $P(24,4)$ ways, since there are 24 letters left (no repetitions being allowed this time). Therefore the answer is $5P(24,4) = 1{,}275{,}120$.

d) First choose the positions for the a and b; this can be done in $C(6,2)$ ways, since once we pick two positions, we put the a in the left-most and the b in the other. There are four remaining positions, and these can be filled in $P(24,4)$ ways, since there are 24 letters left (no repetitions being allowed this time). Therefore the answer is $C(6,2)P(24,4) = 3{,}825{,}360$.

34. Probably the best way to do this is just to break it down into the three cases by sex. There are $C(15,6)$ ways to choose the committee to be composed only of women, $C(15,5)C(10,1)$ ways if there are to be five women and one man, and $C(15,4)C(10,2)$ ways if there are to be four women and two men. Therefore the answer is $C(15,6) + C(15,5)C(10,1) + C(15,4)C(10,2) = 5005 + 30030 + 61425 = 96{,}460$.

36. Glue two 1's to the right of each 0, giving us a collection of nine tokens: five 011's and four 1's. We are asked for the number of strings consisting of these tokens. All that is involved is choosing the positions for the 1's among the nine positions in the string, so the answer is $C(9,4) = 126$.

38. $C(45,3) \cdot C(57,4) \cdot C(69,5) = 14190 \cdot 395010 \cdot 11238513 \approx 6.3 \times 10^{16}$

40. We might as well assume that the first person sits in the northernmost seat. Then there are $P(5,5)$ ways to seat the remaining people, since they form a permutation reading clockwise from the first person. Therefore the answer is $5! = 120$.

42. We can solve this problem by breaking it down into cases depending on the number of ties. There are five cases. (1) If there are no ties, then there are clearly $P(4,4) = 24$ possible ways for the horses to finish. (2) Assume that there are two horses that tie, but the others have distinct finishes. There are $C(4,2) = 6$ ways to choose the horses to be tied; then there are $P(3,3) = 6$ ways to determine the order of finish for the three groups (the pair and the two single horses). Thus there are $6 \cdot 6 = 36$ ways for this to happen. (3) There might be two groups of two horses that are tied. There are $C(4,2) = 6$ ways to choose the winners (and the other two horses are the losers). (4) There might be a group of three horses all tied. There are $C(4,3) = 4$ ways to choose which these horses will be, and then two ways for the race to end (the tied horses win or they lose), so there are $4 \cdot 2 = 8$ possibilities. (5) There is only one way for all the horses to tie. Putting this all together, the answer is $24 + 36 + 6 + 8 + 1 = 75$.

44. a) The complicating factor here is the rule that the penalty kick round (or "group") is over once one team has clinched a victory. For example, if the first team to shoot has missed all of its first four shots and the other team has made two of its first three shots, then the round is over after only seven kicks. There are $2^{10} = 1024$ possible scenarios without this rule (and without worrying yet about whether the score is tied at the end of this round), but it seems rather tedious and dangerous (in the sense of your being likely to make a mistake and leave something out) to try to analyze the more complicated situation by writing out all the possibilities by hand. (This is not impossible, though, and the author has obtained the correct answer in this way.) Rather than do this, one can write a computer program to simulate the situation and do the counting. The result is that there are 672 possible scoring scenarios for a round of penalty kicks, including the possibility that the score is still tied at the end of that round.

Next we need to count the number of ways for the score to end up tied at the end of the round. For this to happen, both teams must score p points, where p is some integer between 0 and 5, inclusive. The scoring scenario is determined by the positions of the kickers who did the scoring. There are $C(5,p)$ ways to choose these positions for each team, or $C(5,p)^2$ ways in all. We need to sum this over the values of p from 0 to 5.

The sum is 252. So there are 252 ways for the score to end up tied. We already noted in the paragraph above that there are 672 different scoring scenarios, so there are $672 - 252 = 420$ scenarios in which the score is not tied. This answers the question for this part of the exercise.

b) This is easy after what we've found above. There are 252 ways for the score to be tied at the end of the first group of penalty kicks, and there are 420 ways for the game to be settled in the second group. So there are $252 \cdot 420 = 105,840$ ways for the game to end during the second round.

c) We have already seen that there are 420 ways for the game to end in the first round, and 105,840 more ways for it to end in the second round. In order for it to go into a sudden death period, the first two rounds must have ended tied, which can happen in $420 \cdot 420 = 176,400$ ways. Thereafter, the game can end after two more kicks in 2 ways (either team can make their kick and have the other team miss theirs), after four more kicks in $2 \cdot 2 = 4$ ways (the first pair of kicks must have the same result, either both made or both missed, and then either team can win), after six more kicks in $2^2 \cdot 2 = 8$ ways (the first two pairs of kicks must have the same results, and then either team can win), after eight more kicks in 16 ways, and after ten more kicks in 32 ways. Thus there are $2 + 4 + 8 + 16 + 32 = 62$ ways for the sudden death round to end within ten kicks. This needs to be multiplied by the 176,400 ways we can reach sudden death, for a total of 10,936,800 scoring scenarios. So the answer to this last question is $420 + 105840 + 10936800 = 11,043,060$.

SECTION 4.4   Binomial Coefficients

2. a) When $(x+y)^5 = (x+y)(x+y)(x+y)(x+y)(x+y)$ is expanded, all products of a term in the first sum, a term in the second sum, a term in the third sum, a term in the fourth sum, and a term in the fifth sum are added. Terms of the form x^5, x^4y, x^3y^2, x^2y^3, xy^4 and y^5 arise. To obtain a term of the form x^5, an x must be chosen in each of the sums, and this can be done in only one way. Thus, the x^5 term in the product has a coefficient of 1. (We can think of this coefficient as $\binom{5}{5}$.) To obtain a term of the form x^4y, an x must be chosen in four of the five sums (and consequently a y in the other sum). Hence, the number of such terms is the number of 4-combinations of five objects, namely $\binom{5}{4} = 5$. Similarly, the number of terms of the form x^3y^2 is the number of ways to pick three of the five sums to obtain x's (and consequently take a y from each of the other two factors). This can be done in $\binom{5}{3} = 10$ ways. By the same reasoning there are $\binom{5}{2} = 10$ ways to obtain the x^2y^3 terms, $\binom{5}{1} = 5$ ways to obtain the xy^4 terms, and only one way (which we can think of as $\binom{5}{0}$) to obtain a y^5 term. Consequently, the product is $x^5 + 5x^4y + 10x^3y^2 + 10x^2y^3 + 5xy^4 + y^5$.

b) This is explained in Example 2. The expansion is $\binom{5}{0}x^5 + \binom{5}{1}x^4y + \binom{5}{2}x^3y^2 + \binom{5}{3}x^2y^3 + \binom{5}{4}xy^4 + \binom{5}{5}y^5 = x^5 + 5x^4y + 10x^3y^2 + 10x^2y^3 + 5xy^4 + y^5$. Note that it does not matter whether we think of the bottom of the binomial coefficient expression as corresponding to the exponent on x, as we did in part **(a)**, or the exponent on y, as we do here.

4. $\binom{13}{8} = 1287$

6. $\binom{11}{7}1^4 = 330$

8. $\binom{17}{9}3^8 2^9 = 24310 \cdot 6561 \cdot 512 = 81,662,929,920$

10. By the binomial theorem, the typical term in this expansion is $\binom{100}{j}x^{100-j}(1/x)^j$, which can be rewritten as $\binom{100}{j}x^{100-2j}$. As j runs from 0 to 100, the exponent runs from 100 down to -100 in decrements of 2. If we let k denote the exponent, then solving $k = 100 - 2j$ for j we obtain $j = (100 - k)/2$. Thus the values of k for which x^k appears in this expansion are -100, -98, ..., -2, 0, 2, 4, ..., 100, and for such values of k the coefficient is $\binom{100}{(100-k)/2}$.

12. We just add adjacent numbers in this row to obtain the next row (starting and ending with 1, of course):

$$1 \quad 11 \quad 55 \quad 165 \quad 330 \quad 462 \quad 462 \quad 330 \quad 165 \quad 55 \quad 11 \quad 1$$

14. Using the factorial formulas for computing binomial coefficients, we see that $\binom{n}{k-1} = \frac{k}{n-k+1}\binom{n}{k}$. If $k \le n/2$, then $\frac{k}{n-k+1} < 1$, so the "less than" signs are correct. Similarly, if $k > n/2$, then $\frac{k}{n-k+1} > 1$, so the "greater than" signs are correct. The middle equality is Corollary 1 in Section 4.3, since $\lfloor n/2 \rfloor + \lceil n/2 \rceil = n$. The equalities at the ends are clear.

16. a) By Exercise 14, we know that $\binom{n}{\lfloor n/2 \rfloor}$ is the largest of the $n-1$ binomial coefficients $\binom{n}{1}$ through $\binom{n}{n-1}$. Therefore it is at least as large as their average, which is $(2^n - 2)/(n-1)$. But since $2n \le 2^n$ for $n \ge 2$, it follows that $(2^n - 2)/(n-1) \ge 2^n/n$, and the proof is complete.
b) This follows from part **(a)** by replacing n with $2n$ when $n \ge 2$, and it is immediate when $n = 1$.

18. The numeral 11 in base b represents the number $b + 1$. Therefore the fourth power of this number is $b^4 + 4b^3 + 6b^2 + 4b + 1$, where the binomial coefficients can be read from Pascal's triangle. As long as $b \ge 7$, these coefficients are single digit numbers in base b, so this is the meaning of the numeral $(14641)_b$. In short, the numeral formed by concatenating the symbols in the fourth row of Pascal's triangle is the answer.

20. It is easy to see that both sides equal

$$\frac{(n-1)!n!(n+1)!}{(k-1)!k!(k+1)!(n-k-1)!(n-k)!(n-k+1)!}.$$

22. a) Suppose that we have a set with n elements, and we wish to choose a subset A with k elements and another, disjoint, subset with $r - k$ elements. The left-hand side gives us the number of ways to do this, namely the product of the number of ways to choose the r elements that are to go into one or the other of the subsets and the number of ways to choose which of *these* elements are to go into the first of the subsets. The right-hand side gives us the number of ways to do this as well, namely the product of the number of ways to choose the first subset and the number of ways to choose the second subset from the elements that remain.
b) On the one hand,

$$\binom{n}{r}\binom{r}{k} = \frac{n!}{r!(n-r)!} \cdot \frac{r!}{k!(r-k)!} = \frac{n!}{k!(n-r)!(r-k)!},$$

and on the other hand

$$\binom{n}{k}\binom{n-k}{r-k} = \frac{n!}{k!(n-k)!} \cdot \frac{(n-k)!}{(r-k)!(n-r)!} = \frac{n!}{k!(n-r)!(r-k)!}.$$

24. We know that

$$\binom{p}{k} = \frac{p!}{k!(p-k)!}.$$

Clearly p divides the numerator. On the other hand, p cannot divide the denominator, since the prime factorizations of these factorials contains only numbers less than p. Therefore the factor p does not cancel when this fraction is reduced to lowest terms (i.e., to a whole number), so p divides $\binom{p}{k}$.

26. First, use Exercise 25 to rewrite the right-hand side of this identity as $\binom{2n}{n+1}$. We give a combinatorial proof, showing that both sides count the number of ways to choose from collection of n men and n women, a subset that has one more man than woman. For the left-hand side, we note that this subset must have k men and $k-1$ women for some k between 1 and n, inclusive. For the (modified) right-hand side, choose any set of $n+1$ people from this collection of n men and n women; the desired subset is the set of men chosen and the women left behind.

28. a) To choose 2 people from a set of n men and n women, we can either choose 2 men ($\binom{n}{2}$ ways to do so) or 2 women ($\binom{n}{2}$ ways to do so) or one of each sex ($n \cdot n$ ways to do so). Therefore the right-hand side counts the number of ways to do this (by the sum rule). The left-hand side counts the same thing, since we are simply choosing 2 people from $2n$ people.

b) $2\binom{n}{2} + n^2 = n(n-1) + n^2 = 2n^2 - n = n(2n-1) = 2n(2n-1)/2 = \binom{2n}{2}$

30. We follow the hint. The number of ways to choose this committee is the number of ways to choose the chairman from among the n mathematicians (n ways) times the number of ways to choose the other $n-1$ members of the committee from among the other $2n-1$ professors. This gives us $n\binom{2n-1}{n-1}$, the expression on the right-hand side. On the other hand, for each k from 1 to n, we can have our committee consist of k mathematicians and $n-k$ computer scientists. There are $\binom{n}{k}$ ways to choose the mathematicians, k ways to choose the chairman from among these, and $\binom{n}{n-k}$ ways to choose the computer scientists. Since this last quantity equals $\binom{n}{k}$, we obtain the expression on the left-hand side of the identity.

32. For $n = 0$ we want

$$(x+y)^0 = \sum_{j=0}^{0} \binom{0}{j} x^{0-j} y^j = \binom{0}{0} x^0 y^0 \,,$$

which is true, since $1 = 1$. Assume the inductive hypothesis. Then we have

$$(x+y)^{n+1} = (x+y) \sum_{j=0}^{n} \binom{n}{j} x^{n-j} y^j$$

$$= \sum_{j=0}^{n} \binom{n}{j} x^{n+1-j} y^j + \sum_{j=0}^{n} \binom{n}{j} x^{n-j} y^{j+1}$$

$$= \sum_{k=0}^{n} \binom{n}{k} x^{n+1-k} y^k + \sum_{k=1}^{n+1} \binom{n}{k-1} x^{n+1-k} y^k$$

$$= \binom{n}{0} x^{n+1} + \left(\sum_{k=1}^{n} [\binom{n}{k} + \binom{n}{k-1}] x^{n+1-k} y^k \right) + \binom{n}{n} y^{n+1}$$

$$= x^{n+1} + \sum_{k=1}^{n} \binom{n+1}{k} x^{n+1-k} y^k + y^{n+1}$$

$$= \sum_{k=0}^{n+1} \binom{n+1}{k} x^{n+1-k} y^k \,,$$

as desired. The key point was the use of Pascal's identity to simplify the expression in brackets in the fourth line of this calculation.

34. By Exercise 33 there are $\binom{n-k+k}{k} = \binom{n}{k}$ paths from $(0,0)$ to $(n-k,k)$ and $\binom{k+n-k}{n-k} = \binom{n}{n-k}$ paths from $(0,0)$ to $(k, n-k)$. By symmetry, these two quantities must be the same (flip the picture around the 45° line).

36. A path ending up at $(n+1-k, k)$ must have made its last step either upward or to the right. If the last step was made upward, then it came from $(n+1-k, k-1)$; if it was made to the right, then it came from $(n-k, k)$. The path cannot have passed through both of these points. Therefore the number of paths to $(n+1-k, k)$ is the sum of the number of paths to $(n+1-k, k-1)$ and the number of paths to $(n-k, k)$. By Exercise 33 this tells us that $\binom{n+1-k+k}{k} = \binom{n+1-k+k-1}{k-1} + \binom{n-k+k}{k}$, which simplifies to $\binom{n+1}{k} = \binom{n}{k-1} + \binom{n}{k}$, Pascal's identity.

38. We follow the hint, first noting that we can start the summation with $k = 1$, since the term with $k = 0$ is 0. The left-hand side counts the number of ways to choose a subset as described in the hint by breaking it down by the number of elements in the subset; note that there are k ways to choose each of the distinguished elements if the subset has size k. For the right-hand side, first note that $n(n+1)2^{n-2} = n(n-1+2)2^{n-2} = n(n-1)2^{n-2} + n2^{n-1}$. The first term counts the number of ways to make this choice if the two distinguished elements are different (choose them, then choose any subset of the remaining elements to be the rest of the subset). The second term counts the number of ways to make this choice if the two distinguished elements are the same (choose it, then choose any subset of the remaining elements to be the rest of the subset). Note that this works even if $n = 1$.

SECTION 4.5   Generalized Permutations and Combinations

2. There are 5 choices each of 5 times, so the answer is $5^5 = 3125$.

4. There are 6 choices each of 7 times, so the answer is $6^7 = 279{,}936$.

6. By Theorem 2 the answer is $C(3 + 5 - 1, 5) = C(7, 5) = C(7, 2) = 21$.

8. By Theorem 2 the answer is $C(21 + 12 - 1, 12) = C(32, 12) = 225{,}792{,}840$.

10. a) $C(6 + 12 - 1, 12) = C(17, 12) = 6188$ **b)** $C(6 + 36 - 1, 36) = C(41, 36) = 749{,}398$
c) If we first pick the two of each kind, then we have picked $2 \cdot 6 = 12$ croissants. This leaves one dozen left to pick without restriction, so the answer is the same as in part **(a)**, namely $C(6 + 12 - 1, 12) = C(17, 12) = 6188$.
d) We first compute the number of ways to violate the restriction, by choosing at least three broccoli croissants. This can be done in $C(6 + 21 - 1, 21) = C(26, 21) = 65780$ ways, since once we have picked the three broccoli croissants there are 21 left to pick without restriction. Since there are $C(6 + 24 - 1, 24) = C(29, 24) = 118755$ ways to pick 24 croissants without any restriction, there must be $118755 - 65780 = 52{,}975$ ways to choose two dozen croissants with no more than two broccoli.
e) Eight croissants are specified, so this problem is the same as choosing $24 - 8 = 16$ croissants without restriction, which can be done in $C(6 + 16 - 1, 16) = C(21, 16) = 20{,}349$ ways.
f) First let us include all the lower bound restrictions. If we choose the required 9 croissants, then there are $24 - 9 = 15$ left to choose, and if there were no restriction on the broccoli croissants then there would be $C(6 + 15 - 1, 15) = C(20, 15) = 15504$ ways to make the selections. If in addition we were to violate the broccoli restriction by choosing at least four broccoli croissants, there would be $C(6 + 11 - 1, 11) = C(16, 11) = 4368$ choices. Therefore the number of ways to make the selection without violating the restriction is $15504 - 4368 - 11{,}136$.

12. There are 5 things to choose from, repetitions allowed, and we want to choose 20 things, order not important. Therefore by Theorem 2 the answer is $C(5 + 20 - 1, 20) = C(24, 20) = C(24, 4) = 10{,}626$.

14. By Theorem 2 the answer is $C(4 + 17 - 1, 17) = C(20, 17) = C(20, 3) = 1140$.

16. a) We require each $x_i \geq 2$. This uses up 12 of the 29 total required, so the problem is the same as finding the number of solutions to $x_1' + x_2' + x_3' + x_4' + x_5' + x_6' = 17$ with each x_i' a nonnegative integer. The number of solutions is therefore $C(6 + 17 - 1, 17) = C(22, 17) = 26{,}334$.

b) The restrictions use up 22 of the total, leaving a free total of 7. Therefore the answer is $C(6 + 7 - 1, 7) = C(12, 7) = 792$.

c) The number of solutions without restriction is $C(6 + 29 - 1, 29) = C(34, 29) = 278256$. The number of solution violating the restriction by having $x_1 \geq 6$ is $C(6 + 23 - 1, 23) = C(28, 23) = 98280$. Therefore the answer is $278256 - 98280 = 179{,}976$.

d) The number of solutions with $x_2 \geq 9$ (as required) but without the restriction on x_1 is $C(6 + 20 - 1, 20) = C(25, 20) = 53130$. The number of solution violating the additional restriction by having $x_1 \geq 8$ is $C(6 + 12 - 1, 12) = C(17, 12) = 6188$. Therefore the answer is $53130 - 6188 = 46{,}942$.

18. It follows directly from Theorem 3 that the answer is

$$\frac{20!}{2!4!3!1!2!3!2!3!} \approx 5.9 \times 10^{13}.$$

20. We introduce the nonnegative slack variable x_4, and our problem becomes the same as the problem of counting the number of nonnegative integer solutions to $x_1 + x_2 + x_3 + x_4 = 11$. By Theorem 2 the answer is $C(4 + 11 - 1, 11) = C(14, 11) = C(14, 3) = 364$.

22. If we think of the balls as doing the choosing, then this is asking for the number of ways to choose 12 bins from the six given bins, with repetition allowed. (The number of times each bin is chosen is the number of balls in that bin.) By Theorem 2 with $n = 6$ and $r = 12$, this choice can be made in $C(6 + 12 - 1, 12) = C(17, 12) = 6188$ ways.

24. We assume that this problem leaves us free to pick which boxes get which numbers of balls. There are several ways to count this. Here is one. Line up the 15 objects in a row (15! ways to do that), and line up the five boxes in a row (5! ways to do that). Now put the first object into the first box, the next two into the second box, the next three into the third box, and so on. This overcounts by a factor of $1! \cdot 2! \cdot 3! \cdot 4! \cdot 5!$, since there are that many ways to swap objects in the permutation without affecting the result. Therefore the answer is $15! \cdot 5!/(1! \cdot 2! \cdot 3! \cdot 4! \cdot 5!) = 4{,}540{,}536{,}000$.

26. We can model this problem by letting x_i be the ith digit of the number for $i = 1, 2, 3, 4, 5, 6$, and asking for the number of solutions to the equation $x_1 + x_2 + x_3 + x_4 + x_5 + x_6 = 13$, where each x_i is between 0 and 8, inclusive, except that one of them equals 9. First, there are 6 ways to decide which of the digits is 9. Without loss of generality assume that $x_6 = 9$. Then the number of ways to choose the remaining digits is the number of nonnegative integer solutions to $x_1 + x_2 + x_3 + x_4 + x_5 = 4$ (note that the restriction that each $x_i \leq 8$ was moot, since the sum was only 4). By Theorem 2 there are $C(5 + 4 - 1, 4) = C(8, 4) = 70$ solutions. Therefore the answer is $6 \cdot 70 = 420$.

28. (Note that the roles of the letters n and r here are reversed from the usual roles, as, for example, in Theorem 2.) We can choose the required objects first, and there are $q_1 + q_2 + \cdots + q_r$ of these. Then $n - (q_1 + q_2 + \cdots + q_r) = n - q_1 - q_2 - \cdots - q_r$ objects remain to be chosen. There are still r types. Therefore by Theorem 2, the number of ways to make this choice is $C(r + (n - q_1 - q_2 - \cdots - q_r) - 1, (n - q_1 - q_2 - \cdots - q_r)) = C(n + r - q_1 - q_2 - \cdots - q_r - 1, n - q_1 - q_2 - \cdots - q_r)$.

30. By Theorem 3 the answer is $11!/(4!4!2!) = 34{,}650$.

32. We can treat the 3 consecutive A's as one letter. Thus we have 6 letters, of which 2 are the same (the two R's), so by Theorem 3 the answer is $6!/2! = 360$.

34. We need to calculate separately, using Theorem 3, the number of strings of length 5, 6, and 7. There are $7!/(3!3!1!) = 140$ strings of length 7. For strings of length 6, we can omit the R and form $6!/(3!3!) = 20$ string; omit an E and form $6!/(3!2!1!) = 60$ strings, or omit an S and also form 60 strings. This gives a total of 140 strings of length 6. For strings of length 5, we can omit two E's or two S's, each giving $5!/(3!1!1!) = 20$ strings; we can omit one E and one S ($5!/(2!2!1!) = 30$ strings); or we can omit the R and either an E or an S ($5!/(3!2!) = 10$ strings each). This gives a total of 90 strings of length 5, for a grand total of 370 strings of length 5 or greater.

36. We simply need to choose the 6 positions, out of the 14 available, to make 1's. There are $C(14,6) = 3003$ ways to do so.

38. We assume that the forty issues are distinguishable.

a) Theorem 4 says that the answer is $40!/10!^4 \approx 4.7 \times 10^{21}$.

b) Each distribution into identical boxes gives rise to $4! = 24$ distributions into labeled boxes, since once we have made the distribution into unlabeled boxes we can arbitrarily label the boxes. Therefore the answer is the same as the answer in part **(a)** divided by 24, namely $(40!/10!^4)/4! \approx 2.0 \times 10^{20}$.

40. We can describe any such travel in a unique way by a sequence of 4 x's, 3 y's, 5 z's, and 4 w's. By Theorem 3, there are

$$\frac{16!}{4!3!5!4!} = 50,450,400$$

such sequences.

42. Theorem 4 says that the answer is $52!/13!^4 \approx 5.4 \times 10^{28}$, since each player gets 13 cards.

44. **a)** All that matters is the number of books on each shelf, so the answer is the number of solutions to $x_1 + x_2 + x_3 + x_4 = 12$, where x_i is being viewed as the number of books on shelf i. The answer is therefore $C(4 + 12 - 1, 12) = C(15, 12) = 455$.

b) No generality is lost if we number the books b_1, b_2, ..., b_{12} and think of placing book b_1, then placing b_2, and so on. There are clearly 4 ways to place b_1, since we can put it as the first book (for now) on any of the shelves. After b_1 is placed, there are 5 ways to place b_2, since it can go to the right of b_1 or it can be the first book on any of the shelves. We continue in this way: there are 6 ways to place b_3 (to the right of b_1, to the right of b_2, or as the first book on any of the shelves), 7 ways to place b_4, ..., 15 ways to place b_{12}. Therefore the answer is the product of these numbers $4 \cdot 5 \cdots 15 = 217,945,728,000$.

46. We follow the hint. There are 5 bars (chosen books), and therefore there are 6 places where the 7 stars (nonchosen books) can fit (before the first bar, between the first and second bars, ..., after the fifth bar). Each of the second through fifth of these slots must have at least one star in it, so that adjacent books are not chosen. Once we have placed these 4 stars, there are 3 stars left to be placed in 6 slots. The number of ways to do this is therefore $C(6 + 3 - 1, 3) = C(8, 3) = 56$.

48. We can think of the n distinguishable objects to be distributed into boxes as numbered from 1 to n. Since such a distribution is completely determined by assigning a box number (from 1 to k) to each object, we can think of a distribution simply as a sequence of box numbers a_1, a_2, ..., a_n, where a_i is the box into which object i goes. Furthermore, since we want n_i objects to go into box i, this sequence must contain n_i copies of the number i (for each i from 1 to k). But this is precisely a permutation of n objects (namely, numbers) with n_i indistinguishable objects of type i (namely, n_i copies of the number i). Thus we have established the desired one-to-one correspondence. Since Theorem 3 tells us that there are $n!/(n_1!n_2!\cdots n_k!)$ permutations, there must also be this many ways to do the distribution into boxes, and the proof of Theorem 4 is complete.

50. This is actually a problem about partitions of sets. Let us call the set of 5 objects $\{a, b, c, d, e\}$. We want to partition this set into three pairwise disjoint subsets (some possibly empty). We count in a fairly ad hoc way. First, we could put all five objects into one subset (i.e., all five objects go into one box, with the other two boxes empty). Second, we could put four of the objects into one subset and one into another, such as $\{a, b, c, d\}$ together with $\{e\}$. There are 5 ways to do this, since each of the five objects can be the singleton. Third, we could put three of the objects into one set (box) and two into another; there are $C(5, 2) = 10$ ways to do this, since there are that many ways to choose which objects are to be the doubleton. Similarly, there are 10 ways to distribute the elements so that three go into one set and one each into the other two sets (for example, $\{a, b, c\}$, $\{d\}$, and $\{e\}$). Finally, we could put two items into one set, two into another, and one into the third (for example, $\{a, b\}$, $\{c, d\}$, and $\{e\}$). Here we need to choose the singleton (5 ways), and then we need to choose one of the 3 ways to separate the remaining four elements into pairs; this gives a total of 15 partitions. In all we have 41 different partitions.

52. Each term must be of the form $Cx_1^{n_1}x_2^{n_2}\cdots x_m^{n_m}$, where the n_i's are nonnegative integers whose sum is n. The number of ways to specify a term, then, is the number of nonnegative integer solutions to $n_1 + n_2 + \cdots + n_m = n$, which by Theorem 2 is $C(m + n - 1, n)$. Note that the coefficients C for these terms can be computed using Theorem 3—see Exercise 53.

54. From Exercise 52, we know that there are $C(3 + 4 - 1, 4) = C(6, 4) = 15$ terms, and the coefficients come from Exercise 53. The answer is $x^4 + y^4 + z^4 + 4x^3y + 4xy^3 + 4x^3z + 4xz^3 + 4y^3z + 4yz^3 + 6x^2y^2 + 6x^2z^2 + 6y^2z^2 + 12x^2yz + 12xy^2z + 12xyz^2$.

56. By Exercise 52, the answer is $C(3 + 100 - 1, 100) = C(102, 100) = C(102, 2) = 5151$.

SECTION 4.6   Generating Permutations and Combinations

2. These can be done using Algorithm 1 or Example 2. This will be explained in detail for part (a); the others are similar. In the last four parts of this exercise, the next permutation exchanges only the last two elements.
   a) The last pair of integers a_j and a_{j+1} where $a_j < a_{j+1}$ is $a_2 = 3$ and $a_3 = 4$. The least integer to the right of 3 that is greater than 3 is 4. Hence 4 is placed in the second position. The integers 2 and 3 are then placed in order in the last two positions, giving the permutation 1423.
   b) 51234   c) 13254   d) 612354   e) 1623574   f) 23587461

4. 156423, 165432, 231456, 231465, 234561, 314562, 432561, 435612, 541236, 543216, 654312, 654321

6. The first subset corresponds to the bit string 0000, namely the empty set. The next subset corresponds to the bit string 0001, namely the set $\{4\}$. The next bit string is 0010, corresponding to the set $\{3\}$, and then 0011, which corresponds to the set $\{3, 4\}$. We continue in this manner, giving the remaining sets: $\{2\}$, $\{2, 4\}$, $\{2, 3\}$, $\{2, 3, 4\}$, $\{1\}$, $\{1, 4\}$, $\{1, 3\}$, $\{1, 3, 4\}$, $\{1, 2\}$, $\{1, 2, 4\}$, $\{1, 2, 3\}$, $\{1, 2, 3, 4\}$.

8. Since the new permutation agrees with the old one in positions 1 to $j - 1$, and since the new permutation has a_k in position j, whereas the old one had a_j, with $a_k > a_j$, the new permutation succeeds the old one in lexicographic order. Furthermore the new permutation is the first one (in lexicographic order) with a_1, a_2, ..., a_{j-1}, a_k in positions 1 to j, and the old permutation was the last one with a_1, a_2, ..., a_{j-1}, a_j in those positions. Since a_k was picked to be the smallest number greater than a_j among a_{j+1}, a_{j+2}, ..., a_n, there can be no permutation between these two.

10. One algorithm would combine Algorithm 3 and Algorithm 1. Using Algorithm 3, we generate all the r-combinations of the set with n elements. At each stage, after we have found each r-combination, we use Algorithm 1, with $n = r$ (and a different collection to be permuted than $\{1, 2, \ldots, n\}$), to generate all the permutations of the elements in this combination. See the solution to Exercise 11 for an example.

12. a) We find that $a_1 = 1$, $a_2 = 1$, $a_3 = 2$, $a_4 = 2$, and $a_5 = 3$. Therefore the number is $1 \cdot 1! + 1 \cdot 2! + 2 \cdot 3! + 2 \cdot 4! + 3 \cdot 5! = 1 + 2 + 12 + 48 + 360 = 423$.
b) Each $a_k = 0$, so the number is 0.
c) We find that $a_1 = 1$, $a_2 = 2$, $a_3 = 3$, $a_4 = 4$, and $a_5 = 5$. Therefore the number is $1 \cdot 1! + 2 \cdot 2! + 3 \cdot 3! + 4 \cdot 4! + 5 \cdot 5! = 1 + 4 + 18 + 96 + 600 = 719 = 6! - 1$, as expected, since this is the last permutation.

14. a) We find the Cantor expansion of 3 to be $1 \cdot 1! + 1 \cdot 2!$. Therefore we know that $a_4 = 0$, $a_3 = 0$, $a_2 = 1$, and $a_1 = 1$. Following the algorithm given in the solution to Exercise 13, we put 5 in position $5 - 0 = 5$, put 4 in position $4 - 0 = 4$, put 3 in position $3 - 1 = 2$, and put 2 in the position that is 1 from the rightmost available position, namely position 1. Therefore the answer is 23145.
b) We find that $89 = 1 \cdot 1! + 2 \cdot 2! + 2 \cdot 3! + 3 \cdot 4!$. Therefore we insert 5, 4, 3, and 2, in order, skipping 3, 2, 2, and 1 positions from the right among the available positions, obtaining 35421.
c) We find that $111 = 1 \cdot 1! + 1 \cdot 2! + 2 \cdot 3! + 4 \cdot 4!$. Therefore we insert 5, 4, 3, and 2, in order, skipping 4, 2, 1, and 1 positions from the right among the available positions, obtaining 52431.

16. Rather than following the hint, we will give a direct argument. The protocol given here has $n!$ possible outcomes, each equally likely, because there are n possible choices for $r(n)$, $n - 1$ possible choices for $r(n - 1)$, and so on. Therefore if we can argue that each outcome gives rise to exactly one permutation, then each permutation will be equally likely. But this is clear. Suppose $(a_1, a_2, a_3, \ldots, a_n)$ is a permutation of $(1, 2, 3, \ldots, n)$. In order for this permutation to be generated by the protocol, it must be the case that $r(n) = a_n$, because it is only on round one of the protocol that anything gets moved into the nth position. Next, $r(n-1)$ must the unique value that picks out a_{n-1} to put in the $(n-1)^{\text{th}}$ position (this is not necessarily a_{n-1}, because it might happen that $a_{n-1} = n$, and n could have been put into one of the other positions as a result of round one). And so on. Thus each permutation corresponds to exactly one sequence of choices of the random numbers.

SUPPLEMENTARY EXERCISES FOR CHAPTER 4

2. a) There are no ways to do this, since there are not enough items.   **b)** $6^{10} = 60,466,176$
c) There are no ways to do this, since there are not enough items.
d) $C(6 + 10 - 1, 10) = C(15, 10) = C(15, 5) = 3003$

4. There are 2^7 bit strings of length 10 that start 000, since each of the last 7 bits can be chosen in either of two ways. Similarly, there are 2^6 bit strings of length 10 that end 1111, and there are 2^3 bit strings of length 10 that both start 000 and end 1111 (since only the 3 middle bits can be freely chosen). Therefore by the inclusion–exclusion principle, the answer is $2^7 + 2^6 - 2^3 = 184$.

6. $9 \cdot 10 \cdot 10 \cdot 10 \cdot 10 = 90,000$

8. a) All the integers from 100 to 999 have three decimal digits, and there are $999 - 100 + 1 = 900$ of these.

b) In addition to the 900 three-digit numbers, there are 9 one-digit positive integers, for a total of 909.

c) There is 1 one-digit number with a 9. Among the two-digit numbers, there are the 10 numbers from 90 to 99, together with the 8 numbers 19, 29, ..., 89, for a total of 18. Among the three-digit numbers, there are the 100 from 900 to 999; and there are, for each century from the 100's to the 800's, again $1 + 18 = 19$ numbers with at least one 9; this gives a total of $100 + 8 \cdot 19 = 252$. Thus our final answer is $1 + 18 + 252 = 271$. Alternately, we can compute this as $10^3 - 9^3 = 271$, since we want to subtract from the number of three-digit nonnegative numbers (with leading 0's allowed) the number of those that use only the nine digits 0 through 8.

d) Since we can use only even digits, there are $5^3 = 125$ ways to specify a three-digit number, allowing leading 0's. Since, however, the number $0 = 000$ is not in our set, we need to subtract 1, obtaining the answer 124.

e) The numbers in question are either of the form $d55$ or $55d$, with $d \neq 5$, or 555. Since d can be any of nine digits, there are $9 + 9 + 1 = 19$ such numbers.

f) All 9 one-digit numbers are palindromes. The 9 two-digit numbers 11, 22, ..., 99 are palindromes. For three-digit numbers, the first digit (which must equal the third digit) can be any of the 9 nonzero digits, and the second digit can be any of the 10 digits, giving $9 \cdot 10 = 90$ possibilities. Therefore the answer is $9 + 9 + 90 = 108$.

10. Using the generalized pigeonhole principle, we see that we need $5 \times 12 + 1 = 61$ people.

12. There are $7 \times 12 = 84$ day-month combinations. Therefore we need 85 people to ensure that two of them were born on the same day of the week and in the same month.

14. We need at least 551 cards to ensure that at least two are identical. Since the cards come in packages of 20, we need $\lceil 551/20 \rceil = 28$ packages.

16. Partition the set of numbers from 1 to $2n$ into the n pigeonholes $\{1, 2\}$, $\{3, 4\}$, ..., $\{2n - 1, 2n\}$. If we have $n + 1$ numbers from this set (the pigeons), then two of them must be in the same hole. This means that among our collection are two consecutive numbers. Clearly consecutive numbers are relatively prime (since every common divisor must divide their difference, 1).

18. Divide the interior of the square, with lines joining the midpoints of opposite sides, into four 1×1 squares. By the pigeonhole principle, at least two of the five points must be in the same small square. The furthest apart two points in a square could be is the length of the diagonal, which is $\sqrt{2}$ for a square 1 unit on a side.

20. A diagonal or a side of the polygon is specified by choosing a pair of vertices, so there are $C(n, 2) = n(n-1)/2$ sides or diagonals. There are n sides, so there must be $[n(n-1)/2] - n = n(n-3)/2$ diagonals.

22. a) We want to solve $n(n-1) = 110$, or $n^2 - n - 110 = 0$. Simple algebra gives $n = 11$ (we ignore $n = -10$, since we need a positive integer for our answer).

b) We recall that $7! = 5040$, so the answer is 7.

c) We need to solve the equation $n(n-1)(n-2)(n-3) = 12n(n-1)$. Since we have $n \geq 4$ in order for $P(n, 4)$ to be defined, this equation reduces to $(n-2)(n-3) = 12$, or $n^2 - 5n - 6 = 0$. Simple algebra gives $n = 6$ (we ignore the solution $n = -1$ since n needs to be a positive integer).

24. An algebraic proof is straightforward. We will give a combinatorial proof of the equivalent identity $P(n + 1, r)(n + 1 - r) = (n + 1)P(n, r)$ (and in fact both of these equal $P(n + 1, r + 1)$). Consider the problem of writing down a permutation of $r + 1$ objects from a collection of $n + 1$ objects. We can first write down a permutation of r of these objects ($P(n+1, r)$ ways to do so), and then write down one more object (and there are $n + 1 - r$ objects left to choose from), thereby obtaining the left-hand side; or we can first choose an object to write down first ($n + 1$ to choose from), and then write down a permutation of length r using the n remaining objects ($P(n, r)$ ways to do so), thereby obtaining the right-hand side.

26. First note that Corollary 2 of Section 4.4 is equivalent to the assertion that the sum of the numbers $C(n, k)$ for even k is equal to the sum of the numbers $C(n, k)$ for odd k. Since $C(n, k)$ counts the number of subsets of size k of a set with n elements, we need to show that a set has as many even-sized subsets as it has odd-sized subsets. Define a function f from the set of all subsets of A to itself (where A is a set with n elements, one of which is a), by setting $f(B) = B \cup \{a\}$ if $a \notin B$, and $f(B) = B - \{a\}$ if $a \in B$. It is clear that f takes even-sized subsets to odd-sized subsets and vice versa, and that f is one-to-one and onto (indeed, $f^{-1} = f$). Therefore f restricted to the set of subsets of odd size gives a one-to-one correspondence between that set and the set of subsets of even size.

28. The base case is $n = 2$, in which case the identity simply states that $1 = 1$. Assume the inductive hypothesis, that $\sum_{j=2}^{n} C(j, 2) = C(n + 1, 3)$. Then

$$\sum_{j=2}^{n+1} C(j, 2) = \left(\sum_{j=2}^{n} C(j, 2) \right) + C(n + 1, 2)$$
$$= C(n + 1, 3) + C(n + 1, 2) = C((n + 1) + 1, 3),$$

as desired. The last equality made use of Pascal's identity.

30. a) For a fixed k, a triple is totally determined by picking i and j; since each can be picked in k ways (each can be any number from 0 to $k - 1$, inclusive), there are k^2 ways to choose the triple. Adding over all possible values of k gives the indicated sum.

b) A triple of this sort is totally determined by knowing the *set* of numbers $\{i, j, k\}$, since the order is fixed. Therefore the number of triples of each kind is just the number of sets of 3 elements chosen from the set $\{0, 1, 2, \ldots, n\}$, and that is clearly $C(n + 1, 3)$.

c) In order for i to equal j (with both less than k), we need to pick two elements from $\{0, 1, 2, \ldots, n\}$, using the larger one for k and the smaller one for both i and j. Therefore there are as many such choices as there are 2-element subsets of this set, namely $C(n + 1, 2)$.

d) This part is its own proof. The last equality follows from elementary algebra.

32. a) If we 2-color the $2d - 1$ elements of S, then there must be at least d elements of one color (if there were $d - 1$ or fewer elements of both colors, then only $2d - 2$ elements would be colored); this is just an application of the generalized pigeonhole principle. Thus there is a d-element subset that does not contain both colors, in violation of the condition for being 2-colorable.

b) We must show that every collection of fewer than three sets each containing two elements is 2-colorable, and that there is a collection of three sets each containing two elements that is not 2-colorable. The second statement follows from part (a), with $d = 2$ (the three sets are $\{1, 2\}$, $\{1, 3\}$, and $\{2, 3\}$). On the other hand, if we have two (or fewer) sets each with two elements, then we can color the two elements of the first set with different colors, and we cannot be prevented from properly coloring the second set, since it must contain an element not in the first set.

c) First we show that the given collection is not 2-colorable. Without loss of generality, assume that 1 is red. If 2 is red, then 6 must be blue (second set). Thus either 4 or 5 must be red (seventh set), which means that 3 must be blue (first or fourth set). This would force 7 to be red (sixth set), which would force both 4 and 5 to be blue (third and fifth sets), a contradiction. Thus 2 is blue. If 3 is red, then we can conclude that 5 is blue, 7 is red, 6 is blue, and 4 is blue, making the last set improperly colored. Thus 3 is blue. This implies that 4 is red, hence 7 is blue, hence 5 and 6 are red, another contradiction. So the given collection cannot be 2-colored. Next we must show that all collections of six sets with three elements each are 2-colorable. Since having more elements in S at our disposable only makes it easier to 2-color the collection, we can assume that S has only five elements; let $S = \{a, b, c, d, e\}$. Since there are 18 occurrences of elements in the collection, some element, say a, must occur at least four times (since $3 \cdot 5 < 18$). If a occurs in six of the sets, then we can color a red and the rest of the elements blue. If a occurs in five of the sets, suppose without loss of generality that b and c occur in the sixth set. Then we can color a and b red and the remaining elements blue. Finally, if a occurs in only four of the sets, then that leaves only four elements for the last two sets, and therefore a pair of elements must be shared by them, say b and c. Again coloring a and b red and the remaining elements blue gives the desired coloring.

34. We might as well assume that the first person sits in the northernmost seat. Then there are $P(7, 7)$ ways to seat the remaining people, since they form a permutation reading clockwise from the first person. Therefore the answer is $7! = 5040$.

36. We need to know the number of solutions to $d + m + g = 12$, where d, m, and g are integers greater than or equal to 3. This is equivalent to the number of nonnegative integer solutions to $d' + m' + g' = 3$, where $d' = d - 3$, $m' = m - 3$, and $g' = g - 3$. By Theorem 2 of Section 4.5, the answer is $C(3 + 3 - 1, 3) = C(5, 3) = 10$.

38. a) By Theorem 3 of Section 4.5, the answer is $10!/(3!2!2!) = 151{,}200$.
b) If we fix the start and the end, then the question concerns only 8 letters, and the answer is $8!/(2!2!) = 10{,}080$.
c) If we think of the three P's as one letter, then the answer is seen to be $8!/(2!2!) = 10{,}080$.

40. There are 26 choices for the third letter. If the digit part of the plate consists of the digits 1, 2, and d, where d is different from 1 or 2, then there are 8 choices for d and $3! = 6$ choices for a permutation of these digits. If $d = 1$ or 2, then there are 2 choices for d and 3 choices for a permutation. Therefore the answer is $26(8 \cdot 6 + 2 \cdot 3) = 1404$.

42. Let us look at the girls first. There are $P(8, 8) = 8! = 40320$ ways to order them relative to each other. This much work produces 9 gaps between girls (including the ends), in each of which at most one boy may sit. We need to choose, in order without repetition, 6 of these gaps, and this can be done in $P(9, 6) = 60480$ ways. Therefore the answer is, by the product rule, $40320 \cdot 60480 = 2{,}438{,}553{,}600$.

44. Assume without loss of generality that we wish to form r-combinations from the set $\{1, 2, \ldots, n\}$. We modify Algorithm 3 in Section 4.6 for generating the next r-combination in lexicographic order, allowing for repetition. Then we generate all such combinations by starting with $11 \ldots 1$ and calling this modified algorithm $C(n + r - 1, r) - 1$ times (this will give us $nn \ldots n$ as the last one).

```
procedure next r-combination(a₁, a₂, …, aᵣ : integers)
{We assume that 1 ≤ a₁ ≤ a₂ ≤ ⋯ ≤ aᵣ ≤ n, with a₁ ≠ n }
i := r
while aᵢ = n
        i := i − 1
aᵢ := aᵢ + 1
for j := i + 1 to r
        aⱼ := aᵢ
```

46. One needs to play around with this enough to eventually discover a situation satisfying the conditions. Here is a way to do it. Suppose the group consists of three men and three women, and suppose that people of the same sex are always enemies and people of the opposite sex are always friends. Then clearly there can be no set of four mutual enemies, because any set of four people must include at least one man and one woman (since there are only three of each sex in the whole group). Also there can be no set of three mutual friends, because any set of three people must include at least two people of the same sex (since there are only two sexes).

CHAPTER 5
Discrete Probability

SECTION 5.1   An Introduction to Discrete Probability

2. The probability is $1/6 \approx 0.17$, since there are six equally likely outcomes.

4. Since April has 30 days, the answer is $30/366 = 5/61 \approx 0.082$.

6. There are 16 cards that qualify as being an ace or a heart, so the answer is $16/52 = 4/13 \approx 0.31$. We could also compute this from Theorem 2 as $4/52 + 13/52 - 1/52$.

8. We saw in Example 5 that there are $C(52,5)$ possible poker hands, and we assume by symmetry that they are all equally likely. In order to solve this problem, we need to compute the number of poker hands that contain the ace of hearts. There is no choice about choosing the ace of hearts. To form the rest of the hand, we need to choose 4 cards from the 51 remaining cards, so there are $C(51,4)$ hands containing the ace of hearts. Therefore the answer to the question is the ratio

$$\frac{C(51,4)}{C(52,5)} = \frac{5}{52} \approx 9.6\%.$$

The problem can also be done by subtracting from 1 the answer to Exercise 9, since a hand contains the ace of hearts if and only if it is not the case that it does not contain the ace of hearts.

10. This is similar to Exercise 8. We need to compute the number of poker hands that contain the two of diamonds and the three of spades. There is no choice about choosing these two cards. To form the rest of the hand, we need to choose 3 cards from the 50 remaining cards, so there are $C(50,3)$ hands containing these two specific cards. Therefore the answer to the question is the ratio

$$\frac{C(50,3)}{C(52,5)} = \frac{5}{663} \approx 0.0075.$$

12. There are 4 ways to specify the ace. Once the ace is chosen for the hand, there are $C(48,4)$ ways to choose nonaces for the remaining four cards. Therefore there are $4C(48,4)$ hands with exactly one ace. Since there are $C(52,5)$ equally likely hands, the answer is the ratio

$$\frac{4C(48,4)}{C(52,5)} \approx 0.30.$$

14. We saw in Example 5 that there are $C(52,5) = 2{,}598{,}960$ different hands, and we assume by symmetry that they are all equally likely. We need to count the number of hands that have 5 different kinds (ranks). There are $C(13,5)$ ways to choose the kinds. For each card, there are then 4 ways to choose the suit. Therefore there are $C(13,5) \cdot 4^5 = 1{,}317{,}888$ ways to choose the hand. Thus the probability is $1317888/2598960 = 2112/4165 \approx 0.51$.

16. Of the $C(52,5) = 2{,}598{,}960$ hands, $4 \cdot C(13,5) = 5148$ are flushes, since we can specify a flush by choosing a suit and then choosing 5 cards from that suit. Therefore the answer is $5148/2598960 = 33/16660 \approx 0.0020$.

18. There are clearly only $10 \cdot 4 = 40$ straight flushes, since all we get to specify for a straight flush is the starting (lowest) kind in the straight (anything from ace up to ten) and the suit. Therefore the answer is $40/C(52,5) = 40/2598960 = 1/64974$.

20. There are 4 royal flushes, one in each suit. Therefore the answer is $4/C(52,5) = 4/2598960 = 1/649740$.

22. There are $\lfloor 100/3 \rfloor = 33$ multiples of 3 among the integers from 1 to 100 (inclusive), so the answer is $33/100 = 0.33$.

24. In each case, if the numbers are chosen from the integers from 1 to n, then there are $C(n,6)$ possible entries, only one of which is the winning one, so the answer is $1/C(n,6)$.
   a) $1/C(30,6) = 1/593775 \approx 1.7 \times 10^{-6}$ **b)** $1/C(36,6) = 1/1947792 \approx 5.1 \times 10^{-7}$
   c) $1/C(42,6) = 1/5245786 \approx 1.9 \times 10^{-7}$ **d)** $1/C(48,6) = 1/12271512 \approx 8.1 \times 10^{-8}$

26. In each case, if the numbers are chosen from the integers from 1 to n, then there are $C(n,6)$ possible entries. If we wish to avoid all the winning numbers, then we must make our choice from the $n-6$ nonwinning numbers, and this can be done in $C(n-6,6)$ ways. Therefore, since the winning numbers are picked at random, the probability is $C(n-6,6)/C(n,6)$.
   a) $C(34,6)/C(40,6) = 1344904/3838380 \approx 0.35$ **b)** $C(42,6)/C(48,6) = 5245786/12271512 \approx 0.43$
   c) $C(50,6)/C(56,6) = 15890700/32468436 \approx 0.49$ **d)** $C(58,6)/C(64,6) = 40475358/74974368 \approx 0.54$

28. We need to compute the number of ways for the Pennsylvania lottery commission to select its 11 numbers, and we need to compute the number of ways for it to select its 11 numbers so as to contain the 7 numbers that we chose. For the former, the number is clearly $C(80,11)$. For the latter, the commission must select four more numbers besides the ones we chose, from the $80-7 = 73$ other numbers, so there are $C(73,4)$ ways to do this. Therefore the probability that we win is the ratio $C(73,4)/C(80,11)$, which works out to $3/28879240$, or about one chance in ten million (1.04×10^{-7}). The same answer can be obtained by counting things in the other direction: the number of ways for us to choose 7 of the commission's predestined 11 numbers divided by the number of ways for us to pick 7 numbers. This gives $C(11,7)/C(80,7)$, which has the same value as before.

30. In order to specify a winning ticket, we must choose five of the six numbers to match ($C(6,5) = 6$ ways to do so) and one number from among the remaining 34 numbers not to match ($C(34,1) = 34$ ways to do so). Therefore there are $6 \cdot 34 = 204$ winning tickets. Since there are $C(40,6) = 3{,}838{,}380$ tickets in all, the answer is $204/3838380 = 17/319865 \approx 5.3 \times 10^{-5}$, or about 1 chance in 19,000.

32. The number of ways for the drawing to turn out is $100 \cdot 99 \cdot 98$. The number of ways of ways for the drawing to cause Kumar, Janice, and Pedro each to win a prize is $3 \cdot 2 \cdot 1$ (three ways for one of these to be picked to win first prize, two ways for one of the others to win second prize, one way for the third to win third prize). Therefore the probability we seek is $(3 \cdot 2 \cdot 1)/(100 \cdot 99 \cdot 98) = 1/161700$.

34. a) There are $50 \cdot 49 \cdot 48 \cdot 47$ equally likely outcomes of the drawings. In only one of these do Bo, Colleen, Jeff, and Rohini win the first, second, third, and fourth prizes, respectively. Therefore the probability is $1/(50 \cdot 49 \cdot 48 \cdot 47) = 1/5527200$.
   b) There are $50 \cdot 50 \cdot 50 \cdot 50$ equally likely outcomes of the drawings. In only one of these do Bo, Colleen, Jeff, and Rohini win the first, second, third, and fourth prizes, respectively. Therefore the probability is $1/50^4 = 1/6250000$.

36. Reasoning as in Example 2, we see that there are 5 ways to get a total of 8 when two dice are rolled: $(6, 2)$, $(5, 3)$, $(4, 4)$, $(3, 5)$, and $(2, 6)$. There are $6^2 = 36$ equally likely possible outcomes of the roll of two dice, so the probability of getting a total of 8 when two dice are rolled is $5/36 \approx 0.139$. For three dice, there are $6^3 = 216$ equally likely possible outcomes, which we can represent as ordered triples (a, b, c). We need to enumerate the possibilities that give a total of 8. This is done in a more systematic way in Section 4.5, but we will do it here by brute force. The first die could turn out to be a 6, giving rise to the 1 triple $(6, 1, 1)$. The first die could be a 5, giving rise to the 2 triples $(5, 2, 1)$, and $(5, 1, 2)$. Continuing in this way, we see that there are 3 triples giving a total of 8 when the first die shows a 4, 4 triples when it shows a 3, 5 triples when it shows a 2, and 6 triples when it shows a 1 (namely $(1, 6, 1)$, $(1, 5, 2)$, $(1, 4, 3)$, $(1, 3, 4)$, $(1, 2, 5)$, and $(1, 1, 6)$). Therefore there are $1 + 2 + 3 + 4 + 5 + 6 = 21$ possible outcomes giving a total of 8. This tells us that the probability of rolling a 9 when three dice are thrown is $21/216 \approx 0.097$, smaller than the corresponding value for two dice. Thus rolling a total of 9 is more likely when using two dice than when using three.

38. a) Intuitively, these should be independent, since the first event seems to have no influence on the second. In fact we can compute as follows. First $p(E_1) = 1/2$ and $p(E_2) = 1/2$ by the symmetry of coin tossing. Furthermore, $E_1 \cap E_2$ is the event that the first two coins come up tails and heads, respectively. Since there are four equally likely outcomes for the first two coins (HH, HT, TH, and TT), $p(E_1 \cap E_2) = 1/4$. Therefore $p(E_1 \cap E_2) = 1/4 = (1/2) \cdot (1/2) = p(E_1)p(E_2)$, so the events are indeed independent.
    b) Again $p(E_1) = 1/2$. For E_2, note that there are 8 equally likely outcomes for the three coins, and in 2 of these cases E_2 occurs (namely HHT and THH); therefore $p(E_2) = 2/8 = 1/4$. Thus $p(E_1)p(E_2) = (1/2) \cdot (1/4) = 1/8$. Now $E_1 \cap E_2$ is the event that the first coin comes up tails, and two but not three heads come up in a row. This occurs precisely when the outcome is THH, so the probability is $1/8$. This is the same as $p(E_1)p(E_2)$, so the events are independent.
    c) As in part (b), $p(E_1) = 1/2$ and $p(E_2) = 1/4$. This time $p(E_1 \cap E_2) = 0$, since there is no way to get two heads in a row if the second coin comes up tails. Since $p(E_1)p(E_2) \neq p(E_1 \cap E_2)$, the events are not independent.

40. You had a 1/4 chance of winning with your original selection. Just as in the original problem, the host's action did not change this, since he would act the same way regardless of whether your selection was a winner or a loser. Therefore you have a 1/4 chance of winning if you do not change. This implies that there is a 3/4 chance of the prize's being behind one of the other doors. Since there are two such doors and by symmetry the probabilities for each of them must be the same, your chance of winning after switching is half of 3/4, or 3/8.

SECTION 5.2   Probability Theory

2. We are told that $p(3) = 2p(x)$ for each $x \neq 3$, but it is implied that $p(1) = p(2) = p(4) = p(5) = p(6)$. We also know that the sum of these six numbers must be 1. It follows easily by algebra that $p(3) = 2/7$ and $p(x) = 1/7$ for $x = 1, 2, 4, 5, 6$.

4. If outcomes are equally likely, then the probability of each outcome is $1/n$, where n is the number of outcomes. Clearly this quantity is between 0 and 1 (inclusive), so (i) is satisfied. Furthermore, there are n outcomes, and the probability of each is $1/n$, so the sum shown in (ii) must equal $n \cdot (1/n) = 1$.

6. We can exploit symmetry in answering these.

a) Since 1 has either to precede 3 or to follow it, and there is no reason that one of these should be any more likely than the other, we immediately see that the answer is $1/2$. We could also simply list all 6 permutations and count that 3 of them have 1 preceding 3, namely 123, 132, and 213.

b) By the same reasoning as in part **(a)**, the answer is again $1/2$.

c) The stated conditions force 3 to come first, so only 312 and 321 are allowed. Therefore the answer is $2/6 = 1/3$.

8. We exploit symmetry in answering many of these.

a) Since 1 has either to precede 2 or to follow it, and there is no reason that one of these should be any more likely than the other, we immediately see that the answer is $1/2$.

b) By the same reasoning as in part **(a)**, the answer is again $1/2$.

c) For 1 immediately to preceded 2, we can think of these two numbers as glued together in forming the permutation. Then we are really permuting $n-1$ numbers—the single numbers from 3 through n and the one glued object, 12. There are $(n-1)!$ ways to do this. Since there are $n!$ permutations in all, the probability of randomly selecting one of these is $(n-1)!/n! = 1/n$.

d) Half of the permutations have n preceding 1. Of these permutations, half of them have $n-1$ preceding 2. Therefore one fourth of the permutations satisfy these conditions, so the probability is $1/4$.

e) Looking at the relative placements of 1, 2, and n, we see that one third of the time, n will come first. Therefore the answer is $1/3$.

10. Note that there are 26! permutations of the letters, so the denominator in all of our answers is 26!. To find the numerator, we have to count the number of ways that the given event can happen. Alternatively, in some cases we may be able to exploit symmetry.

a) There are 13! possible arrangements of the first 13 letters of the permutation, and in only one of these are they in alphabetical order. Therefore the answer is $1/13!$.

b) Once these two conditions are met, there are 24! ways to choose the remaining letters for positions 2 through 25. Therefore the answer is $24!/26! = 1/650$.

c) In effect we are forming a permutation of 25 items—the letters b through y and the double letter combination az or za. There are 25! ways to permute these items, and for each of these permutations there are two choices as to whether a or z comes first. Thus there are $2 \cdot 25!$ ways for form such a permutation, and therefore the answer is $2 \cdot 25!/26! = 1/13$.

d) By part **(c)**, the probability that a and b *are* next to each other is $1/13$. Therefore the probability that a and b are *not* next to each other is $12/13$.

e) There are six ways this can happen: $ax^{24}z$, $zx^{24}a$, $xax^{23}z$, $xzx^{23}a$, $ax^{23}zx$, and $zx^{23}ax$, where x stands for any letter other than a and z (but of course all the x's are different in each permutation). In each of these there are 24! ways to permute the letters other than a and z, so there are 24! permutations of each type. This gives a total of $6 \cdot 24!$ permutations meeting the conditions, so the answer is $(6 \cdot 24!)/26! = 3/325$.

f) Looking at the relative placements of z, a, and b, we see that one third of the time, z will come first. Therefore the answer is $1/3$.

12. Clearly $p(E \cup F) \geq p(E) = 0.8$. Also, $p(E \cup F) \leq 1$. If we apply Theorem 2 from Section 5.1, we can rewrite this as $p(E) + p(F) - p(E \cap F) \leq 1$, or $0.8 + 0.6 - p(E \cap F) \leq 1$. Solving for $p(E \cap F)$ gives $p(E \cap F) \geq 0.4$.

14. The base case $n = 1$ is the trivial statement that $p(E_1) \geq p(E_1)$, and the case $n = 2$ was done in Exercise 13. Assume the inductive hypothesis:

$$p(E_1 \cap E_2 \cap \cdots \cap E_n) \geq p(E_1) + p(E_2) + \cdots + p(E_n) - (n-1)$$

Now let $E = E_1 \cap E_2 \cap \cdots \cap E_n$ and let $F = E_{n+1}$, and apply Exercise 13. We obtain

$$p(E_1 \cap E_2 \cap \cdots \cap E_n \cap E_{n+1}) \geq p(E_1 \cap E_2 \cap \cdots \cap E_n) + p(E_{n+1}) - 1 \,.$$

Substituting from the inductive hypothesis we have

$$p(E_1 \cap E_2 \cap \cdots \cap E_n \cap E_{n+1}) \geq p(E_1) + p(E_2) + \cdots + p(E_n) - (n-1) + p(E_{n+1}) - 1$$
$$= p(E_1) + p(E_2) + \cdots + p(E_n) + p(E_{n+1}) - ((n+1) - 1) \,,$$

as desired.

16. By definition, to say that $\overline{E}$ and $\overline{F}$ are independent is to say that $p(\overline{E} \cap \overline{F}) = p(\overline{E}) \cdot p(\overline{F})$. By De Morgan's Law, $\overline{E} \cap \overline{F} = \overline{E \cup F}$. Therefore

$$p(\overline{E} \cap \overline{F}) = p(\overline{E \cup F}) = 1 - p(E \cup F)$$
$$= 1 - (p(E) + p(F) - p(E \cap F))$$
$$= 1 - p(E) - p(F) + p(E \cap F)$$
$$= 1 - p(E) - p(F) + p(E) \cdot p(F)$$
$$= (1 - p(E)) \cdot (1 - p(F)) = p(\overline{E}) \cdot p(\overline{F}) \,.$$

(We used the two facts presented in the subsection on combinations of events.)

18. We assume for simplicity here that births are independent and the probability of a birth in each day is $1/7$. (This is not exactly true; for example, doctors tend to schedule C-sections on weekdays.)

a) The probability that the second person has the same birth day-of-the-week as the first person (whatever that was) is $1/7$.

b) We proceed as in Example 13. The probability that all the birth days-of-the-week are different is

$$p_n = \frac{6}{7} \cdot \frac{5}{7} \cdot \ldots \cdot \frac{8-n}{7}$$

since each person after the first must have a different birth day-of-the-week from all the previous people in the group. Note that if $n \geq 8$, then $p_n = 0$ since the seventh fraction is 0 (this also follows from the pigeonhole principle). The probability that at least two are born on the same day of the week is therefore $1 - p_n$.

c) We compute $1 - p_n$ for $n = 2, 3, \ldots$ and find that the first time this exceeds $1/2$ is when $n = 4$, so that is our answer. With four people, the probability that at least two will share a birth day-of-the-week is $223/343$, or about 65%.

20. If there are n people in the room (and we assume 366 equally likely and independent birthdays), the probability that none of them has a birthday today is $(365/366)^n$. The question asks for the smallest n such that this quantity is less than $1/2$. We can determine this by trial and error, or we can solve the equation $(365/366)^n = 1/2$ using logarithms. In either case, we find that for $n \leq 253$, $(365/366)^n > 1/2$, but $(365/366)^{254} \approx .4991$. Therefore the answer is 254.

22. a) Given that we are no longer close to the year 1900, which was not a leap year, let us assume that February 29 occurs one time every four years, and that every other date occurs four times every four years. A cycle of four years contains $4 \cdot 365 + 1 = 1461$ days. Therefore the probability that a randomly chosen day is February 29 is $1/1461$, and the probability that a randomly chosen day is any of the other 365 dates is each $4/1461$.

b) We need to compute the probability that in a group of n people, all of them have different birthdays. Rather than compute probabilities at each stage, let us count the number of ways to choose birthdays from the four-year cycle so that all n people have distinct birthdays. There are two cases to consider, depending on whether the group contains a person born on February 29. Let us suppose that there is such a leap-day person; there are n ways to specify which person he is to be. Then there are 1460 days on which the second person can be born so as not to have the same birthday; then there are 1456 days on which the third person can be born so as not to have the same birthday as either of the first two, as so on, until there are $1468 - 4n$ days on which the nth person can be born so as not to have the same birthday as any of the others. This gives a total of

$$n \cdot 1460 \cdot 1456 \cdots (1468 - 4n)$$

ways in all. The other case is that in which there is no leap-day birthday. Then there are 1460 possible birthdays for the first person, 1456 for the second, and so on, down to $1464 - 4n$ for the nth. Thus the total number of ways to choose birthdays without including February 29 is

$$1460 \cdot 1456 \cdots (1464 - 4n).$$

The sum of these two numbers is the numerator of the fraction giving the probability that all the birthdays are distinct. The denominator is 1461^n, since each person can have any birthday within the four-year cycle. Putting this all together, we see that the probability that there are at least two people with the same birthday is

$$1 - \frac{n \cdot 1460 \cdot 1456 \cdots (1468 - 4n) + 1460 \cdot 1456 \cdots (1464 - 4n)}{1461^n}.$$

24. There are 16 equally likely outcomes of flipping a fair coin five times in which the first flip comes up tails (each of the other flips can be either heads or tails). Of these only one will result in four heads appearing, namely $THHHH$. Therefore the answer is 1/16.

26. Intuitively the answer should be yes, because the parity of the number of 1's is a fifty-fifty proposition totally determined by any one of the flips (for example, the last flip). What happened on the other flips is really rather irrelevant. Let us be more rigorous, though. There are 8 bit strings of length 3, and 4 of them contain an odd number of 1's (namely 001, 010, 100, and 111). Therefore $p(E) = 4/8 = 1/2$. Since 4 bit strings of length 3 start with a 1 (namely 100, 101, 110, and 111), we see that $p(F) = 4/8 = 1/2$ as well. Furthermore, since there are 2 strings that start with a 1 and contain an odd number of 1's (namely 100 and 111), we see that $p(E \cap F) = 2/8 = 1/4$. Then since $p(E) \cdot p(F) = (1/2) \cdot (1/2) = 1/4 = p(E \cap F)$, we conclude from the definition that E and F are independent.

28. These questions are applications of the binomial distribution. Following the lead of King Henry VIII, we call having a boy success. Then $p = 0.51$ and $n = 5$ for this problem.
a) We are asked for the probability that $k = 3$. By Theorem 2 the answer is $C(5,3)0.51^3 0.49^2 \approx 0.32$.
b) There will be at least one boy if there are not all girls. The probability of all girls is 0.49^5, so the answer is $1 - 0.49^5 \approx 0.972$.
c) This is just like part (b): The probability of all boys is 0.51^5, so the answer is $1 - 0.51^5 \approx 0.965$.
d) There are two ways this can happen. The answer is clearly $0.51^5 + 0.49^5 \approx 0.063$.

30. a) The probability that all bits are a 1 is $(1/2)^{10} = 1/1024$. This is what is being asked for.
b) This is the same as part (a), except that the probability of a 1 bit is 0.6 rather than 1/2. Thus the answer is $0.6^{10} \approx 0.0060$.
c) We need to multiply the probabilities of each bit being a 1, so the answer is

$$\frac{1}{2} \cdot \frac{1}{2^2} \cdots \frac{1}{2^{10}} = \frac{1}{2^{1+2+\cdots+10}} = \frac{1}{2^{55}} \approx 2.8 \times 10^{-17}.$$

Note that this is essentially 0.

32. Let E be the event that the bit string begins with a 1, and let F be the event that it ends with 00. In each case we need to calculate the probability $p(E \cup F)$, which is the same as $p(E) + p(F) - p(E) \cdot p(F)$. (The fact that $p(E \cap F) = p(E) \cdot p(F)$ follows from the obvious independence of E and F.) So for each part we will compute $p(E)$ and $p(F)$ and then plug into this formula.

a) We have $p(E) = 1/2$ and $p(F) = (1/2) \cdot (1/2) = 1/4$. Therefore the answer is

$$\frac{1}{2} + \frac{1}{4} - \frac{1}{2} \cdot \frac{1}{4} = \frac{5}{8}.$$

b) We have $p(E) = 0.6$ and $p(F) = (0.4) \cdot (0.4) = 0.16$. Therefore the answer is

$$0.6 + 0.16 - 0.6 \cdot 0.16 = 0.664.$$

c) We have $p(E) = 1/2$ and

$$p(F) = (1 - \frac{1}{2^9}) \cdot (1 - \frac{1}{2^{10}}) = 1 - \frac{1}{2^9} - \frac{1}{2^{10}} + \frac{1}{2^{19}}.$$

Therefore the answer is

$$\frac{1}{2} + 1 - \frac{1}{2^9} - \frac{1}{2^{10}} + \frac{1}{2^{19}} - \frac{1}{2} \cdot (1 - \frac{1}{2^9} - \frac{1}{2^{10}} + \frac{1}{2^{19}}) = 1 - \frac{1}{2^9} + \frac{1}{2^{11}} + \frac{1}{2^{19}} - \frac{1}{2^{20}}.$$

34. We need to use the binomial distribution, which tells us that the probability of k successes is

$$b(k; n, p) = C(n, k)p^k (1 - p)^{n-k}.$$

a) Here $k = 0$, since we want all the trials to result in failure. Plugging in and computing, we have $b(0; n, p) = 1 \cdot p^0 \cdot (1 - p)^n = (1 - p)^n$.

b) There is at least one success if and only if it is not the case that there are no successes. Thus we obtain the answer by subtracting the probability in part **(a)** from 1, namely $1 - (1 - p)^n$.

c) There are two ways in which there can be at most one success: no successes or one success. We already computed that the probability of no successes is $(1-p)^n$. Plugging in $k = 1$, we compute that the probability of exactly one success is $b(1; n, p) = n \cdot p^1 \cdot (1 - p)^{n-1}$. Therefore the answer is $(1 - p)^n + np(1 - p)^{n-1}$. This formula only makes sense if $n > 0$, of course; if $n = 0$, then the answer is clearly 1.

d) Since this event is just that the event in part **(c)** does not happen, the answer is $1 - [(1-p)^n + np(1-p)^{n-1}]$. Again, this is for $n > 0$; the probability is clearly 0 if $n = 0$.

36. The basis case here can be taken to be $n = 2$, in which case we have $p(E_1 \cup E_2) = p(E_1) + p(E_2)$. The left-hand side is the sum of $p(x)$ for all $x \in E_1 \cup E_2$. Since E_1 and E_2 are disjoint, this is the sum of $p(x)$ for all $x \in E_1$ added to the sum of $p(x)$ for all $x \in E_2$, which is the right-hand side. Assume the strong inductive hypothesis that the statement is true for $n \le k$, and consider the statement for $n = k + 1$, namely $p\left(\bigcup_{i=1}^{k+1}\right) = \sum_{i=1}^{k+1} p(E_i)$. Let $F = \left(\bigcup_{i=1}^{k}\right)$. Then we can rewrite the left-hand side as $p(F \cup E_{k+1})$. By the inductive hypothesis for $n = 2$ (since $F \cap E_{k+1} = \varnothing$) this equals $p(F) + p(E_{k+1})$. Then by the inductive hypothesis for $n = k$ (since the E_i's are pairwise disjoint), this equals $\sum_{i=1}^{k} p(E_i) + p(E_{k+1}) = \sum_{i=1}^{k+1} p(E_i)$, as desired.

38. a) We assume that the observer was instructed ahead of time to tell us whether or not at least one die came up 6 and to provide no more information than that. If we do not make such an assumption, then the following analysis would not be valid. We use the notation (i, j) to represent that the first die came up i and the second die came up j. Note that there are 36 equally likely outcomes.

a) Let S be the event that at least one die came up 6, and let T be the event that sum of the dice is 7. We want $p(T \mid S)$. By Definition 3, this equals $p(S \cap T)/p(S)$. The outcomes in $S \cap T$ are $(1, 6)$ and $(6, 1)$, so $p(S \cap T) = 2/36$. There are $5^2 = 25$ outcomes in $\overline{S}$ (five ways to choose what happened on each die), so $p(S) = (36 - 25)/36 = 11/36$. Therefore the answer is $(2/36)/(11/36) = 2/11$.

b) The analysis is exactly the same as in part **(a)**, so the answer is again $2/11$.

40. We assume that n is much greater than k, since otherwise, we could simply compare each element with its successor in the list and know for sure whether or not the list is sorted. We choose two distinct random integers i and j from 1 to n, and we compare the ith and j^{th} elements of the given list; if they are in correct order relative to each other, then we answer "unknown" at this step and proceed. If not, then we answer "true" (i.e., the list is not sorted) and halt. We repeat this for k steps (or until we have found elements out of order), choosing new random indices each time. If we have not found any elements out of order after k steps, we halt and answer "false" (i.e., the original list is probably sorted). Since in a random list the probability that two randomly chosen elements are in correct order relative to each other is $1/2$, the probability that we wrongly answer "false" will be about $1/2^k$ if the list is a random permutation. If k is large, this will be very small; for example, if $k = 100$, then this will be less than one chance in 10^{30}.

SECTION 5.3   Expected Value and Variance

2. By Theorem 2 the expected number of successes for n Bernoulli trials is np. In the present problem we have $n = 10$ and $p = 1/2$. Therefore the expected number of successes (i.e., appearances of a head) is $10 \cdot (1/2) = 5$.

4. This is identical to Exercise 2, except that $p = 0.6$. Thus the expected number of heads is $10 \cdot 0.6 = 6$.

6. There are $C(50, 6)$ equally likely possible outcomes when the state picks its winning numbers. The probability of winning \$10 million is therefore $1/C(50, 6)$, and the probability of winning \$0 is $1 - (1/C(50, 6))$. By definition, the expectation is therefore $\$10,000,000 \cdot 1/C(50, 6) + 0 = \$10,000,000/15,890,700 \approx \$0.63$.

8. By Theorem 3 we know that the expectation of a sum is the sum of the expectations. In the current exercise we can let X be the random variable giving the value on the first die, let Y be the random variable giving the value on the second die, and let Z be the random variable giving the value on the third die. In order to compute the expectation of X, of Y, and of Z, we can ignore what happens on the dice not under consideration. Looking just at the first die, then, we compute that the expectation of X is

$$1 \cdot \frac{1}{6} + 2 \cdot \frac{1}{6} + 3 \cdot \frac{1}{6} + 4 \cdot \frac{1}{6} + 5 \cdot \frac{1}{6} + 6 \cdot \frac{1}{6} = 3.5.$$

Similarly, $E(Y) = 3.5$ and $E(Z) = 3.5$. Therefore $E(X + Y + Z) = 3 \cdot 3.5 = 10.5$.

10. There are 6 different outcomes of our experiment. Let the random variable X be the number of times we flip the coin. For $i = 1, 2, \ldots, 6$, we need to compute the probability that $X = i$. In order for this to happen when $i < 6$, the first $i - 1$ flips must contain exactly one tail, and there are $i - 1$ ways this can happen. Therefore $p(X = i) = (i - 1)/2^i$, since there are 2^i equally likely outcomes of i flips. So we have $p(X = 1) = 0$, $p(X = 2) = 1/4$, $p(X = 3) = 2/8 = 1/4$, $p(X = 4) = 3/16$, $p(X = 5) = 4/32 = 1/8$. To compute $p(X = 6)$, we note that this will happen when there is exactly one tail or no tails among the first five flips (probability $5/32 + 1/32 = 6/32 = 3/16$). As a check see that $0 + 1/4 + 1/4 + 3/16 + 1/8 + 3/16 = 1$. We compute the expected number by summing i times $p(X = i)$, so we get $1 \cdot 0 + 2 \cdot 1/4 + 3 \cdot 1/4 + 4 \cdot 3/16 + 5 \cdot 1/8 + 6 \cdot 3/16 = 3.75$.

12. If X is the number of times we roll the die, then X has a geometric distribution with $p = 1/6$.
a) $p(X = n) = (1 - p)^{n-1}p = (5/6)(1/6) = 5^{n-1}/6^n$
b) $1/(1/6) = 6$ by Theorem 4

14. We are asked to show that $\sum_{k=1}^{\infty}(1 - p)^{k-1}p = \sum_{i=0}^{\infty}(1 - p)^i p = 1$. This is a geometric series with initial term p and common ratio $1 - p$, which is less than 1 in absolute value. Therefore the sum converges and equals $p/(1 - (1 - p)) = 1$.

16. We need to show that $p(X = i$ and $Y = j)$ is not always equal to $p(X = i)p(Y = j)$. If we try $i = j = 2$, then we see that the former is 0 (since the sum of the number of heads and the number of tails has to be 2, the number of flips), whereas the latter is $(1/4)(1/4) = 1/16$.

18. Note that by the definition of maximum and the fact that X and Y take on only nonnegative values, $Z(s) \leq X(s) + Y(s)$ for every outcome s. Then

$$E(Z) = \sum_{s \in S} p(s)Z(s) \leq \sum_{s \in S} p(s)(X(s) + Y(s)) = \sum_{s \in S} p(s)X(s) + \sum_{s \in S} p(s)Y(s) = E(X) + E(Y).$$

20. By definition of expectation we have $E(I_A) = \sum_{s \in S} p(s)I_A(s) = \sum_{s \in A} p(s)$, since $I_A(s)$ is 1 when $s \in A$ and 0 when $s \notin A$. But $\sum_{s \in A} p(s) = p(A)$ by definition.

22. By definition, $E(X) = \sum_{k=1}^{\infty} k \cdot p(X = k)$. Let us write this out and regroup (such regrouping is valid even if the sum is infinite since all the terms are positive):

$$E(X) = p(X = 1) + (p(X = 2) + p(X = 2)) + (p(X = 3) + p(X = 3) + p(X = 3)) + \cdots$$
$$= (p(X = 1) + p(X = 2) + p(X = 3) + \cdots) + (p(X = 2) + p(X = 3) + \cdots) + (p(X = 3) + \cdots) + \cdots.$$

But this is precisely $p(A_1) + p(A_2) + p(A_3) + \cdots$, as desired.

24. In Example 18 we saw that the variance of the number of successes in n Bernoulli trials is npq. Here $n = 10$ and $p = 1/6$ and $q = 5/6$. Therefore the variance is $25/18$.

26. A dramatic example is to take $Y = -X$. Then the sum of the two random variables is identically 0, so the variance is certainly 0; but the sum of the variances is $2V(X)$, since Y has the same variance as X. For another (more concrete) example, we can take X to be the number of heads when a coin is flipped and Y to be the number of tails. Then by Example 14, $V(X) = V(Y) = 1/4$; but clearly $X + Y = 1$, so $V(X + Y) = 0$.

28. We proceed as in Example 19, applying Chebyshev's inequality with $V(X) = (0.6)(0.4)n = 0.24n$ by Example 18 and $r = \sqrt{n}$. We have $p(|X(s) - E(X)| \geq \sqrt{n}) \leq V(X)/r^2 = (0.24n)/(\sqrt{n})^2 = 0.24$.

30. It is interesting to note that Markov was Chebyshev's student in Russia. One caution—the variance is not 1000 cans; it is 1000 square cans (the units for the variance of X are the square of the units for X). So a measure of how much the number of cans filled per day varies is about the square root of this, or about 31 cans.

a) We have $E(X) = 10,000$ and we take $a = 11,000$. Then $p(X \geq 11,000) \leq 10,000/11,000 = 10/11$. This is not a terribly good estimate.

b) We apply Theorem 8, with $r = 1000$. The probability that the number of cans filled will differ from the expectation of 10,000 by at least 1000 is at most $1000/1000^2 = 0.001$. Therefore the probability is at least 0.999 that the plant will fill between 9,000 and 11,000 cans. This is also not a very good estimate, since if the number of cans filled per day usually differs by only about 31 from the mean of 10,000, it is virtually impossible that the difference would ever be over 30 times this amount—the probability is much, much less than 1 in 1000.

32. Since

$$\sum_{i=1}^{n} \frac{i}{n(n+1)} = \frac{1}{n(n+1)} \sum_{i=1}^{n} i = \frac{1}{n(n+1)} \frac{n(n+1)}{2} = \frac{1}{2},$$

the probability that the item is not in the list is $1/2$. We know (see Example 8) that if the item is not in the list, then $2n + 2$ comparisons are needed; and if the item is the ith item in the list then $2i + 1$ comparisons are needed. Therefore the expected number of comparisons is given by

$$\frac{1}{2}(2n + 2) + \sum_{i=1}^{n} \frac{i}{n(n+1)}(2i + 1).$$

To evaluate the sum, we use not only the fact that $\sum_{i=1}^{n} i = n(n+1)/2$, but also the fact that $\sum_{i=1}^{n} i^2 = n(n+1)(2n+1)/6$:

$$\frac{1}{2}(2n+2) + \sum_{i=1}^{n}\frac{i}{n(n+1)}(2i+1) = n+1 + \frac{2}{n(n+1)}\sum_{i=1}^{n}i^2 + \frac{1}{n(n+1)}\sum_{i=1}^{n}i$$

$$= n+1 + \frac{2}{n(n+1)}\frac{n(n+1)(2n+1)}{6} + \frac{1}{n(n+1)}\frac{n(n+1)}{2}$$

$$= n+1 + \frac{(2n+1)}{3} + \frac{1}{2} = \frac{10n+11}{6}$$

34. a) Each of the $n!$ permutations occurs with probability $1/n!$, so clearly $E(X)$ is the average number of comparisons, averaged over all these permutations.

b) The summation considers each unordered pair jk once and contributes a 1 if the jth smallest element and the kth smallest element are compared (and contributes 0 otherwise). Therefore the summation counts the number of comparisons, which is what X was defined to be. Note that by the way the algorithm works, the element being compared with at each round is put between the two sublists, so it is never compared with any other elements after that round is finished.

c) Take the expectation of both sides of the equation in part **(b)**. By linearity of expectation we have $E(X) = \sum_{k=2}^{n}\sum_{j=1}^{n-1} E(I_{j,k})$, and $E(I_{j,k})$ is the stated probability by Theorem 2 (with $n = 1$).

d) We prove this by strong induction on n. It is true when $n = 2$, since in this case the two elements are indeed compared once, and $2/(k - j + 1) = 2/(2 - 1 + 1) = 1$. Assume the inductive hypothesis, and consider the first round of quick sort. Suppose that the element in the first position (the element to be compared this round) is the ith smallest element. If $j < i < k$, then the jth smallest element gets put into the first sublist and the kth smallest element gets put into the second sublist, and so these two elements will never be compared. This happens with probability $(k - j - 1)/n$ in a random permutation. If $i = j$ or $i = k$, then the jth smallest element and the kth smallest element will be compared this round. This happens with probability $2/n$. If $i < j$, then both the jth smallest element and the kth smallest element get put into the second sublist and so by induction the probability that they will be compared later on will be $2/(k - j + 1)$. Similarly if $i > k$. The probability that $i < j$ is $(j - 1)/n$, and the probability that $i > k$ is $(n - k)/n$. Putting this all together, the probability of the desired comparison is

$$0 \cdot \frac{k-j-1}{n} + 1 \cdot \frac{2}{n} + \frac{2}{k-j+1}\cdot\left(\frac{j-1}{n} + \frac{n-k}{n}\right),$$

which after a little algebra simplifies to $2/(k - j + 1)$, as desired.

e) From the previous two parts, we need to prove that

$$\sum_{k=2}^{n}\sum_{j-1}^{k-1}\frac{2}{k-j+1} = 2(n+1)\sum_{i=2}^{n}\frac{1}{i} - 2(n-1).$$

This can be done, painfully, by induction.

f) This follows immediately from the previous two parts.

36. We can prove this by doing some algebra on the definition, using the facts (Theorem 3) that the expectation of a sum (or difference) is the sum (or difference) of the expectations and that the expectation of a constant times a random variable equals that constant times the expectation of the random variable:

$$\text{Cov}(X, Y) = E((X - E(X)) \cdot (Y - E(Y))) = E(XY - Y \cdot E(X) - X \cdot E(Y) + E(X) \cdot E(Y))$$
$$= E(XY) - E(Y) \cdot E(X) - E(X) \cdot E(Y) + E(X) \cdot E(Y) = E(XY) - E(X) \cdot E(Y)$$

If X and Y are independent, then by Theorem 5 these last two terms are the same, so their difference is 0.

38. We can use the result of Exercise 36. It is easy to see that $E(X) = 7$ and $E(Y) = 7$ (see Example 4). To find the expectation of XY, we construct the following table to show the value of $2i(i+j)$ for the 36 equally-likely outcomes (i is the row label, j the column label):

	1	2	3	4	5	6
1	4	6	8	10	12	14
2	12	16	20	24	28	32
3	24	30	36	42	48	54
4	40	48	56	64	72	80
5	60	70	80	90	100	110
6	84	96	108	120	132	144

The expected value of XY is therefore the sum of these entries divided by 36, namely $1974/36 = 329/6$. Therefore the covariance is $329/6 - 7 \cdot 7 = 35/6 \approx 5.8$.

40. Let $X = X_1 + X_2 + \cdots + X_m$, where $X_i = 1$ if the ith ball falls into the first bin and $X_i = 0$ otherwise. Then X is the number of balls that fall into the first bin, so we are being asked to compute $E(X)$. Clearly $E(X) = p(X_i = 1) = 1/n$. By linearity of expectation (Theorem 3), the expected number of balls that fall into the first bin is therefore m/n.

SUPPLEMENTARY EXERCISES FOR CHAPTER 5

2. There are $C(52, 13)$ possible hands. A hand with no pairs must contain exactly one card of each kind. The only choice involved, therefore, is the suit for each of the 13 cards. There are 4 ways to specify the suit, and there are 13 tasks to be performed. Therefore there are 4^{13} hands with no pairs. The probability of drawing such a hand is thus $4^{13}/C(52, 13) = 67108864/635013559600 = 4194304/39688347475 \approx 0.000106$.

4. The denominator of each probability is the number of 7-card poker hands, namely $C(52, 7) = 133784560$.
   a) The number of such hands is $13 \cdot 12 \cdot 4$, since there are 13 ways to choose the kind for the four, then 12 ways to choose another kind for the three, then $C(4, 3) = 4$ ways to choose which three cards of that second kind to use. Therefore the probability is $624/133784560 \approx 4.7 \times 10^{-6}$.
   b) The number of such hands is $13 \cdot 4 \cdot 66 \cdot 6^2$, since there are 13 ways to choose the kind for the three, $C(4, 3) = 4$ ways to choose which three cards of that kind to use, then $C(12, 2) = 66$ ways to choose two more kinds for the pairs, then $C(4, 2) = 6$ ways to choose which two cards of each of those kinds to use. Therefore the probability is $123552/133784560 \approx 9.2 \times 10^{-4}$.
   c) The number of such hands is $286 \cdot 6^3 \cdot 10 \cdot 4$, since there are $C(13, 3) = 286$ ways to choose the kinds for the pairs, $C(4, 2) = 6$ ways to choose which two cards of each of those kinds to use, 10 ways to choose the kind for the singleton, and 4 ways to choose which card of that kind to use. Therefore the probability is $2471040/133784560 \approx 0.018$.
   d) The number of such hands is $78 \cdot 6^2 \cdot 165 \cdot 4^3$, since there are $C(13, 2) = 78$ ways to choose the kinds for the pairs, $C(4, 2) = 6$ ways to choose which two cards of each of those kinds to use, $C(11, 3) = 165$ ways to choose the kinds for the singletons, and 4 ways to choose which card of each of those kinds to use. Therefore the probability is $29652480/133784560 \approx 0.22$.
   e) The number of such hands is $1716 \cdot 4^7$, since there are $C(13, 7) = 1716$ ways to choose the kinds and 4 ways to choose which card of each of kind to use. Therefore the probability is $28114944/133784560 \approx 0.21$.

f) The number of such hands is $4 \cdot 1716$, since there are 4 ways to choose the suit for the flush and $C(13, 7) = 1716$ ways to choose the kinds in that suit. Therefore the probability is $6864/133784560 \approx 5.1 \times 10^{-5}$.

g) The number of such hands is $8 \cdot 4^7$, since there are 8 ways to choose the kind for the straight to start at $(A, 2, 3, 4, 5, 6, 7, \text{ or } 8)$ and 4 ways to choose the suit for each kind. Therefore the probability is $131072/133784560 \approx 9.8 \times 10^{-4}$.

h) There are only $4 \cdot 8$ straight flushes, since the only choice is the suit and the starting kind (see part **(g)**). Therefore the probability is $32/133784560 \approx 2.4 \times 10^{-7}$.

6. a) Each of the outcomes 1 through 12 occurs with probability $1/12$, so the expectation is $(1/12)(1 + 2 + 3 + \cdots + 12) = 13/2$.

b) We compute $V(X) = E(X^2) - E(X)^2 = (1/12)(1^2 + 2^2 + 3^2 + \cdots + 12^2) - (13/2)^2 = (325/6) - (169/4) = 143/12$.

8. a) Since expected value is linear, the expected value of the sum is the sum of the expected values, each of which is $13/2$ by Exercise 6a. Therefore the answer is 13.

b) Since variance is linear for independent random variables, and clearly these variables are independent, the variance of the sum is the sum of the variances, each of which is $143/12$ by Exercise 6b. Therefore the answer is $143/6$.

10. a) Since expected value is linear, the expected value of the sum is the sum of the expected values, which are $9/2$ by Exercise 5a and $13/2$ by Exercise 6a. Therefore the answer is $(9/2) + (13/2) = 11$.

b) Since variance is linear for independent random variables, and clearly these variables are independent, the variance of the sum is the sum of the variances, which are $21/4$ by Exercise 5b and $143/12$ by Exercise 6b. Therefore the answer is $(21/4) + (143/12) = 103/6$.

12. We need to determine how many positive integers less than $n = pq$ are divisible by either p or q. Certainly the numbers p, $2p$, $3p$, $\ldots$, $(q - 1)p$ are all divisible by p. This gives $q - 1$ numbers. Similarly, $p - 1$ numbers are divisible by q. None of these numbers is divisible by both p and q since $lcm(p, q) = pq/\gcd(p, q) = pq/1 = pq = n$. Therefore $p + q - 2$ numbers in this range are divisible by p or q, so the remaining $pq - 1 - (p + q - 2) = pq - p - q + 1 = (p - 1)(q - 1)$ are not. Therefore the probability that a randomly chosen integer in this range is not divisible by either p or q is $(p - 1)(q - 1)/(pq - 1)$.

14. Technically a proof by mathematical induction is required, but we will give a somewhat less formal version. We just apply the definition of conditional probability to the right-hand side and observe that practically everything cancels (each denominator with the numerator of the previous term):

$$p(E_1)p(E_2|E_1)p(E_3|E_1 \cap E_2) \cdots p(E_n|E_1 \cap E_2 \cap \cdots \cap E_{n-1})$$
$$= p(E_1) \cdot \frac{p(E_1 \cap E_2)}{p(E_1)} \cdot \frac{p(E_1 \cap E_2 \cap E_3)}{p(E_1 \cap E_2)} \cdots \frac{p(E_1 \cap E_2 \cap \cdots \cap E_n)}{p(E_1 \cap E_2 \cap \cdots \cap E_{n-1})}$$
$$= p(E_1 \cap E_2 \cap \cdots \cap E_n)$$

16. If n is odd, then it is impossible, so the probability is 0. If n is even, then there are $C(n, n/2)$ ways that an equal number of heads and tails can appear (choose the flips that will be heads), and 2^n outcomes in all, so the probability is $C(n, n/2)/2^n$.

18. There are 2^{11} bit strings. There are 2^6 palindromic bit strings, since once the first six bits are specified arbitrarily, the remaining five bits are forced. If a bit string is picked at random, then, the probability that it is a palindrome is $2^6/2^{11} = 1/32$.

20. a) Since there are b bins, each equally likely to receive the ball, the answer is $1/b$.

b) By linearity of expectation, the fact that n balls are tossed, and the answer to part **(a)**, the answer is n/b.

c) In order for this part to make sense, we ignore n, and assume that the ball supply is unlimited and we keep tossing until the bin contains a ball. The number of tosses then has a geometric distribution with $p = 1/b$ from part **(a)**. The expectation is therefore b.

d) Again we have to assume that the ball supply is unlimited and we keep tossing until every bin contains at least one ball. The analysis is identical to that of Exercise 31 in this set, with b here playing the role of n there. By the solution given there, the answer is $b \sum_{j=1}^{b} 1/j$.

22. a) The intersection of two sets is a subset of each of them, so the largest $p(A \cap B)$ could be would occur when the smaller is a subset of the larger. In this case, that would mean that we want $B \subseteq A$, in which case $A \cap B = B$, so $p(A \cap B) = p(B) = 1/2$. To construct an example, we find a common denominator of the fractions involved, namely 6, and let the sample space consist of 6 equally likely outcomes, say numbered 1 through 6. We let $B = \{1, 2, 3\}$ and $A = \{1, 2, 3, 4\}$. The smallest intersection would occur when $A \cup B$ is as large as possible, since $p(A \cup B) = p(A) + p(B) - p(A \cap B)$. The largest $A \cup B$ could ever be is the entire sample space, whose probability is 1, and that certainly can occur here. So we have $1 = (2/3) + (1/2) - p(A \cap B)$, which gives $p(A \cap B) = 1/6$. To construct an example, again we find a common denominator of these fractions, namely 6, and let the sample space consist of 6 equally likely outcomes, say numbered 1 through 6. We let $A = \{1, 2, 3, 4\}$ and $B = \{4, 5, 6\}$. Then $A \cap B = \{4\}$, and $p(A \cap B) = 1/6$.

b) The largest $p(A \cup B)$ could ever be is 1, which occurs when $A \cup B$ is the entire sample space. As we saw in part **(a)**, that is possible here, using the second example above. The union of two sets is a subset of each of them, so the smallest $p(A \cup B)$ could be would occur when the smaller is a subset of the larger. In this case, that would mean that we want $B \subseteq A$, in which case $A \cup B = A$, so $p(A \cup B) = p(A) = 2/3$. This occurs in the first example given above.

24. Note that we can write E as the disjoint union $E = (E \cap F) \cup (E \cap \overline{F})$. Since the probability of a disjoint union is the sum of the probabilities, we have

$$p(E) = p(E \cap F) + p(E \cap \overline{F}) = p(E|F)p(F) + p(E|\overline{F})p(\overline{F}),$$

as desired.

26. Let E be the event that a 0 was received; let F_1 be the event that a 0 was sent; and let F_2 be the event that a 1 was sent. Note that $F_2 = \overline{F_1}$. Then we are told that $p(F_2) = 1/3$, $p(F_1) = 2/3$, $p(E|F_1) = 0.9$, and $p(E|F_2) = 0.2$.

a) $p(E) = p(E|F_1)p(F_1) + p(E|F_2)p(F_2) = 0.9 \cdot (2/3) + 0.2 \cdot (1/3) = 2/3$.

b) We use the formula shown in Exercise 25:

$$p(F_1|E) = \frac{p(E|F_1)p(F_1)}{p(E|F_1)p(F_1) + p(E|F_2)p(F_2)} = \frac{0.9 \cdot (2/3)}{0.9 \cdot (2/3) + 0.2 \cdot (1/3)} = \frac{0.6}{2/3} = 0.9$$

28. By Example 6 in Section 5.3, the expected value of X, the number of people who get their own hat back, is 1. By Exercise 35 in that section, the variance of X is also 1. If we apply Chebyshev's inequality (Theorem 8 in Section 5.3) with $r = 10$, we find that the probability that X is greater than or equal to 11 is at most $1/10^2 = 1/100$.

30. In order for the stated outcome to occur, the first $m + n$ trials must result in exactly m successes and n failures, and the $(m + n)^{\text{th}}$ trial must be a success. There are many ways in which this can occur; specifically, there are $C(n + m - 1, n)$ ways to choose which n of the first $n + m - 1$ trials are to be the failures. Each particular sequence has probability $q^n p^m$ of occurring, since the successes occur with probability p and the failures occur with probability q. The answer follows.

32. a) Clearly each assignment has a probability $1/2^n$.

b) The probability that the random assignment of truth values made the first of the two literals in the clause false is $1/2$, and similarly for the second. Since the coin tosses were independent, the probability that both are false is therefore $(1/2)(1/2) = 1/4$, so the probability that the disjunction is true is $1 - (1/4) = 3/4$.

c) By linearity of expectation, the answer is $(3/4)D$.

d) By part **(c)**, averaged over all possible outcomes of the coin flips, 3/4 of the clauses are true. Since the average cannot be greater than all the numbers being averaged, at least 3/4 of the clauses must be true for at least one outcome of the coin tosses.

CHAPTER 6
Advanced Counting Techniques

SECTION 6.1   Recurrence Relations

2. In each case we simply plug $n = 0, 1, 2, 3, 4, 5$, using the initial conditions for the first few and then the recurrence relation.

   a) $a_0 = -1$, $a_1 = -2a_0 = 2$, $a_2 = -2a_1 = -4$, $a_3 = -2a_2 = 8$, $a_4 = -2a_3 = -16$, $a_5 = -2a_4 = 32$

   b) $a_0 = 2$, $a_1 = -1$, $a_2 = a_1 - a_0 = -3$, $a_3 = a_2 - a_1 = -2$, $a_4 = a_3 - a_2 = 1$, $a_5 = a_4 - a_3 = 3$

   c) $a_0 = 1$, $a_1 = 3a_0^2 = 3$, $a_2 = 3a_1^2 = 27 = 3^3$, $a_3 = 3a_2^2 = 2187 = 3^7$, $a_4 = 3a_3^2 = 14348907 = 3^{15}$, $a_5 = 3a_4^2 = 617673396283947 = 3^{31}$

   d) $a_0 = -1$, $a_1 = 0$, $a_2 = 2a_1 + a_0^2 = 1$, $a_3 = 3a_2 + a_1^2 = 3$, $a_4 = 4a_3 + a_2^2 = 13$, $a_5 = 5a_4 + a_3^2 = 74$

   e) $a_0 = 1$, $a_1 = 1$, $a_2 = 2$, $a_3 = a_2 - a_1 + a_0 = 2$, $a_4 = a_3 - a_2 + a_1 = 1$, $a_5 = a_4 - a_3 + a_2 = 1$

4. a) $-3a_{n-1} + 4a_{n-2} = -3 \cdot 0 + 4 \cdot 0 = 0 = a_n$ **b)** $-3a_{n-1} + 4a_{n-2} = -3 \cdot 1 + 4 \cdot 1 = 1 = a_n$

   c) $-3a_{n-1} + 4a_{n-2} = -3 \cdot (-4)^{n-1} + 4 \cdot (-4)^{n-2} = (-4)^{n-2}\left((-3)(-4) + 4\right) = (-4)^{n-2} \cdot 16 = (-4)^{n-2}(-4)^2 = (-4)^n = a_n$

   d) $-3a_{n-1} + 4a_{n-2} = -3 \cdot \left(2(-4)^{n-1} + 3\right) + 4 \cdot \left(2(-4)^{n-2} + 3\right) = (-4)^{n-2}\left((-6)(-4) + 4 \cdot 2\right) - 9 + 12 = (-4)^{n-2} \cdot 32 + 3 = (-4)^{n-2}(-4)^2 \cdot 2 + 3 = 2 \cdot (-4)^n + 3 = a_n$

6. In each case, one possible answer is just the equation as presented (it is a recurrence relation of degree 0). We will give an alternate answer.

   a) One possible answer is $a_n = a_{n-1}$.

   b) Note that $a_n - a_{n-1} = 2n - (2n - 2) = 2$. Therefore we have $a_n = a_{n-1} + 2$ as one possible answer.

   c) Just as in part **(b)**, we have $a_n = a_{n-1} + 2$.

   d) Probably the simplest answer is $a_n = 5a_{n-1}$.

   e) Since $a_n - a_{n-1} = n^2 - (n-1)^2 = 2n - 1$, we have $a_n = a_{n-1} + 2n - 1$.

   f) This is similar to part **(e)**. One answer is $a_n = a_{n-1} + 2n$.

   g) Note that $a_n - a_{n-1} = n + (-1)^n - (n-1) - (-1)^{n-1} = 1 + 2(-1)^n$. Thus we have $a_n = a_{n-1} + 1 + 2(-1)^n$.

   h) $a_n = na_{n-1}$

8. In the iterative approach, we write a_n in terms of a_{n-1}, then write a_{n-1} in terms of a_{n-2} (using the recurrence relation with $n - 1$ plugged in for n), and so on. When we reach the end of this procedure, we use the given initial value of a_0. This will give us an explicit formula for the answer or it will give us a finite series, which we then sum to obtain an explicit formula for the answer.

   a) $a_n = -a_{n-1} = (-1)^2 a_{n-2} = \cdots = (-1)^n a_{n-n} = (-1)^n a_0 = 5 \cdot (-1)^n$

   b) $a_n = 3 + a_{n-1} = 3 + 3 + a_{n-2} = 2 \cdot 3 + a_{n-2} = 3 \cdot 3 + a_{n-3} = \cdots = n \cdot 3 + a_{n-n} = n \cdot 3 + a_0 = 3n + 1$

c)

$$a_n = -n + a_{n-1}$$
$$= -n + \big(-(n-1) + a_{n-2}\big) = -\big(n + (n-1)\big) + a_{n-2}$$
$$= -\big(n + (n-1)\big) + \big(-(n-2) + a_{n-3}\big) = -\big(n + (n-1) + (n-2)\big) + a_{n-3}$$
$$\vdots$$
$$= -\big(n + (n-1) + (n-2) + \cdots + (n - (n-1))\big) + a_{n-n}$$
$$= -\big(n + (n-1) + (n-2) + \cdots + 1\big) + a_0$$
$$= -\frac{n(n+1)}{2} + 4 = \frac{-n^2 - n + 8}{2}$$

d) $\quad a_n = -3 + 2a_{n-1}$

$$= -3 + 2(-3 + 2a_{n-2}) = -3 + 2(-3) + 4a_{n-2}$$
$$= -3 + 2(-3) + 4(-3 + 2a_{n-3}) = -3 + 2(-3) + 4(-3) + 8a_{n-3}$$
$$= -3 + 2(-3) + 4(-3) + 8(-3 + 2a_{n-4}) = -3 + 2(-3) + 4(-3) + 8(-3) + 16a_{n-4}$$
$$\vdots$$
$$= -3(1 + 2 + 4 + \cdots + 2^{n-1}) + 2^n a_{n-n} = -3(2^n - 1) + 2^n(-1) = -2^{n+2} + 3$$

e)

$$a_n = (n+1)a_{n-1} = (n+1)na_{n-2}$$
$$= (n+1)n(n-1)a_{n-3} = (n+1)n(n-1)(n-2)a_{n-4}$$
$$\vdots$$
$$= (n+1)n(n-1)(n-2)(n-3) \cdots (n - (n-2))\, a_{n-n}$$
$$= (n+1)n(n-1)(n-2)(n-3) \cdots 2 \cdot a_0$$
$$= (n+1)! \cdot 2 = 2(n+1)!$$

f)

$$a_n = 2na_{n-1}$$
$$= 2n\big(2(n-1)a_{n-2}\big) = 2^2\big(n(n-1)\big)a_{n-2}$$
$$= 2^2\big(n(n-1)\big)\big(2(n-2)a_{n-3}\big) = 2^3\big(n(n-1)(n-2)\big)a_{n-3}$$
$$\vdots$$
$$= 2^n n(n-1)(n-2)(n-3) \cdots (n - (n-1))a_{n-n}$$
$$= 2^n n(n-1)(n-2)(n-3) \cdots 1 \cdot a_0$$
$$= 3 \cdot 2^n n!$$

g) $\quad a_n = n - 1 - a_{n-1}$

$$= n - 1 - \big((n-1-1) - a_{n-2}\big) = (n-1) - (n-2) + a_{n-2}$$
$$= (n-1) - (n-2) + \big((n-2-1) - a_{n-3}\big) = (n-1) - (n-2) + (n-3) - a_{n-3}$$
$$\vdots$$
$$= (n-1) - (n-2) + \cdots + (-1)^{n-1}(n-n) + (-1)^n a_{n-n}$$
$$= \frac{2n - 1 + (-1)^n}{4} + (-1)^n \cdot 7$$

10. a) The amount after $n-1$ years is multiplied by 1.09 to give the amount after n years, since 9% of the value must be added to account for the interest. Thus we have $a_n = 1.09a_{n-1}$. The initial condition is $a_0 = 1000$.

b) Since we multiply by 1.09 for each year, the solution is $a_n = 1000(1.09)^n$.

c) $a_{100} = 1000(1.09)^{100} \approx \$5{,}529{,}041$

12. This is just like Exercise 10. We are letting a_n be the population, in billions of people, n years after 2002.

    a) $a_n = 1.013a_{n-1}$, with $a_0 = 6.2$ **b)** $a_n = 6.2 \cdot (1.013)^n$

    c) $a_{20} = 6.2 \cdot (1.013)^{20} \approx 8.0$ billion people

14. We let a_n be the salary, in thousands of dollars, n years after 1999.

    a) $a_n = 1 + 1.05a_{n-1}$, with $a_0 = 50$

    b) Here $n = 8$. We can either iterate the recurrence relation 8 times, or we can use the result of part **(c)**. The answer turns out to be approximately $a_8 = 83.4$, i.e., a salary of approximately \$83,400.

    c) We use the iterative approach.

$$
\begin{aligned}
a_n &= 1 + 1.05a_{n-1} \\
&= 1 + 1.05(1 + 1.05a_{n-2}) \\
&= 1 + 1.05 + (1.05)^2 a_{n-2} \\
&\quad\vdots \\
&= 1 + 1.05 + (1.05)^2 + \cdots + (1.05)^{n-1} + (1.05)^n a_0 \\
&= \frac{(1.05)^n - 1}{1.05 - 1} + 50 \cdot (1.05)^n \\
&= 70 \cdot (1.05)^n - 20
\end{aligned}
$$

16. **a)** Each month our account accrues some interest that must be paid. Since the balance the previous month is $B(k-1)$, the amount of interest we owe is $(r/12)B(k-1)$. After paying this interest, the rest of the P dollar payment we make each month goes toward reducing the principle. Therefore we have $B(k) = B(k-1) - (P - (r/12)B(k-1))$. This can be simplified to $B(k) = (1 + (r/12))B(k-1) - P$. The initial condition is that $B(0) =$ the amount borrowed.

    b) Solving this by iteration yields

$$B(k) = (1 + (r/12))^k (B(0) - 12P/r) + 12P/r.$$

Setting $B(k) = 0$ and solving this for k yields the desired value of T after some messy algebra, namely

$$T = \frac{\log(-12P/(B(0)r - 12P))}{\log(1 + (r/12))}.$$

18. **a)** A permutation of a set with n elements consists of a choice of a first element (which can be done in n ways), followed by a permutation of a set with $n - 1$ elements. Therefore $P_n = nP_{n-1}$. Note that $P_0 = 1$, since there is just one permutation of a set with no objects, namely the empty sequence.

    b) $P_n = nP_{n-1} = n(n-1)P_{n-2} = \cdots = n(n-1)\cdots 2 \cdot 1 \cdot P_0 = n!$

20. This is similar to Exercise 19 and solved in exactly the same way. The recurrence relation is $a_n = a_{n-1} + a_{n-2} + 2a_{n-5} + 2a_{n-10} + a_{n-20} + a_{n-50} + a_{n-100}$. It would be quite tedious to write down the 100 initial conditions.

22. **a)** Let s_n be the number of such sequences. A string ending in n must consist of a string ending in something less than n, followed by an n as the last term. Therefore the recurrence relation is $s_n = s_{n-1} + s_{n-2} + \cdots + s_2 + s_1$. Here is another approach, with a more compact form of the answer. A sequence ending in n is either a sequence ending in $n - 1$, followed by n (and there are clearly s_{n-1} of these), or else it does not contain $n - 1$ as a term at all, in which case it is *identical* to a sequence ending in $n - 1$ in which the $n - 1$ has been replaced by an n (and there are clearly s_{n-1} of these as well). Therefore $s_n = 2s_{n-1}$.

Finally we notice that we can derive the second form from the first (or vice versa) algebraically (for example, $s_4 = 2s_3 = s_3 + s_3 = s_3 + s_2 + s_2 = s_3 + s_2 + s_1$).

b) We need two initial conditions if we use the second formulation above, $s_1 = 1$ and $s_2 = 1$ (otherwise, our argument is invalid, because the first and last terms are the same). There is one sequence ending in 1, namely the sequence with just this 1 in it, and there is only the sequence $1, 2$ ending in 2. If we use the first formulation above, then we can get by with just the initial condition $s_1 = 1$.

c) Clearly the solution to this recurrence relation and initial condition is $s_n = 2^{n-2}$ for all $n \geq 2$.

24. This is very similar to Exercise 23, except that we need to go one level deeper.

a) Let a_n be the number of bit strings of length n containing three consecutive 0's. In order to construct a bit string of length n containing three consecutive 0's we could start with 1 and follow with a string of length $n-1$ containing three consecutive 0's, or we could start with a 01 and follow with a string of length $n-2$ containing three consecutive 0's, or we could start with a 001 and follow with a string of length $n-3$ containing three consecutive 0's, or we could start with a 000 and follow with any string of length $n-3$. These four cases are mutually exclusive and exhaust the possibilities for how the string might start. From this analysis we can immediately write down the recurrence relation, valid for all $n \geq 3$: $a_n = a_{n-1} + a_{n-2} + a_{n-3} + 2^{n-3}$.

b) There are no bit strings of length 0, 1, or 2 containing three consecutive 0's, so the initial conditions are $a_0 = a_1 = a_2 = 0$.

c) We will compute a_3 through a_7 using the recurrence relation:

$$a_3 = a_2 + a_1 + a_0 + 2^0 = 0 + 0 + +0 + 1 = 1$$
$$a_4 = a_3 + a_2 + a_1 + 2^1 = 1 + 0 + 0 + 2 = 3$$
$$a_5 = a_4 + a_3 + a_2 + 2^2 = 3 + 1 + 0 + 4 = 8$$
$$a_6 = a_5 + a_4 + a_3 + 2^3 = 8 + 3 + 1 + 8 = 20$$
$$a_7 = a_6 + a_5 + a_4 + 2^4 = 20 + 8 + 3 + 16 = 47$$

Thus there are 47 bit strings of length 7 containing three consecutive 0's.

26. First let us solve this problem without using recurrence relations at all. It is clear that the only strings that do not contain the string 01 are those that consist of a string of 1's follows by a string of 0's. The string can consist of anywhere from 0 to n 1's, so the number of such strings is $n + 1$. All the rest have at least one occurrence of 01. Therefore the number of bit strings that contain 01 is $2^n - (n+1)$. However, this approach does not meet the instructions of this exercise.

a) Let a_n be the number of bit strings of length n that contain 01. If we want to construct such a string, we could start with a 1 and follow it with a bit string of length $n-1$ that contains 01, and there are a_{n-1} of these. Alternatively, for any k from 1 to $n-1$, we could start with k 0's, follow this by a 1, and then follow this by any $n - k - 1$ bits. For each such k there are 2^{n-k-1} such strings, since the final bits are free. Therefore the number of such strings is $2^0 + 2^1 + 2^2 + \cdots + 2^{n-2}$, which equals $2^{n-1} - 1$. Thus our recurrence relation is $a_n = a_{n-1} + 2^{n-1} - 1$. It is valid for all $n \geq 2$.

b) The initial conditions are $a_0 = a_1 = 0$, since no string of length less than 2 can have 01 in it.

c) We will compute a_2 through a_7 using the recurrence relation:

$$a_2 = a_1 + 2^1 - 1 = 0 + 2 - 1 = 1$$
$$a_3 = a_2 + 2^2 - 1 = 1 + 4 - 1 = 4$$
$$a_4 = a_3 + 2^3 - 1 = 4 + 8 - 1 = 11$$
$$a_5 = a_4 + 2^4 - 1 = 11 + 16 - 1 = 26$$
$$a_6 = a_5 + 2^5 - 1 = 26 + 32 - 1 = 57$$
$$a_7 = a_6 + 2^6 - 1 = 57 + 64 - 1 = 120$$

Thus there are 120 bit strings of length 7 containing 01. Note that this agrees with our nonrecursive analysis, since $2^7 - (7+1) = 120$.

28. This is identical to Exercise 27, one level deeper.

a) Let a_n be the number of ways to climb n stairs. In order to climb n stairs, a person must either start with a step of one stair and then climb $n - 1$ stairs (and this can be done in a_{n-1} ways) or else start with a step of two stairs and then climb $n - 2$ stairs (and this can be done in a_{n-2} ways) or else start with a step of three stairs and then climb $n - 3$ stairs (and this can be done in a_{n-3} ways). From this analysis we can immediately write down the recurrence relation, valid for all $n \geq 3$: $a_n = a_{n-1} + a_{n-2} + a_{n-3}$.

b) The initial conditions are $a_0 = 1$, $a_1 = 1$, and $a_2 = 2$, since there is one way to climb no stairs (do nothing), clearly only one way to climb one stair, and two ways to climb two stairs (one step twice or two steps at once). Note that the recurrence relation is the same as that for Exercise 25.

c) Each term in our sequence $\{a_n\}$ is the sum of the previous three terms, so the sequence begins $a_0 = 1$, $a_1 = 1$, $a_2 = 2$, $a_3 = 4$, $a_4 = 7$, $a_5 = 13$, $a_6 = 24$, $a_7 = 44$, $a_8 = 81$. Thus a person can climb a flight of 8 stairs in 81 ways under the restrictions in this problem.

30. a) Let a_n be the number of ternary strings that contain two consecutive 0's. To construct such a string we could start with either a 1 or a 2 and follow with a string containing two consecutive 0's (and this can be done in $2a_{n-1}$ ways), or we could start with 01 or 02 and follow with a string containing two consecutive 0's (and this can be done in $2a_{n-2}$ ways), we could start with 00 and follow with any ternary string of length $n - 2$ (of which there are clearly 3^{n-2}). Therefore the recurrence relation, valid for all $n \geq 2$, is $a_n = 2a_{n-1} + 2a_{n-2} + 3^{n-2}$.

b) Clearly $a_0 = a_1 = 0$.

c) We will compute a_2 through a_6 using the recurrence relation:

$$a_2 = 2a_1 + 2a_0 + 3^0 = 2 \cdot 0 + 2 \cdot 0 + 1 = 1$$
$$a_3 = 2a_2 + 2a_1 + 3^1 = 2 \cdot 1 + 2 \cdot 0 + 3 = 5$$
$$a_4 = 2a_3 + 2a_2 + 3^2 = 2 \cdot 5 + 2 \cdot 1 + 9 = 21$$
$$a_5 = 2a_4 + 2a_3 + 3^3 = 2 \cdot 21 + 2 \cdot 5 + 27 = 79$$
$$a_6 = 2a_5 + 2a_4 + 3^4 = 2 \cdot 79 + 2 \cdot 21 + 81 = 281$$

Thus there are 281 bit strings of length 6 containing two consecutive 0's.

32. a) Let a_n be the number of ternary strings that contain either two consecutive 0's or two consecutive 1's. To construct such a string we could start with a 2 and follow with a string containing either two consecutive 0's or two consecutive 1's, and this can be done in a_{n-1} ways. There are other possibilities, however. For each k from 0 to $n - 2$, the string could start with $n - 1 - k$ alternating 0's and 1's, followed by a 2, and then be followed by a string of length k containing either two consecutive 0's or two consecutive 1's. The number of such strings is $2a_k$, since there are two ways for the initial part to alternate. The other possibility is that the string has no 2's at all. Then it must consist $n - k - 2$ alternating 0's and 1's, followed by a pair of 0's or 1's, followed by any string of length k. There are $2 \cdot 3^k$ such strings. Now the sum of these quantities as k runs from 0 to $n - 2$ is (since this is a geometric progression) $3^{n-1} - 1$. Putting this all together, we have the following recurrence relation, valid for all $n \geq 2$: $a_n = a_{n-1} + 2a_{n-2} + 2a_{n-3} + \cdots + 2a_0 + 3^{n-1} - 1$. (By subtracting this recurrence relation from the same relation with $n - 1$ substituted for n, we can obtain the following closed form recurrence relation for this problem: $a_n = 2a_{n-1} + a_{n-2} + 2 \cdot 3^{n-2}$.)

b) Clearly $a_0 = a_1 = 0$.

c) We will compute a_2 through a_6 using the recurrence relation:

$$a_2 = a_1 + 2a_0 + 3^1 - 1 = 0 + 2 \cdot 0 + 3 - 1 = 2$$
$$a_3 = a_2 + 2a_1 + 2a_0 + 3^2 - 1 = 2 + 2 \cdot 0 + 2 \cdot 0 + 9 - 1 = 10$$
$$a_4 = a_3 + 2a_2 + 2a_1 + 2a_0 + 3^3 - 1 = 10 + 2 \cdot 2 + 2 \cdot 0 + 2 \cdot 0 + 27 - 1 = 40$$
$$a_5 = a_4 + 2a_3 + 2a_2 + 2a_1 + 2a_0 + 3^4 - 1 = 40 + 2 \cdot 10 + 2 \cdot 2 + 2 \cdot 0 + 2 \cdot 0 + 81 - 1 = 144$$
$$a_6 = a_5 + 2a_4 + 2a_3 + 2a_2 + 2a_1 + 2a_0 + 3^5 - 1$$
$$= 144 + 2 \cdot 40 + 2 \cdot 10 + 2 \cdot 2 + 2 \cdot 0 + 2 \cdot 0 + 243 - 1 = 490$$

Thus there are 490 ternary strings of length 6 containing two consecutive 0's or two consecutive 1's.

34. a) Let a_n be the number of ternary strings that contain two consecutive symbols that are the same. We will develop a recurrence relation for a_n by exploiting the symmetry among the three symbols. In particular, it must be the case that $a_n/3$ such strings start with each of the three symbols. Now let us see how we might specify a string of length n satisfying the condition. We can choose the first symbol in any of three ways. We can follow this by a string that starts with a different symbol but has in it a pair of consecutive symbols; by what we have just said, there are $2a_{n-1}/3$ such strings. Alternatively, we can follow the initial symbol by another copy of itself and then any string of length $n - 2$; there are clearly 3^{n-2} such strings. Thus the recurrence relation is $a_n = 3 \cdot ((2a_{n-1}/3) + 3^{n-2}) = 2a_{n-1} + 3^{n-1}$. It is valid for all $n \geq 2$.

b) Clearly $a_0 = a_1 = 0$.

c) We will compute a_2 through a_6 using the recurrence relation:

$$a_2 = 2a_1 + 3^1 = 2 \cdot 0 + 3 = 3$$
$$a_3 = 2a_2 + 3^2 = 2 \cdot 3 + 9 = 15$$
$$a_4 = 2a_3 + 3^3 = 2 \cdot 15 + 27 = 57$$
$$a_5 = 2a_4 + 3^4 = 2 \cdot 57 + 81 = 195$$
$$a_6 = 2a_5 + 3^5 = 2 \cdot 195 + 243 = 633$$

Thus there are 633 bit strings of length 6 containing two consecutive 0's, 1's, or 2's.

36. We let a_n be the number of ways to pay a toll of $5n$ cents. (Obviously there is no way to pay a toll that is not a multiple of 5 cents.)

a) This problem is isomorphic to Exercise 27, so the answer is the same: $a_n = a_{n-1} + a_{n-2}$, with $a_0 = a_1 = 1$.

b) Iterating, we find that $a_9 = 55$.

38. a) We start by computing the first few terms to get an idea of what's happening. Clearly $R_1 = 2$, since the equator, say, splits the sphere into two hemispheres. Also, $R_2 = 4$ and $R_3 = 8$. Let's try to analyze what happens when the nth great circle is added. It must intersect each of the other circles twice (at diametrically opposite points), and each such intersection results in one prior region being split into two regions, as in Exercise 37. There are $n - 1$ previous great circles, and therefore $2(n - 1)$ new regions. Therefore $R_n = R_{n-1} + 2(n - 1)$. If we impose the initial condition $R_1 = 2$, then our values of R_2 and R_3 found above are consistent with this recurrence. Note that $R_4 = 14$, $R_5 = 22$, and so on.

b) We follow the usual technique, as in Exercise 9. In the last line we use the familiar formula for the sum of the first $n - 1$ positive integers. Note that the formula agrees with the values computed above.

$$R_n = 2(n - 1) + R_{n-1}$$
$$= 2(n - 1) + 2(n - 2) + R_{n-2}$$
$$= 2(n - 1) + 2(n - 2) + 2(n - 3) + R_{n-3}$$
$$\vdots$$

$$= 2(n-1) + 2(n-2) + 2(n-3) + 2 \cdot 1 + R_1$$
$$= n(n-1) + 2 = n^2 - n + 2$$

40. Let e_n be the number of bit sequences of length n with an even number of 0's. Note that therefore there are $2^n - e_n$ bit sequences with an odd number of 0's. There are two ways to get a bit string of length n with an even number of 0's. It can begin with a 1 and be followed by a bit string of length $n-1$ with an even number of 0's, and there are e_{n-1} of these; or it can begin with a 0 and be followed by a bit string of length $n-1$ with an odd number of 0's, and there are $2^{n-1} - e_{n-1}$ of these. Therefore $e_n = e_{n-1} + 2^{n-1} - e_{n-1}$, or simply $e_n = 2^{n-1}$. See also Exercise 31 in Section 4.4.

42. Let a_n be the number of coverings.

a) We follow the hint. If the right-most domino is positioned vertically, then we have a covering of the left-most $n-1$ columns, and this can be done in a_{n-1} ways. If the right-most domino is positioned horizontally, then there must be another domino directly beneath it, and these together cover the last two columns. The first $n-2$ columns therefore will need to contain a covering by dominos, and this can be done in a_{n-2} ways. Thus we obtain the Fibonacci recurrence $a_n = a_{n-1} + a_{n-2}$.

b) Clearly $a_1 = 1$ and $a_2 = 2$.

c) The sequence we obtain is just the Fibonacci sequence, shifted by one. The sequence is thus 1, 2, 3, 5, 8, 13, 21, 34, 55, 89, 144, 233, 377, 610, 987, 1597, 2584, ..., so the answer to this part is 2584.

44. The initial conditions are of course true. We prove the recurrence relation by induction on n, starting with base cases $n = 5$ and $n = 6$, in which cases we find $5f_1 + 3f_0 = 5 = f_5$ and $5f_2 + 3f_1 = 8 = f_6$. Assume the inductive hypothesis. Then we have $5f_{n-4} + 3f_{n-5} = 5(f_{n-5} + f_{n-6}) + 3(f_{n-6} + f_{n-7}) = (5f_{n-5} + 3f_{n-6}) + (5f_{n-6} + 3f_{n-7}) = f_{n-1} + f_{n-2} = f_n$ (we used both the inductive hypothesis and the recursive definition of the Fibonacci numbers). Finally, we prove that f_{5n} is divisible by 5 by induction on n. It is true for $n = 1$, since $f_5 = 5$ is divisible by 5. Assume that it is true for f_{5n}. Then $f_{5(n+1)} = f_{5n+5} = 5f_{5n+1} + 3f_{5n}$ is divisible by 5, since both summands in this expression are divisible by 5.

46. a) We do this systematically, based on the position of the outermost dot, working from left to right:

$$x_0 \cdot (x_1 \cdot (x_2 \cdot (x_3 \cdot x_4)))$$
$$x_0 \cdot (x_1 \cdot ((x_2 \cdot x_3) \cdot x_4))$$
$$x_0 \cdot ((x_1 \cdot x_2) \cdot (x_3 \cdot x_4))$$
$$x_0 \cdot ((x_1 \cdot (x_2 \cdot x_3)) \cdot x_4)$$
$$x_0 \cdot (((x_1 \cdot x_2) \cdot x_3) \cdot x_4)$$
$$(x_0 \cdot x_1) \cdot (x_2 \cdot (x_3 \cdot x_4))$$
$$(x_0 \cdot x_1) \cdot ((x_2 \cdot x_3) \cdot x_4)$$
$$(x_0 \cdot (x_1 \cdot x_2)) \cdot (x_3 \cdot x_4)$$
$$((x_0 \cdot x_1) \cdot x_2) \cdot (x_3 \cdot x_4)$$
$$(x_0 \cdot (x_1 \cdot (x_2 \cdot x_3))) \cdot x_4$$
$$(x_0 \cdot ((x_1 \cdot x_2) \cdot x_3)) \cdot x_4$$
$$((x_0 \cdot x_1) \cdot (x_2 \cdot x_3)) \cdot x_4$$
$$((x_0 \cdot (x_1 \cdot x_2)) \cdot x_3) \cdot x_4$$
$$(((x_0 \cdot x_1) \cdot x_2) \cdot x_3) \cdot x_4$$

b) We know from Example 8 that $C_0 = 1$, $C_1 = 1$, and $C_3 = 5$. It is also easy to see that $C_2 = 2$, since there are only two ways to parenthesize the product of three numbers. Therefore the recurrence relation tells us that $C_4 = C_0C_3 + C_1C_2 + C_2C_1 + C_3C_0 = 1 \cdot 5 + 1 \cdot 2 + 2 \cdot 1 + 5 \cdot 1 = 14$. We have the correct number of solutions listed above.

c) Here $n = 4$, so the formula gives $\frac{1}{5}C(8,4) = \frac{1}{5} \cdot 8 \cdot 7 \cdot 6 \cdot 5/4! = 14$.

48. We let a_n be the number of moves required for this puzzle.

a) In order to move the bottom disk off peg 1, we must have transferred the other $n-1$ disks to peg 3 (since we must move the bottom disk to peg 2); this will require a_{n-1} steps. Then we can move the bottom disk to peg 2 (one more step). Our goal, though, was to move it to peg 3, so now we must move the other $n-1$ disks from peg 3 back to peg 1, leaving the bottom disk quietly resting on peg 2. By symmetry, this again takes a_{n-1} steps. One more step lets us move the bottom disk from peg 2 to peg 3. Now it takes a_{n-1} steps to move the remaining disks from peg 1 to peg 3. So our recurrence relation is $a_n = 3a_{n-1} + 2$. The initial condition is of course that $a_0 = 0$.

b) Computing the first few values, we find that $a_1 = 2$, $a_2 = 8$, $a_3 = 26$, and $a_4 = 80$. It appears that $a_n = 3^n - 1$. This is easily verified by induction: The base case is $a_0 = 3^0 - 1 = 1 - 1 = 0$, and $3a_{n-1} + 2 = 3 \cdot (3^{n-1} - 1) + 2 = 3^n - 3 + 2 = 3^n - 1 = a_n$.

c) The only choice in distributing the disks is which peg each disk goes on, since the order of the disks on a given peg is fixed. Since there are three choices for each disk, the answer is 3^n.

d) The puzzle involves $1 + a_n = 3^n$ arrangements of disks during its solution—the initial arrangement and the arrangement after each move. None of these arrangements can repeat a previous arrangement, since if it did so, there would have been no point in making the moves between the two occurrences of the same arrangement. Therefore these 3^n arrangements are all distinct. We saw in part **(c)** that there are exactly 3^n arrangements, so every arrangement was used.

50. If we follow the hint, then it certainly looks as if $J(n) = 2k + 1$, where k is the amount left over after the largest possible power of 2 has been subtracted from n (i.e., $n = 2^m + k$ and $k < 2^m$).

52. The base case is trivial, since when $n = 1 = 2^0 + 0$, the conjecture in Exercise 50 states that $J(n) = 2 \cdot 0 + 1 = 1$, which is correct. For the inductive step, we look at two cases, depending on whether there are an even or an odd number of players. If there are $2n$ players, suppose that $2n = 2^m + k$, as in the hint for Exercise 50. Then k must be even and we can write $n = 2^{m-1} + (k/2)$, and $k/2 < 2^{m-1}$. By the inductive hypothesis, $J(n) = 2(k/2) + 1 = k + 1$. Then by the recurrence relation from Exercise 51, $J(2n) = 2J(n) - 1 = 2(k+1) - 1 = 2k + 1$, as desired. For the other case, assume that there are $2n + 1$ players, and again write $2n + 1 = 2^m + k$, as in the hint for Exercise 50. Then k must be odd and we can write $n = 2^{m-1} + (k-1)/2$, where $(k-1)/2 < 2^{m-1}$. By the inductive hypothesis, $J(n) = 2((k-1)/2) + 1 = k$. Then by the recurrence relation from Exercise 51, $J(2n+1) = 2J(n) + 1 = 2k + 1$, as desired.

54. Since we can only move one disk at a time, we need one move to lift the smallest disk off the middle disk, and another to lift the middle disk off the largest. Similarly, we need two moves to rejoin these disks. And of course we need at least one move to get the largest disk off peg 1. Therefore we can do no better than five moves. To see that this is possible, we just make the obvious moves (disk 1 is the smallest, and $a \xrightarrow{b} c$ means to move disk b from peg a to peg c: $1 \xrightarrow{1} 2$, $1 \xrightarrow{2} 3$, $1 \xrightarrow{3} 4$, $3 \xrightarrow{2} 4$, $2 \xrightarrow{1} 4$.

56. In our notation, disk 1 is the smallest and disk n is the largest; $a \xrightarrow{b} c$ means to move disk b from peg a to peg c.

a) According to the algorithm, we take $k = 3$, since 5 is between the triangular numbers $t_2 = 3$ and $t_3 = 6$. The moves are to first move $5 - 3 = 2$ disks from peg 1 to peg 2 ($1 \xrightarrow{1} 3$, $1 \xrightarrow{2} 2$, $3 \xrightarrow{1} 2$), then working with pegs 1, 3, and 4 move disks 3, 4, and 5 to peg 4 ($1\xrightarrow{3}4$, $1\xrightarrow{4}3$, $4\xrightarrow{3}3$, $1\xrightarrow{5}4$, $3\xrightarrow{3}1$, $3\xrightarrow{4}4$, $1\xrightarrow{3}4$), and then move disks 1 and 2 from peg 2 to peg 4 ($2\xrightarrow{1}3$, $2\xrightarrow{2}4$, $3\xrightarrow{1}4$). Note that this took 13 moves in all.

b) According to the algorithm, we take $k = 3$, since 6 is between the triangular numbers $t_2 = 3$ and $t_3 = 6$. The moves are to first move $6 - 3 = 3$ disks from peg 1 to peg 2 ($1\xrightarrow{1}3$, $1\xrightarrow{2}4$, $1\xrightarrow{3}2$, $4\xrightarrow{2}2$, $3\xrightarrow{1}2$), then working with pegs 1, 3, and 4 move disks 4, 5, and 6 to peg 4 ($1\xrightarrow{4}4$, $1\xrightarrow{5}3$, $4\xrightarrow{4}3$, $1\xrightarrow{6}4$, $3\xrightarrow{4}1$, $3\xrightarrow{5}4$, $1\xrightarrow{4}4$), and then move disks 1, 2, and 3 from peg 2 to peg 4 ($2\xrightarrow{1}3$, $2\xrightarrow{2}1$, $2\xrightarrow{3}4$, $1\xrightarrow{2}4$, $3\xrightarrow{1}4$). Note that this took 17 moves in all.

c) According to the algorithm, we take $k = 4$, since 7 is between the triangular numbers $t_3 = 6$ and $t_4 = 10$. The moves are to first move $7 - 4 = 3$ disks from peg 1 to peg 2 (five moves, as in part **(b)**), then working with pegs 1, 3, and 4 move disks 4, 5, 6, and 7 to peg 4 (15 moves, using the usual Tower of Hanoi algorithm), and then move disks 1, 2, and 3 from peg 2 to peg 4 (again five moves, as in part **(b)**). Note that this took 25 moves in all.

d) According to the algorithm, we take $k = 4$, since 8 is between the triangular numbers $t_3 = 6$ and $t_4 = 10$. The moves are to first move $8 - 4 = 4$ disks from peg 1 to peg 2 (nine moves, as in Exercise 55, with peg 2 playing the role of peg 4), then working with pegs 1, 3, and 4 move disks 5, 6, 7, and 8 to peg 4 (15 moves, using the usual Tower of Hanoi algorithm), and then move disks 1, 2, 3, and 4 from peg 2 to peg 4 (again nine moves, as above). Note that this took 33 moves in all.

58. To clarify the problem, we note that k is chosen to be the smallest nonnegative integer such that $n \le k(k+1)/2$. If $n - 1 \ne k(k-1)/2$, then this same value of k applies to $n - 1$ as well; otherwise the value for $n - 1$ is $k - 1$. If $n - 1 \ne k(k-1)/2$, it also follows by subtracting k from both sides of the inequality that the smallest nonnegative integer m such that $n - k \le m(m+1)/2$ is $m = k - 1$, so $k - 1$ is the value selected by the Frame-Stewart algorithm for $n - k$. Now we proceed by induction, the base cases being trivial. There are two cases for the inductive step. If $n - 1 \ne k(k-1)/2$, then we have from the recurrence relation in Exercise 57 that $R(n) = 2R(n - k) + 2^k - 1$ and $R(n - 1) = 2R(n - k - 1) + 2^k - 1$. Subtracting yields $R(n) - R(n - 1) = 2(R(n - k) - R(n - k - 1))$. Since $k - 1$ is the value selected for $n - k$, the inductive hypothesis tells us that this difference is $2 \cdot 2^{k-2} = 2^{k-1}$, as desired. On the other hand, if $n - 1 = k(k-1)/2$, then $R(n) - R(n - 1) = 2R(n - k) + 2^k - 1 - (2R(n - 1 - (k - 1)) + 2^{k-1} - 1 = 2^{k-1}$.

60. Since the Frame-Stewart algorithm solves the puzzle, the number of moves it uses, $R(n)$, is an upper bound to the number of moves needed to solve the puzzle. By Exercise 59 we have a recurrence or formula for these numbers. The table below shows n, the corresponding k and t_k, and $R(n)$.

n	k	t_k	$R(n)$
1	1	1	1
2	2	3	3
3	2	3	5
4	3	6	9
5	3	6	13
6	3	6	17
7	4	10	25
8	4	10	33
9	4	10	41
10	4	10	49
11	5	15	65
12	5	15	81
13	5	15	97
14	5	15	113
15	5	15	129

16	6	21	161
17	6	21	193
18	6	21	225
19	6	21	257
20	6	21	289
21	6	21	321
22	7	28	353
23	7	28	417
24	7	28	481
25	7	28	545

62. a) $\nabla a_n = 4 - 4 = 0$ **b)** $\nabla a_n = 2n - 2(n-1) = 2$
c) $\nabla a_n = n^2 - (n-1)^2 = 2n - 1$ **d)** $\nabla a_n = 2^n - 2^{n-1} = 2^{n-1}$

64. This follows immediately (by algebra) from the definition.

66. We prove this by induction on k. The case $k = 1$ was Exercise 64. Assume the inductive hypothesis, that a_{n-k} can be expressed in terms of a_n, ∇a_n, ..., $\nabla^k a_n$, for all n. We will show that $a_{n-(k+1)}$ can be expressed in terms of a_n, ∇a_n, ..., $\nabla^k a_n$, $\nabla^{k+1} a_n$. Note from the definitions that $a_{n-1} = a_n - \nabla a_n$ and that $\nabla^i a_{n-1} = \nabla^i a_n - \nabla^{i+1} a_n$ for all i. By the inductive hypothesis, we know that $a_{(n-1)-k}$ (which is just $a_{n-(k+1)}$ rewritten) can be expressed as $f(a_{n-1}, \nabla a_{n-1}, \ldots, \nabla^k a_{n-1}) = f(a_n - \nabla a_n, \nabla a_n - \nabla^2 a_n, \ldots, \nabla^k a_n - \nabla^{k+1} a_n)$—exactly what we wished to show. Note that in fact all the equations involved are linear.

68. By Exercise 66, each a_{n-i} can be so expressed (as a linear function), so the entire recurrence relation $a_n = c_1 a_{n-1} + c_2 a_{n-2} + \cdots + c_k a_{n-k}$ can be written as $a_n = c_1 f_1 + c_2 f_2 + \cdots + c_k f_k$, where each f_i is a linear expression involving a_n, ∇a_n, ..., $\nabla^k a_n$. This gives us the desired difference equation.

SECTION 6.2   Solving Recurrence Relations

2. a) linear, homogeneous, with constant coefficients; degree 2
b) linear with constant coefficients but not homogeneous
c) not linear
d) linear, homogeneous, with constant coefficients; degree 3
e) linear and homogeneous, but not with constant coefficients
f) linear with constant coefficients, but not homogeneous
g) linear, homogeneous, with constant coefficients; degree 7

4. For each problem, we first write down the characteristic equation and find its roots. Using this we write down the general solution. We then plug in the initial conditions to obtain a system of linear equations. We solve these equations to determine the arbitrary constants in the general solution, and finally we write down the unique answer.
a) $r^2 - r - 6 = 0$ $r = -2, 3$
$$a_n = \alpha_1(-2)^n + \alpha_2 3^n$$
$$3 = \alpha_1 + \alpha_2$$
$$6 = -2\alpha_1 + 3\alpha_2$$
$$\alpha_1 = 3/5 \qquad \alpha_2 = 12/5$$
$$a_n = (3/5)(-2)^n + (12/5)3^n$$

b) $r^2 - 7r + 10 = 0 \qquad r = 2, 5$

$\qquad a_n = \alpha_1 2^n + \alpha_2 5^n$

$\qquad\qquad 2 = \alpha_1 + \alpha_2$

$\qquad\qquad 1 = 2\alpha_1 + 5\alpha_2$

$\qquad\qquad \alpha_1 = 3 \qquad \alpha_2 = -1$

$\qquad a_n = 3 \cdot 2^n - 5^n$

c) $r^2 - 6r + 8 = 0 \qquad r = 2, 4$

$\qquad a_n = \alpha_1 2^n + \alpha_2 4^n$

$\qquad\qquad 4 = \alpha_1 + \alpha_2$

$\qquad\qquad 10 = 2\alpha_1 + 4\alpha_2$

$\qquad\qquad \alpha_1 = 3 \qquad \alpha_2 = 1$

$\qquad a_n = 3 \cdot 2^n + 4^n$

d) $r^2 - 2r + 1 = 0 \qquad r = 1, 1$

$\qquad a_n = \alpha_1 1^n + \alpha_2 n 1^n = \alpha_1 + \alpha_2 n$

$\qquad\qquad 4 = \alpha_1$

$\qquad\qquad 1 = \alpha_1 + \alpha_2$

$\qquad\qquad \alpha_1 = 4 \qquad \alpha_2 = -3$

$\qquad a_n = 4 - 3n$

e) $r^2 - 1 = 0 \qquad r = -1, 1$

$\qquad a_n = \alpha_1(-1)^n + \alpha_2 1^n = \alpha_1(-1)^n + \alpha_2$

$\qquad\qquad 5 = \alpha_1 + \alpha_2$

$\qquad\qquad -1 = -\alpha_1 + \alpha_2$

$\qquad\qquad \alpha_1 = 3 \qquad \alpha_2 = 2$

$\qquad a_n = 3 \cdot (-1)^n + 2$

f) $r^2 + 6r + 9 = 0 \qquad r = -3, -3$

$\qquad a_n = \alpha_1(-3)^n + \alpha_2 n(-3)^n$

$\qquad\qquad 3 = \alpha_1$

$\qquad\qquad -3 = -3\alpha_1 - 3\alpha_2$

$\qquad\qquad \alpha_1 = 3 \qquad \alpha_2 = -2$

$\qquad a_n = 3(-3)^n - 2n(-3)^n = (3 - 2n)(-3)^n$

g) $r^2 + 4r - 5 = 0 \qquad r = -5, 1$

$\qquad a_n = \alpha_1(-5)^n + \alpha_2 1^n = \alpha_1(-5)^n + \alpha_2$

$\qquad\qquad 2 = \alpha_1 + \alpha_2$

$\qquad\qquad 8 = -5\alpha_1 + \alpha_2$

$\qquad\qquad \alpha_1 = -1 \qquad \alpha_2 = 3$

$\qquad a_n = -(-5)^n + 3$

6. The model is the recurrence relation $a_n = a_{n-1} + a_{n-2} + a_{n-2} = a_{n-1} + 2a_{n-2}$, with $a_0 = a_1 = 1$ (see the technique of Exercise 35 in Section 6.1). To solve this, we use the characteristic equation $r^2 - r - 2 = 0$, which has roots -1 and 2. Therefore the general solution is $a_n = \alpha_1(-1)^n + \alpha_2 2^n$. Plugging in the initial conditions gives the equations $1 = \alpha_1 + \alpha_2$ and $1 = -\alpha_1 + 2\alpha_2$, which solve to $\alpha_1 = 1/3$ and $\alpha_2 = 2/3$. Therefore in n microseconds $(1/3)(-1)^n + (2/3)2^n$ messages can be transmitted.

8. a) The recurrence relation is, by the definition of average, $L_n = (1/2)L_{n-1} + (1/2)L_{n-2}$.

$\quad$**b)** The characteristic equation is $r^2 - (1/2)r - (1/2) = 0$, which gives us $r = -1/2$ and $r = 1$. Therefore the general solution is $L_n = \alpha_1(-1/2)^n + \alpha_2$. Plugging in the initial conditions $L_1 = 100000$ and $L_2 = 300000$ gives $100000 = (-1/2)\alpha_1 + \alpha_2$ and $300000 = (1/4)\alpha_1 + \alpha_2$. Solving these yields $\alpha_1 = 800000/3$ and $\alpha_2 = 700000/3$. Therefore the answer is $L_n = (800000/3)(-1/2)^n + (700000/3)$.

10. The proof may be found in textbooks such as *Introduction to Combinatorial Mathematics* by C. L. Liu (McGraw-Hill, 1968), Chapter 3. It is similar to the proof of Theorem 1.

12. The characteristic equation is $r^3 - 2r^2 - r + 2 = 0$. This factors as $(r-1)(r+1)(r-2) = 0$, so the roots are 1, -1, and 2. Therefore the general solution is $a_n = \alpha_1 + \alpha_2(-1)^n + \alpha_3 2^n$. Plugging in initial conditions gives $3 = \alpha_1 + \alpha_2 + \alpha_3$, $6 = \alpha_1 - \alpha_2 + 2\alpha_3$, and $0 = \alpha_1 + \alpha_2 + 4\alpha_3$. The solution to this system of equations is $\alpha_1 = 6$, $\alpha_2 = -2$, and $\alpha_3 = -1$. Therefore the answer is $a_n = 6 - 2(-1)^n - 2^n$.

14. The characteristic equation is $r^4 - 5r^2 + 4 = 0$. This factors as $(r^2-1)(r^2-4) = (r-1)(r+1)(r-2)(r+2) = 0$, so the roots are 1, -1, 2, and -2. Therefore the general solution is $a_n = \alpha_1 + \alpha_2(-1)^n + \alpha_3 2^n + \alpha_4(-2)^n$. Plugging in initial conditions gives $3 = \alpha_1 + \alpha_2 + \alpha_3 + \alpha_4$, $2 = \alpha_1 - \alpha_2 + 2\alpha_3 - 2\alpha_4$, $6 = \alpha_1 + \alpha_2 + 4\alpha_3 + 4\alpha_4$, and $8 = \alpha_1 - \alpha_2 + 8\alpha_3 - 8\alpha_4$. The solution to this system of equations is $\alpha_1 = \alpha_2 = \alpha_3 = 1$ and $\alpha_4 = 0$. Therefore the answer is $a_n = 1 + (-1)^n + 2^n$.

16. This requires some linear algebra, but follows the same basic idea as the proof of Theorem 1. See textbooks such as *Introduction to Combinatorial Mathematics* by C. L. Liu (McGraw-Hill, 1968), Chapter 3.

18. This is a third degree recurrence relation. The characteristic equation is $r^3 - 6r^2 + 12r - 8 = 0$. By the rational root test, the possible rational roots are $\pm 1, \pm 2, \pm 4$. We find that $r = 2$ is a root. Dividing $r - 2$ into $r^3 - 6r^2 + 12r - 8$, we find that $r^3 - 6r^2 + 12r - 8 = (r-2)(r^2 - 4r + 4)$. By inspection we factor the rest, obtaining $r^3 - 6r^2 + 12r - 8 = (r-2)^3$. Hence the only root is 2, with multiplicity 3, so the general solution is (by Theorem 4) $a_n = \alpha_1 2^n + \alpha_2 n 2^n + \alpha_3 n^2 2^n$. To find these coefficients, we plug in the initial conditions:
$$-5 = a_0 = \alpha_1$$
$$4 = a_1 = 2\alpha_1 + 2\alpha_2 + 2\alpha_3$$
$$88 = a_2 = 4\alpha_1 + 8\alpha_2 + 16\alpha_3.$$
Solving this system of equations, we get $\alpha_1 = -5$, $\alpha_2 = 1/2$, and $\alpha_3 = 13/2$. Therefore the answer is $a_n = -5 \cdot 2^n + (n/2) \cdot 2^n + (13n^2/2) \cdot 2^n = -5 \cdot 2^n + n \cdot 2^{n-1} + 13n^2 \cdot 2^{n-1}$.

20. This is a fourth degree recurrence relation. The characteristic polynomial is $r^4 - 8r^2 + 16$, which factors as $(r^2 - 4)^2$, which then further factors into $(r-2)^2(r+2)^2$. The roots are 2 and -2, each with multiplicity 2. Thus we can write down the general solution as usual: $a_n = \alpha_1 2^n + \alpha_2 n \cdot 2^n + \alpha_3(-2)^n + \alpha_4 n \cdot (-2)^n$.

22. This is similar to Example 6. We can immediately write down the general solution using Theorem 4. In this case there are four distinct roots, so $t = 4$. The multiplicities are 3, 2, 2, and 1. So the general solution is $a_n = (\alpha_{1,0} + \alpha_{1,1}n + \alpha_{1,2}n^2)(-1)^n + (\alpha_{2,0} + \alpha_{2,1}n)2^n + (\alpha_{3,0} + \alpha_{3,1}n)5^n + \alpha_{4,0}7^n$.

24. **a)** We compute the right-hand side of the recurrence relation: $2(n-1)2^{n-1} + 2^n = (n-1)2^n + 2^n = n2^n$, which is the left-hand side.

   b) The solution of the associated homogeneous equation $a_n = 2a_{n-1}$ is easily found to be $a_n = \alpha 2^n$. Therefore the general solution of the inhomogeneous equation is $a_n = \alpha 2^n + n2^n$.

   c) Plugging in $a_0 = 2$, we obtain $\alpha = 2$. Therefore the solution is $a_n = 2 \cdot 2^n + n2^n = (n+2)2^n$.

26. We need to use Theorem 6, and so we need to find the roots of the characteristic polynomial of the associated homogeneous recurrence relation. The characteristic equation is $r^3 - 6r^2 + 12r - 8 = 0$, and as we saw in Exercise 18, $r = 2$ is the only root, and it has multiplicity 3.

   a) Since 1 is not a root of the characteristic polynomial of the associated homogeneous recurrence relation, Theorem 6 tells us that the particular solution will be of the form $p_2 n^2 + p_1 n + p_0$. In the notation of Theorem 6, $s = 1$ here.

b) Since 2 is a root with multiplicity 3 of the characteristic polynomial of the associated homogeneous recurrence relation, Theorem 6 tells us that the particular solution will be of the form $n^3 p_0 2^n$.

c) Since 2 is a root with multiplicity 3 of the characteristic polynomial of the associated homogeneous recurrence relation, Theorem 6 tells us that the particular solution will be of the form $n^3(p_1 n + p_0)2^n$.

d) Since -2 is not a root of the characteristic polynomial of the associated homogeneous recurrence relation, Theorem 6 tells us that the particular solution will be of the form $p_0(-2)^n$.

e) Since 2 is a root with multiplicity 3 of the characteristic polynomial of the associated homogeneous recurrence relation, Theorem 6 tells us that the particular solution will be of the form $n^3(p_2 n^2 + p_1 n + p_0)2^n$.

f) Since -2 is not a root of the characteristic polynomial of the associated homogeneous recurrence relation, Theorem 6 tells us that the particular solution will be of the form $(p_3 n^3 + p_2 n^2 + p_1 n + p_0)(-2)^n$.

g) Since 1 is not a root of the characteristic polynomial of the associated homogeneous recurrence relation, Theorem 6 tells us that the particular solution will be of the form p_0. In the notation of Theorem 6, $s = 1$ here.

28. a) The associated homogeneous recurrence relation is $a_n = 2a_{n-1}$. We easily solve it to obtain $a_n^{(h)} = \alpha 2^n$. Next we need a particular solution to the given recurrence relation. By Theorem 6 we want to look for a function of the form $a_n = p_2 n^2 + p_1 n + p_0$. (Note that $s = 1$ here, and 1 is not a root of the characteristic polynomial.) We plug this into our recurrence relation and obtain $p_2 n^2 + p_1 n + p_0 = 2(p_2(n-1)^2 + p_1(n-1) + p_0) + 2n^2$. We rewrite this by grouping terms with equal powers of n, obtaining $(-p_2 - 2)n^2 + (4p_2 - p_1)n + (-2p_2 + 2p_1 - p_0) = 0$. In order for this equation to be true for all n, we must have $p_2 = -2$, $4p_2 = p_1$, and $-2p_2 + 2p_1 - p_0 = 0$. This tells us that $p_1 = -8$ and $p_0 = -12$. Therefore the particular solution we seek is $a_n^{(p)} = -2n^2 - 8n - 12$. So the general solution is the sum of the homogeneous solution and this particular solution, namely $a_n = \alpha 2^n - 2n^2 - 8n - 12$.

b) We plug the initial condition into our solution from part **(a)** to obtain $4 = a_1 = 2\alpha - 2 - 8 - 12$. This tells us that $\alpha = 13$. So the solution is $a_n = 13 \cdot 2^n - 2n^2 - 8n - 12$.

30. a) The associated homogeneous recurrence relation is $a_n = -5a_{n-1} - 6a_{n-2}$. To solve it we find the characteristic equation $r^2 + 5r + 6 = 0$, find that $r = -2$ and $r = -3$ are its solutions, and therefore obtain the homogeneous solution $a_n^{(h)} = \alpha(-2)^n + \beta(-3)^n$. Next we need a particular solution to the given recurrence relation. By Theorem 6 we want to look for a function of the form $a_n = c \cdot 4^n$. We plug this into our recurrence relation and obtain $c \cdot 4^n = -5c \cdot 4^{n-1} - 6c \cdot 4^{n-2} + 42 \cdot 4^n$. We divide through by 4^{n-2}, obtaining $16c = -20c - 6c + 42 \cdot 16$, whence with a little simple algebra $c = 16$. Therefore the particular solution we seek is $a_n^{(p)} = 16 \cdot 4^n = 4^{n+2}$. So the general solution is the sum of the homogeneous solution and this particular solution, namely $a_n = \alpha(-2)^n + \beta(-3)^n + 4^{n+2}$.

b) We plug the initial conditions into our solution from part **(a)** to obtain $56 = a_1 = -2\alpha - 3\beta + 64$ and $278 = a_2 = 4\alpha + 9\beta + 256$. A little algebra yields $\alpha = 1$ and $\beta = 2$. So the solution is $a_n = (-2)^n + 2(-3)^n + 4^{n+2}$.

32. The associated homogeneous recurrence relation is $a_n = 2a_{n-1}$. We easily solve it to obtain $a_n^{(h)} = \alpha 2^n$. Next we need a particular solution to the given recurrence relation. By Theorem 6 we want to look for a function of the form $a_n = cn \cdot 2^n$. We plug this into our recurrence relation and obtain $cn \cdot 2^n = 2c(n-1)2^{n-1} + 3 \cdot 2^n$. We divide through by 2^{n-1}, obtaining $2cn = 2c(n-1) + 6$, whence with a little simple algebra $c = 3$. Therefore the particular solution we seek is $a_n^{(p)} = 3n \cdot 2^n$. So the general solution is the sum of the homogeneous solution and this particular solution, namely $a_n = \alpha 2^n + 3n \cdot 2^n = (3n + \alpha)2^n$.

34. The associated homogeneous recurrence relation is $a_n = 7a_{n-1} - 16a_{n-2} + 12a_{n-3}$. To solve it we find the characteristic equation $r^3 - 7r^2 + 16r - 12 = 0$. By the rational root test we soon discover that $r = 2$ is a root and factor our equation into $(r-2)^2(r-3) = 0$. Therefore the general solution of the homogeneous relation is $a_n^{(h)} = \alpha 2^n + \beta n \cdot 2^n + \gamma 3^n$. Next we need a particular solution to the given recurrence relation. By Theorem 6 we want to look for a function of the form $a_n = (cn+d)4^n$, since the coefficient of 4^n in our given relation is a linear function of n, and 4 is not a root of the characteristic equation. We plug this into our recurrence relation and obtain $(cn+d)4^n = 7(cn-c+d)4^{n-1}-16(cn-2c+d)4^{n-2}+12(cn-3c+d)4^{n-3}+n\cdot 4^n$. We divide through by 4^{n-2}, expand and collect terms (a tedious process, to be sure), obtaining $(c-16)n+(5c+d) = 0$. Therefore $c = 16$ and $d = -80$, so the particular solution we seek is $a_n^{(p)} = (16n-80)4^n$. Thus the general solution is the sum of the homogeneous solution and this particular solution, namely $a_n = \alpha 2^n + \beta n \cdot 2^n + \gamma 3^n + (16n-80)4^n$. Next we plug in the initial conditions to obtain $-2 = a_0 = \alpha + \gamma - 80$, $0 = a_1 = 2\alpha + 2\beta + 3\gamma - 256$, and $5 = a_2 = 4\alpha + 8\beta + 9\gamma - 768$. We solve this system of three linear equations in three unknowns by standard methods to obtain $\alpha = 17$, $\beta = 39/2$, and $\gamma = 61$. So the solution is $a_n = 17\cdot 2^n + 39n\cdot 2^{n-1} + 61\cdot 3^n + (16n-80)4^n$. As a check of our work (it would be too much to hope that we could always get this far without making an algebraic error), we can compute a_3 both from the recurrence and from the solution, and we find that $a_3 = 203$ both ways.

36. Obviously the nth term of the sequence comes from the $(n-1)^{\text{th}}$ term by adding n^2; in symbols, $a_{n-1}+n^2 = \left(\sum_{k=1}^{n-1} k^2\right) + n^2 = \sum_{k=1}^{n} k^2 = a_n$. Also, the sum of the first square is clearly 1. To solve this recurrence relation, we easily see that the homogeneous solution is $a_n = \alpha$, so since the nonhomogeneous term is a second degree polynomial, we need a particular solution of the form $a_n = cn^3 + dn^2 + en$. Plugging this into the recurrence relation gives $cn^3 + dn^2 + en = c(n-1)^3 + d(n-1)^2 + e(n-1) + n^2$. Expanding and collecting terms, we have $(3c-1)n^2 + (-3c+2d)n + (c-d+e) = 0$, whence $c = 1/3$, $d = 1/2$, and $e = 1/6$. Thus $a_n^{(h)} = \frac{1}{3}n^3 + \frac{1}{2}n^2 + \frac{1}{6}n$. So the general solution is $a_n = \alpha + \frac{1}{3}n^3 + \frac{1}{2}n^2 + \frac{1}{6}n$. It is now a simple matter to plug in the initial condition to see that $\alpha = 0$. Note that we can find a common denominator and write our solution in the familiar form $a_n = n(n+1)(2n+1)/6$, as was noted in Table 2 of Section 3.2 and proved by mathematical induction in Exercise 7 of Section 3.3.

38. a) The characteristic equation is $r^2 - 2r + 2 = 0$, whose roots are, by the quadratic formula, $1 \pm \sqrt{-1}$, in other words, $1 + i$ and $1 - i$.

b) The general solution is, by part (**a**), $a_n = \alpha_1(1+i)^n + \alpha_2(1-i)^n$. Plugging in the initial conditions gives us $1 = \alpha_1 + \alpha_2$ and $2 = (1+i)\alpha_1 + (1-i)\alpha_2$. Solving these linear equations tells us that $\alpha_1 = \frac{1}{2} - \frac{1}{2}i$ and $\alpha_2 = \frac{1}{2} + \frac{1}{2}i$. Therefore the solution is $a_n = (\frac{1}{2} - \frac{1}{2}i)(1+i)^n + (\frac{1}{2} + \frac{1}{2}i)(1-i)^n$.

40. First we reduce this system to a recurrence relation and initial conditions involving only a_n. If we subtract the two equations, we obtain $a_n - b_n = 2a_{n-1}$, which gives us $b_n = a_n - 2a_{n-1}$. We plug this back into the first equation to get $a_n = 3a_{n-1} + 2(a_{n-1} - 2a_{n-2}) = 5a_{n-1} - 4a_{n-2}$, our desired recurrence relation in one variable. Note also that the first of the original equations gives us the necessary second initial condition, namely $a_1 = 3a_0 + 2b_0 = 7$. We now solve this problem for $\{a_n\}$ in the usual way. The roots of the characteristic equation $r^2 - 5r + 4 = 0$ are 1 and 4, and the solution, after solving for the arbitrary constants, is $a_n = -1 + 2\cdot 4^n$. Finally, we plug this back into the equation $b_n = a_n - 2a_{n-1}$ to find that $b_n = 1 + 4^n$.

42. We can prove this by induction on n. If $n = 1$, then the assertion is $a_1 = s\cdot f_0 + t\cdot f_1 = s\cdot 0 + t\cdot 1 = t$, which is given; and if $n = 2$, then the assertion is $a_2 = s\cdot f_1 + t\cdot f_2 = s\cdot 1 + t\cdot 1 = s + t$, which is true, since $a_2 = a_1 + a_0 = t + s$. Having taken care of the base cases, we assume the inductive hypothesis, that the statement is true for values less than n. Then $a_n = a_{n-1} + a_{n-2} = (sf_{n-2} + tf_{n-1}) + (sf_{n-3} + tf_{n-2}) = s(f_{n-2} + f_{n-3}) + t(f_{n-1} + f_{n-2}) = sf_{n-1} + tf_n$, as desired.

44. We can compute the first few terms by hand. For $n = 1$, the matrix is just the number 2, so $d_1 = 2$. For

$n = 2$, the matrix is $\begin{bmatrix} 2 & 1 \\ 1 & 2 \end{bmatrix}$, and its determinant is clearly $d_2 = 4 - 1 = 3$. For $n = 3$ the matrix is

$$\begin{bmatrix} 2 & 1 & 0 \\ 1 & 2 & 1 \\ 0 & 1 & 2 \end{bmatrix},$$

and we get $d_3 = 4$ after a little arithmetic. For the general case, our matrix is

$$\mathbf{A}_n = \begin{bmatrix} 2 & 1 & 0 & 0 & \cdots & 0 \\ 1 & 2 & 1 & 0 & \cdots & 0 \\ 0 & 1 & 2 & 1 & \cdots & 0 \\ 0 & 0 & 1 & 2 & \cdots & 0 \\ \vdots & \vdots & \vdots & \vdots & \ddots & \vdots \\ 0 & 0 & 0 & 0 & \cdots & 2 \end{bmatrix}.$$

To compute the determinant, we expand along the top row. This gives us a value of 2 times the determinant of the matrix obtained by deleting the first row and first column minus the determinant of the matrix obtained by deleting the first row and second column. The first of these smaller matrices is just $\mathbf{A}_{n-1}$, with determinant d_{n-1}. The second of these smaller matrices has just one nonzero entry in its first column, so we expand its determinant along the first column and see that it equals d_{n-2}. Therefore our recurrence relation is $d_n = 2d_{n-1} - d_{n-2}$, with initial conditions as computed at the start of this solution. If we compute a few more terms we are led to the conjecture that $d_n = n + 1$. If we show that this satisfies the recurrence, then we have proved that it is indeed the solution. And sure enough, $n + 1 = 2n - (n - 1)$. (Of course, we could have also dragged out the machinery of this section to solve the recurrence relation and initial conditions.)

46. Let a_n represent the number of goats on the island at the start of the nth year.

   a) The initial condition is $a_1 = 2$; we are told that at the beginning of the first year there are two goats. During each subsequent year (year n, with $n \geq 2$), the goats who were on the island the year before (year $n - 1$) double in number, and an extra 100 goats are added in. So $a_n = 2a_{n-1} + 100$.

   b) The associated homogeneous recurrence relation is $a_n = 2a_{n-1}$, whose solution is $a_n^{(h)} = \alpha 2^n$. The particular solution is a polynomial of degree 0, namely a constant, $a_n = c$. Plugging this into the recurrence relation gives $c = 2c + 100$, whence $c = -100$. So the particular solution is $a_n^{(p)} = -100$ and the general solution is $a_n = \alpha 2^n - 100$. Plugging in the initial condition and solving for α gives us $2 = 2\alpha - 100$, or $\alpha = 51$. Hence the desired formula is $a_n = 51 \cdot 2^n - 100$. There are $51 \cdot 2^n - 100$ goats on the island at the start of the nth year.

   c) We are told that $a_1 = 2$, but that is not the relevant initial condition. Instead, since the first two years are special (no goats are removed), the relevant initial condition is $a_2 = 4$. During each subsequent year (year n, with $n \geq 3$), the goats who were on the island the year before (year $n - 1$) double in number, and n goats are removed. So $a_n = 2a_{n-1} - n$. (We assume that the removal occurs after the doubling has occurred; if we assume that the removal takes place first, then we'd have to write $a_n = 2(a_{n-1} - n) = 2a_{n-1} - 2n$.)

   d) The associated homogeneous recurrence relation is $a_n = 2a_{n-1}$, whose solution is $a_n^{(h)} = \alpha 2^n$. The particular solution is a polynomial of degree 1, say $a_n = cn + d$. Plugging this into the recurrence relation and grouping like terms gives $(-c + 1)n + (2c - d) = 0$, whence $c = 1$ and $d = 2$. So the particular solution is $a_n^{(p)} = n + 2$ and the general solution is $a_n = \alpha 2^n + n + 2$. Plugging in the initial condition $a_2 = 4$ and solving for α gives us $4 = 4\alpha + 4$, or $\alpha = 0$. Hence the desired formula is simply $a_n = n + 2$ for all $n \geq 2$ (and $a_1 = 2$). There are $n + 2$ goats on the island at the start of the nth year, for all $n \geq 2$.

48. **a)** This is just a matter of keeping track of what all the symbols mean. First note that $Q(n + 1) = Q(n)f(n)/g(n+1)$. Now the left-hand side of the desired equation is $b_n = g(n+1)Q(n+1)a_n = Q(n)f(n)a_n$. The right-hand side is $b_{n-1} + Q(n)h(n) = g(n)Q(n)a_{n-1} + Q(n)h(n) = Q(n)(g(n)a_{n-1} + h(n))$. That the two sides are the same now follows from the original recurrence relation, $f(n)a_n = g(n)a_{n-1} + h(n)$. Note that

the initial condition for $\{b_n\}$ is $b_0 = g(1)Q(1)a_0 = g(1)(1/g(1))a_0 = a_0 = C$, since it is conventional to view an empty product as the number 1.

b) Since $\{b_n\}$ satisfies the trivial recurrence relation shown in part **(a)**, we see immediately that

$$b_n = Q(n)h(n) + b_{n-1} = Q(n)h(n) + Q(n-1)h(n-1) + b_{n-2} = \cdots$$
$$= \sum_{i=1}^{n} Q(i)h(i) + b_0 = \sum_{i=1}^{n} Q(i)h(i) + C.$$

The value of a_n follows from the definition of b_n given in part **(a)**.

50. a) We can show this by proving that $nC_n - (n+1)C_{n-1} = 2n$, so let us calculate, using the given recurrence:

$$nC_n - (n+1)C_{n-1} = nC_n - (n-1)C_{n-1} - 2C_{n-1}$$
$$= n^2 + n + 2\sum_{k=0}^{n-1} C_k - (n-1)\left(n + \frac{2}{n-1}\sum_{k=0}^{n-2} C_k\right) - 2C_{n-1}$$
$$= n^2 + n + 2\sum_{k=0}^{n-2} C_k + 2C_{n-1} - n^2 + n - 2\sum_{k=0}^{n-2} C_k - 2C_{n-1} = 2n.$$

b) We use the formula given in Exercise 48. Note first that $f(n) = n$, $g(n) = n+1$, and $h(n) = 2n$. Thus $Q(n) = \dfrac{(n-1)!}{(n+1)!} = \dfrac{1}{n(n+1)}$. Plugging this into the formula gives

$$\frac{0 + \sum_{i=1}^{n} \frac{2i}{i(i+1)}}{(n+2) \cdot \frac{1}{(n+1)(n+2)}} = 2(n+1)\sum_{i=1}^{n} \frac{1}{i+1}.$$

There is no nice closed form way to write this sum (the harmonic series), but we can check that both this formula and the recurrence yield the same values of C_n for small n (namely, $C_1 = 2$, $C_2 = 5$, $C_3 = 26/3$, and so on).

52. A proof of this theorem can be found in textbooks such as *Discrete Mathematics with Applications* by H. E. Mattson, Jr. (Wiley, 1993), Chapter 11.

SECTION 6.3   Divide-and-Conquer Algorithms and Recurrence Relations

2. The recurrence relation here is $f(n) = 2f(n/2) + 2$, where $f(1) = 0$, since no comparisons are needed for a set with 1 element. Iterating, we find that $f(2) = 2 \cdot 0 + 2 = 2$, $f(4) = 2 \cdot 2 + 2 = 6$, $f(8) = 2 \cdot 6 + 2 = 14$, $f(16) = 2 \cdot 14 + 2 = 30$, $f(32) = 2 \cdot 30 + 2 = 62$, $f(64) = 2 \cdot 62 + 2 = 126$, and $f(128) = 2 \cdot 126 + 2 = 254$.

4. In this algorithm we assume that $a = (a_{2n-1}a_{2n-2}\cdots a_1a_0)_2$ and $b = (b_{2n-1}b_{2n-2}\cdots b_1b_0)_2$.

```
procedure fast multiply(a, b : nonnegative integers)
if a ≤ 1 and b ≤ 1 then fast multiply(a, b) := ab
else
begin
    A₁ := ⌊a/2ⁿ⌋
    A₀ := a − 2ⁿA₁
    B₁ := ⌊b/2ⁿ⌋
    B₀ := b − 2ⁿB₁
    {we assume that these four numbers have length n; pad if necessary}
    x := fast multiply(A₁, B₁)
    answer := (x shifted left 2n places) + (x shifted left n places)
    x := fast multiply(A₀, B₀)
    answer := answer + x + (x shifted left n places)
    if A₁ ≥ A₀ then A₂ := A₁ − A₀ else A₂ := A₀ − A₁
    if B₀ ≥ B₁ then B₂ := B₀ − B₁ else B₂ := B₁ − B₀
    x := fast multiply(A₂, B₂) shifted left n places
    if (A₁ ≥ A₀ ∧ B₀ ≥ B₁) ∨ (A₁ < A₀ ∧ B₀ < B₁) then
            answer := answer + x
    else answer := answer − x
    fast multiply(a, b) := answer
end
```

6. The recurrence relation is $f(n) = 7f(n/2) + 15n^2/4$, with $f(1) = 1$. Thus we have, iterating, $f(2) = 7 \cdot 1 + 15 \cdot 2^2/4 = 22$, $f(4) = 7 \cdot 22 + 15 \cdot 4^2/4 = 214$, $f(8) = 7 \cdot 214 + 15 \cdot 8^2/4 = 1738$, $f(16) = 7 \cdot 1738 + 15 \cdot 16^2/4 = 13126$, and $f(32) = 7 \cdot 13126 + 15 \cdot 32^2/4 = 95{,}722$.

8. **a)** $f(2) = 2 \cdot 5 + 3 = 13$ **b)** $f(4) = 2 \cdot 13 + 3 = 29$, $f(8) = 2 \cdot 29 + 3 = 61$
   c) $f(16) = 2 \cdot 61 + 3 = 125$, $f(32) = 2 \cdot 125 + 3 = 253$, $f(64) = 2 \cdot 253 + 3 = 509$
   d) $f(128) = 2 \cdot 509 + 3 = 1021$, $f(256) = 2 \cdot 1021 + 3 = 2045$, $f(512) = 2 \cdot 2045 + 3 = 4093$, $f(1024) = 2 \cdot 4093 + 3 = 8189$

10. Since f increases one for each factor of 2 in n, it is clear that $f(2^k) = k + 1$.

12. An exact formula comes from the proof of Theorem 1, namely $f(n) = [f(1) + c/(a-1)]n^{\log_b a} - c/(a-1)$, where $a = 2$, $b = 3$, and $c = 4$ in this exercise. Therefore the answer is $f(n) = 5n^{\log_3 2} - 4$.

14. If there is only one team, then no rounds are needed, so the base case is $R(1) = 0$. Since it takes one round to cut the number of teams in half, we have $R(n) = 1 + R(n/2)$.

16. The solution of this recurrence relation for $n = 2^k$ is $R(2^k) = k$, for the same reason as in Exercise 10.

18. **a)** Our recursive algorithm will take a sequence of $2n$ names (two different names provided by each of n voters) and determine whether the two top vote-getters occur on our list more than $n/2$ times each, and if so, who they are. We assume that our list has the votes of each voter adjacent (the first voter's choices are in positions 1 and 2, the second voter's choices are in positions 3 and 4, and so on). Note that it is possible for more than two candidates to receive more than $n/2$ votes; for example, three voters could have choices AB, AC, and BC, and then all three would qualify. However, there cannot be more than three candidates qualifying, since the sum of four numbers each larger than $n/2$ is larger than $2n$, the total number of votes cast. If $n = 1$, then the two people on the list are both winners. For the recursive step, divide the list into two parts of even size—the first half and the second half—as equally as possible. As is pointed out in the hint

in Exercise 17, no one could have gotten a majority (here that means more than $n/2$ votes) on the whole list without having a majority in one half or the other, since if a candidate got approval from less than or equal to half of the voters in each half, then he got approval from less than or equal to half of the voters in all (this is essentially just the distributive law). Apply the algorithm recursively to each half to come up with at most six names (three from each half). Then run through the entire list to count the number of occurrences of each of those names to decide which, if any, are the winners. This requires at most $12n$ additional comparisons for a list of length $2n$. At the outermost stage of this recursion (i.e., when dealing with the entire list), we have to compare the actual numbers of votes each of the candidates in the running got, since only the top two can be declared winners (subject to the anomaly of three people tied, as illustrated above).

b) We apply the master theorem with $a = 2$, $b = 2$, $c = 12$, and $d = 1$. Since $a = b^d$, we know that the number of comparisons is $O(n^d \log n) = O(n \log n)$.

20. a) We compute $a^n \bmod m$, when n is even, by first computing $y := a^{n/2} \bmod m$ recursively and then doing one modular multiplication, namely $y \cdot y$. When n is odd, we first compute $y := a^{(n-1)/2}$ recursively and then do two multiplications, namely $y \cdot y \cdot a$. So if $f(n)$ is the number of multiplications required, assuming the worst, then we have essentially $f(n) = f(n/2) + 2$.

b) By the master theorem, with $a = 1$, $b = 2$, $c = 2$, and $d = 0$, we see that $f(n)$ is $O(n^0 \log n) = O(\log n)$.

22. a) $f(16) = 2f(4) + 4 = 2(2f(2) + 2) + 4 = 2(2 \cdot 1 + 2) + 4 = 12$

b) Let $m = \log n$, so that $n = 2^m$. Also, let $g(m) = f(2^m)$. Then our recurrence becomes $f(2^m) = 2f(2^{m/2}) + m$, since $\sqrt{2^m} = (2^m)^{1/2} = 2^{m/2}$. Rewriting this in terms of g we have $g(m) = 2g(m/2) + m$. Theorem 2 (with $a = 2$, $b = 2$, $c = 1$, and $d = 1$ now tells us that $g(m)$ is $O(m \log m)$. Since $m = \log n$, this says that our function is $O(\log n \cdot \log \log n)$.

24. To carry this down to its base level would require applying the algorithm three times, so we will show only the outermost step. The points are already sorted for us, and so we divide them into two groups, using x coordinate. The left side will have the first four points listed in it (they all have x coordinates less than 2.5), and the right side will have the rest, all of which have x coordinates greater than 2.5. Thus our vertical line will be taken to be $x = 2.5$. Now assume that we have already applied the algorithm recursively to find the minimum distance between two points on the left, and the minimum distance on the right. It turns out that $d_L = \sqrt{2}$ and $d_R = \sqrt{5}$, so $d = \sqrt{2}$. This is achieved by the points $(1,3)$ and $(2,4)$. Thus we want to concentrate on the strip from $x = 2.5 - \sqrt{2} \approx 1.1$ to $x = 2.5 + \sqrt{2} \approx 3.9$ of width $2d$. The only points in this strip are $(2,4)$, $(2,9)$, $(3,1)$, and $(3,5)$, Working from the bottom up, we compute distances from these points to points as much as $d = \sqrt{2} \approx 1.4$ vertical units above them. According to the discussion in the text, there can never be more than seven such computations for each point in the strip. In this case there is in fact only one, namely $\overline{(2,4)(3,5)}$. This distance is again $\sqrt{2}$, and it ties the minimum distance already obtained. So the minimum distance is $\sqrt{2}$.

26. In our algorithm d contains the shortest distance and is the value returned by the algorithm. We assume a function $dist$ that computes Euclidean distance given two points (a, b) and (c, d), namely $\sqrt{(a - c)^2 + (b - d)^2}$. We also assume that some global preprocessing has been done to sort the points in nondecreasing order of x coordinates before calling this program, and to produce a separate list P of the points in nondecreasing order of y coordinates, but having an identification as to which points in the original list they are.

> **procedure** *closest*$((x_1, y_1), \ldots, (x_n, y_n))$: points in the plane)
> **if** $n = 2$ **then** $d := dist((x_1, y_1), (x_2, y_2))$
> **else**
> **begin**
> $m := (x_{\lfloor n/2 \rfloor} + x_{\lceil n/2 \rceil})/2$
> $d_L := closest((x_1, y_1), \ldots, (x_{\lfloor n/2 \rfloor}, y_{\lfloor n/2 \rfloor}))$
> $d_R := closest((x_{\lceil n/2 \rceil}, y_{\lceil n/2 \rceil}), \ldots, (x_n, y_n))$
> $d := \min(d_L, d_R)$
>   form the sublist P' of P consisting of those points whose x-coordinates are within d of m
>   **for** each point (x, y) in P'
>   **for** each point (x', y') in P' after (x, y) such that $y' - y < d$
>   **if** $dist((x, y), (x', y')) < d$ **then** $d := dist((x, y), (x', y'))$
> **end**
> $\{\, d$ is the minimum distance between points in the list $\}$

28. a) We follow the discussion given here. At each stage, we ask the question twice, "Is x in this part of the set?" if the two answers agree, then we know that they are truthful, and we proceed recursively on the half we then know contains the number. If the two answers disagree, then we ask the question a third time to determine the truth (the first person cannot lie twice, so the third answer is truthful). After we have detected the lie, we no longer need to ask each question twice, since all answers have to be truthful. If the lie occurs on our last query, however, then we have used a full $2 \log n + 1$ questions (the last 1 being the third question when the lie was detected).

b) Divide the set into four (nearly) equal-sized parts, A, B, C, and D. To determine which of the four subsets contains the first person's number, ask these questions: "Is your number in $A \cup B$?" and "Is your number in $A \cup C$?" If the answers are both "yes," then we can eliminate D, since we know that at least one of these answers was truthful and therefore the secret number is in $A \cup B \cup C$. By similar reasoning, if both answers are "no," then we can eliminate A; if the answers are first "yes" and then "no," then we can eliminate C; and if the answers are first "no" and then "yes," then we can eliminate B. Therefore after two questions we have a problem of size about $3n/4$ (exactly this when $4 \mid n$).

c) Since we reduce the problem to one problem of size $3n/4$ at each stage, the number $f(n)$ of questions satisfies $f(n) = f(3n/4) + 2$ when n is divisible by 4.

d) Using iteration, we solve the recurrence relation in part **(c)**. We have $f(n) = 2 + f((3/4)n) = 2 + 2 + f((3/4)^2 n) = 2 + 2 + 2 + f((3/4)^3 n) = \cdots = 2 + 2 + \cdots + 2$, where there are about $\log_{4/3} n$ 2's in the sum. Noting that $\log_{4/3} n = \log n / \log 4/3 \approx 2.4 \log n$, we have that $f(n) \approx 4.8 \log n$.

e) The naive way is better, with fewer than half the number of questions. Another way to see this is to observe that after four questions in the second method, the size of our set is down to $9/16$ of its original size, but after only two questions in the first method, the size of the set is even smaller ($1/2$).

30. The second term obviously dominates the first. Also, $\log_b n$ is just a constant times $\log n$. The statement now follows from the fact that f is increasing.

32. If $a < b^d$, then $\log_b a < d$, so the first term dominates. The statement now follows from the fact that f is increasing.

34. From Exercise 31 (note that here $a = 5$, $b = 4$, $c = 6$, and $d = 1$) we have $f(n) = -24n + 25n^{\log_4 5}$.

36. From Exercise 31 (note that here $a = 8$, $b = 2$, $c = 1$, and $d = 2$) we have $f(n) = -n^2 + 2n^{\log 8} = -n^2 + 2n^3$.

SECTION 6.4   Generating Functions

2. The generating function is $f(x) = 1 + 4x + 16x^2 + 64x^3 + 256x^4$. Since the ith term in this sequence (the coefficient of x^i) is 4^i for $0 \le i \le 4$, we can also write the generating function as

$$f(x) = \sum_{i=0}^{4}(4x)^i = \frac{1 - (4x)^5}{1 - 4x}.$$

4. We will use Table 1 in much of this solution.

a) Apparently all the terms are 0 except for the seven -1's shown. Thus $f(x) = -1 - x - x^2 - x^3 - x^4 - x^5 - x^6$. This is already in closed form, but we can also write it more compactly as $f(x) = -(1 - x^7)/(1 - x)$, making use of the identity from Example 2.

b) This sequence fits the pattern in Table 1 for $1/(1 - ax)$ with $a = 3$. Therefore the generating function is $1/(1 - 3x)$.

c) We can factor out $3x^2$ and write the generating function as $3x^2(1 - x + x^2 - x^3 + \cdots) = 3x^2/(1 + x)$, again using the identity in Table 1.

d) Except for the extra x (the coefficient of x is 2 rather than 1), the generating function is just $1/(1 - x)$. Therefore the answer is $x + (1/(1 - x))$.

e) From Table 1, we see that the binomial theorem applies and we can write this as $(1 + 2x)^7$.

f) We can factor out -3 and write the generating function as $-3(1 - x + x^2 - x^3 + \cdots) = -3/(1 + x)$, using the identity in Table 1.

g) We can factor out x and write the generating function as $x(1 - 2x + 4x^2 - 8x^3 + \cdots) = x/(1 + 2x)$, using the sixth identity in Table 1 with $a = -2$.

h) From Table 1 we see that the generating function here is $1/(1 - x^2)$.

6. a) Since the sequence with $a_n = 1$ for all n has generating function $1/(1 - x)$, this sequence has generating function $-1/(1 - x)$.

b) By Table 1, the generating function for the sequence in which $a_n = 2^n$ for *all* n is $1/(1 - 2x)$. Here we can either think of subtracting out the missing constant term (since $a_0 = 0$) or factoring out $2x$. Therefore the answer can be written as either $1/(1 - 2x) - 1$ or $2x/(1 - 2x)$, which are of course algebraically equivalent.

c) We need to split this into two parts. Since we know that the generating function for the sequence $\{n + 1\}$ is $1/(1 - x)^2$, we write $n - 1 = (n + 1) - 2$. Therefore the generating function is $(1/(1 - x)^2) - (2/(1 - x))$. We can combine terms and write this function as $(2x - 1)/(1 - x)^2$, but there is no particular reason to prefer that form in general.

d) The power series for the function e^x is $\sum_{n=0}^{\infty} x^n/n!$. That is almost what we have here; the difference is that the denominator is $(n + 1)!$ instead of $n!$. So we have

$$\sum_{n=0}^{\infty} \frac{x^n}{(n+1)!} = \frac{1}{x}\sum_{n=0}^{\infty} \frac{x^{n+1}}{(n+1)!} = \frac{1}{x}\sum_{n=1}^{\infty} \frac{x^n}{n!}$$

by a change of variable. This last sum is $e^x - 1$ (only the first term is missing), so our answer is $(e^x - 1)/x$.

e) Let $f(x)$ be the generating function we seek. From Table 1 we know that $1/(1-x)^3 = \sum_{n=0}^{\infty} C(n+2, 2)x^n$, and that is almost what we have here. To transform this to $f(x)$ need to factor out x^2 and change the variable of summation:

$$\frac{1}{(1-x)^3} = \sum_{n=0}^{\infty} C(n+2, 2)x^n = \frac{1}{x^2}\sum_{n=0}^{\infty} C(n+2,2)x^{n+2} = \frac{1}{x^2}\sum_{n=2}^{\infty} C(n,2)x^n = \frac{1}{x^2}\cdot(f(x) - f(0) - f(1))$$

Noting that $f(0) = f(1) = 0$ by definition, we have $f(x) = x^2/(1-x)^3$.

f) We again use Table 1:

$$\sum_{n=0}^{\infty} C(10, n+1)x^n = \sum_{n=1}^{\infty} C(10, n)x^{n-1} = \frac{1}{x}\sum_{n=1}^{\infty} C(10, n)x^n = \frac{1}{x}((1+x)^{10} - 1)$$

8. a) By the binomial theorem (the third line of Table 1) we get $a_{2n} = C(3, n)$ for $n = 0, 1, 2, 3$, and the other coefficients are all 0. Alternatively, we could just multiply out this finite polynomial and note the nonzero coefficients: $a_0 = 1$, $a_2 = 3$, $a_4 = 3$, $a_6 = 1$.

b) This is like part **(a)**. First we need to factor out -1 and write this as $-(1 - 3x)^3$. Then by the binomial theorem (the second line of Table 1) we get $a_n = -C(3, n)(-3)^n$ for $n = 0, 1, 2, 3$, and the other coefficients are all 0. Alternatively, we could (by hand or with maple) just multiply out this finite polynomial and note the nonzero coefficients: $a_0 = -1$, $a_1 = 9$, $a_2 = -27$, $a_3 = 27$.

c) This problem requires a combination of the results of the sixth and seventh identities in Table 1. The coefficient of x^{2n} is 2^n, and the odd coefficients are all 0.

d) We know that $x^2/(1-x)^3 = x^2 \sum_{n=0}^{\infty} C(n+2, 2)x^n = \sum_{n=0}^{\infty} C(n+2, 2)x^{n+2} = \sum_{n=2}^{\infty} C(n, 2)x^n$. Therefore $a_n = C(n, 2) = n(n-1)/2$ for $n \geq 2$ and $a_0 = a_1 = 0$. (Actually, since $C(0, 2) = C(1, 2) = 0$, we really don't need to make a special statement for $n < 2$.)

e) The last term gives us, from Table 1, $a_n = 3^n$. We need to adjust this for $n = 0$ and $n = 1$ because of the first two terms. Thus $a_0 = -1 + 3^0 = 0$, and $a_1 = 1 + 3^1 = 4$.

f) We split this into two parts and proceed as in part **(d)**:

$$\frac{1}{(1+x)^3} + \frac{x^3}{(1+x)^3} = \sum_{n=0}^{\infty}(-1)^n C(n+2, 2)x^n + x^3\sum_{n=0}^{\infty}(-1)^n C(n+2, 2)x^n$$

$$= \sum_{n=0}^{\infty}(-1)^n C(n+2, 2)x^n + \sum_{n=0}^{\infty}(-1)^n C(n+2, 2)x^{n+3}$$

$$= \sum_{n=0}^{\infty}(-1)^n C(n+2, 2)x^n + \sum_{n=3}^{\infty}(-1)^{n-3} C(n-1, 2)x^n$$

Note that n and $n - 3$ have opposite parities. Therefore $a_n = (-1)^n C(n+2, 2) + (-1)^{n-3}C(n-1, 2) = (-1)^n(C(n+2, 2) - C(n-1, 2)) = (-1)^n 3n$ for $n \geq 3$ and $a_n = (-1)^n C(n+2, 2) = (-1)^n(n+2)(n+1)/2$ for $n < 3$. This answer can be confirmed using the **series** command in maple.

g) The key here is to recall the algebraic identity $1 - x^3 = (1-x)(1+x+x^2)$. Therefore the given function can be rewritten as $x(1-x)/(1-x^3)$, which can then be split into $x/(1-x^3)$ plus $-x^2/(1-x^3)$. From Table 1 we know that $1/(1-x^3) = 1 + x^3 + x^6 + x^9 + \cdots$. Therefore $x/(1-x^3) = x + x^4 + x^7 + x^{10} + \cdots$, and $-x^2/(1-x^3) = -x^2 - x^5 - x^8 - x^{11} - \cdots$. Thus we see that a_n is 0 when n is a multiple of 3, it is 1 when n is 1 greater than a multiple of 3, and it is -1 when n is 2 greater than a multiple of 3. One can check this answer with maple.

h) From Table 1 we know that $e^x = 1 + x + x^2/2! + x^3/3! + \cdots$. It follows that

$$e^{3x^2} = 1 + 3x^2 + \frac{(3x^2)^2}{2!} + \frac{(3x^2)^3}{3!} + \cdots.$$

We can therefore read off the coefficients of the generating function for $e^{3x^2} - 1$. First, clearly $a_0 = 0$. Second, $a_n = 0$ when n is odd. Finally, when n is even, we have $a_{2m} = 3^m/m!$.

10. Different approaches are possible for obtaining these answers. One can use brute force algebra and just multiply everything out, either by hand or with computer algebra software such as maple. One can view the problem as asking for the solution to a particular combinatorial problem and solve the problem by other means (e.g., listing all the possibilities). Or one can get a closed form expression for the coefficients, using the generating function theory developed in this section.

a) First we view this combinatorially. By brute force we can list the ten ways to obtain x^9 when this product is multiplied out (where "ijk" means choose an x^i term from the first factor, an x^j term from the second factor, and an x^k term from the third factor): 009, 036, 063, 090, 306, 333, 360, 603, 630, 900. Second, it is clear that we can view this problem as asking for the coefficient of x^3 in $(1 + x + x^2 + x^3 + \cdots)^3$, since each x^3 in the original is playing the role of x here. Since $(1 + x + x^2 + x^3 + \cdots)^3 = 1/(1-x)^3 = \sum_{n=0}^{\infty} C(n+2, 2)x^n$, the answer is clearly $C(3+2, 2) = C(5, 2) = 10$. A third way to get the answer is to ask maple to expand $(1 + x^3 + x^6 + x^9)^3$ and look at the coefficient of x^9, which will turn out to be 10. Note that we don't have to go beyond x^9 in each factor, because the higher terms can't contribute to an x^9 term in the answer.

b) If we factor out x^2 from each factor, we can write this as $x^6(1 + x + x^2 + \cdots)^3$. Thus we are seeking the coefficient of x^3 in $(1 + x + x^2 + \cdots)^3 = \sum_{n=0}^{\infty} C(n+2, 2)x^n$, so the answer is $C(3+2, 2) = 10$. The other two methods explained in part **(a)** work here as well.

c) If we factor out as high a power of x from each factor as we can, then we can write this as

$$x^7(1 + x^2 + x^3)(1 + x)(1 + x + x^2 + x^3 + \cdots),$$

and so we seek the coefficient of x^2 in $(1 + x^2 + x^3)(1 + x)(1 + x + x^2 + x^3 + \cdots)$. We could do this by brute force, but let's try it more analytically. We write our expression in closed form as

$$\frac{(1 + x^2 + x^3)(1 + x)}{1 - x} = \frac{1 + x + x^2 + \text{higher order terms}}{1 - x} = \frac{1}{1-x} + x \cdot \frac{1}{1-x} + x^2 \cdot \frac{1}{1-x} + \text{irrelevant terms}.$$

The coefficient of x^2 in this power series comes either from the coefficient of x^2 in the first term in the final expression displayed above, or from the coefficient of x^1 in the second factor of the second term of that expression, or from the coefficient of x^0 in the second factor of the third term. Each of these coefficients is 1, so our answer is 3. This could also be confirmed by having maple multiply out ("**expand**") the original expression (truncating the last factor at x^3).

d) The easiest approach here is simply to note that there are only two combinations of terms that will give us an x^9 term in the product: $x \cdot x^8$ and $x^7 \cdot x^2$. So the answer is 2.

e) The highest power of x appearing in this expression when multiplied out is x^6. Therefore the answer is 0.

12. These can all be checked by using the **series** command in maple.

　　a) By Table 1, the coefficient of x^n in this power series is $(-3)^n$. Therefore the answer is $(-3)^{12} = 531{,}441$.

　　b) By Table 1, the coefficient of x^n in this power series is $2^n C(n+1, 1)$. Thus the answer is $2^{12} C(12+1, 1) = 53{,}248$.

　　c) By Table 1, the coefficient of x^n in this power series is $(-1)^n C(n+7, 7)$. Therefore the answer is $(-1)^{12} C(12+7, 7) = 50{,}388$.

　　d) By Table 1, the coefficient of x^n in this power series is $4^n C(n+2, 2)$. Thus the answer is $4^{12} C(12+2, 2) = 1{,}526{,}726{,}656$.

　　e) This is really asking for the coefficient of x^9 in $1/(1+4x)^2$. Following the same idea as in part **(d)**, we see that the answer is $(-4)^9 C(9+1, 1) = -2{,}621{,}440$.

14. Each child will correspond to a factor in our generating function. We can give 0, 1, 2, or 3 figures to the child; therefore the generating function for each child is $1 + x + x^2 + x^3$. We want to find the coefficient of x^{12} in the expansion of $(1 + x + x^2 + x^3)^5$. We can multiply this out (preferably with a computer algebra package such as maple), and the coefficient of x^{12} turns out to be 35. To solve it analytically, we write our generating function as

$$\left(\frac{1 - x^4}{1 - x}\right)^5 = \frac{1 - 5x^4 + 10x^8 - 10x^{12} + \text{higher order terms}}{(1 - x)^5}.$$

There are four contributions to the coefficient of x^{12}, one for each term in the numerator, from the power series for $1/(1-x)^5$. Since the coefficient of x^n in $1/(1-x)^5$ is $C(n+4, 4)$, our answer is $C(12+4, 4) - 5C(8+4, 4) + 10C(4+4, 4) - 10C(0+4, 4) = 1820 - 2475 + 700 - 10 = 35$.

16. The factors in the generating function for choosing the egg and plain bagels are both $x^2 + x^3 + x^4 + \cdots$. The factor for choosing the salty bagels is $x^2 + x^3$. Therefore the generating function for this problem is $(x^2 + x^3 + x^4 + \cdots)^2(x^2 + x^3)$. We want to find the coefficient of x^{12}, since we want 12 bagels. This is equivalent to finding the coefficient of x^6 in $(1 + x + x^2 + \cdots)^2(1 + x)$ This function is $(1 + x)/(1 - x)^2$, so we want the coefficient of x^6 in $1/(1 - x)^2$, which is 7, plus the coefficient of x^5 in $1/(1 - x)^2$, which is 6. Thus the answer is 13.

18. Without changing the answer, we can assume that the jar has an infinite number of balls of each color; this will make the algebra easier. For the red and green balls the generating function is $1 + x + x^2 + \cdots$, but for the blue balls the generating function is $x^3 + x^4 + \cdots + x^{10}$, so the generating function for the whole problem is $(1 + x + x^2 + \cdots)^2(x^3 + x^4 + \cdots + x^{10})$. We seek the coefficient of x^{14}. This is the same as the coefficient of x^{11} in

$$(1 + x + x^2 + \cdots)^2(1 + x + \cdots + x^7) = \frac{1 - x^8}{(1 - x)^3}.$$

Since the coefficient of x^n in $1/(1 - x)^3$ is $C(n + 2, 2)$, and we have two contributing terms determined by the numerator, our answer is $C(11 + 2, 2) - C(3 + 2, 2) = 68$.

20. We want the coefficient of x^k to be the number of ways to make change for k pesos. Ten-peso bills contribute 10 each to the exponent of x. Thus we can model the choice of the number of 10-peso bills by the choice of a term from $1 + x^{10} + x^{20} + x^{30} + \cdots$. Twenty-peso bills contribute 20 each to the exponent of x. Thus we can model the choice of the number of 20-peso bills by the choice of a term from $1 + x^{20} + x^{40} + x^{60} + \cdots$. Similarly, 50-peso bills contribute 50 each to the exponent of x, so we can model the choice of the number of 50-peso bills by the choice of a term from $1 + x^{50} + x^{100} + x^{150} + \cdots$. Similar reasoning applies to 100-peso bills. Thus the generating function is $f(x) = (1 + x^{10} + x^{20} + x^{30} + \cdots)(1 + x^{20} + x^{40} + x^{60} + \cdots)(1 + x^{50} + x^{100} + x^{150} + \cdots)(1 + x^{100} + x^{200} + x^{300} + \cdots)$, which can also be written as

$$f(x) = \frac{1}{(1 - x^{10})(1 - x^{20})(1 - x^{50})(1 - x^{100})}$$

by Table 1. Note that $c_k = 0$ unless k is a multiple of 10, and the power series has no terms whose exponents are not powers of 10.

22. Let e_i, for $i = 1, 2, \ldots, n$, be the exponent of x taken from the ith factor in forming a term x^6 in the expansion. Thus $e_1 + e_2 + \cdots + e_n = 6$. The coefficient of x^6 is therefore the number of ways to solve this equation with nonnegative integers, which, from Section 4.5, is $C(n + 6 - 1, 6) = C(n + 5, 6)$. Its value, of course, depends on n.

24. a) The restriction on x_1 gives us the factor $x^3 + x^4 + x^5 + \cdots$. The restriction on x_2 gives us the factor $x + x^2 + x^3 + x^4 + x^5$. The restriction on x_3 gives us the factor $1 + x + x^2 + x^3 + x^4$. And the restriction on x_4 gives us the factor $x + x^2 + x^3 + \cdots$. Thus the answer is the product of these:

$$(x^3 + x^4 + x^5 + \cdots)(x + x^2 + x^3 + x^4 + x^5)(1 + x + x^2 + x^3 + x^4)(x + x^2 + x^3 + \cdots)$$

We can use algebra to rewrite this in closed form as $x^5(1 + x + x^2 + x^3 + x^4)^2/(1 - x)^2$.

b) We want the coefficient of x^7 in this series, which is the same as the coefficient of x^2 in the series for

$$\frac{(1 + x + x^2 + x^3 + x^4)^2}{(1 - x)^2} = \frac{1 + 2x + 3x^2 + \text{higher order terms}}{(1 - x)^2}.$$

Since the coefficient of x^n in $1/(1 - x)^2$ is $n + 1$, our answer is $1 \cdot 3 + 2 \cdot 2 + 3 \cdot 1 = 10$.

26. a) On each roll, we can get a total of one pip, two pips, ..., six pips. So the generating function for each roll is $x + x^2 + x^3 + x^4 + x^5 + x^6$. The exponent on x gives the number of pips. If we want to achieve a total of k pips in n rolls, then we need the coefficient of x^k in $(x + x^2 + x^3 + x^4 + x^5 + x^6)^n$. Since n is free to vary here, we must add these generating functions for all possible values of n. Therefore the generating function for this problem is $\sum_{n=0}^{\infty} (x + x^2 + x^3 + x^4 + x^5 + x^6)^n$. By the formula for summing a geometric series, this is the same as $1/(1 - (x + x^2 + x^3 + x^4 + x^5 + x^6)) = 1/(1 - x - x^2 - x^3 - x^4 - x^5 - x^6)$.

b) We seek the coefficient of x^8 in the power series for our answer to part **(a)**. The best way to get the answer is probably asking maple or another computer algebra package to find this power series, which it will probably do using calculus. If we do so, the answer turns out to be 125 (the series starts out $1 + x + 2x^2 + 4x^3 + 8x^4 + 16x^5 + 32x^6 + 63x^7 + 125x^8 + 248x^9$).

28. In each case, the generating function for the choice of pennies is $1 + x + x^2 + \cdots = 1/(1-x)$ or some portion of this to account for restrictions on the number of pennies used. Similarly, the generating function for the choice of nickels is $1 + x^5 + x^{10} + \cdots = 1/(1 - x^5)$ (or some portion); and similarly for the dimes and quarters. For each part we will write down the generating function (a product of the generating functions for each coin) and then invoke a computer algebra system to get the answer.

a) The generating function for the pennies is $1 + x + x^2 + \cdots + x^{10} = (1 - x^{11})/(1-x)$. Thus our entire generating function is

$$\frac{1 - x^{11}}{1 - x} \cdot \frac{1}{1 - x^5} \cdot \frac{1}{1 - x^{10}} \cdot \frac{1}{1 - x^{25}}.$$

Maple says that the coefficient of x^{100} in this is 79.

b) This is just like part **(a)**, except that now the generating function is

$$\frac{1 - x^{11}}{1 - x} \cdot \frac{1 - (x^5)^{11}}{1 - x^5} \cdot \frac{1}{1 - x^{10}} \cdot \frac{1}{1 - x^{25}}.$$

This time maple reports that the answer is 58.

c) This problem can be solved by using a generating function with two variables, one for the number of coins (say y) and one for the values (say x). Then the generating function for nickels, for instance, is

$$1 + x^5 y + x^{10} y^2 + \cdots = \frac{1}{1 - x^5 y}.$$

We multiply the four generating functions together, for the four different denominations, and get a function of x and y. Then we ask maple to expand this as a power series and get the coefficient of x^{100}. This coefficient is a polynomial in y. We ask maple to extract and simplify this polynomial and it turns out to be $y^4 + y^6 + 2y^7 + 2y^8 + 2y^9 + 4y^{10}$ plus higher order terms that we don't want, since we need the number of coins (which is what the exponent on y tells us) to be less than 11. Since the total of these coefficients is 12, the answer is 12, which can be confirmed by brute force enumeration.

30. a) Multiplication distributes over addition, even when we are talking about infinite sums, so the generating function is just $2G(x)$.

b) What used to be the coefficient of x^0 is now the coefficient of x^1, and similarly for the other terms. The way that happened is that the whole series got multiplied by x. Therefore the generating function for this series is $xG(x)$. In symbols,

$$a_0 x + a_1 x^2 + a_2 x^3 + \cdots = x(a_0 + a_1 x + a_2 x^2 + \cdots) = xG(x).$$

c) The terms involving a_0 and a_1 are missing; $G(x) - a_0 - a_1 x = a_2 x^2 + a_3 x^3 + \cdots$. Here, however, we want a_2 to be the coefficient of x^4, not x^2 (and similarly for the other powers), so we must throw in an extra factor. Thus the answer is $x^2(G(x) - a_0 - a_1 x)$.

d) This is just like part **(c)**, except that we slide the powers down. Thus the answer is $(G(x) - a_0 - a_1 x)/x^2$.

e) Following the hint, we differentiate $G(x) = \sum_{n=0}^{\infty} a_n x^n$ to obtain $G'(x) = \sum_{n=0}^{\infty} n a_n x^{n-1}$. By a change of variable this becomes $\sum_{n=0}^{\infty} (n+1) a_{n+1} x^n = a_1 + 2a_2 x + 3a_3 x^2 + \cdots$, which is the generating function for precisely the sequence we are given. Thus $G'(x)$ is the generating function for this sequence.

f) If we look at Theorem 1, it is not hard to see that the sequence shown here is precisely the coefficients of $G(x) \cdot G(x)$.

32. This problem is like Example 16. First let $G(x) = \sum_{k=0}^{\infty} a_k x^k$. Then $xG(x) = \sum_{k=0}^{\infty} a_k x^{k+1} = \sum_{k=1}^{\infty} a_{k-1} x^k$ (by changing the name of the variable from k to $k+1$). Thus

$$G(x) - 7xG(x) = \sum_{k=0}^{\infty} a_k x^k - \sum_{k=1}^{\infty} 7a_{k-1} x^k = a_0 + \sum_{k=1}^{\infty} (a_k - 7a_{k-1}) x^k = a_0 + 0 = 5 \,,$$

because of the given recurrence relation and initial condition. Thus $G(x)(1 - 7x) = 5$, so $G(x) = 5/(1 - 7x)$. From Table 1 we know then that $a_k = 5 \cdot 7^k$.

34. Let $G(x) = \sum_{k=0}^{\infty} a_k x^k$. Then $xG(x) = \sum_{k=0}^{\infty} a_k x^{k+1} = \sum_{k=1}^{\infty} a_{k-1} x^k$ (by changing the name of the variable from k to $k+1$). Thus

$$G(x) - 3xG(x) = \sum_{k=0}^{\infty} a_k x^k - \sum_{k=1}^{\infty} 3a_{k-1} x^k = a_0 + \sum_{k=1}^{\infty} (a_k - 3a_{k-1}) x^k = 1 + \sum_{k=1}^{\infty} 4^{k-1} x^k$$

$$= 1 + x \sum_{k=1}^{\infty} 4^{k-1} x^{k-1} = 1 + x \sum_{k=0}^{\infty} 4^k x^k = 1 + x \cdot \frac{1}{1 - 4x} = \frac{1 - 3x}{1 - 4x} \,.$$

Thus $G(x)(1 - 3x) = (1 - 3x)/(1 - 4x)$, so $G(x) = 1/(1 - 4x)$. Therefore $a_k = 4^k$, from Table 1.

36. Let $G(x) = \sum_{k=0}^{\infty} a_k x^k$. Then $xG(x) = \sum_{k=0}^{\infty} a_k x^{k+1} = \sum_{k=1}^{\infty} a_{k-1} x^k$ (by changing the name of the variable from k to $k+1$), and $x^2 G(x) = \sum_{k=0}^{\infty} a_k x^{k+2} = \sum_{k=2}^{\infty} a_{k-2} x^k$. Thus

$$G(x) - xG(x) - 2x^2 G(x) = \sum_{k=0}^{\infty} a_k x^k - \sum_{k=1}^{\infty} a_{k-1} x^k - \sum_{k=2}^{\infty} 2a_{k-2} x^k = a_0 + a_1 x - a_0 x + \sum_{k=2}^{\infty} 2^k \cdot x^k$$

$$= 4 + 8x + \frac{1}{1 - 2x} - 1 - 2x = \frac{4 - 12x^2}{1 - 2x} \,,$$

because of the given recurrence relation, the initial conditions, Table 1, and algebra. Since the left-hand side of this equation factors as $G(x)(1 - 2x)(1 + x)$, we have $G(x) = (4 - 12x^2)/((1 + x)(1 - 2x)^2)$. At this point we must use partial fractions to break up the denominator. Setting

$$\frac{4 - 12x^2}{(1 + x)(1 - 2x)^2} = \frac{A}{1 + x} + \frac{B}{1 - 2x} + \frac{C}{(1 - 2x)^2} \,,$$

multiplying through by the common denominator, and equating coefficients, we find that $A = -8/9$, $B = 38/9$, and $C = 2/3$. Thus

$$G(x) = \frac{-8/9}{1 + x} + \frac{38/9}{1 - 2x} + \frac{2/3}{(1 - 2x)^2} = \sum_{k=0}^{\infty} \left(-\frac{8}{9}(-1)^k + \frac{38}{9} \cdot 2^k + \frac{2}{3}(k+1)2^k \right) x^k$$

(from Table 1). Therefore $a_k = (-8/9)(-1)^k + (38/9)2^k + (2/3)(k+1)2^k$. Incidentally, it would be wise to check our answers, either with a computer algebra package, or by computing the next term of the sequence from both the recurrence and the formula (here $a_2 = 24$ both ways).

38. Let $G(x) = \sum_{k=0}^{\infty} a_k x^k$. Then $xG(x) = \sum_{k=0}^{\infty} a_k x^{k+1} = \sum_{k=1}^{\infty} a_{k-1} x^k$ (by changing the name of the variable from k to $k + 1$), and similarly $x^2 G(x) = \sum_{k=0}^{\infty} a_k x^{k+2} = \sum_{k=2}^{\infty} a_{k-2} x^k$. Thus

$$G(x) - 2xG(x) - 3x^2 G(x) = \sum_{k=0}^{\infty} a_k x^k - \sum_{k=1}^{\infty} 2a_{k-1} x^k - \sum_{k=2}^{\infty} 3a_{k-2} x^k = a_0 + a_1 x - 2a_0 x + \sum_{k=2}^{\infty} (4^k + 6) \cdot x^k$$

$$= 20 + 20x + \frac{1}{1 - 4x} + \frac{6}{1 - x} - 7 - 10x = 13 + 10x + \frac{1}{1 - 4x} + \frac{6}{1 - x}$$

$$= \frac{20 - 80x + 2x^2 + 40x^3}{(1 - 4x)(1 - x)},$$

because of the given recurrence relation, the initial conditions, and Table 1. Since the left-hand side of this equation factors as $G(x)(1 - 3x)(1 + x)$, we know that

$$G(x) = \frac{20 - 80x + 2x^2 + 40x^3}{(1 - 4x)(1 - x)(1 + x)(1 - 3x)}.$$

At this point we must use partial fractions to break up the denominator. Setting this last expression equal to

$$\frac{A}{1 - 4x} + \frac{B}{1 - x} + \frac{C}{1 + x} + \frac{D}{1 - 3x},$$

multiplying through by the common denominator, and equating coefficients, we find that $A = 16/5$, $B = -3/2$, $C = 31/20$, and $D = 67/4$. Thus

$$G(x) = \frac{16/5}{1 - 4x} + \frac{-3/2}{1 - x} + \frac{31/20}{1 + x} + \frac{67/4}{1 - 3x} = \sum_{k=0}^{\infty} \left(\frac{16}{5} \cdot 4^k - \frac{3}{2} + \frac{31}{20}(-1)^k + \frac{67}{4} \cdot 3^k \right) x^k$$

(from Table 1). Therefore $a_k = (16/5)4^k - (3/2) + (31/20)(-1)^k + (67/4)3^k$. We check our answer by computing the next term of the sequence from both the recurrence and the formula (here $a_2 = 202$ both ways). Alternatively, we ask maple for the solution:

$$\mathtt{rsolve(\{a(k) = 2 * a(k - 1) + 3 * a(k - 2) + 4\char`\^k + 6, a(0) = 20, a(1) = 60\}, a(k));}$$

40. a) By definition,

$$\binom{-1/2}{n} = \frac{(-1/2)(-3/2)(-5/2) \cdots (-(2n - 1)/2)}{n!}$$

$$= (-1)^n \frac{1 \cdot 3 \cdot 5 \cdots (2n - 1)}{2^n \, n!}$$

$$= (-1)^n \frac{1 \cdot 3 \cdot 5 \cdots (2n - 1)}{2^n \, n!} \cdot \frac{2 \cdot 4 \cdot 6 \cdot (2n)}{2^n \, n!}$$

$$= (-1)^n \frac{(2n)!}{n! \, n! \, 4^n}$$

$$= (-1)^n \binom{2n}{n} \frac{1}{4^n} = \binom{2n}{n} \frac{1}{(-4)^n}$$

b) By the extended binomial theorem (Theorem 2), with $-4x$ in place of x and $u = -1/2$, we have

$$(1 - 4x)^{-1/2} = \sum_{n=0}^{\infty} \binom{-1/2}{n} (-4x)^n = \sum_{n=0}^{\infty} \frac{\binom{2n}{n}}{(-4)^n} (-4x)^n = \sum_{n=0}^{\infty} \binom{2n}{n} x^n.$$

42. First we note, as the hint suggests, that $(1 + x)^n = (1 + x)(1 + x)^{n-1} = (1 + x)^{n-1} + x(1 + x)^{n-1}$. Expanding both sides of this equality using the binomial theorem, we have

$$\sum_{r=0}^{n} C(n, r) x^r = \sum_{r=0}^{n-1} C(n - 1, r) x^r + \sum_{r=0}^{n-1} C(n - 1, r) x^{r+1}$$

$$= \sum_{r=0}^{n-1} C(n - 1, r) x^r + \sum_{r=1}^{n} C(n - 1, r - 1) x^r.$$

Thus

$$1 + \left(\sum_{r=1}^{n-1} C(n,r)x^r \right) + x^n = 1 + \left(\sum_{r=1}^{n-1} (C(n-1,r) + C(n-1,r-1))x^r \right) + x^n \,.$$

Comparing these two expressions, coefficient by coefficient, we see that $C(n,r)$ must equal $C(n-1,r)+C(n-1,r-1)$ for $1 \le r \le n-1$, as desired.

44. Let $G(x) = \sum_{n=0}^{\infty} a_n x^n$ be the generating function for the sequence $\{a_n\}$, where $a_n = 1^2 + 2^2 + 3^2 + \cdots + n^2$.

a) We use the method of generating functions to solve the recurrence relation and initial condition that our sequence satisfies: $a_n = a_{n-1} + n^2$ with $a_0 = 0$ (as in, for example, Exercise 34):

$$G(x) - xG(x) = \sum_{n=0}^{\infty} a_n x^n - \sum_{n=1}^{\infty} a_{n-1} x^n = \sum_{n=0}^{\infty} n^2 x^n \,.$$

By Exercise 37, the generating function for $\{n^2\}$ is

$$\frac{2}{(1-x)^3} - \frac{3}{(1-x)^2} + \frac{1}{1-x} = \frac{x^2+x}{(1-x)^3} \,,$$

so $(1-x)G(x) = (x^2+x)/(1-x)^3$. Dividing both sides by $1-x$ gives the desired expression for $G(x)$.

b) We split the generating function we found for $G(x) = \sum_{n=0}^{\infty} a_n x^n$ into two pieces and use Table 1:

$$\frac{x^2}{(1-x)^4} + \frac{x}{(1-x)^4} = \sum_{n=0}^{\infty} C(n+3,3)x^{n+2} + \sum_{n=0}^{\infty} C(n+3,3)x^{n+1}$$

$$= \sum_{n=0}^{\infty} C(n+1,3)x^n + \sum_{n=0}^{\infty} C(n+2,3)x^n$$

$$= \sum_{n=0}^{\infty} \frac{(n+1)n(n-1) + (n+2)(n+1)n}{6} x^n$$

$$= \sum_{n=0}^{\infty} \frac{n(n+1)(2n+1)}{6} x^n \,,$$

as desired. (Note that we did not need to change the limits of summation in line 3 because $C(1,3) = C(2,3) = 0$.)

46. We will make heavy use of the identity $e^x = \sum_{n=0}^{\infty} \frac{1}{n!} x^n$.

a) $\sum_{n=0}^{\infty} \frac{(-2)^n}{n!} x^n = 2 \sum_{n=0}^{\infty} \frac{1}{n!} (-2x)^n = e^{-2x}$.

b) $\sum_{n=0}^{\infty} \frac{-1}{n!} x^n = -\sum_{n=0}^{\infty} \frac{1}{n!} x^n = -e^x$

c) $\sum_{n=0}^{\infty} \frac{n}{n!} x^n = \sum_{n=1}^{\infty} \frac{x^n}{(n-1)!} = x \sum_{n=0}^{\infty} \frac{x^n}{n!} = xe^x$, by a change of variable (This could also be done using calculus.)

d) This generating function can be obtained either with calculus or without. To do it without calculus, write

$$\sum_{n=0}^{\infty} n(n-1) \frac{x^n}{n!} = \sum_{n=2}^{\infty} \frac{x^n}{(n-2)!} = x^2 \sum_{n=0}^{\infty} \frac{x^n}{n!} = x^2 e^x, \text{ by a change of variable. To do it with calculus, start}$$

with $e^x = \sum_{n=0}^{\infty} \frac{x^n}{n!}$ and differentiate both sides twice to obtain $e^x = \sum_{n=0}^{\infty} \frac{n(n-1)}{n!} x^{n-2} = \frac{1}{x^2} \sum_{n=0}^{\infty} n(n-1) \frac{x^n}{n!}$.

Therefore $\sum_{n=0}^{\infty} n(n-1) \frac{x^n}{n!} = x^2 e^x$.

e) This generating function can be obtained either with calculus or without. To do it without calculus, write

$$\sum_{n=0}^{\infty} \frac{1}{(n+1)(n+2)} \cdot \frac{x^n}{n!} = \sum_{n=0}^{\infty} \frac{x^n}{(n+2)!} = \frac{1}{x^2} \sum_{n=0}^{\infty} \frac{x^{n+2}}{(n+2)!} = \frac{1}{x^2} \sum_{n=2}^{\infty} \frac{x^n}{n!} = \frac{1}{x^2}(e^x - x - 1).$$

To do it with calculus, integrate $e^s = \sum_{n=0}^{\infty} \frac{s^n}{n!}$ from 0 to t to obtain

$$e^t - 1 = \sum_{n=0}^{\infty} \frac{t^{n+1}}{n+1} \cdot \frac{1}{n!}.$$

Then differentiate again, from 0 to x, to obtain

$$e^x - x - 1 = \sum_{n=0}^{\infty} \frac{x^{n+2}}{(n+2)(n+1)n!} = x^2 \sum_{n=0}^{\infty} \frac{x^n}{(n+2)(n+1)n!}.$$

Thus $\sum_{n=0}^{\infty} \frac{1}{(n+1)(n+2)} \cdot \frac{x^n}{n!} = (e^x - x - 1)/x^2$.

48. In many of these cases, it's a matter of plugging the exponent of e into the generating function for e^x. We let a_n denote the nth term of the sequence whose generating function is given.

a) The generating function is $e^{3x} = \sum_{n=0}^{\infty} \frac{(3x)^n}{n!} = \sum_{n=0}^{\infty} 3^n \frac{x^n}{n!}$, so the sequence is $a_n = 3^n$.

b) The generating function is $2e^{-3x+1} = (2e)e^{-3x} = 2e \sum_{n=0}^{\infty} \frac{(-3x)^n}{n!} = \sum_{n=0}^{\infty} (2e(-3)^n) \frac{x^n}{n!}$, so the sequence is $a_n = 2e(-3)^n$.

c) The generating function is $e^{4x} + e^{-4x} = \sum_{n=0}^{\infty} \frac{(4x)^n}{n!} + \sum_{n=0}^{\infty} \frac{(-4x)^n}{n!} = \sum_{n=0}^{\infty} (4^n + (-4)^n) \frac{x^n}{n!}$, so the sequence is $a_n = 4^n + (-4)^n$.

d) The sequence whose exponential generating function is e^{3x} is clearly $\{3^n\}$, as in part **(a)**. Since

$$1 + 2x = \frac{1}{0!}x^0 + \frac{2}{1!}x^1 + \sum_{n=2}^{\infty} \frac{0}{n!}x^n,$$

we know that $a_n = 3^n$ for $n \geq 2$, with $a_1 = 3^1 + 2 = 5$ and $a_0 = 3^0 + 1 = 2$.

e) We know that

$$\frac{1}{1+x} = \sum_{n=0}^{\infty} (-1)^n x^n = \sum_{n=0}^{\infty} \frac{(-1)^n n!}{n!} x^n,$$

so the sequence for which $1/(1+x)$ is the exponential generating function is $\{(-1)^n n!\}$. Combining this with the rest of the function (where the generating function is just $\{1\}$), we have $a_n = 1 - (-1)^n n!$.

f) Note that

$$xe^x = \sum_{n=0}^{\infty} x \cdot \frac{x^n}{n!} = \sum_{n=0}^{\infty} \frac{x^{n+1}}{n!} = \sum_{n=1}^{\infty} \frac{x^n}{(n-1)!} = \sum_{n=1}^{\infty} n \cdot \frac{x^n}{n!} = \sum_{n=0}^{\infty} n \cdot \frac{x^n}{n!}.$$

(We changed variable in the middle.) Therefore $a_n = n$, as in Exercise 46c.

g) First we note that

$$e^{x^3} = \sum_{n=0}^{\infty} \frac{(x^3)^n}{n!} = 1 + \frac{x^3}{1!} + \frac{x^6}{2!} + \frac{x^9}{3!} + \cdots$$

$$= \frac{x^0}{0!} \cdot \frac{0!}{0!} + \frac{x^3}{3!} \cdot \frac{3!}{1!} + \frac{x^6}{6!} \cdot \frac{6!}{2!} + \frac{x^9}{9!} \cdot \frac{9!}{3!} + \cdots.$$

Therefore we see that $a_n = 0$ if n is not a multiple of 3, and $a_n = n!/(n/3)!$ if n is a multiple of 3.

50. a) Since all 4^n base-four strings of length n fall into one of the four categories counted by a_n, b_n, c_n, and d_n, obviously $d_n = 4^n - a_n - b_n - c_n$. Next let's see how a string of various types of length $n+1$ can be obtained from a string of length n by adding one digit. To get a string of length $n+1$ with an even number of 0s and an even number of 1s, we can take a string of length n with these same parities and append a 2 or a 3 (thus there are $2a_n$ such strings of this type), or we can take a string of length n with an even number of 0s and an odd number of 1s and append a 1 (thus there are b_n such strings of this type), or we can take a string of length n with an odd number of 0s and an even number of 1s and append a 0 (thus there are c_n such strings of this type). Therefore we have $a_{n+1} = 2a_n + b_n + c_n$. In the same way we find that $b_{n+1} = 2b_n + a_n + d_n$, which equals $b_n - c_n + 4^n$ after substituting the identity with which we began this solution. Similarly, $c_{n+1} = 2c_n + a_n + d_n = c_n - b_n + 4^n$.

b) The strings of length 1 are 0, 1, 2, and 3. So clearly $a_1 = 2$, $b_1 = c_1 = 1$, and $d_1 = 0$. (Note that 0 is an even number.) In fact we can also say that $a_0 = 1$ (the empty string) and $b_0 = c_0 = d_0 = 0$.

c) We apply the recurrences from part **(a)** twice:

$$a_2 = 2 \cdot 2 + 1 + 1 = 6 \qquad a_3 = 2 \cdot 6 + 4 + 4 = 20$$
$$b_2 = 1 - 1 + 4 = 4 \qquad b_3 = 4 + 16 - 4 = 16$$
$$c_2 = 1 - 1 + 4 = 4 \qquad c_3 = 4 + 16 - 4 = 16$$
$$d_2 = 16 - 6 - 4 - 4 = 2 \qquad d_3 = 64 - 20 - 16 - 16 = 12$$

d) Before proceeding as the problem asks, we note a shortcut. By symmetry, b_n must be the same as c_n. Substituting this into our recurrences, we find immediately that $b_n = c_n = 4^{n-1}$ for $n \geq 1$. Therefore $a_n = 2a_{n-1} + 2 \cdot 4^{n-2}$. This recurrence with the initial condition $a_1 = 2$ can easily be solved by the methods of either this section or Section 6.2 to give $a_n = 2^{n-1} + 4^{n-1}$. But let's proceed as instructed.

Let $A(x)$, $B(x)$, and $C(x)$ be the desired generating functions. Then $xA(x) = \sum_{n=0}^{\infty} a_n x^{n+1} = \sum_{n=1}^{\infty} a_{n-1} x^n$ and similarly for B and C, so we have

$$A(x) - xB(x) - xC(x) - 2xA(x) = \sum_{n=0}^{\infty} a_n x^n - \sum_{n=1}^{\infty} b_{n-1} x^n - \sum_{n=1}^{\infty} c_{n-1} x^n - \sum_{n=1}^{\infty} 2a_{n-1} x^n = a_0 = 1.$$

Similarly,

$$B(x) - xB(x) + xC(x) = \sum_{n=0}^{\infty} b_n x^n - \sum_{n=1}^{\infty} b_{n-1} x^n + \sum_{n=1}^{\infty} c_{n-1} x^n$$

$$= b_0 + \sum_{n=1}^{\infty} 4^{n-1} x^n = 0 + x \sum_{n=0}^{\infty} 4^n x^n = \frac{x}{1-4x}.$$

Obviously C satisfies the same equation. Therefore our system of three equations (suppressing the arguments on A, B, and C) is

$$(1 - 2x)A - xB - xC = 1$$
$$(1 - x)B + xC = \frac{x}{1 - 4x}$$
$$xB + (1 - x)C = \frac{x}{1 - 4x}.$$

e) Subtracting the third equation in part **(d)** from the second shows that $B = C$, and then plugging that back into the second equation immediately gives

$$B(x) = C(x) = \frac{x}{1 - 4x}.$$

Plugging these into the first equation yields

$$(1 - 2x)A - 2x \cdot \frac{x}{1 - 4x} = 1,$$

and solving for A gives us

$$A(x) = \frac{1 - 4x + 2x^2}{(1 - 2x)(1 - 4x)}.$$

Now that we know the generating functions, we can recover the coefficients. For B and C (using Table 1) we immediately get a coefficient of 4^{n-1} for all $n \geq 1$, with $b_0 = c_0 = 0$. We rewrite $A(x)$ using partial fractions as

$$A(x) = \frac{1}{4} + \frac{1/2}{1 - 2x} + \frac{1/4}{1 - 4x},$$

so we have $a_n = \frac{1}{2} \cdot 2^n + \frac{1}{4} \cdot 4^n = 2^{n-1} + 4^{n-1}$ for $n \geq 1$, with $a_0 = \frac{1}{4} + \frac{1}{2} + \frac{1}{4} = 1$.

52. To form a partition of n using only odd-sized parts, we must choose some 1s, some 3s, some 5s, and so on. The generating function for choosing 1s is

$$1 + x + x^2 + x^3 + \cdots = \frac{1}{1 - x}$$

(the exponent gives the number so obtained). Similarly, the generating function for choosing 3s is

$$1 + x^3 + x^6 + x^9 + \cdots = \frac{1}{1 - x^3}$$

(again the exponent gives the number so obtained). The other choices have analogous generating functions. Therefore the generating function for the entire problem, so that the coefficient of x^n will give $p_o(n)$, the number of partitions of n into odd-sized part, is the infinite product

$$\frac{1}{1 - x} \cdot \frac{1}{1 - x^3} \cdot \frac{1}{1 - x^5} \cdots .$$

54. We need to carefully organize our work so as not to miss any of the partitions. We start with largest-sized parts first in all cases. For $n = 1$, we have $1 = 1$ as the only partition of either type, and so $p_o(1) = p_d(1) = 1$. For $n = 2$, we have $2 = 2$ as the only partition into distinct parts, and $2 = 1 + 1$ as the only partition into odd parts, so $p_o(1) = p_d(1) = 1$. For $n = 3$, we have $3 = 3$ and $3 = 2 + 1$ as the only partitions into distinct parts, and $3 = 3$ and $3 = 1 + 1 + 1$ as the only partitions into odd parts, so $p_o(1) = p_d(1) = 2$. For $n = 4$, we have $4 = 4$ and $4 = 3 + 1$ as the only partitions into distinct parts, and $4 = 3 + 1$ and $4 = 1 + 1 + 1 + 1$ as the only partitions into odd parts, so $p_o(1) = p_d(1) = 2$. For $n = 5$, we have $5 = 5$, $5 = 4 + 1$, and $5 = 3 + 2$ as the only partitions into distinct parts, and $5 = 5$, $5 = 3 + 1 + 1$, and $5 = 1 + 1 + 1 + 1 + 1$ as the only partitions into odd parts, so $p_o(1) = p_d(1) = 3$. For $n = 6$, we have $6 = 6$, $6 = 5 + 1$, $6 = 4 + 2$, and $6 = 3 + 2 + 1$ as the only partitions into distinct parts, and $6 = 5 + 1$, $6 = 3 + 3$, $6 = 3 + 1 + 1 + 1$, and $6 = 1 + 1 + 1 + 1 + 1 + 1$ as the only partitions into odd parts, so $p_o(1) = p_d(1) = 4$. For $n = 7$, we have $7 = 7$, $7 = 6 + 1$, $7 = 5 + 2$, $7 = 4 + 3$, and $7 = 4 + 2 + 1$ as the only partitions into distinct parts, and $7 = 7$, $7 = 5 + 1 + 1$, $7 = 3 + 3 + 1$, $7 = 3 + 1 + 1 + 1 + 1$, and $7 = 1 + 1 + 1 + 1 + 1 + 1 + 1$ as the only partitions into odd parts, so $p_o(1) = p_d(1) = 5$. Finally, for $n = 8$, we have $8 = 8$, $8 = 7 + 1$, $8 = 6 + 2$, $8 = 5 + 3$, $8 = 5 + 2 + 1$, and $8 = 4 + 3 + 1$ as the only partitions into distinct parts, and $8 = 7 + 1$, $8 = 5 + 3$ $8 = 5 + 1 + 1 + 1$, $8 = 3 + 3 + 1 + 1$, $8 = 3 + 1 + 1 + 1 + 1 + 1$, and $8 = 1 + 1 + 1 + 1 + 1 + 1 + 1 + 1$ as the only partitions into odd parts, so $p_o(1) = p_d(1) = 6$. As we will prove in Exercise 55, it is no coincidence that these numbers all agree.

56. This is a very difficult problem. A solution can be found in *The Theory of Partitions* by George Andrews (Addison-Wesley, 1976), Chapter 6.

58. a) In order to have the first success on the nth trial, where $n \geq 1$, we must have $n - 1$ failures followed by a success. Therefore $p(X = n) = q^{n-1}p$, where p is the probability of success and $q = 1 - p$ is the probability of failure. Therefore the probability generating function is

$$G(x) = \sum_{n=1}^{\infty} q^{n-1}px^n = px \sum_{n=1}^{\infty} (qx)^{n-1} = px \sum_{n=0}^{\infty} (qx)^n = \frac{px}{1 - qx}.$$

b) By Exercise 57, $E(X)$ is the derivative of $G(x)$ at $x = 1$. Here we have

$$G'(x) = \frac{p}{(1 - qx)^2}, \quad \text{so} \quad G'(1) = \frac{p}{(1 - q)^2} = \frac{p}{p^2} = \frac{1}{p}.$$

From the same exercise, we know that the variance is $G''(1) + G'(1) - G'(1)^2$; so we compute:

$$G''(x) = \frac{2pq}{(1 - qx)^3}, \quad \text{so} \quad G''(1) = \frac{2pq}{(1 - q)^3} = \frac{2pq}{p^3} = \frac{2q}{p^2},$$

and therefore

$$V(X) = G''(1) + G'(1) - G'(1)^2 = \frac{2q}{p^2} + \frac{1}{p} - \frac{1}{p^2} = \frac{q}{p^2}.$$

60. We start with the definition and then use the fact that the only way for the sum of two nonnegative integers to be k is for one of them to be i and the other to be $k - i$, for some i between 0 and k, inclusive. We then invoke independence, and finally the definition of multiplication of infinite series:

$$G_{X+Y}(x) = \sum_{k=0}^{\infty} p(X + Y = k)x^k$$

$$= \sum_{k=0}^{\infty} \left(\sum_{i=0}^{k} p(X = i \text{ and } Y = k - i) \right) x^k$$

$$= \sum_{k=0}^{\infty} \left(\sum_{i=0}^{k} p(X = i) \cdot p(Y = k - i) \right) x^k$$

$$= G_X(x) \cdot G_Y(x)$$

SECTION 6.5   Inclusion–Exclusion

2. $|C \cup D| = |C| + |D| - |C \cap D| = 345 + 212 - 188 = 369$

4. $|M \cap S| = |M| + |S| - |M \cup S| = 650000 + 1250000 - 1450000 = 450{,}000$

6. a) In this case the union is just A_3, so the answer is $|A_3| = 10{,}000$.
  b) The cardinality of the union is the sum of the cardinalities in this case, so the answer is $100 + 1000 + 10000 = 11{,}100$.
  c) $|A_1 \cup A_2 \cup A_3| = |A_1| + |A_2| + |A_3| - |A_1 \cap A_2| - |A_1 \cap A_3| - |A_2 \cap A_3| + |A_1 \cap A_2 \cap A_3| = 100 + 1000 + 10000 - 2 - 2 - 2 + 1 = 11{,}095$

8. $270 - 64 - 94 - 58 + 26 + 28 + 22 - 14 = 116$

10. $100 - \lfloor 100/5 \rfloor - \lfloor 100/7 \rfloor + \lfloor 100/(5 \cdot 7) \rfloor = 100 - 20 - 14 + 2 = 68$

12. There are $\lfloor \sqrt{1000} \rfloor = 31$ squares and $\lfloor \sqrt[3]{1000} \rfloor = 10$ cubes. Furthermore there are $\lfloor \sqrt[6]{1000} \rfloor = 3$ numbers that are both squares and cubes, i.e., sixth powers. Therefore the answer is $31 + 10 - 3 = 38$.

14. There are 26! strings in all. To count the strings that contain *fish*, we glue these four letters together as one and permute it and the 22 other letters, so there are 23! such strings. Similarly there are 24! strings that contain *rat* and 23! strings that contain *bird*. Furthermore, there are 21! strings that contain both *fish* and *rat* (glue each of these sets of letters together), but there are no strings that contain both *bird* and another of these strings. Therefore the answer is $26! - 23! - 24! - 23! + 21! \approx 4.0 \times 10^{26}$.

16. $4 \cdot 100 - 6 \cdot 50 + 4 \cdot 25 - 5 = 195$

18. There are $C(10,1) + C(10,2) + \cdots + C(10,10) = 2^{10} - C(10,0) = 1023$ terms on the right-hand side of the equation.

20. $5 \cdot 10000 - 10 \cdot 1000 + 10 \cdot 100 - 5 \cdot 10 + 1 = 40{,}951$

22. The base case is $n = 2$, for which we already know the formula to be valid. Assume that the formula is true for n sets. Look at a situation with $n+1$ sets, and temporarily consider $A_n \cup A_{n+1}$ as one set. Then by the inductive hypothesis we have

$$|A_1 \cup \cdots \cup A_{n+1}| = \sum_{i<n} |A_i| + |A_n \cup A_{n+1}| - \sum_{i<j<n} |A_i \cap A_j|$$
$$- \sum_{i<n} |A_i \cap (A_n \cup A_{n+1})| + \cdots + (-1)^n |A_1 \cap \cdots \cap A_{n-1} \cap (A_n \cup A_{n+1})|.$$

Next we apply the distributive law to each term on the right involving $A_n \cup A_{n+1}$, giving us

$$\sum |(A_{i_1} \cap \cdots \cap A_{i_m}) \cap (A_n \cup A_{n+1})| = \sum |(A_{i_1} \cap \cdots \cap A_{i_m} \cap A_n) \cup (A_{i_1} \cap \cdots \cap A_{i_m} \cap A_{n+1})|.$$

Now we apply the base case to rewrite each of these terms as

$$\sum |A_{i_1} \cap \cdots \cap A_{i_m} \cap A_n| + \sum |A_{i_1} \cap \cdots \cap A_{i_m} \cap A_{n+1}| - \sum |A_{i_1} \cap \cdots \cap A_{i_m} \cap A_n \cap A_{n+1}|,$$

which gives us precisely the summation we want.

24. Let E_1, E_2, and E_3 be these three events, in the order given. Then $p(E_1) = C(5,3)/2^5 = 10/32$; $p(E_2) = 2^3/2^5 = 8/32$; and $p(E_3) = 2^3/2^5 = 8/32$. Furthermore $p(E_1 \cap E_2) = C(3,1)/2^5 = 3/32$; $p(E_1 \cap E_3) = 1/32$; and $p(E_2 \cap E_3) = 2/32$. Finally $p(E_1 \cap E_2 \cap E_3) = 1/32$. Therefore the probability that at least one of these events occurs is $(10 + 8 + 8 - 3 - 1 - 2 + 1)/32 = 21/32$.

26. We only need to list the terms that have one or two events in them. Thus we have

$$p(E_1 \cup E_2 \cup E_3 \cup E_4) = \sum_{1 \le i \le 4} p(E_i) - \sum_{1 \le i < j \le 4} p(E_i \cap E_j),$$

or, explicitly, $p(E_1 \cup E_2 \cup E_3 \cup E_4) = p(E_1) + p(E_2) + p(E_3) + p(E_4) - p(E_1 \cap E_2) - p(E_1 \cap E_3) - p(E_1 \cap E_4) - p(E_2 \cap E_3) - p(E_2 \cap E_4) - p(E_3 \cap E_4)$.

28. The probability of the union, in this case, is the sum of the probabilities of the events:

$$p(E_1 \cup E_2 \cup \cdots \cup E_n) = \sum_{i=1}^{n} p(E_i) = p(E_1) + p(E_2) + \cdots + p(E_n)$$

SECTION 6.6   Applications of Inclusion–Exclusion

2. $1000 - 450 - 622 - 30 + 111 + 14 + 18 - 9 = 32$

4. $C(4+17-1, 17) - C(4+13-1, 13) - C(4+12-1, 12) - C(4+11-1, 11) - C(4+8-1, 8) + C(4+8-1, 8) + C(4+7-1, 7) + C(4+4-1, 4) + C(4+6-1, 6) + C(4+3-1, 3) + C(4+2-1, 2) - C(4+2-1, 2) = 20$

6. Square-free numbers are those not divisible by the square of a prime. We count them as follows: $99 - \lfloor 99/2^2 \rfloor - \lfloor 99/3^2 \rfloor - \lfloor 99/5^2 \rfloor - \lfloor 99/7^2 \rfloor + \lfloor 99/(2^2 3^2) \rfloor = 61$.

8. $5^7 - C(5,1)4^7 + C(5,2)3^7 - C(5,3)2^7 + C(5,4)1^7 = 16{,}800$

10. This problem is asking for the number of onto functions from a set with 8 elements (the balls) to a set with 3 elements (the urns). Therefore the answer is $3^8 - C(3,1)2^8 + C(3,2)1^8 = 5796$.

12. 2143, 2341, 2413, 3142, 3412, 3421, 4123, 4312, 4321

14. We use Theorem 2 with $n = 10$, which gives us

$$\frac{D_{10}}{10!} = 1 - \frac{1}{1!} + \frac{1}{2!} - \cdots + \frac{1}{10!} = \frac{1334961}{3628800} = \frac{16481}{44800} \approx 0.3678794643\,,$$

which is almost exactly $e^{-1} \approx 0.3678794412\ldots$.

16. There are $n!$ ways to make the first assignment. We can think of this first seating as assigning student n to a chair we will label n. Then the next seating must be a derangement with respect to this numbering, so there are D_n second seatings possible. Therefore the answer is $n! D_n$.

18. In a derangement of the numbers from 1 to n, the number 1 cannot go first, so let $k \neq 1$ be the number that goes first. There are $n-1$ choices for k. Now there are two ways to get a derangement with k first. One way is to have 1 in the kth position. If we do this, then there are exactly D_{n-2} ways to derange the rest of the numbers. On the other hand, if 1 does not go into the kth position, then think of the number 1 as being temporarily relabeled k. A derangement is completed in this case by finding a derangement of the numbers 2 through n in positions 2 through n, so there are D_{n-1} of them. Combining all this, by the product rule and the sum rule, we obtain the desired recurrence relation. The initial conditions are $D_0 = 1$ and $D_1 = 0$.

20. We apply iteration to the formula $D_n = nD_{n-1} + (-1)^n$, obtaining

$$\begin{aligned}
D_n &= n\big((n-1)D_{n-2} + (-1)^{n-1}\big) + (-1)^n \\
&= n(n-1)D_{n-2} + n(-1)^{n-1} + (-1)^n \\
&= n(n-1)\big((n-2)D_{n-3} + (-1)^{n-2}\big) + n(-1)^{n-1} + (-1)^n \\
&= n(n-1)(n-2)D_{n-3} + n(n-1)(-1)^{n-2} + n(-1)^{n-1} + (-1)^n \\
&\;\;\vdots \\
&= n(n-1)\cdots 2D_1 + n(n-1)\cdots 3 - n(n-1)\cdots 4 + \cdots + n(-1)^{n-1} + (-1)^n \\
&= n(n-1)\cdots 3 - n(n-1)\cdots 4 + \cdots + n(-1)^{n-1} + (-1)^n\,,
\end{aligned}$$

which yields the formula in Theorem 2 after factoring out $n!$.

22. The numbers not relatively prime to pq are the ones that have p and/or q as a factor. Thus we have

$$\phi(pq) = pq - \frac{pq}{p} - \frac{pq}{q} + \frac{pq}{pq} = pq - q - p + 1 = (p-1)(q-1)\,.$$

24. The left-hand side of course counts the number of permutations of the set of integers from 1 to n. The right-hand side counts it, too, by a two-step process: first decide how many and which elements are to be fixed (this can be done in $C(n, k)$ ways, for each of $k = 0, 1, \ldots, n$), and in each case derange the remaining elements (which can be done in D_{n-k} ways).

26. This permutation starts with $4, 5, 6$ in some order ($3! = 6$ ways to choose this), followed by $1, 2, 3$ in some order ($3! = 6$ ways to decide this). Therefore the answer is $6 \cdot 6 = 36$.

SUPPLEMENTARY EXERCISES FOR CHAPTER 6

2. a) Let a_n be the amount that remains after n hours. Then $a_n = 0.99a_{n-1}$.
   b) By iteration we find the solution $a_n = (0.99)^n a_0$, where a_0 is the original amount of the isotope.

4. a) Let B_n be the number of bacteria after n hours. The initial conditions are $B_0 = 100$ and $B_1 = 300$. Thereafter, $B_n = B_{n-1} + 2B_{n-1} - B_{n-2} = 3B_{n-1} - B_{n-2}$.
   b) The characteristic equation is $r^2 - 3r + 1 = 0$, which has roots $(3 \pm \sqrt{5})/2$. Therefore the general solution is $B_n = \alpha_1((3 + \sqrt{5})/2)^n + \alpha_2((3 - \sqrt{5})/2)^n$. Plugging in the initial conditions we determine that $\alpha_1 = 50 + 30\sqrt{5}$ and $\alpha_2 = 50 - 30\sqrt{5}$. Therefore the solution is $B_n = (50 + 30\sqrt{5})((3 + \sqrt{5})/2)^n + (50 - 30\sqrt{5})((3 - \sqrt{5})/2)^n$.
   c) Plugging in small values of n, we find that $B_9 = 676{,}500$ and $B_{10} = 1{,}771{,}100$. Therefore the colony will contain more than one million bacteria after 10 hours.

6. We can put any of the stamps on first, leaving a problem with a smaller number of cents to solve. Thus the recurrence relation is $a_n = a_{n-4} + a_{n-6} + a_{n-10}$. We need 10 initial conditions, and it is easy to see that $a_0 = 1$, $a_1 = a_2 = a_3 = a_5 = a_7 = a_9 = 0$, and $a_4 = a_6 = a_8 = 1$.

8. If we add the equations, we obtain $a_n + b_n = 2a_{n-1}$, which means that $b_n = 2a_{n-1} - a_n$. If we now substitute this back into the first equation, we have $a_n = a_{n-1} + (2a_{n-2} - a_{n-1}) = 2a_{n-2}$. The initial conditions are $a_0 = 1$ (given) and $a_1 = 3$ (follows from the first recurrence relation and the given initial conditions). We can solve this using the characteristic equation $r^2 - 2 = 0$, but a simpler approach, that avoids irrational numbers, is as follows. It is clear that $a_{2n} = 2^n a_0 = 2^n$, and $a_{2n+1} = 2^n a_1 = 3 \cdot 2^n$. This is a nice explicit formula, which is all that "solution" really means. We also need a formula for b_n, of course. From $b_n = 2a_{n-1} - a_n$ (obtained above), we have $b_{2n} = 3 \cdot 2^n - 2^n = 2^{n+1}$, and $b_{2n+1} = 2 \cdot 2^n - 3 \cdot 2^n = -2^n$.

10. Following the hint, we let $b_n = \log a_n$. Then the recurrence relation becomes $b_n = 3b_{n-1} + 2b_{n-2}$, with initial conditions $b_0 = b_1 = 1$. This is solved in the usual manner. The characteristic equation is $r^2 - 3r - 2 = 0$, which gives roots $(3 \pm \sqrt{17})/2$. Plugging the initial conditions into the general solution and doing some messy algebra gives

$$b_n = \frac{17 - \sqrt{17}}{34}\left(\frac{3 + \sqrt{17}}{2}\right)^n + \frac{17 + \sqrt{17}}{34}\left(\frac{3 - \sqrt{17}}{2}\right)^n.$$

The solution to the original problem is then $a_n = 2^{b_n}$.

12. The characteristic equation is $r^3 - 3r^2 + 3r - 1 = 0$. This factors as $(r - 1)^3 = 0$, so there is only one root, 1, and its multiplicity is 3. Therefore the general solution is $a_n = \alpha_1 + \alpha_2 n + \alpha_3 n^2$. Plugging in the initial conditions gives us $2 = \alpha_1$, $2 = \alpha_1 + \alpha_2 + \alpha_3$, and $4 = \alpha_1 + 2\alpha_2 + 4\alpha_3$. Solving yields $\alpha_1 = 2$, $\alpha_2 = -1$, and $\alpha_3 = 1$. Therefore the solution is $a_n = 2 - n + n^2$.

14. We use the result of Exercise 31 in Section 6.3, with $a = 3$, $b = 5$, $c = 2$, and $d = 4$. Thus the solution is $f(n) = 625n^4/311 - 314n^{\log_5 3}/311$.

16. The algorithm compares the largest elements of the two halves (this is one comparison), and then it compares the smaller largest element with the second largest element of the other half (one more comparison). This is sufficient to determine the largest and second largest elements of the list. (If the list has only one element in it, then the second largest element is declared to be $-\infty$.) Let $f(n)$ be the number of comparisons used by this algorithm on a list of size n. The list is split into two lists, of size $\lfloor n/2 \rfloor$ and $\lceil n/2 \rceil$, respectively. Thus our recurrence relation is $f(n) = f(\lfloor n/2 \rfloor) + f(\lceil n/2 \rceil) + 2$, with initial condition $f(1) = 0$. (This algorithm could be made slightly more efficient by having the base cases be $n = 2$ and $n = 3$, rather than $n = 1$.)

18. a) $\Delta a_n = 3 - 3 = 0$ **b)** $\Delta a_n = 4(n+1) + 7 - (4n+7) = 4$
   c) $\Delta a_n = \left((n+1)^2 + (n+1) + 1\right) - (n^2 + n + 1) = 2n + 2$

20. We prove something a bit stronger. If $a_n = P(n)$ is a polynomial of degree at most d, then Δa_n is a polynomial of degree at most $d - 1$. To see this, let $P(n) = c_d n^d + \text{(lower order terms)}$. Then

$$\Delta P(n) = c_d(n+1)^d + \text{(lower order terms)} - c_d n^d + \text{(lower order terms)}$$
$$= c_d n^d + \text{(lower order terms)} - c_d n^d + \text{(lower order terms)}$$
$$= \text{(lower order terms)}.$$

If we apply this result $d + 1$ times, then we get that $\Delta^{d+1} a_n$ has degree at most -1, i.e., is identically 0.

22. Since it is valid to use the commutative, associative, and distributive laws for absolutely convergent infinite series, we simply write

$$(cF + dG)(x) = cF(x) + dG(x) = c\sum_{k=0}^{\infty} a_k x^k + d\sum_{k=0}^{\infty} b_k x^k = \sum_{k=0}^{\infty}(ca_k + db_k)x^k.$$

24. $14 + 18 - 22 = 10$

26. If the queries are correct, then by inclusion-exclusion the number of students who are freshmen and have not taken courses in either subject must equal $2175 - 1675 - 1074 - 444 + 607 + 350 + 201 - 143 = -3$. Since a negative number here is not possible, we conclude that the responses cannot all be accurate.

28. There will be $C(7, i)$ terms involving combinations of i of the sets at a time. Therefore the answer is $C(7, 1) + C(7, 2) + C(7, 3) + C(7, 4) + C(7, 5) = 119$.

30. For a more compact notation, let us write $1{,}000{,}000$ as M.
   a) $\lfloor M/2 \rfloor + \lfloor M/3 \rfloor + \lfloor M/5 \rfloor - \lfloor M/(2 \cdot 3) \rfloor - \lfloor M/(2 \cdot 5) \rfloor - \lfloor M/(3 \cdot 5) \rfloor + \lfloor M/(2 \cdot 3 \cdot 5) \rfloor = 733{,}334$
   b) $M - \lfloor M/7 \rfloor - \lfloor M/11 \rfloor - \lfloor M/13 \rfloor + \lfloor M/(7 \cdot 11) \rfloor + \lfloor M/(7 \cdot 13) \rfloor + \lfloor M/(11 \cdot 13) \rfloor - \lfloor M/(7 \cdot 11 \cdot 13) \rfloor = 719{,}281$
   c) This is asking for numbers divisible by 3 but not by 21. Since the set of numbers divisible by 21 is a subset of the set of numbers divisible by 3, this is simply $\lfloor M/3 \rfloor - \lfloor M/21 \rfloor = 285{,}714$.

32. After the assignments of the hardest and easiest job have been made, there are 4 different jobs to assign to 3 different employees. No restrictions are stated, so we assume that there are none. Therefore we are just looking for the number of functions from a set with 4 elements to a set with 3 elements, and there are $3^4 = 81$ such functions. (If we impose the restriction that every employee must get at least one job, then it is a little harder. In particular, we must rule out all the assignments in which the jobs go only to the two employees that already have jobs. There are $2^4 = 16$ such assignments, so the answer would be $81 - 16 = 65$ in this case.)

34. We will count the number of bit strings that do contain four consecutive 1's. Bits 1 through 4 could be 1's, or bits 2 through 5, or bits 3 through 6, and in each case there are 4 strings meeting those conditions (since the other two bits are free). This gives a total of 12. However we overcounted, since there are ways in which more than one of these can happen. There are 2 strings in which bits 1 through 4 and bits 2 through 5 are 1's, 2 strings in which bits 2 through 5 and bits 3 through 6 are 1's, and 1 string in which bits 1 through 4 and bits 3 through 6 are 1's. Finally, there is 1 string in which all three substrings are 1's. Thus the number of bit strings with 4 consecutive 1's is $12 - 2 - 2 - 1 + 1 = 8$. Therefore the answer to the exercise is $2^6 - 8 = 56$.

CHAPTER 7
Relations

SECTION 7.1   Relations and Their Properties

2. a) $(1,1)$, $(1,2)$, $(1,3)$, $(1,4)$, $(1,5)$, $(1,6)$, $(2,2)$, $(2,4)$, $(2,6)$, $(3,3)$, $(3,6)$, $(4,4)$, $(5,5)$, $(6,6)$

b) We draw a line from a to b whenever a divides b, using separate sets of points; an alternate form of this graph would have just one set of points.

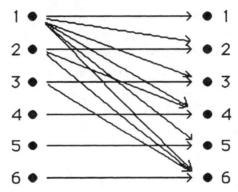

c) We put an $\times$ in the ith row and j^{th} column if and only if i divides j.

R	1	2	3	4	5	6
1	×	×	×	×	×	×
2		×		×		×
3			×			×
4				×		
5					×	
6						×

4. a) Being taller than is not reflexive (I am not taller than myself), nor symmetric (I am taller than my daughter, but she is not taller than I). It is antisymmetric (vacuously, since we never have A taller than B, and B taller than A, even if $A = B$). It is clearly transitive.

b) This is clearly reflexive, symmetric, and transitive (it is an equivalence relation—see Section 7.5). It is not antisymmetric, since twins, for example, are unequal people born on the same day.

c) This has exactly the same answers as part **(b)**, since having the same first name is just like having the same birthday.

d) This is clearly reflexive and symmetric. It is not antisymmetric, since my cousin and I have a common grandparent, and I and my cousin have a common grandparent, but I am not equal to my cousin. This relation is not transitive. My cousin and I have a common grandparent; my cousin and her cousin on the other side of her family have a common grandparent. My cousin's cousin and I do not have a common grandparent.

6. a) Since $1 + 1 \neq 0$, this relation is not reflexive. Since $x + y = y + x$, it follows that $x + y = 0$ if and only if $y + x = 0$, so the relation is symmetric. Since $(1, -1)$ and $(-1, 1)$ are both in R, the relation is not antisymmetric. The relation is not transitive; for example, $(1, -1) \in R$ and $(-1, 1) \in R$, but $(1, 1) \notin R$.

b) Since $x = \pm x$ (choosing the plus sign), the relation is reflexive. Since $x = \pm y$ if and only if $y = \pm x$, the relation is symmetric. Since $(1, -1)$ and $(-1, 1)$ are both in R, the relation is not antisymmetric. The relation is transitive, essentially because the product of 1's and -1's is ± 1.

c) The relation is reflexive, since $x - x = 0$ is a rational number. The relation is symmetric, because if $x - y$ is rational, then so is $-(x - y) = y - x$. Since $(1, -1)$ and $(-1, 1)$ are both in R, the relation is not antisymmetric. To see that the relation is transitive, not that if $(x, y) \in R$ and $(y, z) \in R$, then $x - y$ and $y - z$ are rational numbers. Therefore their sum $x - z$ is rational, and that means that $(x, z) \in R$.

d) Since $1 \neq 2 \cdot 1$, this relation is not reflexive. It is not symmetric, since $(2, 1) \in R$, but $(1, 2) \notin R$. To see that it is antisymmetric, suppose that $x = 2y$ and $y = 2x$. Then $y = 4y$, from which it follows that $y = 0$ and hence $x = 0$. Thus the only time that (x, y) and (y, x) are both is R is when $x = y$ (and both are 0). This relation is clearly not transitive, since $(4, 2) \in R$ and $(2, 1) \in R$, but $(4, 1) \notin R$.

e) This relation is reflexive since squares are always nonnegative. It is clearly symmetric (the roles of x and y in the statement are interchangeable). It is not antisymmetric, since $(2, 3)$ and $(3, 2)$ are both in R. It is not transitive; for example, $(1, 0) \in R$ and $(0, -2) \in R$, but $(1, -2) \notin R$.

f) This is not reflexive, since $(1, 1) \notin R$. It is clearly symmetric (the roles of x and y in the statement are interchangeable). It is not antisymmetric, since $(2, 0)$ and $(0, 2)$ are both in R. It is not transitive; for example, $(1, 0) \in R$ and $(0, -2) \in R$, but $(1, -2) \notin R$.

g) This is not reflexive, since $(2, 2) \notin R$. It is not symmetric, since $(1, 2) \in R$ but $(2, 1) \notin R$. It is antisymmetric, because if $(x, y) \in R$ and $(y, x) \in R$, then $x = 1$ and $y = 1$, so $x = y$. It is transitive, because if $(x, y) \in R$ and $(y, z) \in R$, then $x = 1$ (and $y = 1$, although that doesn't matter), so $(x, z) \in R$.

h) This is not reflexive, since $(2, 2) \notin R$. It is clearly symmetric (the roles of x and y in the statement are interchangeable). It is not antisymmetric, since $(2, 1)$ and $(1, 2)$ are both in R. It is not transitive; for example, $(3, 1) \in R$ and $(1, 7) \in R$, but $(3, 7) \notin R$.

8. We give the simplest example in each case.
a) the empty set on $\{a\}$ (vacuously symmetric and antisymmetric)
b) $\{(a, b), (b, a), (a, c)\}$ on $\{a, b, c\}$

10. Only the relation in part **(a)** is irreflexive (the others are all reflexive).

12. a) not irreflexive, since $(0, 0) \in R$.   **b)** not irreflexive, since $(0, 0) \in R$.
c) not irreflexive, since $(0, 0) \in R$.   **d)** not irreflexive, since $(0, 0) \in R$.
e) not irreflexive, since $(0, 0) \in R$.   **f)** not irreflexive, since $(0, 0) \in R$.
g) not irreflexive, since $(1, 1) \in R$.   **h)** not irreflexive, since $(1, 1) \in R$.

14. $\forall x \, ((x, x) \notin R)$

16. The relations in parts **(a)**, **(b)**, and **(e)** are not asymmetric since they contain pairs of the form (x, x). Clearly the relation in part **(c)** is not asymmetric. The relation in part **(f)** is not asymmetric (both $(1, 3)$ and $(3, 1)$ are in the relation). It is easy to see that the relation in part **(d)** is asymmetric.

18. According to the preamble to Exercise 16, an asymmetric relation is one for which $(a, b) \in R$ and $(b, a) \in R$ can never hold simultaneously, even if $a = b$. Thus R is asymmetric if and only if R is antisymmetric and also irreflexive.

a) This is not asymmetric, since in fact (a, a) is always in R.

b) For any page a with no links, $(a, a) \in R$, so this is not asymmetric.

c) For any page a with links, $(a, a) \in R$, so this is not asymmetric.

d) For any page a that is linked to, $(a, a) \in R$, so this is not asymmetric.

20. An asymmetric relation must be antisymmetric, since the hypothesis of the condition for antisymmetry is false if the relation is asymmetric. The relation $\{(a, a)\}$ on $\{a\}$ is antisymmetric but not asymmetric, however, so the answer to the second question is no. In fact, it is easy to see that R is asymmetric if and only if R is antisymmetric and irreflexive.

22. Of course many answers are possible. The empty relation is always asymmetric (x is never related to y). A less trivial example would be $(a, b) \in R$ if and only if a is taller than b. Clearly it is impossible that both a is taller than b and b is taller than a at the same time.

24. a) $R^{-1} = \{(b, a) \mid (a, b) \in R\} = \{(b, a) \mid a < b\} = \{(a, b) \mid a > b\}$

b) $\overline{R} = \{(a, b) \mid (a, b) \notin R\} = \{(a, b) \mid a \not< b\} = \{(a, b) \mid a \geq b\}$

26. a) Since this relation is symmetric, $R^{-1} = R$.

b) This relation consists of all pairs (a, b) in which state a does not border state b.

28. These are merely routine exercises in set theory. Note that $R_1 \subseteq R_2$.

a) $\{(1, 1), (1, 2), (2, 1), (2, 2), (2, 3), (3, 1), (3, 2), (3, 3), (3, 4)\} = R_2$ **b)** $\{(1, 2), (2, 3), (3, 4)\} = R_1$

c) $\varnothing$ **d)** $\{(1, 1), (2, 1), (2, 2), (3, 1), (3, 2), (3, 3)\}$

30. Since $(1, 2) \in R$ and $(2, 1) \in S$, we have $(1, 1) \in S \circ R$. We use similar reasoning to form the rest of the pairs in the composition, giving us the answer $\{(1, 1), (1, 2), (2, 1), (2, 2)\}$.

32. a) The union of two relations is the union of these sets. Thus $R_1 \cup R_3$ holds between two real numbers if R_1 holds or R_3 holds (or both, it goes without saying). Here this means that the first number is greater than the second or vice versa—in other words, that the two numbers are not equal. This is just relation R_6.

b) For (a, b) to be in $R_3 \cup R_6$, we must have $a > b$ or $a = b$. Since this happens precisely when $a \geq b$, we see that the answer is R_2.

c) The intersection of two relations is the intersection of these sets. Thus $R_2 \cap R_4$ holds between two real numbers if R_2 holds and R_4 holds as well. Thus for (a, b) to be in $R_2 \cap R_4$, we must have $a \geq b$ and $a \leq b$. Since this happens precisely when $a = b$, we see that the answer is R_5.

d) For (a, b) to be in $R_3 \cap R_5$, we must have $a < b$ and $a = b$. It is impossible for $a < b$ and $a = b$ to hold at the same time, so the answer is $\varnothing$, i.e., the relation that never holds.

e) Recall that $R_1 - R_2 = R_1 \cap \overline{R_2}$. But $\overline{R_2} = R_3$, so we are asked for $R_1 \cap R_3$. It is impossible for $a > b$ and $a < b$ to hold at the same time, so the answer is $\varnothing$, i.e., the relation that never holds.

f) Reasoning as in part (**f**), we want $R_2 \cap \overline{R_1} = R_2 \cap R_4$, which is R_5 (this was part (**c**)).

g) Recall that $R_1 \oplus R_3 = (R_1 \cap \overline{R_3}) \cup (R_3 \cap \overline{R_1})$. We see that $R_1 \cap \overline{R_3} = R_1 \cap R_2 = R_1$, and $R_3 \cap \overline{R_1} = R_3 \cap R_4 = R_3$. Thus our answer is $R_1 \cup R_3 = R_6$ (as in part (**a**)).

h) Recall that $R_2 \oplus R_4 = (R_2 \cap \overline{R_4}) \cup (R_4 \cap \overline{R_2})$. We see that $R_2 \cap \overline{R_4} = R_2 \cap R_1 = R_1$, and $R_4 \cap \overline{R_2} = R_4 \cap R_3 = R_3$. Thus our answer is $R_1 \cup R_3 = R_6$ (as in part (**a**)).

34. Recall that the composition of two relations all defined on a common set is defined as follows: $(a, c) \in S \circ R$ if and only if there is some element b such that $(a, b) \in R$ and $(b, c) \in S$. We have to apply this in each case.

a) For (a, c) to be in $R_1 \circ R_1$, we must find an element b such that $(a, b) \in R_1$ and $(b, c) \in R_1$. This means that $a > b$ and $b > c$. Clearly this can be done if and only if $a > c$ to begin with. But that is precisely the statement that $(a, c) \in R_1$. Therefore we have $R_1 \circ R_1 = R_1$. We can interpret (part of) this as showing that R_1 is transitive.

b) For (a, c) to be in $R_1 \circ R_2$, we must find an element b such that $(a, b) \in R_2$ and $(b, c) \in R_1$. This means that $a \geq b$ and $b > c$. Clearly this can be done if and only if $a > c$ to begin with. But that is precisely the statement that $(a, c) \in R_1$. Therefore we have $R_1 \circ R_2 = R_1$.

c) For (a, c) to be in $R_1 \circ R_3$, we must find an element b such that $(a, b) \in R_3$ and $(b, c) \in R_1$. This means that $a < b$ and $b > c$. Clearly this can always be done simply by choosing b to be large enough. Therefore we have $R_1 \circ R_3 = \mathbf{R}^2$, the relation that always holds.

d) For (a, c) to be in $R_1 \circ R_4$, we must find an element b such that $(a, b) \in R_4$ and $(b, c) \in R_1$. This means that $a \leq b$ and $b > c$. Clearly this can always be done simply by choosing b to be large enough. Therefore we have $R_1 \circ R_4 = \mathbf{R}^2$, the relation that always holds.

e) For (a, c) to be in $R_1 \circ R_5$, we must find an element b such that $(a, b) \in R_5$ and $(b, c) \in R_1$. This means that $a = b$ and $b > c$. Clearly this can be done if and only if $a > c$ to begin with (choose $b = a$). But that is precisely the statement that $(a, c) \in R_1$. Therefore we have $R_1 \circ R_5 = R_1$. One way to look at this is to say that R_5, the equality relation, acts as an identity for the composition operation (on the right—although it is also an identity on the left as well).

f) For (a, c) to be in $R_1 \circ R_6$, we must find an element b such that $(a, b) \in R_6$ and $(b, c) \in R_1$. This means that $a \neq b$ and $b > c$. Clearly this can always be done simply by choosing b to be large enough. Therefore we have $R_1 \circ R_6 = \mathbf{R}^2$, the relation that always holds.

g) For (a, c) to be in $R_2 \circ R_3$, we must find an element b such that $(a, b) \in R_3$ and $(b, c) \in R_2$. This means that $a < b$ and $b \geq c$. Clearly this can always be done simply by choosing b to be large enough. Therefore we have $R_2 \circ R_3 = \mathbf{R}^2$, the relation that always holds.

h) For (a, c) to be in $R_3 \circ R_3$, we must find an element b such that $(a, b) \in R_3$ and $(b, c) \in R_3$. This means that $a < b$ and $b < c$. Clearly this can be done if and only if $a < c$ to begin with. But that is precisely the statement that $(a, c) \in R_3$. Therefore we have $R_3 \circ R_3 = R_3$. We can interpret (part of) this as showing that R_3 is transitive.

36. For (a, b) to be an element of R^3, we must find people c and d such that $(a, c) \in R$, $(c, d) \in R$, and $(d, b) \in R$. In words, this says that a is the parent of someone who is the parent of someone who is the parent of b. More simply, a is a great-grandparent of b.

38. Note that these two relations are inverses of each other, since a is a multiple of b if and only if b divides a (see the preamble to Exercise 24).

a) The union of two relations is the union of these sets. Thus $R_1 \cup R_2$ holds between two integers if R_1 holds or R_2 holds (or both, it goes without saying). Thus $(a, b) \in R_1 \cup R_2$ if and only if $a \mid b$ or $b \mid a$. There is not a good easier way to state this.

b) The intersection of two relations is the intersection of these sets. Thus $R_1 \cap R_2$ holds between two integers if R_1 holds and R_2 holds. Thus $(a, b) \in R_1 \cap R_2$ if and only if $a \mid b$ and $b \mid a$. This happens if and only if $a = \pm b$ and $a \neq 0$.

c) By definition $R_1 - R_2 = R_1 \cap \overline{R_2}$. Thus this relation holds between two integers if R_1 holds and R_2 does not hold. We can write this in symbols by saying that $(a, b) \in R_1 - R_2$ if and only if $a \mid b$ and $b \nmid a$. This is equivalent to saying that $a \mid b$ and $a \neq \pm b$.

d) By definition $R_2 - R_1 = R_2 \cap \overline{R_1}$. Thus this relation holds between two integers if R_2 holds and R_1 does not hold. We can write this in symbols by saying that $(a, b) \in R_2 - R_1$ if and only if $b \mid a$ and $a \nmid b$. This is equivalent to saying that $b \mid a$ and $a \neq \pm b$.

e) We know that $R_1 \oplus R_2 = (R_1 - R_2) \cup (R_2 - R_1)$, so we look at our solutions to part **(c)** and part **(d)**. Thus this relation holds between two integers if R_1 holds and R_2 does not hold, or vice versa. This happens if and only if $a \mid b$ or $b \mid a$, but $a \neq \pm b$.

40. These are just the 16 different subsets of $\{(0,0), (0,1), (1,0), (1,1)\}$.

   1. $\varnothing$
   2. $\{(0,0)\}$
   3. $\{(0,1)\}$
   4. $\{(1,0)\}$
   5. $\{(1,1)\}$
   6. $\{(0,0), (0,1)\}$
   7. $\{(0,0), (1,0)\}$
   8. $\{(0,0), (1,1)\}$
   9. $\{(0,1), (1,0)\}$
   10. $\{(0,1), (1,1)\}$
   11. $\{(1,0), (1,1)\}$
   12. $\{(0,0), (0,1), (1,0)\}$
   13. $\{(0,0), (0,1), (1,1)\}$
   14. $\{(0,0), (1,0), (1,1)\}$
   15. $\{(0,1), (1,0), (1,1)\}$
   16. $\{(0,0), (0,1), (1,0), (1,1)\}$

42. We list the relations by number as given in the solution above.
   a) 8, 13, 14, 16   **b)** 1, 3, 4, 9   **c)** 1, 2, 5, 8, 9, 12, 15, 16
   d) 1, 2, 3, 4, 5, 6, 7, 8, 10, 11, 13, 14   **e)** 1, 3, 4   **f)** 1, 2, 3, 4, 5, 6, 7, 8, 10, 11, 13, 14, 16

44. This is similar to Example 16 in this section. A relation on a set S with n elements is a subset of $S \times S$. Since $S \times S$ has n^2 elements, so there are 2^{n^2} relations on S if no restrictions are imposed. One might observe here that the condition that $a \neq b$ is not relevant.

a) Half of these relations contain (a, b) and half do not, so the answer is $2^{n^2}/2 = 2^{n^2-1}$. Looking at it another way, we see that there are $n^2 - 1$ choices involved in specifying such a relation, since we have no choice about (a, b).

b) The analysis and answer are exactly the same as in part **(a)**.

c) Of the n^2 possible pairs to put in S, exactly n of them have a as their first element. We must use none of these, so there are $n^2 - n$ pairs that we are free to work with. Therefore there are 2^{n^2-n} possible choices for S.

d) By part **(c)** we know that there are 2^{n^2-n} relations that do not contain at least one ordered pair with a as its first element, so all the other relations, namely $2^{n^2} - 2^{n^2-n}$ of them, do contain at least one ordered pair with a as its first element.

e) We reason as in part **(c)**. There are n ordered pairs that have a as their first element, and n more that have b as their second element, although this counts (a, b) twice, so there are a total of $2n - 1$ pairs that violated the condition. This means that there are $n^2 - 2n + 1 = (n-1)^2$ pairs that we are free to choose for S. Thus the answer is $2^{(n-1)^2}$. Another way to look at this is to visualize the matrix representing S. The ath row must be all 0's, as must the bth column. If we cross out that row and column we have in effect an $n - 1$ by $n - 1$ matrix, with $(n-1)^2$ entries. Since we can fill each entry with either a 0 or a 1, there are $2^{(n-1)^2}$ choices for specifying S.

f) This is the opposite condition from part **(e)**. Therefore reasoning as in part **(d)**, we have $2^{n^2} - 2^{(n-1)^2}$ possible relations.

46. a) There are two relations on a set with only one element, and they are both transitive.

   b) There are 16 relations on a set with two elements, and we saw in Exercise 42f that 13 of them are transitive.

   c) For $n = 3$ there are $2^{3^2} = 512$ relations. One way to find out how many of them are transitive is to use a computer to generate them all and check each one for transitivity. If we do this, then we find that 171 of them are transitive. Doing this by hand is not pleasant, since there are many cases to consider.

48. a) Since R contains all the pairs (x, x), so does $R \cup S$. Therefore $R \cup S$ is reflexive.

   b) Since R and S each contain all the pairs (x, x), so does $R \cap S$. Therefore $R \cap S$ is reflexive.

   c) Since R and S each contain all the pairs (x, x), we know that $R \oplus S$ contains none of these pairs. Therefore $R \oplus S$ is irreflexive.

   d) Since R and S each contain all the pairs (x, x), we know that $R - S$ contains none of these pairs. Therefore $R - S$ is irreflexive.

   e) Since R and S each contain all the pairs (x, x), so does $S \circ R$. Therefore $S \circ R$ is reflexive.

50. By definition, to say that R is antisymmetric is to say that $R \cap R^{-1}$ contains only pairs of the form (a, a). The statement we are asked to prove is just a rephrasing of this.

52. This is immediate from the definition, since R is reflexive if and only if it contains all the pairs (x, x), which in turn happens if and only if $\overline{R}$ contains none of these pairs, i.e., $\overline{R}$ is irreflexive.

54. We just apply the definition each time. We find that R^2 contains all the pairs in $\{1, 2, 3, 4, 5\} \times \{1, 2, 3, 4, 5\}$ except $(2, 3)$ and $(4, 5)$; and R^3, R^4, and R^5 contain all the pairs.

56. We prove this by induction on n. There is nothing to prove in the base case $n = 1$. Assume the inductive hypothesis that R^n is symmetric, and let $(a, c) \in R^{n+1} = R^n \circ R$. Then there is a $b \in A$ such that $(a, b) \in R$ and $(b, c) \in R^n$. Since R^n and R are symmetric, $(b, a) \in R$ and $(c, b) \in R^n$. Thus by definition $(c, a) \in R \circ R^n$. We will have completed the proof if we can show that $R \circ R^n = R^{n+1}$. This we do in two steps. First, composition of relations is associative, that is, $(R \circ S) \circ T = R \circ (S \circ T)$ for all relations with appropriate domains and codomains. (The proof of this is straightforward applications of the definition.) Second we show that $R \circ R^n = R^{n+1}$ by induction on n. Again the base case is trivial. Under the inductive hypothesis, then, $R \circ R^{n+1} = R \circ (R^n \circ R) = (R \circ R^n) \circ R = R^{n+1} \circ R = R^{n+2}$, as desired.

SECTION 7.2   *n*-ary Relations and Their Applications

2. We have to find all the solutions to this equation, making sure to include all the permutations. The 4-tuples are $(6, 1, 1, 1)$, $(1, 6, 1, 1)$, $(1, 1, 6, 1)$, $(1, 1, 1, 6)$, $(3, 2, 1, 1)$, $(3, 1, 2, 1)$, $(3, 1, 1, 2)$, $(2, 3, 1, 1)$, $(2, 1, 3, 1)$, $(2, 1, 1, 3)$, $(1, 3, 2, 1)$, $(1, 3, 1, 2)$, $(1, 2, 3, 1)$, $(1, 2, 1, 3)$, $(1, 1, 3, 2)$, and $(1, 1, 2, 3)$.

4. Primary keys are the domains that have all different entries.

   a) The only primary key is *Course*.   **b)** The only primary key is *Course_number*.

   c) The only primary key is *Course_number*.   **d)** The only primary key is *Departure_time*.

6. We see that the *Professor* field by itself is not a key, since there is more than one 5-tuple containing the same professor. We can make the identification of the tuple unique by including the course number as well, or by including the time as well. Thus either *Professor–Course_number* or *Professor–Time* will work. Note, however, that either of these might not work if more data are added, since different departments can have the same course number, and a professor can be teaching two courses in the same room at the same time (e.g., a graduate course and the undergraduate version of that same course).

8. **a)** The ISBN is unique for each book, so that is a likely the one and only primary key (and certainly the best one in any case).

   b) This would work as long as there were not two books published the same year (date is usually given only as a year) with the same title. In practice, this could easily not happen.

   c) This would work as long as there were not two book with the same title and the same number of pages. In practice, this could possibly not happen, although it is perhaps less likely than in part **(b)**.

10. The selection operator picks out all the tuples that match the criteria. The 5-tuples in Table 7 that have A100 as their room are (Cruz, Zoology, 335, A100, 9: 00 A.M.), (Cruz, Zoology, 412, A100, 8: 00 A.M.), and (Farber, Psychology, 501, A100, 3: 00 P.M.).

12. The selection operator picks out all the tuples that match the criteria. There is only one 4-tuple in Table 10 that has a quantity of at least 50 and project number 2, namely $(9191, 2, 80, 4)$.

14. We keep only the second, third, and fifth columns, obtaining (b, c, e).

16. The table uses columns 1, 2, and 4 of Table 8. We start by deleting columns 3 and 5 from Table 8. Since no rows are duplicates of earlier rows, this table is the answer.

Airline	*Flight_number*	*Destination*
Nadir	122	Detroit
Acme	221	Denver
Acme	122	Anchorage
Acme	323	Honolulu
Nadir	199	Detroit
Acme	222	Denver
Nadir	322	Detroit

18. By definition, there are $5 + 8 - 3 = 10$ components.

20. Both sides of this equation pick out the subset of R consisting of those n-tuples satisfying both conditions C_1 and C_2. This follows immediately from the definitions of conjunction and the selection operator.

22. Both sides of this equation pick out the set of n-tuples that satisfy condition C, and furthermore are in R or S (or both, of course). This follows immediately from the definitions of union and the selection operator.

24. Both sides of this equation pick out the set of n-tuples that satisfy condition C, and are in R and are not in S. This follows immediately from the definitions of set difference and the selection operator.

26. Note that we lose information when we delete columns. Therefore we might have more in the second set than in the first, since it could be easier to be in the intersection in the second case. A simple example would be to let $R = \{(a, b)\}$ and $S = \{(a, c)\}$, $n = 2$, $m = 1$, and $i_1 = 1$. Then $R \cap S = \emptyset$, so $P_1(R \cap S) = \emptyset$. On the other hand, $P_1(R) = P_1(S) = \{(a)\}$, so $P_1(R) \cap P_1(S) = \{(a)\}$.

28. This is similar to Example 11.

   a) We apply the selection operator with the condition "$1000 \le$ Part_number ≤ 5000" to the 3-tuples given in Table 9, picking out those rows that have a part number in the indicated range. Then we choose the supplier field from those rows, and delete duplicates.

   b) Five of the 3-tuples in the joined database satisfy the condition, namely $(23, 1092, 1)$, $(23, 1101, 3)$, $(31, 4975, 3)$, $(31, 3477, 2)$, and $(33, 1001, 1)$. The suppliers appearing here are $23, 31, 33$.

SECTION 7.3   Representing Relations

2. In each case we use a 4×4 matrix, putting a 1 in position (i,j) if the pair (i,j) is in the relation and a 0 in position (i,j) if the pair (i,j) is not in the relation.

a) $\begin{bmatrix} 0 & 1 & 1 & 1 \\ 0 & 0 & 1 & 1 \\ 0 & 0 & 0 & 1 \\ 0 & 0 & 0 & 0 \end{bmatrix}$
b) $\begin{bmatrix} 1 & 0 & 0 & 1 \\ 0 & 1 & 0 & 0 \\ 0 & 0 & 1 & 0 \\ 1 & 0 & 0 & 0 \end{bmatrix}$
c) $\begin{bmatrix} 0 & 1 & 1 & 1 \\ 1 & 0 & 1 & 1 \\ 1 & 1 & 0 & 1 \\ 1 & 1 & 1 & 0 \end{bmatrix}$
d) $\begin{bmatrix} 0 & 0 & 0 & 0 \\ 0 & 0 & 0 & 1 \\ 1 & 1 & 0 & 1 \\ 0 & 0 & 0 & 0 \end{bmatrix}$

4. a) Since the $(1,1)^{\text{th}}$ entry is a 1, $(1,1)$ is in the relation. Since $(1,3)^{\text{th}}$ entry is a 0, $(1,3)$ is not in the relation. Continuing in this manner, we see that the relation contains $(1,1)$, $(1,2)$, $(1,4)$, $(2,1)$, $(2,3)$, $(3,2)$, $(3,3)$, $(3,4)$, $(4,1)$, $(4,3)$, and $(4,4)$.

b) $(1,1)$, $(1,2)$, $(1,3)$, $(2,2)$, $(3,3)$, $(3,4)$, $(4,1)$, and $(1,4)$

c) $(1,2)$, $(1,4)$, $(2,1)$, $(2,3)$, $(3,2)$, $(3,4)$, $(4,1)$, and $(4,3)$

6. An asymmetric relation (see the preamble to Exercise 16 in Section 7.1) is one for which $(a,b) \in R$ and $(b,a) \in R$ can never hold simultaneously, even if $a = b$. In the directed graph, this means that there are no loops and no pairs of edges that join the same two vertices in the opposite directions.

8. For reflexivity we want all 1's on the main diagonal; for irreflexivity we want all 0's on the main diagonal; for symmetry, we want the matrix to be symmetric about the main diagonal (equivalently, the matrix equals its transpose); for antisymmetry we want there never to be two 1's symmetrically placed about the main diagonal (equivalently, the meet of the matrix and its transpose has no 1's off the main diagonal); and for transitivity we want the Boolean square of the matrix (the Boolean product of the matrix and itself) to be "less than or equal to" the original matrix in the sense that there is a 1 in the original matrix at every location where there is a 1 in the Boolean square.

a) Since some 1's and some 0's on the main diagonal, this relation is neither reflexive nor irreflexive. Since the matrix is symmetric, the relation is symmetric. The relation is not antisymmetric—look at positions $(1,2)$ and $(2,1)$. Finally, the relation is not transitive; for example, the 1's in positions $(1,2)$ and $(2,3)$ would require a 1 in position $(1,3)$ if the relation were to be transitive.

b) Since there are all 1's on the main diagonal, this relation is reflexive and not irreflexive. Since the matrix is not symmetric, the relation is not symmetric (look at positions $(1,2)$ and $(2,1)$, for example). The relation is antisymmetric since there are never two 1's symmetrically placed with respect to the main diagonal. Finally, the Boolean square of this matrix is not itself (look at position $(1,4)$ in the square), so the relation is not transitive.

c) Since there are all 0's on the main diagonal, this relation is not reflexive but is irreflexive. Since the matrix is symmetric, the relation is symmetric. The relation is not antisymmetric—look at positions $(1,2)$ and $(2,1)$, for example. Finally, the Boolean square of this matrix has a 1 in position $(1,1)$, so the relation is not transitive.

10. Note that the total number of entries in the matrix is $1000^2 = 1{,}000{,}000$.

a) There is a 1 in the matrix for each pair of distinct positive integers not exceeding 100, namely in position (a,b) where $a \leq b$, as well as 1's along the diagonal. Thus the answer is the number of subsets of size 2 from a set of 100 elements, plus 1000, i.e., $C(1000,2) + 1000 = 499500 + 1000 = 500{,}500$.

b) There two 1's in each row of the matrix except the first and last rows, in which there is one 1. Therefore the answer is $998 \cdot 2 + 2 = 1998$.

c) There is a 1 in the matrix at each entry just above and to the left of the "anti-diagonal" (i.e., in positions $(1,999)$, $(2,998)$, $\ldots$, $(999,1)$. Therefore the answer is 999.

d) There is a 1 in the matrix at each entry on or above (to the left of) the "anti-diagonal." This is the same number of 1's as in part **(a)**, so the answer is again 500,500.

e) Every row has all 1's except for the first row, so the answer is $999 \cdot 1000 = 999{,}500$.

12. We take the transpose of the matrix, since we want the $(i,j)^{\text{th}}$ entry of the matrix for R^{-1} to be 1 if and only if the $(j,i)^{\text{th}}$ entry of R is 1.

14. a) The matrix for the union is formed by taking the join: $\begin{bmatrix} 0 & 1 & 0 \\ 1 & 1 & 1 \\ 1 & 1 & 1 \end{bmatrix}$.

b) The matrix for the intersection is formed by taking the meet: $\begin{bmatrix} 0 & 1 & 0 \\ 0 & 1 & 1 \\ 1 & 0 & 0 \end{bmatrix}$.

c) The matrix is the Boolean product $\mathbf{M}_{R_1} \odot \mathbf{M}_{R_2} = \begin{bmatrix} 0 & 1 & 1 \\ 1 & 1 & 1 \\ 0 & 1 & 0 \end{bmatrix}$.

d) The matrix is the Boolean product $\mathbf{M}_{R_1} \odot \mathbf{M}_{R_1} = \begin{bmatrix} 1 & 1 & 1 \\ 1 & 1 & 1 \\ 0 & 1 & 0 \end{bmatrix}$.

e) The matrix is the entrywise XOR: $\begin{bmatrix} 0 & 0 & 0 \\ 1 & 0 & 0 \\ 0 & 1 & 1 \end{bmatrix}$.

16. Since the matrix for R^{-1} is just the transpose of the matrix for R (see Exercise 12), the entries are the same collection of 0's and 1's, so there are k nonzero entries in $\mathbf{M}_{R^{-1}}$ as well.

18. We draw the directed graphs, in each case with the vertex set being $\{1,2,3\}$ and an edge from i to j whenever (i,j) is in the relation.

20. In each case we draw a directed graph on three vertices with an edge from a to b for each pair (a,b) in the relation, i.e., whenever there is a 1 in position (a,b) in the matrix. In part **(a)**, for instance, we need an edge from 1 to itself since there is a 1 in position $(1,1)$ in the matrix, and an edge from 1 to 3, but no edge from 1 to 2.

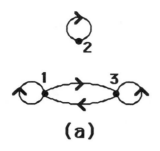   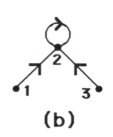   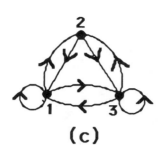

(a)   **(b)**   **(c)**

22. We draw the directed graph with the vertex set being $\{a, b, c, d\}$ and an edge from i to j whenever (i, j) is in the relation.

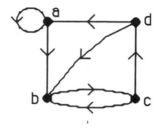

24. We list all the pairs (x, y) for which there is an edge from x to y in the directed graph:
    $\{(a, a), (a, c), (b, a), (b, b), (b, c), (c, c)\}$.

26. We list all the pairs (x, y) for which there is an edge from x to y in the directed graph:
    $\{(a, a), (a, b), (b, a), (b, b), (c, a), (c, c), (c, d), (d, d)\}$.

28. We list all the pairs (x, y) for which there is an edge from x to y in the directed graph:
    $\{(a, a), (a, b), (b, a), (b, b), (c, c), (c, d), (d, c), (d, d)\}$.

30. Clearly R is irreflexive if and only if there are no loops in the directed graph for R.

32. Recall that the relation is reflexive if there is a loop at each vertex; irreflexive if there are no loops at all; symmetric if edges appear only in **antiparallel** pairs (edges from one vertex to a second vertex and from the second back to the first); antisymmetric if there is no pair of antiparallel edges; asymmetric if is both antisymmetric and irreflexive; and transitive if all paths of length 2 (a pair of edges (x, y) and (y, z)) are accompanied by the corresponding path of length 1 (the edge (x, z)). The relation drawn in Exercise 26 is reflexive but not irreflexive since there are loops at each vertex. It is not symmetric, since, for instance, the edge (c, a) is present but not the edge (a, c). It is not antisymmetric, since both edges (a, b) and (b, a) are present. So it is not asymmetric either. It is not transitive, since the path $(c, a), (a, b)$ from c to b is not accompanied by the edge (c, b). The relation drawn in Exercise 27 is neither reflexive nor irreflexive since there are some loops but not a loop at each vertex. It is symmetric, since the edges appear in antiparallel pairs. It is not antisymmetric, since, for instance, both edges (a, b) and (b, a) are present. So it is not asymmetric either. It is not transitive, since edges (c, a) and (a, c) are present, but not (c, c). The relation drawn in Exercise 28 is reflexive and not irreflexive since there are loops at all vertices. It is symmetric but not antisymmetric or asymmetric. It is transitive; the only nontrivial paths of length 2 have the necessary loop shortcuts.

34. For each pair (a, b) of vertices (including the pairs (a, a) in which the two vertices are the same), if there is an edge from a to b, then erase it, and if there is no edge from a to b, put add it in.

36. We assume that the two relations are on the same set. For the union, we simply take the union of the directed graphs, i.e., take the directed graph on the same vertices and put in an edge from i to j whenever there is an edge from i to j in either of them. For intersection, we simply take the intersection of the directed graphs, i.e., take the directed graph on the same vertices and put in an edge from i to j whenever there are edges from i to j in both of them. For symmetric difference, we simply take the symmetric difference of the directed graphs, i.e., take the directed graph on the same vertices and put in an edge from i to j whenever there is an edge from i to j in one, but not both, of them. Similarly, to form the difference, we take the difference of the directed graphs, i.e., take the directed graph on the same vertices and put in an edge from i to j whenever there is an edge from i to j in the first but not the second. To form the directed graph for the composition $S \circ R$ of relations R and S, we draw a directed graph on the same set of vertices and put in an edge from i to j whenever there is a vertex k such that there is an edge from i to k in R, and an edge from k to j in S.

SECTION 7.4   Closures of Relations

2. When we add all the pairs (x, x) to the given relation we have all of $\mathbf{Z} \times \mathbf{Z}$; in other words, we have the relation that always holds.

4. To form the reflexive closure, we simply need to add a loop at each vertex that does not already have one.

6. We form the reflexive closure by taking the given directed graph and appending loops at all vertices at which there are not already loops.

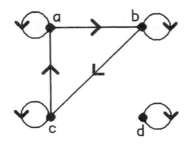

8. To form the digraph of the symmetric closure, we simply need to add an edge from x to y whenever this edge is not already in the directed graph but the edge from y to x is.

10. The symmetric closure was found in Example 2 to be the "is not equal to" relation. If we now make this relation reflexive as well, we will have the relation that always holds.

12. $\mathbf{M}_R \vee \mathbf{I}_n$ is by definition the same as $\mathbf{M}_R$ except that it has all 1's on the main diagonal. This must represent the reflexive closure of R, since this closure is the same as R except for the addition of all the pairs (x, x) that were not already present.

14. Suppose that the closure C exists. We must show that C is the intersection I of all the relations S that have property **P** and contain R. Certainly $I \subseteq C$, since C is one of the sets in the intersection. Conversely, by definition of closure, C is a subset of every relation S that has property **P** and contains R; therefore C is contained in their intersection.

16. In each case, the sequence is a path if and only if there is an edge from each vertex in the sequence to the vertex following it.

a) This is a path. **b)** This is not a path (there is no edge from e to c). **c)** This is a path.

d) This is not a path (there is no edge from d to a). **e)** This is a path.

f) This is not a path (there is no loop at b).

18. a) One path is a, b.

b) There is no way to get to a from any other vertex, so there is no path from b to a.

c) One path is b, c, b. **d)** One path is a, e. **e)** One path is b, e, d.

f) One path is c, e, d. **g)** One path is d, e, d.

h) There is no way to get to a from any other vertex, so there is no path from e to a.

i) There is no way to get from e to any other vertex except d, so there is no path from e to c.

20. a) The pair (a, b) is in R^2 precisely when there is a city c such that there is a direct flight from a to c and a direct flight from c to b—in other words, when it is possible to fly from a to b with a scheduled stop (and possibly a plane change) in some intermediate city.

b) The pair (a, b) is in R^3 precisely when there are cities c and d such that there is a direct flight from a to c, a direct flight from c to d, and a direct flight from d to b—in other words, when it is possible to fly from a to b with two scheduled stops (and possibly a plane change at one or both) in intermediate cities.

c) The pair (a, b) is in R^* precisely when it is possible to fly from a to b.

22. Since $R \subseteq R^*$, clearly if $\Delta \subseteq R$, then $\Delta \subseteq R^*$.

24. It is certainly possibly for R^2 to contain some pairs (a, a). For example, let $R = \{(1, 2), (2, 1)\}$.

26. a) We show the various matrices that are involved. First,

$$\mathbf{A} = \begin{bmatrix} 0 & 0 & 1 & 0 & 0 \\ 0 & 0 & 0 & 1 & 0 \\ 1 & 0 & 0 & 0 & 0 \\ 0 & 1 & 0 & 0 & 0 \\ 0 & 0 & 0 & 1 & 0 \end{bmatrix}, \quad \mathbf{A}^{[2]} = \begin{bmatrix} 1 & 0 & 0 & 0 & 0 \\ 0 & 1 & 0 & 0 & 0 \\ 0 & 0 & 1 & 0 & 0 \\ 0 & 0 & 0 & 1 & 0 \\ 0 & 1 & 0 & 0 & 0 \end{bmatrix}, \quad \text{and} \quad \mathbf{A}^{[3]} = \begin{bmatrix} 0 & 0 & 1 & 0 & 0 \\ 0 & 0 & 0 & 1 & 0 \\ 1 & 0 & 0 & 0 & 0 \\ 0 & 1 & 0 & 0 & 0 \\ 0 & 0 & 0 & 1 & 0 \end{bmatrix} = \mathbf{A}.$$

It follows that $\mathbf{A}^{[4]} = \mathbf{A}^{[2]}$ and $\mathbf{A}^{[5]} = \mathbf{A}^{[3]}$. Therefore the answer $\mathbf{B}$, the meet of all the $\mathbf{A}$'s, is $\mathbf{A} \vee \mathbf{A}^{[2]}$, namely

$$\begin{bmatrix} 1 & 0 & 1 & 0 & 0 \\ 0 & 1 & 0 & 1 & 0 \\ 1 & 0 & 1 & 0 & 0 \\ 0 & 1 & 0 & 1 & 0 \\ 0 & 1 & 0 & 1 & 0 \end{bmatrix}.$$

b) For this and the remaining parts we just exhibit the matrices that arise.

$$\mathbf{A} = \begin{bmatrix} 0 & 0 & 0 & 0 & 0 \\ 0 & 0 & 1 & 0 & 1 \\ 0 & 0 & 0 & 0 & 1 \\ 1 & 0 & 0 & 0 & 0 \\ 0 & 1 & 1 & 0 & 0 \end{bmatrix} \quad \mathbf{A}^{[2]} = \begin{bmatrix} 0 & 0 & 0 & 0 & 0 \\ 0 & 1 & 1 & 0 & 1 \\ 0 & 1 & 1 & 0 & 0 \\ 0 & 0 & 0 & 0 & 0 \\ 0 & 0 & 1 & 0 & 1 \end{bmatrix} \quad \mathbf{A}^{[3]} = \begin{bmatrix} 0 & 0 & 0 & 0 & 0 \\ 0 & 1 & 1 & 0 & 1 \\ 0 & 0 & 1 & 0 & 1 \\ 0 & 0 & 0 & 0 & 0 \\ 0 & 1 & 1 & 0 & 1 \end{bmatrix}$$

$$\mathbf{A}^{[4]} = \begin{bmatrix} 0 & 0 & 0 & 0 & 0 \\ 0 & 1 & 1 & 0 & 1 \\ 0 & 1 & 1 & 0 & 1 \\ 0 & 0 & 0 & 0 & 0 \\ 0 & 1 & 1 & 0 & 1 \end{bmatrix} = \mathbf{A}^{[5]} \quad \mathbf{B} = \begin{bmatrix} 0 & 0 & 0 & 0 & 0 \\ 0 & 1 & 1 & 0 & 1 \\ 0 & 1 & 1 & 0 & 1 \\ 1 & 0 & 0 & 0 & 0 \\ 0 & 1 & 1 & 0 & 1 \end{bmatrix}$$

c)

$$\mathbf{A} = \begin{bmatrix} 0 & 1 & 1 & 0 & 1 \\ 1 & 0 & 1 & 0 & 0 \\ 1 & 1 & 0 & 0 & 0 \\ 1 & 0 & 0 & 0 & 0 \\ 0 & 0 & 0 & 1 & 0 \end{bmatrix} \quad \mathbf{A}^{[2]} = \begin{bmatrix} 1 & 1 & 1 & 1 & 0 \\ 1 & 1 & 1 & 0 & 1 \\ 1 & 1 & 1 & 0 & 1 \\ 0 & 1 & 1 & 0 & 1 \\ 1 & 0 & 0 & 0 & 0 \end{bmatrix} \quad \mathbf{A}^{[3]} = \begin{bmatrix} 1 & 1 & 1 & 0 & 1 \\ 1 & 1 & 1 & 1 & 1 \\ 1 & 1 & 1 & 1 & 1 \\ 1 & 1 & 1 & 1 & 0 \\ 0 & 1 & 1 & 0 & 1 \end{bmatrix}$$

$$\mathbf{A}^{[4]} = \begin{bmatrix} 1 & 1 & 1 & 1 & 1 \\ 1 & 1 & 1 & 1 & 1 \\ 1 & 1 & 1 & 1 & 1 \\ 1 & 1 & 1 & 0 & 1 \\ 1 & 1 & 1 & 1 & 0 \end{bmatrix} \quad \mathbf{A}^{[5]} = \begin{bmatrix} 1 & 1 & 1 & 1 & 1 \\ 1 & 1 & 1 & 1 & 1 \\ 1 & 1 & 1 & 1 & 1 \\ 1 & 1 & 1 & 1 & 1 \\ 1 & 1 & 1 & 0 & 1 \end{bmatrix} \quad \mathbf{B} = \begin{bmatrix} 1 & 1 & 1 & 1 & 1 \\ 1 & 1 & 1 & 1 & 1 \\ 1 & 1 & 1 & 1 & 1 \\ 1 & 1 & 1 & 1 & 1 \\ 1 & 1 & 1 & 1 & 1 \end{bmatrix}$$

d)

$$\mathbf{A} = \begin{bmatrix} 0 & 0 & 0 & 0 & 1 \\ 1 & 0 & 0 & 1 & 0 \\ 0 & 0 & 0 & 1 & 0 \\ 1 & 0 & 1 & 0 & 0 \\ 1 & 1 & 1 & 0 & 1 \end{bmatrix} \quad \mathbf{A}^{[2]} = \begin{bmatrix} 1 & 1 & 1 & 0 & 1 \\ 1 & 0 & 1 & 0 & 1 \\ 1 & 0 & 1 & 0 & 0 \\ 0 & 0 & 0 & 1 & 1 \\ 1 & 1 & 1 & 1 & 1 \end{bmatrix} \quad \mathbf{A}^{[3]} = \begin{bmatrix} 1 & 1 & 1 & 1 & 1 \\ 1 & 1 & 1 & 1 & 1 \\ 0 & 0 & 0 & 1 & 1 \\ 1 & 1 & 1 & 0 & 1 \\ 1 & 1 & 1 & 1 & 1 \end{bmatrix}$$

$$\mathbf{A}^{[4]} = \begin{bmatrix} 1 & 1 & 1 & 1 & 1 \\ 1 & 1 & 1 & 1 & 1 \\ 1 & 1 & 1 & 0 & 1 \\ 1 & 1 & 1 & 1 & 1 \\ 1 & 1 & 1 & 1 & 1 \end{bmatrix} \quad \mathbf{A}^{[5]} = \begin{bmatrix} 1 & 1 & 1 & 1 & 1 \\ 1 & 1 & 1 & 1 & 1 \\ 1 & 1 & 1 & 1 & 1 \\ 1 & 1 & 1 & 1 & 1 \\ 1 & 1 & 1 & 1 & 1 \end{bmatrix} = \mathbf{B}$$

28. We compute the matrices $\mathbf{W}_i$ for $i = 0, 1, 2, 3, 4, 5$, and then $\mathbf{W}_5$ is the answer.

a)

$$\mathbf{W}_0 = \begin{bmatrix} 0 & 0 & 1 & 0 & 0 \\ 0 & 0 & 0 & 1 & 0 \\ 1 & 0 & 0 & 0 & 0 \\ 0 & 1 & 0 & 0 & 0 \\ 0 & 0 & 0 & 1 & 0 \end{bmatrix} \quad \mathbf{W}_1 = \begin{bmatrix} 0 & 0 & 1 & 0 & 0 \\ 0 & 0 & 0 & 1 & 0 \\ 1 & 0 & 1 & 0 & 0 \\ 0 & 1 & 0 & 0 & 0 \\ 0 & 0 & 0 & 1 & 0 \end{bmatrix} \quad \mathbf{W}_2 = \begin{bmatrix} 0 & 0 & 1 & 0 & 0 \\ 0 & 0 & 0 & 1 & 0 \\ 1 & 0 & 1 & 0 & 0 \\ 0 & 1 & 0 & 1 & 0 \\ 0 & 0 & 0 & 1 & 0 \end{bmatrix}$$

$$\mathbf{W}_3 = \begin{bmatrix} 1 & 0 & 1 & 0 & 0 \\ 0 & 0 & 0 & 1 & 0 \\ 1 & 0 & 1 & 0 & 0 \\ 0 & 1 & 0 & 1 & 0 \\ 0 & 0 & 0 & 1 & 0 \end{bmatrix} \quad \mathbf{W}_4 = \begin{bmatrix} 1 & 0 & 1 & 0 & 0 \\ 0 & 1 & 0 & 1 & 0 \\ 1 & 0 & 1 & 0 & 0 \\ 0 & 1 & 0 & 1 & 0 \\ 0 & 1 & 0 & 1 & 0 \end{bmatrix} = \mathbf{W}_5$$

b)

$$\mathbf{W}_0 = \begin{bmatrix} 0 & 0 & 0 & 0 & 0 \\ 0 & 0 & 1 & 0 & 1 \\ 0 & 0 & 0 & 0 & 1 \\ 1 & 0 & 0 & 0 & 0 \\ 0 & 1 & 1 & 0 & 0 \end{bmatrix} = \mathbf{W}_1 \quad \mathbf{W}_2 = \begin{bmatrix} 0 & 0 & 0 & 0 & 0 \\ 0 & 0 & 1 & 0 & 1 \\ 0 & 0 & 0 & 0 & 1 \\ 1 & 0 & 0 & 0 & 0 \\ 0 & 1 & 1 & 0 & 1 \end{bmatrix} = \mathbf{W}_3 = \mathbf{W}_4$$

$$\mathbf{W}_5 = \begin{bmatrix} 0 & 0 & 0 & 0 & 0 \\ 0 & 1 & 1 & 0 & 1 \\ 0 & 1 & 1 & 0 & 1 \\ 1 & 0 & 0 & 0 & 0 \\ 0 & 1 & 1 & 0 & 1 \end{bmatrix}$$

c)

$$\mathbf{W}_0 = \begin{bmatrix} 0 & 1 & 1 & 0 & 1 \\ 1 & 0 & 1 & 0 & 0 \\ 1 & 1 & 0 & 0 & 0 \\ 1 & 0 & 0 & 0 & 0 \\ 0 & 0 & 0 & 1 & 0 \end{bmatrix} \quad \mathbf{W}_1 = \begin{bmatrix} 0 & 1 & 1 & 0 & 1 \\ 1 & 1 & 1 & 0 & 1 \\ 1 & 1 & 1 & 0 & 1 \\ 1 & 1 & 1 & 0 & 1 \\ 0 & 0 & 0 & 1 & 0 \end{bmatrix} \quad \mathbf{W}_2 = \begin{bmatrix} 1 & 1 & 1 & 0 & 1 \\ 1 & 1 & 1 & 0 & 1 \\ 1 & 1 & 1 & 0 & 1 \\ 1 & 1 & 1 & 0 & 1 \\ 0 & 0 & 0 & 1 & 0 \end{bmatrix} = \mathbf{W}_3$$

$$\mathbf{W}_4 = \begin{bmatrix} 1 & 1 & 1 & 0 & 1 \\ 1 & 1 & 1 & 0 & 1 \\ 1 & 1 & 1 & 0 & 1 \\ 1 & 1 & 1 & 0 & 1 \\ 1 & 1 & 1 & 1 & 1 \end{bmatrix} \quad \mathbf{W}_5 = \begin{bmatrix} 1 & 1 & 1 & 1 & 1 \\ 1 & 1 & 1 & 1 & 1 \\ 1 & 1 & 1 & 1 & 1 \\ 1 & 1 & 1 & 1 & 1 \\ 1 & 1 & 1 & 1 & 1 \end{bmatrix}$$

d)

$$\mathbf{W}_0 = \begin{bmatrix} 0 & 0 & 0 & 0 & 1 \\ 1 & 0 & 0 & 1 & 0 \\ 0 & 0 & 0 & 1 & 0 \\ 1 & 0 & 1 & 0 & 0 \\ 1 & 1 & 1 & 0 & 1 \end{bmatrix} \quad \mathbf{W}_1 = \begin{bmatrix} 0 & 0 & 0 & 0 & 1 \\ 1 & 0 & 0 & 1 & 1 \\ 0 & 0 & 0 & 1 & 0 \\ 1 & 0 & 1 & 0 & 1 \\ 1 & 1 & 1 & 0 & 1 \end{bmatrix} \quad \mathbf{W}_2 = \begin{bmatrix} 0 & 0 & 0 & 0 & 1 \\ 1 & 0 & 0 & 1 & 1 \\ 0 & 0 & 0 & 1 & 0 \\ 1 & 0 & 1 & 0 & 1 \\ 1 & 1 & 1 & 1 & 1 \end{bmatrix}$$

$$\mathbf{W}_3 = \begin{bmatrix} 0 & 0 & 0 & 0 & 1 \\ 1 & 0 & 0 & 1 & 1 \\ 0 & 0 & 0 & 1 & 0 \\ 1 & 0 & 1 & 1 & 1 \\ 1 & 1 & 1 & 1 & 1 \end{bmatrix} \quad \mathbf{W}_4 = \begin{bmatrix} 0 & 0 & 0 & 0 & 1 \\ 1 & 0 & 1 & 1 & 1 \\ 1 & 0 & 0 & 1 & 1 \\ 1 & 0 & 1 & 1 & 1 \\ 1 & 1 & 1 & 1 & 1 \end{bmatrix} \quad \mathbf{W}_5 = \begin{bmatrix} 1 & 1 & 1 & 1 & 1 \\ 1 & 1 & 1 & 1 & 1 \\ 1 & 1 & 1 & 1 & 1 \\ 1 & 1 & 1 & 1 & 1 \\ 1 & 1 & 1 & 1 & 1 \end{bmatrix}$$

30. Let m be the length of the shortest path from a to b, and let $a = x_0, x_1, \ldots, x_{m-1}, x_m = b$ be such a path. If $m > n - 1$, then $m \geq n$, so $m + 1 \geq n + 1$, which means that not all of the vertices x_0, x_1, x_2, $\ldots$, x_m are distinct. Thus $x_i = x_j$ for some i and j with $0 \leq i < j \leq m$ (but not both $i = 0$ and $j = m$, since $a \neq b$). We can then excise the circuit from x_i to x_j, leaving a shorter path from a to b, namely $x_0, \ldots, x_i, x_{j+1}, \ldots, x_m$. This contradicts the choice of m. Therefore $m \leq n - 1$, as desired.

32. Warshall's algorithm determines the existence of paths. If instead we keep track of the lengths of paths, then we can get the desired information. Thus we make the following changes in Algorithm 2. First, instead of initializing $\mathbf{W}$ to be $\mathbf{M}_R$, we initialize it to be $\mathbf{M}_R$ with each 0 replaced by ∞. Second, the computational step becomes $w_{ij} := \min(w_{ij}, w_{ik} + w_{kj})$.

34. All we need to do is make sure that all the pairs (x, x) are included. An easy way to accomplish this is to add them at the end, by setting $\mathbf{W} := \mathbf{W} \vee \mathbf{I}_n$.

SECTION 7.5   Equivalence Relations

2. a) This is an equivalence relation by Exercise 5.   **b)** This is an equivalence relation by Exercise 5.

   c) This is not an equivalence relation, since it need not be transitive. (We assume that biological parentage is at issue here, so it is possible for A to be the child of W and X, B to be the child of X and Y, and C to be the child of Y and Z. Then A is related to B, and B is related to C, but A is not related to C.)

   d) This is not an equivalence relation since it is clearly not transitive.

   e) Again, just as in part **(c)**, this is not transitive.

4. One relation is that a and b are related if were born in the same state (with "outside the U.S." counting as one state). Here the equivalence classes are the nonempty sets of students from each state. Another example is for a to be related to b if a and b have lived the same number of complete decades. The equivalence classes are the set of all 10-to-19 year-olds, the set of all 20-to-29 year-olds, and so on (the sets among these that are nonempty, that is). A third example is for a to be related to b if 10 is a divisor of the difference between a's age and b's age, where "age" means the whole number of years since birth, as of the first day of class. For each $i = 0, 1, \ldots, 9$, there is the equivalence class (if it is nonempty) of those students whose age ends with the digit i.

6. The function that sends each $x \in A$ to its equivalence class $[x]$ is obviously such a function.

8. This follows from Exercise 5, where f is the function that takes a bit string of length $n \geq 3$ to its last $n - 3$ bits.

10. This follows from Exercise 5, where f is the function from the set of pairs of positive integers to the set of positive rational numbers that takes (a,b) to a/b, since clearly $ad = bc$ if and only if $a/b = c/d$.

12. a) This follows from Exercise 5, where the function f from the set of polynomials to the set of polynomials is the operator that takes the derivative n times—i.e., f of a function g is the function $g^{(n)}$. The best way to think about this is that any relation defined by a statement of the form "a and b are equivalent if they have the same whatever" is an equivalence relation. Here "whatever" is "n^{th} derivative"; in the general situation of Exercise 5, "whatever" is "function value under f."
b) The third derivative of x^4 is $24x$. Since the third derivative of a polynomial of degree 2 or less is 0, the polynomials of the form $x^4 + ax^2 + bx + c$ have the same third derivative. Thus these are the functions in the same equivalence class as f.

14. This follows from Exercise 5, where the function f from the set of people to the set of Web-traversing behaviors starting at the given particular Web page takes the person to the behavior that person exhibited.

16. We need to observe whether the relation is reflexive (there is a loop at each vertex), symmetric (every edge that appears is accompanied by its antiparallel mate—an edge involving the same two vertices but pointing in the opposite direction), and transitive (paths of length 2 are accompanied by the path of length 1—i.e., edge—between the same two vertices in the same direction). We see that this relation is an equivalence relation, satisfying all three properties. The equivalence classes are $\{a,d\}$ and $\{b,c\}$.

18. a) This is not an equivalence relation, since it is not symmetric.
b) This is an equivalence relation; one equivalence class consists of the first and third elements, and the other consists of the second and fourth elements.
c) This is an equivalence relation; one equivalence class consists of the first, second, and third elements, and the other consists of the fourth element.

20. Only part **(a)** and part **(c)** are equivalence relations. In part **(a)** each element is in an equivalence class by itself. In part **(c)** the elements 1 and 2 are in one equivalence class, and 0 and 3 are each in their own equivalence class.

22. Only part **(a)** and part **(d)** are equivalence relations. In part **(a)** there is one equivalence class for each $n \in \mathbf{Z}$, and it contains all those functions whose value at 1 is n. In part **(d)** there really is no good way to describe the equivalence classes. For one thing, the set of equivalence classes is uncountable. For each function $f : \mathbf{Z} \to \mathbf{Z}$, there is the equivalence class consisting of all those functions g for which there is a constant C such that $g(n) = f(n) + C$ for all $n \in \mathbf{Z}$.

24. a) all the strings whose first three bits are 010   **b)** all the strings whose first three bits are 101
c) all the strings whose first three bits are 111   **d)** all the strings whose first three bits are 010

26. In each case, the equivalence class of 4 is the set of all integers congruent to 4, modulo m.
a) $\{4 + 2n \mid n \in \mathbf{Z}\} = \{\ldots, -2, 0, 2, 4, \ldots\}$ **b)** $\{4 + 3n \mid n \in \mathbf{Z}\} = \{\ldots, -2, 1, 4, 7, \ldots\}$
c) $\{4 + 6n \mid n \in \mathbf{Z}\} = \{\ldots, -2, 4, 10, 16, \ldots\}$ **d)** $\{4 + 8n \mid n \in \mathbf{Z}\} = \{\ldots, -4, 4, 12, 20, \ldots\}$

28. a) By our observation in the solution to Exercise 10, the equivalence class of $(1,2)$ is the set of all pairs (a,b) such that the fraction a/b equals $1/2$.
b) Again by our observation, the equivalence classes are the positive rational numbers. (Indeed, this is the way one can rigorously define what a rational number is, and this is why fractions are so difficult for children to understand.)

30. a) This is a partition, since it satisfies the definition.

   b) This is not a partition, since the subsets are not disjoint.

   c) This is a partition, since it satisfies the definition.

   d) This is not a partition, since the union of the subsets leaves out 0.

32. a) This is clearly a partition.   **b)** This is not a partition, since 0 is in neither set.

   c) This is a partition by the division algorithm.

   d) This is a partition, since the second set mentioned is the set of all number between -100 and 100, inclusive.

   e) The first two sets are not disjoint (4 is in both), so this is not a partition.

34. a) This is a partition, since it satisfies the definition.

   b) This is a partition, since it satisfies the definition.

   c) This is not a partition, since the intervals are not disjoint (they share endpoints).

   d) This is not a partition, since the union of the subsets leaves out the integers.

   e) This is a partition, since it satisfies the definition.

   f) This is a partition, since it satisfies the definition. Each equivalence class consists of all real numbers with a fixed fractional part.

36. In each case, we need to list all the pairs we can where both coordinates are chosen from the same subset. We should proceed in an organized fashion, listing all the pairs corresponding to each part of the partition.

   a) $\{(a,a),(a,b),(b,a),(b,b),(c,c),(c,d),(d,c),(d,d),(e,e),(e,f),(e,g),(f,e),(f,f),(f,g),(g,e),(g,f),(g,g)\}$

   b) $\{(a,a),(b,b),(c,c),(c,d),(d,c),(d,d),(e,e),(e,f),(f,e),(f,f),(g,g)\}$

   c) $\{(a,a),(a,b),(a,c),(a,d),(b,a),(b,b),(b,c),(b,d),(c,a),(c,b),(c,c),(c,d),(d,a),(d,b),(d,c),(d,d),$
   $(e,e),(e,f),(e,g),(f,e),(f,f),(f,g),(g,e),(g,f),(g,g)\}$

   d) $\{(a,a),(a,c),(a,e),(a,g),(c,a),(c,c),(c,e),(c,g),(e,a),(e,c),(e,e),(e,g),(g,a),(g,c),(g,e),(g,g),$
   $(b,b),(b,d),(d,b),(d,d),(f,f)\}$

38. We need to show that every equivalence class consisting of people living in the same county (or parish) and same state is contained in an equivalence class of all people living in the same state. This is clear. The equivalence class of all people living in county c in state s is a subset of the set of people living in state s.

40. First, suppose that $R_1 \subseteq R_2$. We must show that P_1 is a refinement of P_2. Let $[a]_{R_1}$ be an equivalence class in P_1. We must show that $[a]_{R_1}$ is contained in an equivalence class in P_2. In fact, we will show that $[a]_{R_1} \subseteq [a]_{R_2}$. To this end, let $b \in [a]_{R_1}$. Then $(a,b) \in R_1 \subseteq R_2$. Therefore $b \in [a]_{R_2}$, as desired.

   Conversely, suppose that P_1 is a refinement of P_2. Since $a \in [a]_{R_2}$, the definition of "refinement" forces $[a]_{R_1} \subseteq [a]_{R_2}$ for all $a \in A$. This means that for all $b \in A$ we have $(a,b) \in R_1 \rightarrow (a,b) \in R_2$; in other words, $R_1 \subseteq R_2$.

42. a) This need not be an equivalence relation, since it need not be transitive.

   b) Since the intersection of reflexive, symmetric, and transitive relations also have these properties (see Section 7.1), the intersection of equivalence relations is an equivalence relation.

   c) This will never be an equivalence relation on a nonempty set, since it is not reflexive.

44. This exercise is very similar to Exercise 45, and the reader should look at the solution there for details.

   a) As in Exercise 45, the motions of the bracelet form a dihedral group, in this case consisting of six motions: rotations of $0°$, $120°$, and $240°$, and three reflections, each keeping one bead fixed and interchanging the other two. The composition of any two of these operations is again one of these operations. The $0°$ rotation plays the role of the identity, which says that the relation is reflexive. Each operation has an inverse (reflections are their own inverses, the $0°$ rotation is its own inverse, and the $120°$ and $240°$ rotations are inverses of each other); this proves symmetry. And transitivity follows from the group table.

b) The equivalence classes are the indistinguishable bracelets. If we denote a bracelet by the colors of its beads, then these classes can be described as RRR, WWW, BBB, RRW, RRB, WWR, WWB, BBR, BBW, and RWB. Note that once we specify the colors, then every two bracelets with those colors are equivalent. This would not be the case if there were four or more beads, however. For example, in a 4-bead bracelet with two reds and two whites, the bracelet in which the red beads are adjacent is not equivalent to the one in which they are not.

46. a) In Exercise 25 of Section 2.2, we showed that $f(x)$ is $\Theta(g(x))$ if and only if $f(x)$ is $O(g(x))$ and $g(x)$ is $O(f(x))$. To show that R is reflexive, we need to show that $f(x)$ is $O(f(x))$, which is clear by taking $C = 1$ and $k = 1$ in the definition. Symmetry is immediate from the definition, since if $f(x)$ is $O(g(x))$ and $g(x)$ is $O(f(x))$, then $g(x)$ is $O(f(x))$ and $f(x)$ is $O(g(x))$. Finally, transitivity follows immediately from the transitive of the "is big-O of" relation, which was proved in Exercise 17 of Section 2.2.

b) This is the class of all functions that asymptotically (i.e., as $n \to \infty$) grow just as fast as a multiple of $f(n) = n^2$. So, for example, functions such as $g(n) = 5n^2 + \log n$, or $g(n) = (n^3 - 17)/(100n + 10^{10})$ belong to this class, but $g(n) = n^{2.01}$ does not (it grows too fast), and $g(n) = n^2/\log n$ does not (it grows too slowly). Another way to express this class is to say that it is the set of all functions g such that there exist constants positive C_1 and C_2 such that the ratio $f(n)/g(n)$ always lies between C_1 and C_2.

48. We will count partitions instead, since equivalence relations are in one-to-one correspondence with partitions. Without loss of generality let the set be $\{1, 2, 3, 4\}$. There is 1 partition in which all the elements are in the same set, namely $\{\{1, 2, 3, 4\}\}$. There are 4 partitions in which the sizes of the sets are 1 and 3, namely $\{\{1\}, \{2, 3, 4\}\}$ and three more like it. There are 3 partitions in which the sizes of the sets are 2 and 2, namely $\{\{1, 2\}, \{3, 4\}\}$ and two more like it. There are 6 partitions in which the sizes of the sets are 2, 1, and 1, namely $\{\{1, 2\}, \{3\}, \{4\}\}$ and five more like it. Finally, there is 1 partition in which all the elements are in separate sets. This gives a total of 15. To actually list the 15 relations would be tedious.

50. No. Here is a counterexample. Start with $\{(1, 2), (3, 2)\}$ on the set $\{1, 2, 3\}$. Its transitive closure is itself. The reflexive closure of that is $\{(1, 1), (1, 2), (2, 2), (3, 2), (3, 3)\}$. The symmetric closure of that is $\{(1, 1), (1, 2), (2, 1), (2, 2), (2, 3), (3, 2), (3, 3)\}$. The result is not transitive; for example, $(1, 3)$ is missing. Therefore this is not an equivalence relation.

52. We end up with the original partition P.

54. We will develop this recurrence relation in the context of partitions of the set $\{1, 2, \ldots, n\}$. Note that $p(0) = 1$, since there is only one way to partition the empty set (namely, into the empty collection of subsets). For warm-up, we also note that $p(1) = 1$, since $\{\{1\}\}$ is the only partition of $\{1\}$; that $p(2) = 2$, since we can partition $\{1, 2\}$ either as $\{\{1, 2\}\}$ or as $\{\{1\}, \{2\}\}$; and that $p(3) = 5$, since there are the following partitions: $\{\{1, 2, 3\}\}$, $\{\{1, 2\}, \{3\}\}$, $\{\{1, 3\}, \{2\}\}$, $\{\{2, 3\}, \{1\}\}$, $\{\{1\}, \{2\}, \{3\}\}$. Now to partition $\{1, 2, \ldots, n\}$, we first decide how many other elements of this set will go into the same subset as n goes into. Call this number j, and note that j can take any value from 0 through $n - 1$. Once we have determined j, we can specify the partition by deciding on the subset of j elements from $\{1, 2, \ldots, n - 1\}$ that will go into the same subset as n (and this can be done in $C(n - 1, j)$ ways), and then we need to decide how to partition the remaining $n - 1 - j$ elements (and this can be done in $p(n - j - 1)$ ways). The given recurrence relation now follows.

SECTION 7.6   Partial Orderings

2. a) This relation is $\{(1,1),(1,3),(2,1),(2,2),(3,3)\}$. It is clearly reflexive and antisymmetric. The only pairs that might present problems with transitivity are the nondiagonal pairs, $(2,1)$ and $(1,3)$. If the relation were to be transitive, then we would also need the pair $(2,3)$ in the relation. Since it is not there, the relation is not a partial order.

b) Reasoning as in part **(a)**, we see that this relation is a partial order, since the pair $(3,1)$ can cause no problem with transitivity.

c) A little trial and error shows that this relation is not transitive ($(1,3)$ and $(3,4)$ are present, but not $(1,4)$) and therefore not a partial order.

4. This relation is not transitive (there is no arrow from c to b), so it is not a partial order.

6. This follows immediately from the definition. Clearly R^{-1} is reflexive if R is. For antisymmetry, suppose that $(a,b) \in R^{-1}$ and $a \neq b$. Then $(b,a) \in R$, so $(a,b) \notin R$, whence $(b,a) \notin R^{-1}$. Finally, if $(a,b) \in R^{-1}$ and $(b,c) \in R^{-1}$, then $(b,a) \in R$ and $(c,b) \in R$, so $(c,a) \in R$ (since R is transitive), and therefore $(a,c) \in R^{-1}$; thus R^{-1} is transitive.

8. a) These are comparable, since $5 \mid 15$.

b) These are not comparable since neither divides the other.

c) These are comparable, since $8 \mid 16$.

d) These are comparable, since $7 \mid 7$.

10. a) We need either a number less than 2 in the first coordinate, or a 2 in the first coordinate and a number less than 3 in the second coordinate. Therefore the answer is $(1,1)$, $(1,2)$, $(1,3)$, $(1,4)$, $(2,1)$, and $(2,2)$.

b) We need either a number greater than 3 in the first coordinate, or a 3 in the first coordinate and a number greater than 1 in the second coordinate. Therefore the answer is $(4,1)$, $(4,2)$, $(4,3)$, $(4,4)$, $(3,2)$, $(3,3)$, and $(3,4)$.

c) The Hasse diagram is a straight line with 16 points on it, since this is a total order. The pair $(4,4)$ is at the top, $(4,3)$ beneath it, $(4,2)$ beneath that, and so on, with $(1,1)$ at the bottom. To save space, we will not actually draw this picture.

12. a) The string *quack* comes first, since it is an initial substring of *quacking*, which comes next (since the other three strings all begin *qui*, not *qua*). Similarly, these last three strings are in the order *quick*, *quicksand*, *quicksilver*.

b) The order is *open*, *opened*, *opener*, *opera*, *operand*.

c) The order is *zero*, *zoo*, *zoological*, *zoology*, *zoom*.

14. The Hasse diagram for this total order is a straight line, as shown, with 0 at the top (it is the "largest" element under the "is greater than or equal to" relation) and 5 at the bottom.

16. In each case we put a above b and draw a line between them if $b\,|\,a$ but there is no element c other than a and b such that $b\,|\,c$ and $c\,|\,a$.

a) Note that 1 divides all numbers, so the numbers on the second level from the bottom are the primes.

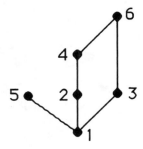

b) In this case these numbers are pairwise relatively prime, so there are no lines in the Hasse diagram.

c) Note that we can place the points as we wish, as long as a is above b when $b\,|\,a$.

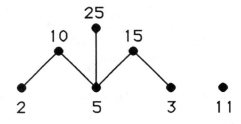

d) In this case these numbers each divide the next, so the Hasse diagram is a straight line.

18. This picture is a four-dimensional cube. We draw the sets with k elements at level k: the empty set at level 0 (the bottom), the entire set at level 4 (the top).

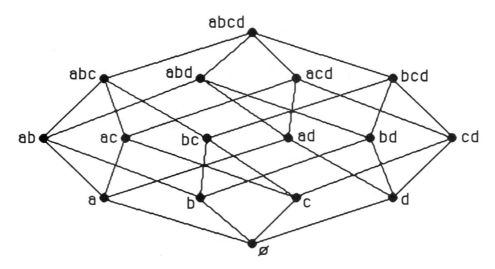

20. The procedure is the same as in Exercise 19: $\{(a,a),(a,b),(a,c),(a,d),(a,e),(b,b),(b,d),(b,e),(c,c),(c,d),$ $(d,d),(e,e)\}$

22. In this problem $a \preceq b$ when $a \,|\, b$. For (a,b) to be in the covering relation, we need a to be a proper divisor of b but we also must have no element in our set $\{1,2,3,4,6,12\}$ being a proper multiple of a and a proper divisor of b. For example, $(2,12)$ is not in the covering relation, since $2\,|\,6$ and $6\,|\,12$. With this understanding it is easy to list the pairs in the covering relation: $(1,2)$, $(1,3)$, $(2,4)$, $(2,6)$, $(3,6)$, $(4,12)$, and $(6,12)$.

24. In the Hasse diagram, if x is lower than y and there is an edge joining x and y, then $x \prec y$. We claim that in this case (x,y) is also in the covering relation. Indeed, the definition of the Hasse diagram stated that there is to be no edge from x to y if there is some z with $x \prec z \prec y$ (such edges forced by transitivity were to be removed in the construction). This is equivalent to having (x,y) in the covering relation. Conversely, if (x,y) is in the covering relation, the $x \prec y$, and there is no z that would have caused the edge between x and y to be removed in the construction of the Hasse diagram. This completes the proof.

26. a) The maximal elements are the ones with no other elements above them, namely l and m.
   b) The minimal elements are the ones with no other elements below them, namely a, b, and c.
   c) There is no greatest element, since neither l nor m is greater than the other.
   d) There is no least element, since neither a nor b is less than the other.
   e) We need to find elements from which we can find downward paths to all of a, b, and c. It is clear that k, l, and m are the elements fitting this description.
   f) Since k is less than both l and m, it is the least upper bound of a, b, and c.
   g) No element is less than both f and h, so there are no lower bounds.
   h) Since there are no lower bounds, there can be no greatest lower bound.

28. The reader should draw the Hasse diagram to aid in answering these questions.
   a) Clearly the numbers 27, 48, 60, and 72 are maximal, since each divides no number in the list other than itself. All of the other numbers divide 72, however, so they are not maximal.
   b) Only 2 and 9 are minimal. Every other element is divisible by either 2 or 9.
   c) There is no greatest element, since, for example, there is no number in the set that both 60 and 72 divide.
   d) There is no least element, since there is no number in the set that divides both 2 and 9.
   e) We need to find numbers in the list that are multiples of both 2 and 9. Clearly 18, 36, and 72 are the numbers we are looking for.

f) Of the numbers we found in the previous part, 18 satisfies the definition of the least upper bound, since it divides the other two upper bounds.

g) We need to find numbers in the list that are divisors of both 60 and 72. Clearly 2, 4, 6, and 12 are the numbers we are looking for.

h) Of the numbers we found in the previous part, 12 satisfies the definition of the greatest lower bound, since the other three lower bounds divide it.

30. a) One example is the natural numbers under "is less than or equal to." Here 1 is the (only) minimal element, and there are no maximal elements.

b) Dual to part (a), the answer is the natural numbers under "is greater than or equal to."

c) Combining the answers for the first two parts, we look at the set of integers under "is less than or equal to." Clearly there are no maximal or minimal elements.

32. Reflexivity is clear from the definition. To show antisymmetry, suppose that $a_1 \ldots a_m < b_1 \ldots b_n$, and let $t = \min(m,n)$. This means that either $a_1 \ldots a_t = b_1 \ldots b_t$ and $m < n$, so that $b_1 \ldots b_n \not< a_1 \ldots a_m$, or else $a_1 \ldots a_t < b_1 \ldots b_t$, so that $b_1 \ldots b_t \not< a_1 \ldots a_t$ and hence again $b_1 \ldots b_n \not< a_1 \ldots a_m$. Finally for transitivity, suppose that $a_1 \ldots a_m < b_1 \ldots b_n < c_1 \ldots c_p$. Let $t = \min(m,n)$, $r = \min(n,p)$, $s = \min(m,p)$, and $l = \min(m,n,p)$. Now if $a_1 \ldots a_l < b_1 \ldots b_l < c_1 \ldots c_l$, then clearly $a_1 \ldots a_m < c_1 \ldots c_p$. Otherwise, without loss of generality we may assume that $a_1 \ldots a_l = b_1 \ldots b_l$. If $l = t$, then $m < n$ and $m \le p$. Furthermore, either $b_1 \ldots b_r < c_1 \ldots c_r$, or $b_1 \ldots b_r = c_1 \ldots c_r$ and $n < p$. In the former case, if $r > l$, then since $p > m$ we have $a_1 \ldots a_m < c_1 \ldots c_p$, whereas if $r = l$, then $a_1 \ldots a_l < c_1 \ldots c_l$. In the latter case, $a_1 \ldots a_s = c_1 \ldots c_s$ and $m < p$, so again $a_1 \ldots a_m < c_1 \ldots c_p$. If $l < t$, then we must have $b_1 \ldots b_l < c_1 \ldots c_l$, whence $a_1 \ldots a_l < c_1 \ldots c_l$.

34. a) If x and y are both greatest elements, then by definition, $x \preceq y$ and $y \preceq x$, whence $x = y$.

b) This is dual to part (a). If x and y are both least elements, then by definition, $x \preceq y$ and $y \preceq x$, whence $x = y$.

36. a) If x and y are both least upper bounds, then by definition, $x \preceq y$ and $y \preceq x$, whence $x = y$.

b) This is dual to part (a). If x and y are both greatest lower bounds, then by definition, $x \preceq y$ and $y \preceq x$, whence $x = y$.

38. In each case, we need to decide whether every pair of elements has a least upper bound and a greatest lower bound.

a) This is not a lattice, since the elements 6 and 9 have no upper bound (no element in our set is a multiple of both of them).

b) This is a lattice; in fact it is a linear order, since each element in the list divides the next one. The least upper bound of two numbers in the list is the larger, and the greatest lower bound is the smaller.

c) Again, this is a lattice because it is a linear order. The least upper bound of two numbers in the list is the smaller number (since here "greater" really means "less"!), and the greatest lower bound is the larger of the two numbers.

d) This is similar to Example 23, with the roles of subset and superset reversed. Here the g.l.b. of two subsets A and B is $A \cup B$, and their l.u.b. is $A \cap B$.

40. By the duality in the definitions, the greatest lower bound of two elements of S under R is their least upper bound under R^{-1}, and their least upper bound under R is their greatest lower bound under R^{-1}. Therefore, if (S, R) is a lattice (i.e., all the l.u.b.'s and g.l.b.'s exist), then so is (S, R^{-1}).

42. We need to verify the various defining properties of a lattice. First, we need to show that S is a poset under the given $\preceq$ relation. Clearly $(A, C) \preceq (A, C)$, since $A \leq A$ and $C \subseteq C$; thus we have established reflexivity. For antisymmetry, suppose that $(A_1, C_1) \preceq (A_2, C_2)$ and $(A_2, C_2) \preceq (A_1, C_1)$. This means that $A_1 \leq A_2$, $C_1 \subseteq C_2$, $A_2 \leq A_1$, and $C_2 \subseteq C_1$. By the properties of $\leq$ and $\subseteq$ it immediately follows that $A_1 = A_2$ and $C_1 = C_2$, so $(A_1, C_1) = (A_2, C_2)$. Transitivity is proved in a similar way, using the transitivity of $\leq$ and $\subseteq$. Second, we need to show that greatest lower bounds and least upper bounds exist. Suppose that (A_1, C_1) and (A_2, C_2) are two elements of S; we claim that $(\min(A_1, A_2), C_1 \cap C_2)$ is their greatest lower bound. Clearly $\min(A_1, A_2) \leq A_1$ and $\min(A_1, A_2) \leq A_2$; and $C_1 \cap C_2 \subseteq C_1$ and $C_1 \cap C_2 \subseteq C_2$. Therefore $(\min(A_1, A_2), C_1 \cap C_2) \preceq (A_1, C_1)$ and $(\min(A_1, A_2), C_1 \cap C_2) \preceq (A_2, C_2)$, so this is a lower bound. On the other hand, if (A, C) is any lower bound, then $A \leq A_1$, $A \leq A_2$, $C \subseteq C_1$, and $C \subseteq C_2$. It follows from the properties of $\leq$ and $\subseteq$ that $A \leq \min(A_1, A_2)$ and $C \subseteq C_1 \cap C_2$. Therefore $(A, C) \preceq (\min(A_1, A_2), C_1 \cap C_2)$. This means that $(\min(A_1, A_2), C_1 \cap C_2)$ is the greatest lower bound. The proof that $(\max(A_1, A_2), C_1 \cup C_2)$ is the least upper bound is exactly dual to this argument.

44. This issue was already dealt with in our solution to Exercise 38, parts **(b)** and **(c)**. If $(S, \leq)$ is a total (linear) order, then the least upper bound of two elements is the larger one, and their greatest lower bound is the smaller.

46. By Exercise 44, we can try to choose our examples from among total orders, such as subsets of $\mathbf{Z}$ under $\leq$.
   a) $(\mathbf{Z}, \leq)$ **b)** $(\mathbf{Z}^+, \leq)$ **c)** $(\mathbf{Z}^-, \leq)$, where $\mathbf{Z}^-$ is the set of negative integers   **d)** $(\{1\}, \leq)$

48. In each case, the issue is whether every subset contains a least element.
   a) The is well-ordered, since the minimum element in each set is its smallest element.
   b) This is not well-ordered. For example, the set $\{\frac{1}{n} \mid n \in \mathbf{N}\}$ contains no minimum element.
   c) This is a finite totally-ordered set, so it is well-ordered.
   d) This is well-ordered, since has the same structure as the positive integers under $\leq$, because $x \geq y$ if and only if $-x \leq -y$.

50. Let x_0 and x_1 be two elements in the dense poset, with $x_0 \prec x_1$ (guaranteed by the conditions stated). By density, there is an element x_2 between x_0 and x_1, i.e., with $x_0 \prec x_2 \prec x_1$. Again by density, there is an element x_3 between x_0 and x_2, i.e., with $x_0 \prec x_3 \prec x_2$. We continue in this manner and have produced an infinite decreasing sequence: $\cdots \prec x_4 \prec x_3 \prec x_2 \prec x_1$. THus the poset is not well-founded.

52. It is not well-founded because of the infinite decreasing sequence $\cdots \prec aaab \prec aab \prec ab \prec b$. It is not dense, because there is no element between a and aa in this order.

54. This is dual to Lemma 1. We can simply copy the proof, changing every "minimal" to "maximal" and reversing each inequality.

56. Since a larger number can never divide a smaller one, the "is less than or equal to" relation on any set is a compatible total order for the divisibility relation. In this case we have $1 \prec 2 \prec 3 \prec 6 \prec 8 \prec 12 \prec 24 \prec 36$.

58. There are many compatible total orders here. We just need to work from the bottom up. One answer is to take Foundation $\prec$ Framing $\prec$ Roof $\prec$ Exterior siding $\prec$ Wiring $\prec$ Plumbing $\prec$ Flooring $\prec$ Wall $-$ board $\prec$ Exterior painting $\prec$ Interior painting $\prec$ Carpeting $\prec$ Interior fixtures $\prec$ Exterior fixtures $\prec$ Completion.

SUPPLEMENTARY EXERCISES FOR CHAPTER 7

2. In each case we will construct a simplest such relation.

    a) $\{(a, a), (b, b), (c, c), (a, b), (b, a), (b, c), (c, b), (d, d)\}$ **b)** $\varnothing$ **c)** $\{(a, b), (b, c)\}$

    d) $\{(a, a), (b, b), (c, c), (a, b), (b, a), (c, a), (c, b), (d, d)\}$ **e)** $\{(a, b), (b, a), (c, c), (c, a)\}$

4. Suppose that $R_1 \subseteq R_2$ and that R_2 is antisymmetric. We must show that R_1 is also antisymmetric. Let $(a, b) \in R_1$ and $(b, a) \in R_1$. Since these two pairs are also both in R_2, we know that $a = b$, as desired.

6. Since $(a, a) \in R_1$ and $(a, a) \in R_2$ for all $a \in A$, it follows that $(a, a) \notin R_1 \oplus R_2$ for all $a \in A$.

8. Under this hypothesis, $\overline{R}$ must also be symmetric, for if $(a, b) \in \overline{R}$, then $(a, b) \notin R$, whence (b, a) cannot be in R, either (by the symmetry of R); in other words, (b, a) is also in $\overline{R}$.

10. First suppose that R is reflexive and circular. We need to show that R is symmetric and transitive. Let $(a, b) \in R$. Since also $(b, b) \in R$, it follows by circularity that $(b, a) \in R$; this proves symmetry. Now if $(a, b) \in R$ and $(b, c) \in R$, then by circularity $(c, a) \in R$ and so by symmetry $(a, c) \in R$; thus R is transitive. Conversely, transitivity and symmetry immediately imply circularity, so every equivalence relation is reflexive and circular.

12. A primary key in the first relation need not be a primary key in the join. Let the first relation contain the pairs (John, boy) and (Mary, girl); and let the second relation contain the pairs (boy, vain), (girl, athletic), and (girl, smart). Clearly *Name* is a primary key for the first relation. If we take the join on the *Sex* column, then we obtain the relation containing the pairs (John, boy, vain), (Mary, girl, athletic), and (Mary, girl, smart); in this relation *Name* is not a primary key.

14. **a)** Two mathematicians are related under R^2 if and only if each has written a joint paper with some mathematician c.

    b) Two mathematicians are related under R^* if there is a finite sequence of mathematicians $a = c_0$, c_1, c_2, ..., c_{m-1}, $c_m = b$, with $m \geq 1$, such that for each i from 1 to m, mathematician c_i has written a joint paper with mathematician c_{i-1}.

    c) The Erdős number of a is the length of a shortest path in R from a to Erdős, if such a path exists. (Some mathematicians have no Erdős number.)

16. We assume that the notion of calling is a potential one—subroutine **P** is related to subroutine **Q** if it might be possible for **P** to call **Q** during its execution (in other words, there is a call to **Q** as one of the steps in the subroutine **P**). Otherwise this exercise would not be well-defined, since *actual* calls are unpredictable—they depend on what actually happens as the programs execute.

    a) Let **P** and **Q** be subroutines. Then **P** is related to **Q** under the transitive closure of R if and only if at some time during an active invocation of **P** it might be possible for **Q** to be called.

    b) Routines such as this are usually called recursive—it might be possible for **P** to be called again while it is still active.

    c) The reflexive closure of the transitive closure of any relation is just the transitive closure (see part **(a)**) with all the loops adjoined.

18. We can prove this symbolically, since the symmetric closure of a relation is the union of the relation and its inverse. Thus we have $(R \cup S) \cup (R \cup S)^{-1} = R \cup S \cup R^{-1} \cup S^{-1} = (R \cup R^{-1}) \cup (S \cup S^{-1})$.

20. a) This is an equivalence relation by Exercise 5 in Section 7.5, letting $f(x)$ be the sign of the zodiac under which x was born.

    b) This is an equivalence relation by Exercise 5 in Section 7.5, letting $f(x)$ be the year in which x was born.

    c) This is not an equivalence relation (it is not transitive).

22. This relation is reflexive, since $x - x = 0 \in \mathbf{Q}$. To see that it is symmetric, suppose that $x - y \in \mathbf{Q}$. Then $y - x = -(x - y)$ is again a rational number. For transitivity, if $x - y \in \mathbf{Q}$ and $y - z \in \mathbf{Q}$, then their sum, namely $x - z$, is also rational (the rational numbers are closed under addition). The equivalence class of 1 and of $1/2$ are both just the set of rational numbers. The equivalence class of π is the set of real numbers that differ from π by a rational number; in other words it is $\{\pi + r \mid r \in \mathbf{Q}\}$.

24. Let S be the transitive closure of the symmetric closure of the reflexive closure of R. Then by Exercise 23 in Section 7.4, S is symmetric. Since it is also clearly transitive and reflexive, S is an equivalence relation. Furthermore, every element added to R to produce S was forced to be added in order to insure reflexivity, symmetry, or transitivity; therefore S is the smallest equivalence relation containing R.

26. This follows from the fact (Exercise 40 in Section 7.5) that two partitions are related under the refinement relation if and only if their corresponding equivalence relations are related under the $\subseteq$ relation, together with the fact that $\subseteq$ is a partial order on every collection of sets.

28. A subset of a chain is again a chain, so we list only the maximal chains.

    a) $\{a, b, c\}$ and $\{a, b, d\}$ **b)** $\{a, b, e\}$, $\{a, b, d\}$, and $\{a, c, d\}$

    c) In this case there are 9 maximal chains, each consisting of one element from the top row, the element in the middle, and one element in the bottom row.

30. The vertices are arranged in three columns. Each pair of vertices in the same column are clearly comparable. Therefore the largest antichain can have at most three elements. One such antichain is $\{a, b, c\}$.

32. This result is known as Dilworth's theorem. For a proof, see, for instance, page 58 of *Graph Theory* by Béla Bollobás (Springer-Verlag, 1979).

34. Let x be a minimal element in S. Then the hypothesis $\forall y(y \prec x \rightarrow P(y))$ is vacuously true, so the conclusion $P(x)$ is true, which is what we wanted to show.

36. Reflexivity is the statement that f is $O(f)$. This is trivial, by taking $C = 1$ and $k = 1$ in the definition of the big-O relation. Transitivity was proved in Exercise 17 of Section 2.2.

38. It was proved in Exercise 37 that $R \cap R^{-1}$ is an equivalence relation whenever R is a quasi-ordering on a set A. Therefore it makes sense to speak of the equivalence classes of $R \cap R^{-1}$, and the relation S is well-defined from its syntax. To show that S is a partial order, we must show that it is reflexive, anti-symmetric, and transitive. For the first of these, we need to show that (C, C) belongs to S, which means that there are elements $c \in C$ and $d \in C$ such that (c, d) belongs to R. By the definition of equivalence class, C is not empty, so let c be any element of C, and let $d = c$. Then (c, c) belongs to R by the reflexivity of R. Next, for antisymmetry, suppose that (C, D) and (D, C) both belong to S; we must show that $C = D$. We have that (c, d) belongs to R for some $c \in C$ and $d \in D$; and we have that (d', c') belongs to R for some $d' \in D$ and $c' \in C$. If we show that (c, d) also belongs to R^{-1}, then we will know that c and d are in the same equivalence class of $R \cap R'$, and therefore that $C = D$. To do this, we need to show that (d, c) belongs to R. Since d and d' are in the same equivalence class, we know that (d, d') belongs to R; we already mentioned that (d', c') belongs to R; and since c' and c are in the same equivalence class, we know that (c', c) belongs to R. Applying the transitivity of R three times, we conclude that (d, c) belongs to R, as desired.

Finally, to show the transitivity of S, we must show that if (C, D) belongs to S and (D, E) belongs to S, then (C, E) belongs to S. The hypothesis tells us that (c, d) belongs to R for some $c \in C$ and $d \in D$, and that (d', e) belongs to R for some $d' \in D$ and $e \in E$. As in the previous paragraph, we know that (d, d') belongs to R. Therefore by the transitivity of R (thrice), (c, e) belongs to R, and our proof is complete.

40. This follows in essentially one step from part **(c)** of Exercise 39. Suppose that $x \vee y = y$. Then by the first absorption law, $x = x \wedge (x \vee y) = x \wedge y$. Conversely, if $x \wedge y = x$, then by the second absorption law (with the roles of x and y reversed), $y = y \vee (x \wedge y) = y \vee x$. (We are using the commutative law as well, of course.)

42. By Exercise 45 in Section 7.6, every finite lattice has a least element and a greatest element. These elements are the 0 and 1, respectively, discussed in the preamble to this exercise.

44. We learned in Example 23 of Section 7.6 that the meet and join in this lattice are $\cap$ and $\cup$. We know from Section 1.7 that these operations are distributive over each other. There is nothing more to prove.

46. Here is one example. The reader should draw the Hasse diagram to see it more vividly. The elements in the lattice are 0, 1, a, b, c, d, and e. The relations are that 0 precedes all other elements; all other elements precede 1; b, d, and e precede c; and b precedes a. Then both d and e are complements of a, but b has no complement (since $b \vee x \neq 1$ unless $x = 1$).

48. This can be proved by playing around with the symbolism. Suppose that a and b are both complements of x. This means that $x \vee a = 1$, $x \wedge a = 0$, $x \vee b = 1$, and $x \wedge b = 0$. Now using the various identities in Exercises 39 and 41 and the preamble to Exercise 43, we have $a = a \wedge 1 = a \wedge (x \vee b) = (a \wedge x) \vee (a \wedge b) = 0 \vee (a \wedge b) = a \wedge b$. By the same argument, we can also show that $b = a \wedge b$. By transitivity of equality, it follows that $a = b$.

CHAPTER 8
Graphs

SECTION 8.1   Introduction to Graphs

2. a) A simple graph would be the model here, since there are no parallel edges or loops, and the edges are undirected.

b) A multigraph would, in theory, be needed here, since there may be more than one interstate highway between the same pair of cities.

c) A pseudograph is needed here, to allow for loops.

4. This is a multigraph; the edges are undirected, and there are no loops, but there are parallel edges.

6. This is a multigraph; the edges are undirected, and there are no loops, but there are parallel edges.

8. This is a directed multigraph; the edges are directed, and there are parallel edges.

10. The graph in Exercise 3 is simple. The multigraph in Exercise 4 can be made simple by removing one of the edges between a and b, and two of the edges between b and d. The pseudograph in Exercise 5 can be made simple by removing the three loops and one edge in each of the three pairs of parallel edges. The multigraph in Exercise 6 can be made simple by removing one of the edges between a and c, and one of the edges between b and d. The other three are not undirected graphs. (Of course removing any supersets of the answers given here are equally valid answers; in particular, we could remove *all* the edges in each case.)

12. Since there are edges from Hawk to Crow, Owl, and Raccoon, the graph is telling us that the hawk competes with these three animals.

14. Each person is represented by a vertex, with an edge between two vertices if and only if the people are acquainted.

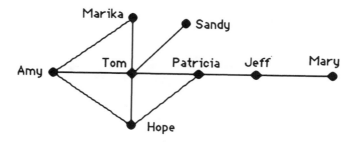

16. Fred influences Brian, since there is an edge from Fred to Brian. Yvonne and Deborah influence Fred, since there are edges from these vertices to Fred.

18. Team four beat the vertices to which there are edges from Team four, namely only Team three. The other teams—Team one, Team two, Team five, and Team six—all beat Team four, since there are edges from them to Team four.

20. This is a directed multigraph with one edge from a to b for each call made by a to b. Rather than draw the parallel edges with parallel lines, we have indicated what is intended by writing a numeral on the edge to indicate how many calls were made, if it was more than one.

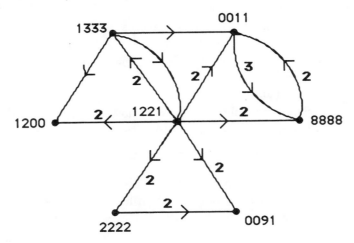

22. This is similar to the use of directed graphs to model telephone calls.

a) We can have a vertex for each mailbox or e-mail address in the network, with a directed edge between two vertices if a message is sent from the tail of the edge to the head.

b) As in part **(a)** we use a directed edge for each message sent during the week.

24. Vertices with thousands or millions of edges going out from them could be such lists.

26. The model says that the statements for which there are edges to S_6 must be executed before S_6, namely the statements S_1, S_2, S_3, and S_4.

28. The vertices in the directed graph represent cities. Whenever there is a nonstop flight from city A to city B, we put a directed edge into our directed graph from vertex A to vertex B, and furthermore we label that edge with the flight time. Let us see how to incorporate this into the mathematical definition. Let us call such a thing a directed graph with weighted edges. It is defined to be a triple (V, E, W), where (V, E) is a directed graph (i.e., V is a set of vertices and E is a set of ordered pairs of elements of V) and W is a function from E to the set of nonnegative real numbers. Here we are simply thinking of $W(e)$ as the weight of edge e, which in this case is the flight time.

SECTION 8.2   Graph Terminology

2. In this pseudograph there are 5 vertices and 13 edges. The degree of vertex a is 6, since in addition to the 4 nonloops incident to a, there is a loop contributing 2 to the degree. The degrees of the other vertices are $\deg(b) = 6$, $\deg(c) = 6$, $\deg(d) = 5$, and $\deg(e) = 3$. There are no pendant or isolated vertices in this pseudograph.

4. For the graph in Exercise 1, the sum is $2 + 4 + 1 + 0 + 2 + 3 = 12 = 2 \cdot 6$; there are 6 edges. For the pseudograph in Exercise 2, the sum is $6 + 6 + 6 + 5 + 3 = 26 = 2 \cdot 13$; there are 13 edges. For the pseudograph in Exercise 3, the sum is $3 + 2 + 4 + 0 + 6 + 0 + 4 + 2 + 3 = 24 = 2 \cdot 12$; there are 12 edges.

6. Model this problem by letting the vertices of a graph be the people at the party, with an edge between two people if they shake hands. Then the degree of each vertex is the number of people the person that vertex represents shakes hands with. By Theorem 1 the sum of the degrees is even (it is $2e$).

8. In this directed multigraph there are 4 vertices and 8 edges. The degrees are $\deg^-(a) = 2$, $\deg^+(a) = 2$, $\deg^-(b) = 3$, $\deg^+(b) = 4$, $\deg^-(c) = 2$, $\deg^+(c) = 1$, $\deg^-(d) = 1$, and $\deg^+(d) = 1$.

10. For Exercise 7 the sum of the in-degrees is $3 + 1 + 2 + 1 = 7$, and the sum of the out-degrees is $1 + 2 + 1 + 3 = 7$; there are 7 edges. For Exercise 8 the sum of the in-degrees is $2 + 3 + 2 + 1 = 8$, and the sum of the out-degrees is $2 + 4 + 1 + 1 = 8$; there are 8 edges. For Exercise 9 the sum of the in-degrees is $6 + 1 + 2 + 4 + 0 = 13$, and the sum of the out-degrees is $1 + 5 + 5 + 2 + 0 = 13$; there are 13 edges.

12. Since there is an edge from a person to each of his or her acquaintances, the degree of v is the number of people v knows. An isolated vertex would be a person who knew on one, and a pendant vertex would be a person who knew just one other person (it is doubtful that there are many, if any, isolated or pendant vertices). If the average degree is 1000, then the average person knows 1000 other people.

14. Since there is an edge from a person to each of the other actors that person has appeared with in a movie, the degree of v is the number of other actors that person has appeared with. An isolated vertex would be a person who has appeared only in movies in which he or she was the only actor, and a pendant vertex would be a person who has appeared with only one other actor in any movie (it is doubtful that there are many, if any, isolated or pendant vertices).

16. Since there is an edge from a page to each page that it links to, the outdegree of a vertex is the number of links on that page, and the in-degree of a vertex is the number of other pages that have a link to it.

18. a) This graph has 7 vertices, with an edge joining each pair of distinct vertices.

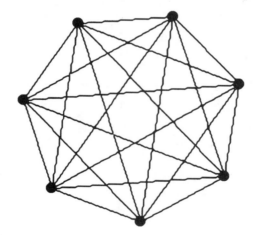

b) This graph is the complete bipartite graph on parts of size 1 and 8; we have put the part of size 1 in the middle.

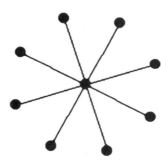

c) This is the complete bipartite graph with 4 vertices in each part.

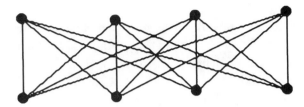

d) This is the 7-cycle.

e) The 7-wheel is the 7-cycle with an extra vertex joined to the other 7 vertices.

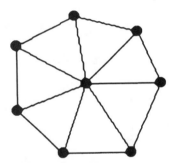

f) We take two copies of Q_3 and join corresponding vertices.

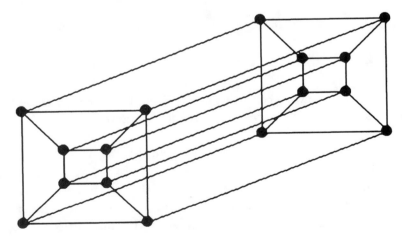

20. This graph is bipartite, with bipartition $\{a, c\}$ and $\{b, d, e\}$. In fact this is the complete bipartite graph $K_{2,3}$. If this graph were missing the edge between a and d, then it would still be bipartite on the same sets, but not a complete bipartite graph.

22. This is just like Exercise 20, but here we have the complete bipartite graph $K_{2,4}$. The vertices in the part of size 2 are c and f, and the vertices in the part of size 4 are a, b, d, and e.

24. a) By the definition given in the text, K_1 does not have enough vertices to be bipartite. Clearly K_2 is bipartite. There is a triangle in K_n for $n > 2$, so those complete graphs are not bipartite. (See Exercise 21.)
b) First we need $n \geq 3$ for C_n to be defined. If n is even, then C_n is bipartite, since we can take one part to be every other vertex. If n is odd, then C_n is not bipartite.
c) Every wheel contains triangles, so no W_n is bipartite.
d) Q_n is bipartite for all $n \geq 1$, since we can divide the vertices into these two classes: those bit strings with an odd number of 1's, and those bit strings with an even number of 1's.

26. The 4-wheel (see Figure 5) with one edge along the rim deleted is such a graph. It has $(4+3+3+2+2)/2 = 7$ edges.

28. a) Since the number of odd-degree vertices has to be even, no graph exists with these degrees. Another reason no such graph exists is that the vertex of degree 0 would have to be isolated but the vertex of degree 5 would have to be adjacent to every other vertex, and these two statements are contradictory.
b) Since the number of odd-degree vertices has to be even, no graph exists with these degrees. Another reason no such graph exists is that the degree of a vertex in a simple graph is at most 1 less than the number of vertices.
c) A 6-cycle is such a graph. (See picture below.)
d) Since the number of odd-degree vertices has to be even, no graph exists with these degrees.
e) A 6-cycle with one of its diagonals added is such a graph. (See picture below.)
f) A graph consisting of three edges with no common vertices is such a graph. (See picture below.)
g) The 5-wheel is such a graph. (See picture below.)
h) Each of the vertices of degree 5 is adjacent to all the other vertices. Thus there can be no vertex of degree 1. So no such graph exists.

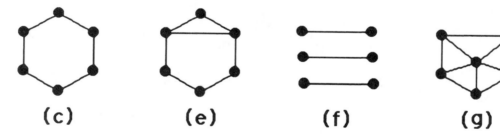

$$\textbf{(c)} \qquad\qquad \textbf{(e)} \qquad\qquad \textbf{(f)} \qquad\qquad \textbf{(g)}$$

30. We list the subgraphs: the subgraph consisting of K_2 itself, the subgraph consisting of two vertices and no edges, and two subgraphs with 1 vertex each. Therefore the answer is 4.

32. We need to count this in an organized manner. First note that W_3 is the same as K_4, and it will be easier if we think of it as K_4. We will count the subgraphs in terms of the number of vertices they contain. There are clearly just 4 subgraphs consisting of just one vertex. If a subgraph is to have two vertices, then there are $C(4, 2) = 6$ ways to choose the vertices, and then 2 ways in each case to decide whether or not to include the edge joining them. This gives us $6 \cdot 2 = 12$ subgraphs with two vertices. If a subgraph is to have three vertices, then there are $C(4, 3) = 4$ ways to choose the vertices, and then $2^3 = 8$ ways in each case to decide whether or not to include each of the edges joining pairs of them. This gives us $4 \cdot 8 = 32$ subgraphs with three vertices. Finally, there are the subgraphs containing all four vertices. Here there are $2^6 = 64$ ways to decide which edges to include. Thus our answer is $4 + 12 + 32 + 64 = 112$.

34. a) We want to show that $2e \geq vm$. We know from Theorem 1 that $2e$ is the sum of the degrees of the vertices. This certainly cannot be less than the sum of m for each vertex, since each degree is no less than m.
b) We want to show that $2e \leq vM$. We know from Theorem 1 that $2e$ is the sum of the degrees of the vertices. This certainly cannot exceed the sum of M for each vertex, since each degree is no greater than M.

36. Since the vertices in one part have degree m, and vertices in the other part have degree n, we conclude that $K_{m,n}$ is regular if and only if $m = n$.

38. We draw the answer by superimposing the graphs (keeping the positions of the vertices the same).

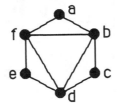

40. The union is shown here. The only common vertex is a, so we have reoriented the drawing so that the pieces will not overlap.

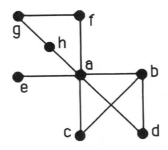

42. The given information tells us that $G \cup \overline{G}$ has 28 edges. However, $G \cup \overline{G}$ is the complete graph on the number of vertices n that G has. Since this graph has $n(n-1)/2$ edges, we want to solve $n(n-1)/2 = 28$. Thus $n = 8$.

44. Suppose the parts are of sizes k and $v - k$. Then the maximum number of edges the graph may have is $k(v - k)$ (an edge between each pair of vertices in different parts). By algebra or calculus, we know that the function $f(k) = k(v - k)$ achieves its maximum when $k = v/2$, giving $f(k) = v^2/4$. Thus there are at most $v^2/4$ edges.

46. We start by coloring any vertex red. Then we color all the vertices adjacent to this vertex blue. Then we color all the vertices adjacent to blue vertices red, then color all the vertices adjacent to red vertices blue, and so on. If we ever are in the position of trying to color a vertex with the color opposite to the color it already has, then we stop and know that the graph is not bipartite. If the process terminates (successfully) before all the vertices have been colored, then we color some uncolored vertex red (it will necessarily not be adjacent to any vertices we have already colored) and begin the process again. Eventually we will have either colored all the vertices (producing the bipartition) or stopped and decided that the graph is not bipartite.

48. Obviously $(G^c)^c$ and G have the same vertex set, so we need only show that they have the same directed edges. But this is clear, since an edge (u, v) is in $(G^c)^c$ if and only if the edge (v, u) is in G^c if and only if the edge (u, v) is in G.

50. If $G = (V, E)$ is a directed multigraph with function f from the edge set to the set of ordered pairs of vertices (see the definition), then the converse can be taken to be $G^c = (V, E)$ with the function f^c defined so that heads become tails and vice versa. Specifically, if $e \in E$ and $f(e) = (u, v)$, then we set $f^c(e) = (v, u)$.

52. In addition to the connections shown in Figure 12, we need to make connections between $P(i, 3)$ and $P(i, 0)$ for each i, and between $P(3, j)$ and $P(0, j)$ for each j. The complete network is shown here. We can imagine this drawn on a torus.

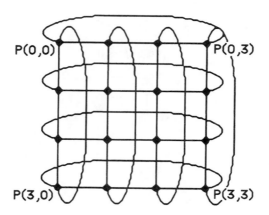

SECTION 8.3   Representing Graphs and Graph Isomorphism

2. This is similar to Exercise 1. The list is as follows.

Vertex	Adjacent vertices
a	b, d
b	a, d, e
c	d, e
d	a, b, c
e	b, c

4. This is similar to Exercise 3. The list is as follows.

Initial vertex	Terminal vertices
a	b, d
b	a, c, d, e
c	b, c
d	a, e
e	c, e

6. This is similar to Exercise 5. The vertices are assumed to be listed in alphabetical order.

$$\begin{bmatrix} 0 & 1 & 0 & 1 & 0 \\ 1 & 0 & 0 & 1 & 1 \\ 0 & 0 & 0 & 1 & 1 \\ 1 & 1 & 1 & 0 & 0 \\ 0 & 1 & 1 & 0 & 0 \end{bmatrix}$$

8. This is similar to Exercise 7.

$$\begin{bmatrix} 0 & 1 & 0 & 1 & 0 \\ 1 & 0 & 1 & 1 & 1 \\ 0 & 1 & 1 & 0 & 0 \\ 1 & 0 & 0 & 0 & 1 \\ 0 & 0 & 1 & 0 & 1 \end{bmatrix}$$

10. This graph has three vertices and is undirected, since the matrix is symmetric.

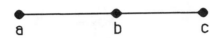

12. This graph is directed, since the matrix is not symmetric.

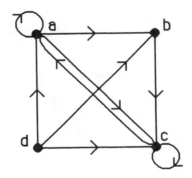

14. This is similar to Exercise 13.

$$\begin{bmatrix} 0 & 3 & 0 & 1 \\ 3 & 0 & 1 & 0 \\ 0 & 1 & 0 & 3 \\ 1 & 0 & 3 & 0 \end{bmatrix}$$

16. Because of the numbers larger than 1, we need multiple edges in this graph.

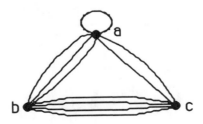

18. This is similar to Exercise 16.

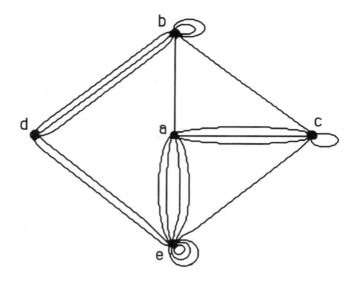

20. This is similar to Exercise 19.

$$\begin{bmatrix} 1 & 1 & 1 & 1 \\ 0 & 1 & 0 & 1 \\ 1 & 0 & 1 & 0 \\ 1 & 1 & 1 & 1 \end{bmatrix}$$

22. a) This matrix is symmetric, so we can take the graph to be undirected. No parallel edges are present, since no entries exceed 1.

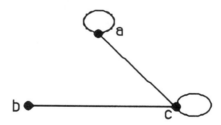

24. This is the adjacency matrix of a directed multigraph, because the matrix is not symmetric and it contains entries greater than 1.

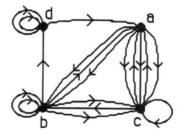

26. Each column represents an edge; the two 1's in the column are in the rows for the endpoints of the edge.

Exercise 1
$$\begin{bmatrix} 1 & 1 & 1 & 0 & 0 \\ 1 & 0 & 0 & 1 & 0 \\ 0 & 1 & 0 & 0 & 1 \\ 0 & 0 & 1 & 1 & 1 \end{bmatrix}$$

Exercise 2
$$\begin{bmatrix} 1 & 1 & 0 & 0 & 0 & 0 \\ 1 & 0 & 1 & 1 & 0 & 0 \\ 0 & 0 & 0 & 0 & 1 & 1 \\ 0 & 1 & 1 & 0 & 1 & 0 \\ 0 & 0 & 0 & 1 & 0 & 1 \end{bmatrix}$$

28. For an undirected graph, the sum of the entries in the ith row is the same as the corresponding column sum, namely the number of edges incident to the vertex i, which is the same as the degree of i minus the number of loops at i. (See the solution to Exercise 29.)

In a directed graph, the answer is dual to the answer for Exercise 29. The sum of the entries in the ith row is the number of edges that have i as their initial vertex, i.e., the out-degree of i.

30. The sum of the entries in the ith row of the incidence matrix is the number of edges incident to vertex i, since there is one column with a 1 in row i for each such edge.

32. a) This is just the matrix that has 0's on the main diagonal and 1's elsewhere, namely

$$\begin{bmatrix} 0 & 1 & 1 & \cdots & 1 \\ 1 & 0 & 1 & \cdots & 1 \\ 1 & 1 & 0 & \cdots & 1 \\ \vdots & \vdots & \vdots & \ddots & \vdots \\ 1 & 1 & 1 & \cdots & 0 \end{bmatrix}.$$

b) We label the vertices so that the cycle goes $v_1, v_2, \ldots, v_n, v_1$. Then the matrix has 1's on the diagonals just above and below the main diagonal and in positions $(1, n)$ and $(n, 1)$, and 0's elsewhere:

$$\begin{bmatrix} 0 & 1 & 0 & \cdots & 0 & 1 \\ 1 & 0 & 1 & \cdots & 0 & 0 \\ 0 & 1 & 0 & \cdots & 0 & 0 \\ \vdots & \vdots & \vdots & \ddots & \vdots & \vdots \\ 0 & 0 & 0 & \cdots & 0 & 1 \\ 1 & 0 & 0 & \cdots & 1 & 0 \end{bmatrix}$$

c) This matrix is the same as the answer in part **(b)**, except that we add one row and column for the vertex in the middle of the wheel; in our matrix it is the last row and column:

$$\begin{bmatrix} 0 & 1 & 0 & \cdots & 0 & 1 & 1 \\ 1 & 0 & 1 & \cdots & 0 & 0 & 1 \\ 0 & 1 & 0 & \cdots & 0 & 0 & 1 \\ \vdots & \vdots & \vdots & \ddots & \vdots & \vdots & \vdots \\ 0 & 0 & 0 & \cdots & 0 & 1 & 1 \\ 1 & 0 & 0 & \cdots & 1 & 0 & 1 \\ 1 & 1 & 1 & \cdots & 1 & 1 & 0 \end{bmatrix}$$

d) Since the first m vertices are adjacent to none of the first m vertices but all of the last n, and vice versa, this matrix splits up into four pieces:

$$\begin{bmatrix} 0 & \cdots & 0 & 1 & \cdots & 1 \\ \vdots & \ddots & \vdots & \vdots & \ddots & \vdots \\ 0 & \cdots & 0 & 1 & \cdots & 1 \\ 1 & \cdots & 1 & 0 & \cdots & 0 \\ \vdots & \ddots & \vdots & \vdots & \ddots & \vdots \\ 1 & \cdots & 1 & 0 & \cdots & 0 \end{bmatrix}$$

e) It is not convenient to show these matrices explicitly. Instead, we will give a recursive definition. Let $\mathbf{Q}_n$ be the adjacency matrix for the graph Q_n. Then

$$\mathbf{Q}_1 = \begin{bmatrix} 0 & 1 \\ 1 & 0 \end{bmatrix}$$

and

$$\mathbf{Q}_{n+1} = \begin{bmatrix} \mathbf{Q}_n & \mathbf{I}_n \\ \mathbf{I}_n & \mathbf{Q}_n \end{bmatrix},$$

where $\mathbf{I}_n$ is the identity matrix (since the corresponding vertices of the two n-cubes are joined by edges in the $(n+1)$-cube).

34. These graphs are isomorphic, since each is a path with five vertices. One isomorphism is $f(u_1) = v_1$, $f(u_2) = v_2$, $f(u_3) = v_4$, $f(u_4) = v_5$, and $f(u_5) = v_3$.

36. These graphs are not isomorphic. The second has a vertex of degree 4, whereas the first does not.

38. These two graphs are isomorphic. Each consists of a K_4 with a fifth vertex adjacent to two of the vertices in the K_4. Many isomorphisms are possible. One is $f(u_1) = v_1$, $f(u_2) = v_3$, $f(u_3) = v_2$, $f(u_4) = v_5$, and $f(u_5) = v_4$.

40. These graphs are not isomorphic—the degrees of the vertices are not the same (the graph on the right has a vertex of degree 4, which the graph on the left lacks).

42. These graphs are not isomorphic. In the first graph the vertices of degree 4 are adjacent. This is not true of the second graph.

44. The easiest way to show that these graphs are not isomorphic is to look at their complements. The complement of the graph on the left consists of two 4-cycles. The complement of the graph on the right is an 8-cycle. Since the complements are not isomorphic, the graphs are also not isomorphic.

46. This is immediate from the definition, since an edge is in $\overline{G}$ if and only if it is not in G, if and only if the corresponding edge is not in H, if and only if the corresponding edge is in $\overline{H}$.

48. An isolated vertex has no incident edges, so the row consists of all 0's.

50. The complementary graph consists of edges $\{a,c\}$, $\{c,d\}$, and $\{d,b\}$; it is clearly isomorphic to the original graph (send d to a, a to c, b to d, and c to b).

52. If G is self-complementary, then the number of edges of G must equal the number of edges of $\overline{G}$. But the sum of these two numbers is $n(n-1)/2$, where n is the number of vertices of G, since the union of the two graphs is K_n. Therefore the number of edges of G must be $n(n-1)/4$. Since this number must be an integer, a look at the four cases shows that n may be congruent to either 0 or 1, but not congruent to either 2 or 3, modulo 4.

54. **a)** There are just two graphs with 2 vertices—the one with no edges, and the one with one edge.
b) A graph with three vertices can contain 0, 1, 2, or 3 edges. There is only one graph for each number of edges, up to isomorphism. Therefore the answer is 4.
c) Here we look at graphs with 4 vertices. There is 1 graph with no edges, and 1 (up to isomorphism) with a single edge. If there are two edges, then these edges may or may not be adjacent, giving us 2 possibilities. If there are three edges, then the edges may form a triangle, a star, or a path, giving us 3 possibilities. Since graphs with four, five, or six edges are just complements of graphs with two, one, or no edges (respectively), the number of isomorphism classes must be the same as for these earlier cases. Thus our answer is $1 + 1 + 2 + 3 + 2 + 1 + 1 = 11$.

56. There are 9 such graphs. Let us first look at the graphs that have a cycle in them. There is only 1 with a 4-cycle. There are 2 with a triangle, since the fourth edge can either be incident to the triangle or not. If there are no cycles, then the edges may all be in one connected component (see Section 8.4), in which case there are 3 possibilities (a path of length four, a path of length three with an edge incident to one of the middle vertices on the path, and a star). Otherwise, there are two components, which are necessarily either two paths of length two, a path of length three plus a single edge, or a star with three edges plus a single edge (3 possibilities in this case as well).

58. a) These graphs are both K_3, so they are isomorphic.

b) These are both simple graphs with 4 vertices and 5 edges. Up to isomorphism there is only one such graph (its complement is a single edge), so the graphs have to be isomorphic.

60. We need only modify the definition of isomorphism of simple graphs slightly. The directed graphs $G_1 = (V_1, E_1)$ and $G_2 = (V_2, E_2)$ are isomorphic if there is a one-to-one and onto function $f : V_1 \to V_2$ such that for all pairs of vertices a and b in V_1, $(a, b) \in E_1$ if and only if $(f(a), f(b)) \in E_2$.

62. These two graphs are not isomorphic. In the first there is no edge from the unique vertex of in-degree 0 (u_1) to the unique vertex of out-degree 0 (u_2), whereas in the second graph there is such an edge, namely $v_3 v_4$.

64. We claim that the digraphs are isomorphic. To discover an isomorphism, we first note that vertices u_1, u_2, and u_3 in the first digraph are independent (i.e., have no edges joining them), as are u_4, u_5, and u_6. Therefore these two groups of vertices will have to correspond to similar groups in the second digraph, namely v_1, v_3, and v_5, and v_2, v_4, and v_6, in some order. Furthermore, u_3 is the only vertex among one of these groups of u's to be the only one in the group with out-degree 2, so it must correspond to v_6, the vertex with the similar property in the other digraph; and in the same manner, u_4 must correspond to v_5. Now it is an easy matter, by looking at where the edges lead, to see that the isomorphism (if there is one) must also pair up u_1 with v_2; u_2 with v_4; u_5 with v_1; and u_6 with v_3. Finally, we easily verify that this indeed gives an isomorphism—each directed edge in the first digraph is present precisely when the corresponding directed edge is present in the second digraph.

66. a) There are 10 nonisomorphic directed graphs with 2 vertices. To see this, first consider graphs that have no edges from one vertex to the other. There are 3 such graphs, depending on whether they have no, one, or two loops. Similarly there are 3 in which there is an edge from each vertex to the other. Finally, there are 4 graphs that have exactly one edge between the vertices, because now the vertices are distinguished, and there can be or fail to be a loop at each vertex.

b) A detailed discussion of the number of directed graphs with 3 vertices would be rather long, so we will just give the answer, namely 104. There are some useful pictures relevant to this problem (and part **(c)** as well) in the appendix to *Graph Theory* by Frank Harary (Addison-Wesley, 1969).

c) The answer is 3069.

68. The answers depend on exactly how the storage is done, of course, but we will give naive answers that are at least correct as approximations.

a) We need one adjacency list for each vertex, and the list needs some sort of name or header; this requires v storage locations. In addition, each edge will appear twice, once in the list of each of its endpoints; this will require $2e$ storage locations. Therefore we need $v + 2e$ locations in all.

b) The adjacency matrix is a $v \times v$ matrix, so it requires v^2 bits of storage.

c) The incidence matrix is a $v \times e$ matrix, so it requires ve bits of storage.

SECTION 8.4   Connectivity

2. **a)** This is a path of length 4, but it is not a circuit, since it ends at a vertex other than the one at which it began. It is simple, since no edges are repeated.

   b) This is a path of length 4, which is a circuit. It is not simple, since it uses an edge more than once.

   c) This is not a path, since there is no edge from d to b.

   d) This is not a path, since there is no edge from b to d.

4. This graph is connected—it is easy to see that there is a path from every vertex to every other vertex.

6. The graph in Exercise 3 has three components: the piece that looks like a $\wedge$, the piece that looks like a $\vee$, and the isolated vertex. The graph in Exercise 4 is connected, with just one component. The graph in Exercise 5 has two components, each a triangle.

8. A connected component of a collaboration graph represent a maximal set of people with the property that for any two of them, we can find a string of joint works that takes us from one to the other. The word "maximal" here implies that nobody else can be added to this set of people without destroying this property.

10. An actor is in the same connected component as Kevin Bacon if there is a path from that person to Bacon. This means that the actor was in a movie with someone who was in a movie with someone who ... who was in a movie with Kevin Bacon. This includes Kevin Bacon, all actors who appeared in a movie with Kevin Bacon, all actors who appeared in movies with those people, and so on.

12. **a)** The cycle $baeb$ guarantees that these three vertices are in one strongly connected component. Since there is no path from c to any other vertex, and there is no path from any other vertex to d, these two vertices are in strong components by themselves. Therefore the strongly connected components are $\{a, b, e\}$, $\{c\}$, and $\{d\}$.

   b) The cycle $cdec$ guarantees that these three vertices are in one strongly connected component. The vertices a, b, and f are in strong components by themselves, since there are no paths both to and from each of these to every other vertex. Therefore the strongly connected components are $\{a\}$, $\{b\}$ $\{c, d, e\}$, and $\{f\}$.

   c) The cycle $abcdfghia$ guarantees that these eight vertices are in one strongly connected component. Since there is no path from e to any other vertex, this vertex is in a strong component by itself. Therefore the strongly connected components are $\{a, b, c, d, f, g, h, i\}$ and $\{e\}$.

14. Let $a, b, c, \ldots, z$ be the directed path. Since z and a are in the same strongly connected component, there is a directed path from z to a. This path appended to the given path gives us a circuit. We can reach any vertex on the original path from any other vertex on that path by going around this circuit.

16. **a)** Adjacent vertices are in different parts, so every path between them must have odd length. Therefore there are no paths of length 2.

   b) A path of length 3 is specified by choosing a vertex in one part for the second vertex in the path and a vertex in the other part for the third vertex in the path (the first and fourth vertices are the given adjacent vertices). Therefore there are $3 \cdot 3 = 9$ paths.

   c) As in part (a), the answer is 0.

   d) This is similar to part (b); therefore the answer is $3^4 = 81$.

18. Probably the best way to do this is to write down the adjacency matrix for this graph and then compute its

powers. The matrix is

$$\mathbf{A} = \begin{bmatrix} 0 & 1 & 0 & 1 & 1 & 0 \\ 1 & 0 & 1 & 0 & 1 & 1 \\ 0 & 1 & 0 & 1 & 0 & 1 \\ 1 & 0 & 1 & 0 & 1 & 0 \\ 1 & 1 & 0 & 1 & 0 & 1 \\ 0 & 1 & 1 & 0 & 1 & 0 \end{bmatrix}.$$

a) To find the number of paths of length 2, we need to look at $\mathbf{A}^2$, which is

$$\begin{bmatrix} 3 & 1 & 2 & 1 & 2 & 2 \\ 1 & 4 & 1 & 3 & 2 & 2 \\ 2 & 1 & 3 & 0 & 3 & 1 \\ 1 & 3 & 0 & 3 & 1 & 2 \\ 2 & 2 & 3 & 1 & 4 & 1 \\ 2 & 2 & 1 & 2 & 1 & 3 \end{bmatrix}.$$

Since the $(3,4)^{\text{th}}$ entry is 0, so there are no paths of length 2.

b) The $(3,4)^{\text{th}}$ entry of $\mathbf{A}^3$ turns out to be 8, so there are 8 paths of length 3.

c) The $(3,4)^{\text{th}}$ entry of $\mathbf{A}^4$ turns out to be 10, so there are 10 paths of length 4.

d) The $(3,4)^{\text{th}}$ entry of $\mathbf{A}^5$ turns out to be 73, so there are 73 paths of length 5.

e) The $(3,4)^{\text{th}}$ entry of $\mathbf{A}^6$ turns out to be 160, so there are 160 paths of length 6.

f) The $(3,4)^{\text{th}}$ entry of $\mathbf{A}^7$ turns out to be 739, so there are 739 paths of length 7.

20. We show this by induction on n. For $n = 1$ there is nothing to prove. Now assume the inductive hypothesis, and let G be a connected graph with $n+1$ vertices and fewer than n edges, where $n \geq 1$. Since the sum of the degrees of the vertices of G is equal to 2 times the number of edges, we know that the sum of the degrees is less than $2n$, which is less than $2(n+1)$. Therefore some vertex has degree less than 2. Since G is connected, this vertex is not isolated, so it must have degree 1. Remove this vertex and its edge. Clearly the result is still connected, and it has n vertices and fewer than $n-1$ edges, contradicting the inductive hypothesis. Therefore the statement holds for G, and the proof is complete.

22. Let v be a vertex of odd degree, and let H be the component of G containing v. Then H is a graph itself, so it has an even number of vertices of odd degree. In particular, there is another vertex w in H with odd degree. By definition of connectivity, there is a path from v to w.

24. Vertices c and d are the cut vertices. The removal of either one creates a graph with two components. The removal of any other vertex does not disconnect the graph.

26. The graph in Exercise 23 has no cut edges; any edge can be removed, and the result is still connected. For the graph in Exercise 24, $\{c, d\}$ is the only cut edge. There are several cut edges for the graph in Exercise 25: $\{a, b\}$, $\{b, c\}$, $\{c, d\}$, $\{c, e\}$, $\{e, i\}$, and $\{h, i\}$.

28. First we show that if c is a cut vertex, then there exist vertices u and v such that every path between them passes through c. Since the removal of c increases the number of components, there must be two vertices in G that are in different components after the removal of c. Then every path between these two vertices has to pass through c. Conversely, if u and v are as specified, then they must be in different components of the graph with c removed. Therefore the removal of c resulted in at least two components, so c is a cut vertex.

30. First suppose that $e = \{u, v\}$ is a cut edge. Every circuit containing e must contain a path from u to v in addition to just the edge e. Since there are no such paths if e is removed from the graph, every such path must contain e. Thus e appears twice in the circuit, so the circuit is not simple. Conversely, suppose that e

is not a cut edge. Then in the graph with e deleted u and v are still in the same component. Therefore there is a simple path P from u to v in this deleted graph. The circuit consisting of P followed by e is a simple circuit containing e.

32. (The answers given here are not unique.) In the directed graph in Exercise 7, there is a path from b to each of the other three vertices, so $\{b\}$ is a vertex basis (and a smallest one). For the directed graph in Exercise 8, there is a path from b to each of a and c; on the other hand, d must clearly be in every vertex basis. Thus $\{b, d\}$ is a smallest vertex basis. Every vertex basis for the directed graph in Exercise 9 must contain vertex e, since it has no incoming edges. On the other hand, from any other vertex we can reach all the other vertices, so e together with any one of the other four vertices will form a vertex basis.

34. By definition of graph, both G_1 and G_2 are nonempty. If they have no common vertex, then there clearly can be no paths from $v_1 \in G_1$ to $v_2 \in G_2$. In that case G would not be connected, contradicting the hypothesis.

36. First we obtain the inequality given in the hint. We claim that the maximum value of $\sum n_i^2$, subject to the constraint that $\sum n_i = n$, is obtained when one of the n_i's is as large as possible, namely $n - k + 1$, and the remaining n_i's (there are $k - 1$ of them) are all equal to 1. To justify this claim, suppose instead that two of the n_i's were a and b, with $a \geq b \geq 2$. If we replace a by $a + 1$ and b by $b - 1$, then the constraint is still satisfied, and the sum of the squares has changed by $(a + 1)^2 + (b - 1)^2 - a^2 - b^2 = 2(a - b) + 2 \geq 2$. Therefore the maximum cannot be attained unless the n_i's are as we claimed. Since there are only a finite number of possibilities for the distribution of the n_i's, the arrangement we give must in fact yield the maximum. Therefore $\sum n_i^2 \leq (n - k + 1)^2 + (k - 1) \cdot 1^2 = n^2 - (k - 1)(2n - k)$, as desired.

Now by Exercise 35, the number of edges of the given graph does not exceed $\sum C(n_i, 2) = \sum (n_i^2 + n_i)/2 = ((\sum n_i^2) + n)/2$. Applying the inequality obtained above, we see that this does not exceed $(n^2 - (k - 1)(2n - k) + n)/2$, which after a little algebra is seen to equal $(n - k)(n - k + 1)/2$. The upshot of all this is that the most edges are obtained if there is one component as large as possible, with all the other components consisting of isolated vertices.

38. Under these conditions, the matrix has a block structure, with all the 1's confined to small squares (of various sizes) along the main diagonal. The reason for this is that there are no edges between different components. See the picture for a schematic view. The only 1's occur inside the small submatrices (but not all the entries in these squares are 1's, of course).

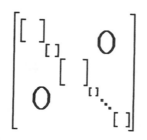

40. The length of a shortest path is the smallest l such that there is at least one path of length l from v to w. Therefore we can find the length by computing successively $\mathbf{A}^1$, $\mathbf{A}^2$, $\mathbf{A}^3$, ..., until we find the first l such that the $(i, j)^{\text{th}}$ entry of $\mathbf{A}^l$ is not 0, where v is the ith vertex and w is the jth.

42. First we write down the adjacency matrix for this graph, namely

$$\mathbf{A} = \begin{bmatrix} 0 & 1 & 0 & 1 & 0 \\ 1 & 0 & 0 & 0 & 1 \\ 0 & 1 & 0 & 0 & 0 \\ 1 & 0 & 0 & 0 & 0 \\ 0 & 0 & 1 & 1 & 0 \end{bmatrix}.$$

Then we compute $\mathbf{A}^2$ and $\mathbf{A}^3$, and look at the $(1,3)^{\text{th}}$ entry of each. We find that these entries are 0 and 1, respectively. By the reasoning given in Exercise 40, we conclude that a shortest path has length 3.

44. Suppose that f is an isomorphism from graph G to graph H. If G has a simple circuit of length k, say $u_1, u_2, \ldots, u_k, u_1$, then we claim that $f(u_1), f(u_2), \ldots, f(u_k), f(u_1)$ is a simple circuit in H. Certainly this is a circuit, since each edge $u_i u_{i+1}$ (and $u_k u_1$) in G corresponds to an edge $f(u_i)f(u_{i+1})$ (and $f(u_k)f(u_1)$) in H. Furthermore, since no edge was repeated in this circuit in G, no edge will be repeated when we use f to move over to H.

46. The adjacency matrix of G is as follows:

$$\mathbf{A} = \begin{bmatrix} 0 & 1 & 1 & 0 & 0 & 0 & 0 \\ 1 & 0 & 1 & 0 & 0 & 0 & 0 \\ 1 & 1 & 0 & 1 & 0 & 1 & 0 \\ 0 & 0 & 1 & 0 & 1 & 1 & 0 \\ 0 & 0 & 0 & 1 & 0 & 0 & 0 \\ 0 & 0 & 1 & 1 & 0 & 0 & 1 \\ 0 & 0 & 0 & 0 & 0 & 1 & 0 \end{bmatrix}$$

We compute $\mathbf{A}^2$ and $\mathbf{A}^3$, obtaining

$$\mathbf{A}^2 = \begin{bmatrix} 2 & 1 & 1 & 1 & 0 & 1 & 0 \\ 1 & 2 & 1 & 1 & 0 & 1 & 0 \\ 1 & 1 & 4 & 1 & 1 & 1 & 1 \\ 1 & 1 & 1 & 3 & 0 & 1 & 1 \\ 0 & 0 & 1 & 0 & 1 & 1 & 0 \\ 1 & 1 & 1 & 1 & 1 & 3 & 0 \\ 0 & 0 & 1 & 1 & 0 & 0 & 1 \end{bmatrix} \quad \text{and} \quad \mathbf{A}^3 = \begin{bmatrix} 2 & 3 & 5 & 2 & 1 & 2 & 1 \\ 3 & 2 & 5 & 2 & 1 & 2 & 1 \\ 5 & 5 & 4 & 6 & 1 & 6 & 1 \\ 2 & 2 & 6 & 2 & 3 & 5 & 1 \\ 1 & 1 & 1 & 3 & 0 & 1 & 1 \\ 2 & 2 & 6 & 5 & 1 & 2 & 3 \\ 1 & 1 & 1 & 1 & 1 & 3 & 0 \end{bmatrix}.$$

Already every off-diagonal entry in $\mathbf{A}^3$ is nonzero, so we know that there is a path of length 3 between every pair of distinct vertices in this graph. Therefore the graph G is connected.

On the other hand, the adjacency matrix of H is as follows:

$$\mathbf{A} = \begin{bmatrix} 0 & 1 & 1 & 0 & 0 & 0 \\ 1 & 0 & 0 & 0 & 0 & 0 \\ 1 & 0 & 0 & 0 & 0 & 0 \\ 0 & 0 & 0 & 0 & 1 & 1 \\ 0 & 0 & 0 & 1 & 0 & 1 \\ 0 & 0 & 0 & 1 & 1 & 0 \end{bmatrix}$$

We compute $\mathbf{A}^2$ through $\mathbf{A}^5$, obtaining the following matrices:

$$\mathbf{A}^2 = \begin{bmatrix} 2 & 0 & 0 & 0 & 0 & 0 \\ 0 & 1 & 1 & 0 & 0 & 0 \\ 0 & 1 & 1 & 0 & 0 & 0 \\ 0 & 0 & 0 & 2 & 1 & 1 \\ 0 & 0 & 0 & 1 & 2 & 1 \\ 0 & 0 & 0 & 1 & 1 & 2 \end{bmatrix} \quad \mathbf{A}^3 = \begin{bmatrix} 0 & 2 & 2 & 0 & 0 & 0 \\ 2 & 0 & 0 & 0 & 0 & 0 \\ 2 & 0 & 0 & 0 & 0 & 0 \\ 0 & 0 & 0 & 2 & 3 & 3 \\ 0 & 0 & 0 & 3 & 2 & 3 \\ 0 & 0 & 0 & 3 & 3 & 2 \end{bmatrix}$$

$$\mathbf{A}^4 = \begin{bmatrix} 4 & 0 & 0 & 0 & 0 & 0 \\ 0 & 2 & 2 & 0 & 0 & 0 \\ 0 & 2 & 2 & 0 & 0 & 0 \\ 0 & 0 & 0 & 6 & 5 & 5 \\ 0 & 0 & 0 & 5 & 6 & 5 \\ 0 & 0 & 0 & 5 & 5 & 6 \end{bmatrix} \quad \mathbf{A}^5 = \begin{bmatrix} 0 & 4 & 4 & 0 & 0 & 0 \\ 4 & 0 & 0 & 0 & 0 & 0 \\ 4 & 0 & 0 & 0 & 0 & 0 \\ 0 & 0 & 0 & 10 & 11 & 11 \\ 0 & 0 & 0 & 11 & 10 & 11 \\ 0 & 0 & 0 & 11 & 11 & 10 \end{bmatrix}$$

If we compute the sum $\mathbf{A} + \mathbf{A}^2 + \mathbf{A}^3 + \mathbf{A}^4 + \mathbf{A}^5$ we obtain

$$\begin{bmatrix} 6 & 7 & 7 & 0 & 0 & 0 \\ 7 & 3 & 3 & 0 & 0 & 0 \\ 7 & 3 & 3 & 0 & 0 & 0 \\ 0 & 0 & 0 & 20 & 21 & 21 \\ 0 & 0 & 0 & 21 & 20 & 21 \\ 0 & 0 & 0 & 21 & 21 & 20 \end{bmatrix}.$$

There is a 0 in the $(1,4)$ position, telling us that there is no path of length at most 5 from vertex a to vertex d. Since the graph only has six vertices, this tells us that there is no path at all from a to d. Thus the fact that there was a 0 as an off-diagonal entry in the sum told us that the graph was not connected.

SECTION 8.5   Euler and Hamilton Paths

2. All the vertex degrees are even, so there is an Euler circuit. We can find one by trial and error, or by using Algorithm 1. One such circuit is $a, b, c, f, i, h, g, d, e, h, f, e, b, d, a$.

4. This graph has no Euler circuit, since the degree of vertex c (for one) is odd. There is an Euler path between the two vertices of odd degree. One such path is $f, a, b, c, d, e, f, b, d, a, e, c$.

6. This graph has no Euler circuit, since the degree of vertex b (for one) is odd. There is an Euler path between the two vertices of odd degree. One such path is $b, c, d, e, f, d, g, i, d, a, h, i, a, b, i, c$.

8. All the vertex degrees are even, so there is an Euler circuit. We can find one by trial and error, or by using Algorithm 1. One such circuit is $a, b, c, d, e, j, c, h, i, d, b, g, h, m, n, o, j, i, n, l, m, f, g, l, k, f, a$.

10. The graph model for this exercise is as shown here.

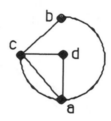

Vertices a and b are the banks of the river, and vertices c and d are the islands. Each vertex has even degree, so the graph has an Euler circuit, such as a, c, b, a, d, c, a. Therefore a walk of the type described is possible.

12. The algorithm is essentially the same as Algorithm 1. If there are no vertices of odd degree, then we simply use Algorithm 1, of course. If there are exactly two vertices of odd degree, then we begin constructing the initial path at one such vertex, and it will necessarily end at the other when it cannot be extended any further. Thereafter we follow Algorithm 1 exactly, splicing new circuits into the path we have constructed so far until no unused edges remain.

14. See the comments in the solution to Exercise 13. This graph has exactly two vertices of odd degree; therefore it has an Euler path and can be so traced.

16. First suppose that the directed multigraph has an Euler circuit. Since this circuit provides a path from every vertex to every other vertex, the graph must be strongly connected (and hence also weakly connected). Also, we can count the in-degrees and out-degrees of the vertices by following this circuit; as the circuit passes through a vertex, it adds one to the count of both the in-degree (as it comes in) and the out-degree (as it leaves). Therefore the two degrees are equal for each vertex.

Conversely, suppose that the graph meets the conditions stated. Then we can proceed as in the proof of Theorem 1 and construct an Euler circuit.

18. For Exercises 18–23 we use the results of Exercises 16 and 17. This directed graph satisfies the condition of Exercise 17 but not that of Exercise 16. Therefore there is no Euler circuit. The Euler path must go from a to d. One such path is $a, b, d, b, c, d, c, a, d$.

20. The conditions of Exercise 16 are met, so there is an Euler circuit, which is perforce also an Euler path. One such path is $a, d, b, d, e, b, e, c, b, a$.

22. This directed graph satisfies the condition of Exercise 17 but not that of Exercise 16. Therefore there is no Euler circuit. The Euler path must go from c to b. One such path is $c, e, b, d, c, b, f, d, e, f, e, a, f, a, b, c, b$. (There is no Euler circuit, however, since the conditions of Exercise 22 are not met.)

24. The algorithm is identical to Algorithm 1.

26. **a)** The degrees of the vertices $(n-1)$ are even if and only if n is odd. Therefore there is an Euler circuit if and only if n is odd (and greater than 1, of course).
b) For all $n \geq 3$, clearly C_n has an Euler circuit, namely itself.
c) Since the degrees of the vertices around the rim are all odd, no wheel has an Euler circuit.
d) The degrees of the vertices are all n. Therefore there is an Euler circuit if and only if n is even (and greater than 0, of course).

28. **a)** Since the degrees of the vertices are all m and n, this graph has an Euler circuit if and only if both of the positive integers m and n are even.
b) All the graphs listed in part **(a)** have an Euler circuit, which is also an Euler path. In addition, the graphs $K_{n,2}$ for odd n have exactly 2 vertices of odd degree, so they have an Euler path but not an Euler circuit. Also, $K_{1,1}$ obviously has an Euler path. All other complete bipartite graphs have too many vertices of odd degree.

30. This graph can have no Hamilton circuit because of the cut edge $\{c, f\}$. Every simple circuit must be confined to one of the two components obtained by deleting this edge.

32. As in Exercise 30, the cut edge ($\{e, f\}$ in this case) prevents a Hamilton circuit.

34. This graph has no Hamilton circuit. If it did, then certainly the circuit would have to contain edges $\{d, a\}$ and $\{a, b\}$, since these are the only edges incident to vertex a. By the same reasoning, the circuit would have to contain the other six edges around the outside of the figure. These eight edges already complete a circuit, and this circuit omits the nine vertices on the inside. Therefore there is no Hamilton circuit.

36. It is easy to find a Hamilton circuit here, such as $a, d, g, h, i, f, c, e, b$, and back to a.

38. This graph has the Hamilton path a, b, c, d, e.

40. This graph has no Hamilton path. There are three vertices of degree 1; each of them would have to be an end vertex of every Hamilton path. Since a path has only 2 ends, this is impossible.

42. It is easy to find the Hamilton path d, c, a, b, e here.

44. a) Obviously K_n has a Hamilton circuit for all $n \geq 3$ but not for $n \leq 2$.

b) Obviously C_n has a Hamilton circuit for all $n \geq 3$.

c) A Hamilton circuit for C_n can easily be extended to one for W_n by replacing one edge along the rim of the wheel by two edges, one going to the center and the other leading from the center. Therefore W_n has a Hamilton circuit for all $n \geq 3$.

d) This is Exercise 49; see the solution given for it.

46. We do the easy part first, showing that the graph obtained by deleting a vertex from the Petersen graph has a Hamilton circuit. By symmetry, it makes no difference which vertex we delete, so assume that it is vertex j. Then a Hamilton circuit in what remains is $a, e, d, i, g, b, c, h, f, a$. Now we show that the entire graph has no Hamilton circuit. Assume that a Hamilton circuit exists. Not all the edges around the outside can be used, so without loss of generality assume that $\{c, d\}$ is not used. Then $\{e, d\}$, $\{d, i\}$, $\{h, c\}$, and $\{b, c\}$ must all be used. If $\{a, f\}$ is not used, then $\{e, a\}$, $\{a, b\}$, $\{f, i\}$, and $\{f, h\}$ must be used, forming a premature circuit. Therefore $\{a, f\}$ is used. Without loss of generality we may assume that $\{e, a\}$ is also used, and $\{a, b\}$ is not used. Then $\{b, g\}$ is also used, and $\{e, j\}$ is not. But this requires $\{g, j\}$ and $\{h, j\}$ to be used, forming a premature circuit b, c, h, j, g, b. Hence no Hamilton circuit can exist in this graph.

48. We want to look only at odd n, since if n is even, then being at least $(n-1)/2$ is the same as being at least $n/2$, in which case Dirac's theorem would apply. One way to avoid having a Hamilton circuit is to have a cut vertex—a vertex whose removal disconnects the graph. The simplest example would be the "bow-tie" graph with five vertices (a, b, c, d, and e), where cut vertex c is adjacent to each of the other vertices, and the only other edges are ab and de. Every vertex has degree at least $(5-1)/2 = 2$, but there is no Hamilton circuit.

50. Let us begin at vertex a and walk toward vertex b. Then the circuit begins a, b, c. At this point we must choose among three edges to continue the circuit. If we choose edge $\{c, f\}$, then we will have disconnected the graph that remains, so we must not choose this edge. Suppose instead that the circuit continues with edge $\{c, d\}$. Then the entire circuit is forced to be a, b, c, d, e, c, f, a.

52. This proof is rather hard. See page 63 of *Graph Theory with Applications* by J. A. Bondy and U. S. R. Murty (American Elsevier, 1976).

54. An Euler path will cover every link, so it can be used to test the links. A Hamilton path will cover all the devices, so it can be used to test the devices.

56. We draw one vertex for each of the 9 squares on the board. We then draw an edge from a vertex to each vertex that can be reached by moving 2 units horizontally and 1 unit vertically or vice versa. The result is as shown.

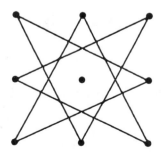

58. a) In a Hamilton path we need to visit each vertex once, moving along the edges. A knight's tour is precisely such a path, since we visit each square once, making legal moves.

b) This is the same as part **(a)**, except that a re-entrant tour must return to its starting point, just as a Hamilton circuit must return to its starting point.

60. In a 3×3 board, the middle vertex is isolated (see solution to Exercise 56). In other words, there is no knight move to or from the middle square. Thus there can clearly be no knight's tour. There is a tour of the rest of the squares, however, as the picture above shows.

62. Each square of the board can be thought of as a pair of integers (x, y). Let A be the set of squares for which $x + y$ is odd, and let B be the set of squares for which $x + y$ is even. This partitions the vertex set of the graph representing the legal moves of a knight on the board into two parts. Now every move of the knight changes $x + y$ by an odd number—either $1 + 2 = 3$, $2 - 1 = 1$, $1 - 2 = -1$, or $-1 - 2 = -3$. Therefore every edge in this graph joins a vertex in A to a vertex in B. Thus the graph is bipartite.

64. A little trial and error, loosely following the hint, produced the following solution. The numbers show the order in which the squares are to be traversed.

1	28	13	26	3	38	41	16
64	25	2	39	52	15	4	37
29	12	27	14	57	40	17	42
24	63	56	53	60	51	36	5
11	30	49	62	55	58	43	18
48	23	54	59	50	61	6	35
31	10	21	46	33	8	19	44
22	47	32	9	20	45	34	7

SECTION 8.6   Shortest-Path Problems

2. In the solution to Exercise 5 we find a shortest path. Its length is 7.

4. In the solution to Exercise 5 we find a shortest path. Its length is 16.

6. The solution to this problem is given in the solution to Exercise 7, where the paths themselves are found.

8. In theory, we can use Dijkstra's algorithm. In practice with graphs of this size and shape, we can tell by observation what the conceivable answers will be and find the one that produces the minimum total length by inspection.

a) The direct path is the shortest.

b) The path via Chicago only is the shortest.

c) The path via Atlanta and Chicago is the shortest.

d) The path via Atlanta, Chicago and Denver is the shortest.

10. The comments for Exercise 8 apply.

   a) The direct flight is the cheapest.

   b) The path via New York is the cheapest.

   c) The path via New York and Chicago is the cheapest.

   d) The path via New York is the cheapest.

12. The comments for Exercise 8 apply.

   a) The path through Chicago is the fastest.

   b) The path via Chicago is the fastest.

   c) The path via Denver (or the path via Los Angeles) is the fastest.

   d) The path via Dallas (or the path via Chicago) is the fastest.

14. Here we simply assign the weight of 1 to each edge.

16. We need to keep track of the vertex from which a shortest path known so far comes, as well as the length of that path. Thus we add an array P to the algorithm, where $P(v)$ is the previous vertex in the best known path to v. We modify Algorithm 1 so that when L is updated by the statement $L(v) := L(u) + w(u, v)$, we also set $P(v) := u$. Once the **while** loop has terminated, we can obtain a shortest path from a to z *in reverse* by starting with z and following the pointers in P. Thus the path in reverse is z, $P(z)$, $P(P(z))$, ..., $P(P(\cdots P(z) \cdots)) = a$.

18. The shortest path need not be unique. For example, we could have a graph with vertices a, b, c, and d, with edges $\{a, b\}$ of weight 3, $\{b, c\}$ of weight 7, $\{a, d\}$ of weight 4, and $\{d, c\}$ of weight 6. There are two shortest paths from a to c.

20. We give an ad hoc analysis. Recall that a simple path cannot use any edge more than once. Furthermore, since the path must use an odd number of edges incident to a and an odd number of edges incident to z, the path must omit at least two edges, one at each end. The best we could hope for, then, in trying for a path of maximum length, is that the path leaves out the shortest such edges—$\{a, c\}$ and $\{e, z\}$. If the path leaves out these two edges, then it must also leave out one more edge incident to c, since the path must use an even number of the three remaining edges incident to c. The best we could hope for is that the path omits the two aforementioned edges and edge $\{b, c\}$. Since $2 + 1 < 4$, this is better than the other possibility, namely omitting edge $\{a, b\}$ instead of edge $\{a, c\}$. Finally, we find a simple path omitting only these three edges, namely a, b, d, c, e, d, z, with length 35, and thus we conclude that it is a longest simple path from a to z.

   A similar argument shows that the longest simple path from c to z is c, a, b, d, c, e, d, z

22. It follows by induction on i that after the ith pass through the triply nested **for** loop in the pseudocode, $d(v_j, v_k)$ gives, for each j and k, the shortest distance between v_j and v_k using only intermediate vertices v_m for $m \leq i$. Therefore after the final path, we have obtained the shortest distance.

24. Consider the graph with vertices a, b, and z, where the weight of $\{a, z\}$ is 2, the weight of $\{a, b\}$ is 3, and the weight of $\{b, z\}$ is -2. Then Dijkstra's algorithm will decide that $L(z) = 2$ and stop, whereas the path a, b, z is shorter (has length 1).

26. The following table shows the twelve different Hamilton circuits and their weights:

Circuit	Weight
a-b-c-d-e-a	$3 + 10 + 6 + 1 + 7 = 27$
a-b-c-e-d-a	$3 + 10 + 5 + 1 + 4 = 23$
a-b-d-c-e-a	$3 + 9 + 6 + 5 + 7 = 30$
a-b-d-e-c-a	$3 + 9 + 1 + 5 + 8 = 26$
a-b-e-c-d-a	$3 + 2 + 5 + 6 + 4 = 20$
a-b-e-d-c-a	$3 + 2 + 1 + 6 + 8 = 20$
a-c-b-d-e-a	$8 + 10 + 9 + 1 + 7 = 35$
a-c-b-e-d-a	$8 + 10 + 2 + 1 + 4 = 25$
a-c-d-b-e-a	$8 + 6 + 9 + 2 + 7 = 32$
a-c-e-b-d-a	$8 + 5 + 2 + 9 + 4 = 28$
a-d-b-c-e-a	$4 + 9 + 10 + 5 + 7 = 35$
a-d-c-b-e-a	$4 + 6 + 10 + 2 + 7 = 29$

Thus we see that the circuits a-b-e-c-d-a and a-b-e-d-c-a (or the same circuits starting at some other point but traversing the vertices in the same or exactly opposite order) are the ones with minimum total weight.

28. The following table shows the twelve different Hamilton circuits and their weights, where we abbreviate the cities with the beginning letter of their name, except that New Orleans is O:

Circuit	Weight
S-B-N-O-P-S	$409 + 109 + 229 + 309 + 119 = 1175$
S-B-N-P-O-S	$409 + 109 + 319 + 309 + 429 = 1575$
S-B-O-N-P-S	$409 + 239 + 229 + 319 + 119 = 1315$
S-B-O-P-N-S	$409 + 239 + 309 + 319 + 389 = 1665$
S-B-P-N-O-S	$409 + 379 + 319 + 229 + 429 = 1765$
S-B-P-O-N-S	$409 + 379 + 309 + 229 + 389 = 1715$
S-N-B-O-P-S	$389 + 109 + 239 + 309 + 119 = 1165$
S-N-B-P-O-S	$389 + 109 + 379 + 309 + 429 = 1615$
S-N-O-B-P-S	$389 + 229 + 239 + 379 + 119 = 1355$
S-N-P-B-O-S	$389 + 319 + 379 + 239 + 429 = 1755$
S-O-B-N-P-S	$429 + 239 + 109 + 319 + 119 = 1215$
S-O-N-B-P-S	$429 + 229 + 109 + 379 + 119 = 1265$

As a check of our arithmetic, we can compute the total weight (price) of all the trips (it comes to 17580) and check that it is equal to 6 times the sum of the weights (which here is 2930), since each edge appears in six paths (and sure enough, $17580 = 6 \cdot 2930$). We see that the circuit S-N-B-O-P-S (or the same circuit starting at some other point but traversing the vertices in the same or exactly opposite order) is the one with minimum total weight, 1165.

30. We follow the hint. Let G be our original weighted graph, and construct a new graph G' as follows. The vertices and edges of G' are the same as the vertices and edges of G. For each pair of vertices u and v in G, use an algorithm such as Dijkstra's algorithm to find a shortest path (i.e., one of minimum total weight) between u and v. Record this path in a table, and assign to the edge $\{u, v\}$ in G' the weight of this path. It is now clear that finding the circuit of minimum total weight in G' that visits each vertex exactly once is equivalent to finding the circuit of minimum total weight in G that visits each vertex at least once.

SECTION 8.7   Planar Graphs

2. For convenience we label the vertices a, b, c, d, e, starting with the vertex in the lower left corner and proceeding clockwise around the outside of the figure as drawn in the exercise. If we move vertex d down, then the crossings can be avoided.

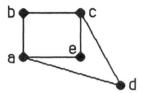

4. For convenience we label the vertices a, b, c, d, e, starting with the vertex in the lower left corner and proceeding clockwise around the outside of the figure as drawn in the exercise. If we move vertex b far to the right, and squeeze vertices d and e in a little, then we can avoid crossings.

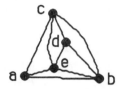

6. This graph is easily untangled and drawn in the following planar representation.

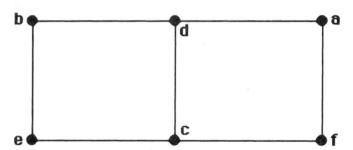

8. If one has access to software such as Geometer's Sketchpad, then this problem can be solved by drawing the graph and moving the points around, trying to find a planar drawing. If we are unable to find one, then we look for a reason why—either a subgraph homeomorphic to K_5 or one homeomorphic to $K_{3,3}$ (always try the latter first). In this case we find that there is in fact an actual copy of $K_{3,3}$, with vertices a, c, and e in one set and b, d, and f in the other.

10. The argument is similar to the argument when v_3 is inside region R_2. In the case at hand the edges between v_3 and v_4 and between v_3 and v_5 separate R_1 into two subregions, R_{11} (bounded by v_1, v_4, v_3, and v_5) and R_{12} (bounded by v_2, v_4, v_3, and v_5). Now again there is no way to place vertex v_6 without forcing a crossing. If v_6 is in R_2, then there is no way to draw the edge $\{v_3, v_6\}$ without crossing another edge. If v_6 is in R_{11}, then the edge between v_2 and v_6 cannot be drawn; whereas if v_6 is in R_{12}, then the edge between v_1 and v_6 cannot be drawn.

12. Euler's formula says that $v - e + r = 2$. We are given $v = 8$, and from the fact that the sum of the degrees equals twice the number of edges, we deduce that $e = (3 \cdot 8)/2 = 12$. Therefore $r = 2 - v + e = 2 - 8 + 12 = 6$.

14. Euler's formula says that $v - e + r = 2$. We are given $e = 30$ and $r = 20$. Therefore $v = 2 - r + e = 2 - 20 + 30 = 12$.

16. A bipartite simple graph has no simple circuits of length three. Therefore the inequality follows from Corollary 3.

18. If we add $k-1$ edges, we can make the graph connected, create no new regions, and still avoid edge crossings. (We just add an edge from one vertex in one component, incident to the unbounded region, to one vertex in each of the other components.) For this new graph, Euler's formula tells us that $v-(e+k-1)+r=2$. This simplifies algebraically to $r=e-v+k+1$.

20. This graph is not homeomorphic to $K_{3,3}$, since by rerouting the edge between a and h we see that it is planar.

22. Replace each vertex of degree two and its incident edges by a single edge. Then the result is $K_{3,3}$: the parts are $\{a,e,i\}$ and $\{c,g,k\}$. Therefore this graph is homeomorphic to $K_{3,3}$.

24. This graph is nonplanar. If we delete the five curved edges outside the big pentagon, then the graph is homeomorphic to K_5. We can see this by replacing each vertex of degree 2 and its two edges by one edge.

26. If we follow the proof in Example 3, we see how to construct a planar representation of all of $K_{3,3}$ except for one edge. In particular, if we place vertex v_6 inside region R_{22} of Figure 7(b), then we can draw edges from v_6 to v_2 and v_3 with no crossings, and to v_1 with only one crossing. Furthermore, since $K_{3,3}$ is not planar, its crossing number cannot be 0. Hence its crossing number is 1.

28. First note that the Petersen graph with one edge removed is not planar; indeed, by Example 8, the Petersen graph with three mutually adjacent edges removed is not planar. Therefore the crossing number must be greater than 1. (If it were only 1, then removing the edge that crossed would give a planar drawing of the Petersen graph minus one edge.) The following figure shows a drawing with only two crossings. (This drawing was obtained by a little trial and error.) Therefore the crossing number must be 2. (In this figure, the vertices are labeled as in Figure 14(a).)

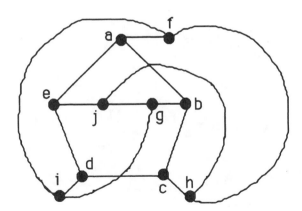

30. Since by Exercise 26 we know how to embed all but one edge of $K_{3,3}$ in one plane with no crossings, we can embed all of $K_{3,3}$ in two planes with no crossings simply by drawing the last edge in the second plane.

32. By Corollary 1 to Euler's formula, we know that in one plane we can draw without crossing at most $3v-6$ edges from a graph with v vertices. Therefore if a graph has v vertices and e edges, then it will require at least $e/(3v-6)$ planes in order to draw all the edges without crossing. Since the thickness is a whole number, it must be greater than or equal to the smallest integer at least this large, i.e., $\lceil e/(3v-6)\rceil$.

34. This is essentially the same as Exercise 32, using Corollary 3 in place of Corollary 1.

36. As in the solution to Exercise 37, we represent the torus by a rectangle. The figure below shows how K_5 is embedded without crossings. (The reader might try to embed K_6 or K_7 on a torus.)

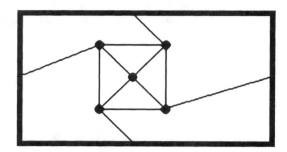

SECTION 8.8   Graph Coloring

2. We construct the dual as in Exercise 1.

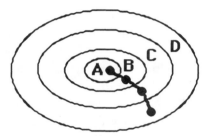

As in Exercise 1, the number of colors needed to color this map is the same as the number of colors needed to color the dual graph. Clearly two colors are necessary and sufficient: one for vertices (regions) A and C, and the other for B and D.

4. We construct the dual as in Exercise 1.

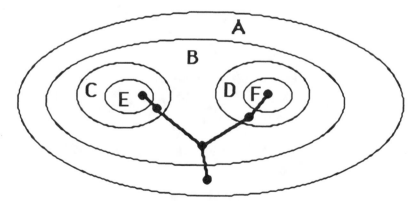

As in Exercise 1, the number of colors needed to color this map is the same as the number of colors needed to color the dual graph. Clearly two colors are necessary and sufficient: one for vertices (regions) A, C, and D, and the other for B, E, and F.

6. Since there is a triangle, at least 3 colors are needed. To show that 3 colors suffice, notice that we can color the vertices around the outside alternately using red and blue, and color vertex g green.

8. Since there is a triangle, at least 3 colors are needed. The coloring in which b and c are blue, a and f are red, and d and e are green shows that 3 colors suffice.

10. Since vertices b, c, h, and i form a K_4, at least 4 colors are required. A coloring using only 4 colors (and we can get this by trial and error, without much difficulty) is to let a and c be red; b, d, and f, blue; g and i, green; and e and h, yellow.

12. In Exercise 5 the chromatic number is 3, but if we remove vertex a, then the chromatic number will fall to 2. In Exercise 6 the chromatic number is 3, but if we remove vertex g, then the chromatic number will fall to 2. In Exercise 7 the chromatic number is 3, but if we remove vertex b, then the chromatic number will fall to 2. In Exercise 8 the chromatic number was shown to be 3. Even if we remove a vertex, at least one of the two triangles ace and bdf must remain, since they share no vertices. Therefore the smaller graph will still have chromatic number 3. In Exercise 9 the chromatic number is 2. Obviously it is not possible to reduce it to 1 by removing one vertex, since at least one edge will remain. In Exercise 10 the chromatic number was shown to be 4, and a coloring was provided. If we remove vertex h and recolor vertex e red, then we can eliminate color yellow from that solution. Therefore we will have reduced the chromatic number to 3. Finally, the graph in Exercise 11 will still have a triangle, no matter what vertex is removed, so we cannot lower its chromatic number below 3 by removing a vertex.

14. Since the map is planar, we know that four colors suffice. That four colors are necessary can be seen by looking at Kentucky. It is surrounded by Tennessee, Missouri, Illinois, Indiana, Ohio, West Virginia, and Virginia; furthermore the states in this list form a C_7, each one adjacent to the next. Therefore at least three colors are needed to color these seven states (see Exercise 16), and then a fourth is necessary for Kentucky.

16. Let the circuit be v_1, v_2, ..., v_n, v_1, where n is odd. Suppose that two colors (red and blue) sufficed to color the graph containing this circuit. Without loss of generality let the color of v_1 be red. Then v_2 must be blue, v_3 must be red, and so on, until finally v_n must be red (since n is odd). But this is a contradiction, since v_n is adjacent to v_1. Therefore at least three colors are needed.

18. We draw the graph in which two vertices (representing locations) are adjacent if the locations are within 150 miles of each other.

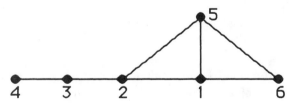

Clearly three colors are necessary and sufficient to color this graph, say red for vertices 4, 2, and 6; blue for 3 and 5; and yellow for 1. Thus three channels are necessary and sufficient.

20. We let the vertices of a graph be the animals, and we draw an edge between two vertices if the animals they represent cannot be in the same habitat because of their eating habits. A coloring of this graph gives an assignment of habitats (the colors are the habitats).

22. **a)** See Section 20 of *Introduction to Graph Theory*, second edition, by Robin J. Wilson (Academic Press, 1979), for a proof that the edge chromatic number of K_n is $n-1$ if n is even, and n if n is odd. The proof is nontrivial.

b) Let t be the larger of m and n. Since all the vertices in one part have degree t, it is clear that at least t colors are needed. That t colors suffice is less clear. See the reference given in part **(a)** for a proof that they do.

c) If n is even, then clearly we can alternate 2 colors around the cycle, so the edge chromatic number is 2. If n is odd, then by the same reasoning the edge chromatic number cannot be 2 and yet is equal to 3.

d) The edges incident to the middle of the wheel must be painted different colors, so n colors are necessary. Furthermore, it is easy to find a free color for each edge along the rim, so n is sufficient as well.

24. Since each of the n vertices in this subgraph must have a different color, the chromatic number must be at least n.

26. Since there are no edges within a part, we can color the vertices in one part red and the vertices in the other part blue. Therefore the chromatic number is at most 2. Since the graph is connected, there is at least one edge joining the parts, so the chromatic number must be at least 2. Thus the chromatic number is exactly 2.

28. Our pseudocode is as follows. The comments should explain how it implements the algorithm.

```
procedure coloring(G : simple graph)
{assume that the vertices are labeled 1, 2, . . . , n so that
   deg(1) ≥ deg(2) ≥ · · · ≥ deg(n) }
for i := 1 to n
       c(i) := 0  {originally no vertices are colored}
count := 0  {no vertices colored yet}
color := 1  {try the first color}
while count < n  {there are still vertices to be colored}
begin
       for i := 1 to n  {try to color vertex i with color color}
           if c(i) = 0  {vertex i is not yet colored} then
               begin
                   c(i) := color  {assume we can do it until we find out otherwise}
                   for j := 1 to n
                       if {i, j} is an edge and c(j) = color
                           then c(i) := 0  {we found out otherwise}
                   if c(i) = color
                       then count := count + 1  {the new coloring of i worked}
               end
       color := color + 1  {we have to go on to the next color}
end  {the coloring is complete}
```

30. First let us prove some general results. In a complete graph, each vertex is adjacent to every other vertex, so each vertex must get its own set of k different colors. Therefore if there are n vertices, kn colors are clearly necessary and sufficient. Thus $\chi_k(K_n) = kn$. In a bipartite graph, every vertex in one part can get the same set of k colors, and every vertex in the other part can get the same set of k colors (a disjoint set from the colors assigned to the vertices in the first part). Therefore $2k$ colors are sufficient, and clearly $2k$ colors are required if there is at least one edge. Let us now look at the specific graphs.

a) For this complete graph situation we have $k = 2$ and $n = 3$, so $2 \cdot 3 = 6$ colors are necessary and sufficient.

b) As in part (**a**), the answer is kn, which here is $2 \cdot 4 = 8$.

c) Call the vertex in the middle of the wheel m, and call the vertices around the rim, in order, a, b, c, and d. Since m, a, and b form a triangle, we need at least 6 colors. Assign colors 1 and 2 to m, 3 and 4 to a, and 5 and 6 to b. Then we can also assign 3 and 4 to c, and 5 and 6 to d, completing a 2-tuple coloring with 6 colors. Therefore $\chi_2(W_4) = 6$.

d) First we show that 4 colors are not sufficient. If we had only colors 1 through 4, then as we went around the cycle we would have to assign, say, 1 and 2 to the first vertex, 3 and 4 to the second, 1 and 2 to the third, and 3 and 4 to the fourth. This gives us no colors for the final vertex. To see that 5 colors are sufficient, we simply give the coloring: In order around the cycle the colors are $\{1,2\}$, $\{3,4\}$, $\{1,5\}$, $\{2,4\}$, and $\{3,5\}$. Therefore $\chi_2(C_5) = 5$.

e) By our general result on bipartite graphs, the answer is $2k = 2 \cdot 2 = 4$.

f) By our general result on complete graphs, the answer is $kn = 3 \cdot 5 = 15$.

g) We claim that the answer is 8. To see that eight colors suffice, we can color the vertices as follows in order around the cycle: $\{1,2,3\}$, $\{4,5,6\}$, $\{1,2,7\}$, $\{3,6,8\}$, and $\{4,5,7\}$. Showing that seven colors are not sufficient is harder. Assume that a coloring with seven colors exists. Without loss of generality, color the first vertex $\{1,2,3\}$ and color the second vertex $\{4,5,6\}$. If the third vertex is colored $\{1,2,3\}$, then the fourth and fifth vertices would need to use six colors different from 1, 2, and 3, for a total of nine colors. Therefore without loss of generality, assume that the third vertex is colored $\{1,2,7\}$. But now the other two vertices cannot have colors 1 or 2, and they must have six different colors, so eight colors would be required in all. This is a contradiction, so there is in fact no coloring with just seven colors.

h) By our general result on bipartite graphs, the answer is $2k = 2 \cdot 3 = 6$.

32. As we observed in the solution to Exercise 30, the answer is $2k$ if G has at least one edge (and it is clearly k if G has no edges, since every vertex can get the same colors).

34. We use induction on the number of vertices of the graph. Every graph with six or fewer vertices can be colored with six or fewer colors, since each vertex can get a different color. That takes care of the basis case(s). So we assume that all graphs with k vertices can be 6-colored and consider a graph G with $k+1$ vertices. By Corollary 2 in Section 8.7, G has a vertex v with degree at most 5. Remove v to form the graph G'. Since G' has only k vertices, we 6-color it by the inductive hypothesis. Now we can 6-color G by assigning to v a color not used by any of its five or fewer neighbors. This completes the inductive step, and the theorem is proved.

SUPPLEMENTARY EXERCISES FOR CHAPTER 8

2. A graph must be nonempty, so the subgraph can have 1, 2, or 3 vertices. If it has 1 vertex, then it has no edges, so there is clearly just one possibility, K_1. If the subgraph has 2 vertices, then it can have no edges or the one edge joining these two vertices; this gives 2 subgraphs. Finally, if all three vertices are in the subgraph, then the graph can contain no edges, one edge (and we get isomorphic graphs, no matter which edge is used), two edges (ditto), or all three edges. This gives 4 different subgraphs with 3 vertices. Therefore the answer is $1 + 2 + 4 = 7$.

4. Each vertex in the first graph has degree 4. This statement is not true for the second graph. Therefore the graphs cannot be isomorphic. (In fact, the number of edges is different.)

6. We draw these graphs by putting the points in each part close together in clumps, and joining all vertices in different clumps.

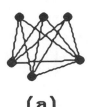
(a)

(b)

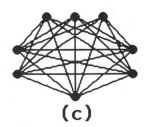
(c)

8. a) The statement is true, and we can prove it using the pigeonhole principle. Suppose that the graph has n vertices. The degrees have to be numbers from 0 to $n-1$, inclusive, a total of n possibilities. Now if there is a vertex of degree $n-1$, then it is adjacent to every other vertex, and hence there can be no vertex of degree 0. Thus not all n of the possible degrees can be used. Therefore by the pigeonhole principle, some degree must occur twice.

b) The statement is false for multigraphs. As a simple example, let the multigraph have three vertices a, b, and c. Let there be one edge between a and b, and two edges between b and c. Then it is easy to see that the degrees of the vertices are 1, 3, and 2.

10. Since all the vertices in the subgraph are adjacent in K_n, they are adjacent in the subgraph, i.e., the subgraph is complete.

12. Some staring at the graph convinces us that there are no K_6's. There is one K_5, namely the clique *ceghi*. There are two K_4's not contained in this K_5, which therefore are cliques: *abce*, and *cdeg*. All the K_3's not contained in any of the cliques listed so far are also cliques. We find only *aef* and *efg*. All the edges are in at least one of the cliques listed so far (and there are no isolated vertices), so we are done.

14. Since e is adjacent to every other vertex, the (unique) minimum dominating set is $\{e\}$.

16. It is easy to check that the set $\{c, e, j, l\}$ is dominating. We must show that no set with only three vertices is dominating. Suppose that there were such a set. First suppose that the vertex f is to be included. Then at least two more vertices are needed to take care of vertices a and i, unless vertex e is chosen. If vertex e is not chosen, therefore, the dominating set must have more than three vertices, since no pair of vertices covering a and i can cover d, for instance. On the other hand, if e is chosen, then since no single vertex covers c and l, again at least four vertices are required. Thus we may assume that f (and by symmetry g as well) is not in the dominating set with only three elements. This means that we need to find three vertices from the 10-cycle $a, b, c, d, h, l, k, j, i, e, a$ that cover all ten of these vertices. This is impossible, since each vertex covers only three, and $3 \cdot 3 < 10$. Therefore we conclude that there is no dominating set with only three vertices.

18. If G is the graph representing the $n \times n$ chessboard, then a minimum dominating set for G corresponds exactly to a set of squares on which we may place the minimum number of queens to control the board.

20. This isomorphism need not hold. For the simplest counterexample, let G_1, G_2, and H_1 each be the graph consisting of the single vertex v, and let H_2 be the graph consisting of the single vertex w. Then of course G_1 and H_1 are isomorphic, as are G_2 and H_2. But $G_1 \cup G_2$ is a graph with one vertex, and $H_1 \cup H_2$ is a graph with two vertices.

22. Since a 1 in the adjacency matrix indicates the presence of an edge and a 0 the absence of an edge, to obtain the adjacency matrix for $\overline{G}$ we change each 1 in the adjacency matrix for G to a 0, and we change each 0 not on the main diagonal to a 1 (we do not want to introduce loops).

24. a) If no degree is greater than 2, then the graph must consist either of the 5-cycle or a path with no vertices repeated. Therefore there are just two graphs.

b) Certainly every graph besides K_5 that contains K_4 as a subgraph will have chromatic number 4. There are 3 such graphs, since the vertex not in "the" K_4 can be adjacent to one, two or three of the other four vertices. A little further trial and error will convince one that there are no other graphs meeting these conditions, so the answer is 3.

c) Since every proper subgraph of K_5 is planar, there is only one such graph, namely K_5.

26. This follows from the transitivity of the "is isomorphic to" relation and Exercise 65 in Section 8.3. If G is self-converse, then G is isomorphic to G^c. Since H is isomorphic to G, H^c is also isomorphic to G^c. Stringing together these isomorphisms, we see that H is isomorphic to H^c, as desired.

28. This graph is not orientable because of the cut edge $\{c, d\}$, exactly as in Exercise 27.

30. Since we need the city to be strongly connected, we need to find an orientation of the undirected graph representing the city's streets, where the edges represent streets and the vertices represent intersections.

32. There are $C(n, 2) = n(n-1)/2$ edges in a tournament. We must decide how to orient each one, and there are 2 ways to do this for each edge. Therefore the answer is $2^{n(n-1)/2}$. Note that we have not answered the question of how many nonisomorphic tournaments there are—that is much harder.

34. We proceed by induction on n, the number of vertices in the tournament. The base case is $n = 2$, and the single edge is the Hamilton path. Now let G be a tournament with $n + 1$ vertices. Delete one vertex, say v, and find (by the inductive hypothesis) a Hamilton path $v_1, v_2, \ldots, v_n$ in the tournament that remains. Now if (v_n, v) is an edge of G, then we have the Hamilton path $v_1, v_2, \ldots, v_n, v$; similarly if (v, v_1) is an edge of G, then we have the Hamilton path $v, v_1, v_2, \ldots, v_n$. Otherwise, there must exist a smallest i such that (v_i, v) and (v, v_{i+1}) are edges of G. We can then splice v into the previous path to obtain the Hamilton path $v_1, v_2, \ldots, v_i, v, v_{i+1}, \ldots, v_n$.

36. We follow the hint, arbitrarily pairing the vertices of odd degree and adding an extra edge joining the vertices in each pair. The resulting multigraph has all vertices of even degree, and so it has an Euler circuit. If we delete the new edges, then this circuit is split into k paths. Since no two of the added edges were adjacent, each path is nonempty. The edges and vertices in each of these paths constitute a subgraph, and these subgraphs constitute the desired collection.

38. **a)** The diameter is clearly 1, since the maximum distance between two vertices is 1. The radius is also 1, with any vertex serving as the center.

b) The diameter is clearly 2, since vertices in the same part are not adjacent, but no pair of vertices are at a distance greater than 2. Similarly, the radius is 2, with any vertex serving as the center.

c) Vertices at diagonally opposite corners of the cube are a distance 3 from each other, and this is the worst case, so the diameter is 3. By symmetry we can take any vertex as the center, so it is clear that the radius is also 3.

d) Vertices at opposite corners of the hexagon are a distance 3 from each other, and this is the worst case, so the diameter is 3. By symmetry we can take any vertex as the center, so it is clear that the radius is also 3. (Despite the appearances in this exercise, it is not always the case that the radius equals the diameter; for example, $K_{1,n}$ has radius 1 and diameter 2.)

40. Suppose that we follow the given circuit through the multigraph, but instead of using edges more than once, we put in a new parallel edge whenever needed. The result is an Euler circuit through a larger multigraph. If we added new parallel edges in only $m - 1$ or fewer places in this process, then we have modified at most $2(m - 1)$ vertex degrees. This means that there are at least $2m - 2(m - 1) = 2$ vertices of odd degree remaining, which is impossible in a multigraph with an Euler circuit. Therefore we must have added new edges in at least m places, which means the circuit must have used at least m edges more than once.

42. We assume that only simple paths are of interest here. There may be no such path, so no such algorithm is possible. If we want an algorithm that looks for such a path and either finds one or determines that none exists, we can proceed as follows. First we use Dijkstra's algorithm (or some other algorithm) to find a shortest path from a to z (the given vertices). Then for each edge e in that path (one at a time), we delete e from the graph and find a shortest path between a and z in the graph that remains, or determine that no such path exists (again using, say, Dijkstra's algorithm). The second shortest path from a to z is a path of minimum length among all the paths so found, or does not exist if no such paths are found.

44. If we want a shortest path from a to z that passes through m, then clearly we need to find a shortest path from a to m and a shortest path from m to z, and then concatenate them. Each of these paths can be found using Dijkstra's algorithm.

46. a) No two vertices are not adjacent, so the independence number is 1.

b) If n is even, then we can take every other vertex as our independent set, so the independence number is $n/2$. If n is odd, then this does not quite work, but clearly we can take every other vertex except for one vertex. In this case the independence number is $(n-1)/2$. We can state this answer succinctly as $\lfloor n/2 \rfloor$.

c) Since Q_n is a bipartite graph with 2^{n-1} vertices in each part, the independence number is at least 2^{n-1} (take one of the parts as the independent set). We prove that there can be no more than this many independent vertices by induction on n. It is trivial for $n = 1$. Assume the inductive hypothesis, and suppose that there are more than 2^n independent vertices in Q_{n+1}. Recall that Q_{n+1} contains two copies of Q_n in it (with each pair of corresponding points joined by an edge). By the pigeonhole principle, at least one of these Q_n's must contain more than $2^n/2 = 2^{n-1}$ independent vertices. This contradicts the inductive hypothesis. Thus Q_{n+1} has only 2^n independent vertices, as desired.

d) The independence number is clearly the larger of m and n; the independent set to take is the part with this number of vertices.

48. In order to prove this statement it is sufficient to find a coloring with $v - i + 1$ colors. We color the graph as follows. Let S be an independent set with i vertices. Color each vertex of S with color $v - i + 1$. Color each of the other $v - i$ vertices a different color.

50. a) Obviously adding edges can only help in making the graph connected, so this property is monotone increasing. It is not monotone decreasing, because by removing edges one can disconnect a connected graph.

b) This is dual to part (a); the property is monotone decreasing. To see this, note that removing edges from a nonconnected graph cannot possibly make it connected, while adding edges certainly can.

c) This property is neither monotone increasing nor monotone decreasing. We need to provide examples to verify this. Consider the graph C_4, a square. It has an Euler circuit. However, if we add one edge or remove one edge, then the resulting graph will no longer have an Euler circuit.

d) This property is monotone increasing (since the extra edges do not interfere with the Hamilton circuit already there) but not monotone decreasing (e.g., start with a cycle).

e) This property is monotone decreasing. If a graph can be drawn in the plane, then clearly each of its subgraphs can also be drawn in the plane (just get out your eraser!). The property is not monotone increasing; for example, adding the missing edge to the complete graph on five vertices minus an edge changes the graph from being planar to being nonplanar.

f) This property is neither monotone increasing nor monotone decreasing. It is easy to find examples in which adding edges increases the chromatic number and removing them decreases it (e.g., start with C_5).

g) As in part (f), adding edges can easily decrease the radius and removing them can easily increase it, so this property is neither monotone increasing nor monotone decreasing. For example, C_7 has radius three, but adding enough edges to make K_7 reduces the radius to 1, and removing enough edges to disconnect the graph renders the radius infinite.

h) As in part (g), this is neither monotone increasing nor monotone decreasing.

52. Suppose that G is a graph on n vertices randomly generated using edge probability p, and G' is a graph on n vertices randomly generated using edge probability p', where $p < p'$. Recall that this means that for G we go through all pairs of vertices and independently put an edge between them with probability p; and similarly for G'. We must show that G is no more likely to have property P than G' is. To see this, we will imagine a different way of forming G. First we generate a random graph G' using edge probability p'; then we go through the edges that are present, and independently erase each of them with probability $1 - (p/p')$. Clearly, for an edge to end up in G, it must first get generated and then not get erased, which has probability $p' \cdot (p/p') = p$; therefore this is a valid way to generate G. Now whenever G has property P, then so does G', since P is monotone increasing. Thus the probability that G has property P is no greater than the probability that G' does; in fact it will usually be less, since once a G' having property P is generated, it is possible that it will lose the property as edges are erased.

CHAPTER 9
Trees

SECTION 9.1   Introduction to Trees

2. a) This is a tree since it is connected and has no simple circuits.

b) This is a tree since it is connected and has no simple circuits.

c) This is not a tree, since it is not connected.

d) This is a tree since it is connected and has no simple circuits.

e) This is not a tree, since it has a simple circuit.

f) This is a tree since it is connected and has no simple circuits.

4. a) Vertex a is the root, since it is drawn at the top.

b) The internal vertices are the vertices with children, namely a, b, d, e, g, h, i, and o.

c) The leaves are the vertices without children, namely c, f, j, k, l, m, n, p, q, r, and s.

d) The children of j are the vertices adjacent to j and below j. There are no such vertices, so there are no children.

e) The parent of h is the vertex adjacent to h and above h, namely d.

f) Vertex o has only one sibling, namely p, which is the other child of o's parent, i.

g) The ancestors of m are all the vertices on the unique simple path from m back to the root, namely g, b, and a.

h) The descendants of b are all the vertices that have b as an ancestor, namely e, f, g, j, k, l, and m.

6. This is not a full m-ary tree for any m. It is an m-ary tree for all $m \geq 3$, since each vertex has at most 3 children, but since some vertices have 3 children, while others have 1 or 2, it is not full for any m.

8. We can easily determine the levels from the drawing. The root a is at level 0. The vertices in the row below a are at level 1, namely b, c, and d. The vertices below that, namely e through i (in alphabetical order), are at level 2. Similarly j through p are at level 3, and q, r, and s are at level 4.

10. We describe the answers, rather than actually drawing pictures.

a) The subtree rooted at a is the entire tree, since a is the root.

b) The subtree rooted at c consists of just the vertex c.

c) The subtree rooted at e consists of e, j, and k, and the edges ej and ek.

12. We find the answer by carefully enumerating these trees, i.e., drawing a full set of nonisomorphic trees. One way to organize this work so as to avoid leaving any trees out or counting the same tree (up to isomorphism) more than once is to list the trees by the length of their longest simple path (or longest simple path from the root in the case of rooted trees).

a) There are two trees with four vertices, namely $K_{1,3}$ and the simple path of length 3. See the first two trees below.

b) The longest path from the root can have length 1, 2 or 3. There is only one tree with longest path of length 1 (the other three vertices are at level 1), and only one with longest path of length 3. If the longest path has length 2, then the fourth vertex (after using three vertices to draw this path) can be "attached" to either the root or the vertex at level 1, giving us two nonisomorphic trees. Thus there are a total of four nonisomorphic rooted trees on 4 vertices, as shown below.

14. There are two things to prove. First suppose that T is a tree. By definition it is connected, so we need to show that the deletion of any of its edges produces a graph that is not connected. Let $\{x, y\}$ be an edge of T, and note that $x \neq y$. Now T with $\{x, y\}$ deleted has no path from x to y, since there was only one simple path from x to y in T, and the edge itself was it. (We use Theorem 1 here, as well as the fact that if there is a path from a vertex u to another vertex v, then there is a simple path from u to v by Theorem 1 in Section 8.4.) Therefore the graph with $\{x, y\}$ deleted is not connected.

Conversely, suppose that a simple connected graph T satisfies the condition that the removal of any edge will disconnect it. We must show that T is a tree. If not, then T has a simple circuit, say $x_1, x_2, \ldots, x_r, x_1$. If we delete edge $\{x_r, x_1\}$ from T, then the graph will remain connected, since wherever the deleted edge was used in forming paths between vertices we can instead use the rest of the circuit: $x_1, x_2, \ldots, x_r$ or its reverse, depending on which direction we need to go. This is a contradiction to the condition. Therefore our assumption was wrong, and T is a tree.

16. If both m and n are at least 2, then clearly there is a simple circuit of length 4 in $K_{m,n}$. On the other hand, $K_{m,1}$ is clearly a tree (as is $K_{1,n}$). Thus we conclude that $K_{m,n}$ is a tree if and only if $m = 1$ or $n = 1$.

18. By Theorem 4(ii), the answer is $mi + 1 = 5 \cdot 100 + 1 = 501$.

20. By Theorem 4(i), the answer is $[(m - 1)n + 1]/m = (2 \cdot 100 + 1)/3 = 67$.

22. The model here is a full 5-ary tree. We are told that there are 10,000 internal vertices (these represent the people who send out the letter). By Theorem 4(ii) we see that $n = mi + 1 = 5 \cdot 10000 + 1 = 50,001$. Everyone but the root receives the letter, so we conclude that 50,000 people receive the letter. There are $50001 - 10000 = 40,001$ leaves in the tree, so that is the number of people who receive the letter but do not send it out.

24. Such a tree does exist. By Theorem 4(iii), we note that such a tree must have $i = 75/(m-1)$ internal vertices. This has to be a whole number, so $m - 1$ must divide 75. This is possible, for example, if $m = 6$, so let us try it. A complete 6-ary tree (see preamble to Exercise 27) of height 2 would have 36 leaves. We therefore need to add 40 leaves. This can be accomplished by changing 8 vertices at level 2 to internal vertices; each such change adds 5 leaves to the tree (6 new leaves at level 3, less the one leaf at level 5 that has been changed to an internal vertex). We will not show a picture of this tree, but just summarize its appearance. The root has 6 children, each of which has 6 children, giving 36 vertices at level 2. Of these, 28 are leaves, and each of the remaining 8 vertices at level 2 has 6 children, living at level 3, for a total of 48 leaves at level 3. The total number of leaves is therefore $28 + 48 = 76$, as desired.

26. By Theorem 4(iii), we note that such a tree must have $i = 80/(m-1)$ internal vertices. This has to be a whole number, so $m - 1$ must divide 80. By enumerating the divisors of 80, we see that m can equal 2, 3, 5, 6, 9, 11, 17, 21, 41, or 81. Some of these are incompatible with the height requirements, however.

a) Since the height is 4, we cannot have $m = 2$, since that will give us at most $1 + 2 + 4 + 8 + 16 = 31$ vertices. Any of the larger values of m shown above, up to 21, allows us to form a tree with 81 leaves and height 4. In each case we could get m^4 leaves if we made all vertices at levels smaller than 4 internal; and we can get as few as $4(m-1) + 1$ leaves by putting only one internal vertex at each such level. We can get 81 leaves in the former case by taking $m = 3$; on the other hand, if $m > 21$, then we would be forced to have more than 81 leaves. Therefore the bounds on m are $3 \le m \le 21$ (with m also restricted to being in the list above).

b) If T must be balanced, then the smallest possible number of leaves is obtained when level 3 has only one internal vertex and $m^3 - 1$ leaves, giving a total of $m^3 - 1 + m$ leaves in T. Again, the maximum number of leaves will be m^4. With these restriction, we see that $m = 5$ is already too big, since this would require at least $5^3 - 1 + 5 = 129$ leaves. Therefore the only possibility is $m = 3$.

28. This tree has 1 vertex at level 0, m vertices at level 1, m^2 vertices at level 2, ..., m^h vertices at level h. Therefore it has

$$1 + m + m^2 + \cdots + m^h = \frac{m^{h+1} - 1}{m - 1}$$

vertices in all. The vertices at level h are the only leaves, so it has m^h leaves.

30. (We assume $m \ge 2$.) First we delete all the vertices at level h; there is at least one such vertex, and they are all leaves. The result must be a complete m-ary tree of height $h - 1$. By the result of Exercise 28, this tree has m^{h-1} leaves. In the original tree, then, there are more than this many leaves, since every internal vertex at level $h - 1$ (which counts as a leaf in our reduced tree) spawns at least two leaves at level h.

32. The root of the tree represents the entire book. The vertices at level 1 represent the chapters—each chapter is a chapter of (read "child of") the book. The vertices at level 2 represent the sections (the parent of each such vertex is the chapter in which the section resides). Similarly the vertices at level 3 are the subsections.

34. **a)** The parent of a vertex is that vertex's boss.

b) The child of a vertex is an immediate subordinate of that vertex (one he or she directly supervises).

c) The sibling of a vertex is a coworker with the same boss.

d) The ancestors of a vertex are that vertex's boss, his/her boss's boss, etc.

e) The descendants of a vertex are all the people that that vertex ultimately supervises (directly or indirectly).

f) The level of a vertex is the number of levels away from the top of the organization that vertex is.

g) The height of the tree is the depth of the structure.

36. **a)** We simply add one more row to the tree in Figure 12, obtaining the following tree.

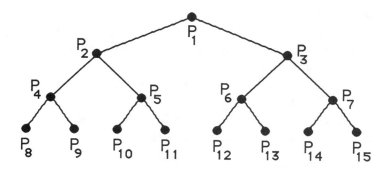

b) During the first step we use the bottom row of the network to add $x_1 + x_2$, $x_3 + x_4$, $x_5 + x_6$, ..., $x_{15} + x_{16}$. During the second step we use the next row up to add the results of the computations from the first step, namely $(x_1 + x_2) + (x_3 + x_4)$, $(x_5 + x_6) + (x_7 + x_8)$, ..., $(x_{13} + x_{14}) + (x_{15} + x_{16})$. The third step uses the sums obtained in the second, and the two processors in the second row of the tree perform $(x_1 + x_2 + x_3 + x_4) + (x_5 + x_6 + x_7 + x_8)$ and $(x_9 + x_{10} + x_{11} + x_{12}) + (x_{13} + x_{14} + x_{15} + x_{16})$. Finally, during the fourth step the root processor adds these two quantities to obtain the desired sum.

38. For $n = 3$, there is only one tree to consider, the one that is a simple path of length 2. There are 3 choices for the label to put in the middle of the path, and once that choice is made, the labeled tree is determined up to isomorphism. Therefore there are 3 labeled trees with 3 vertices.

For $n = 4$, there are two structures the tree might have. If it is a simple path with length 3, then there are 12 different labelings; this follows from the fact that there are $P(4,4) = 4! = 24$ permutations of the integers from 1 to 4, but a permutation and its reverse lead to the same labeled tree. If the tree structure is $K_{1,3}$, then the only choice is which label to put on the vertex that is adjacent to the other three, so there are 4 such trees. Thus in all there are 16 labeled trees with 4 vertices.

In fact it is a theorem that the number of labeled trees with n vertices is n^{n-2} for all $n \geq 2$.

40. The eccentricity of vertex e is 3, and it is the only vertex with eccentricity this small. Therefore e is the only center.

42. Since the height of a tree is the maximum distance from the root to another vertex, this is clear from the definition of center.

44. We choose a root and color it red. Then we color all the vertices at odd levels blue and all the vertices at even levels red.

46. The number of vertices in the tree T_n satisfies the recurrence relation $v_n = v_{n-1} + v_{n-2} + 1$ (the "+1" is for the root), with $v_1 = v_2 = 1$. Thus the sequence begins 1, 1, 3, 5, 9, 15, 25, ... It is easy to prove by induction that $v_n = 2f_n - 1$, where f_n is the nth Fibonacci number. The number of leaves satisfies the recurrence relation $l_n = l_{n-1} + l_{n-2}$, with $l_1 = l_2 = 1$, so $l_n = f_n$. Since $i_n = v_n - l_n$, we have $i_n = f_n - 1$. Finally, it is clear that the height of the tree T_n is one more than the height of the tree T_{n-1} for $n \geq 3$, with the height of T_2 being 0. Therefore the height of T_n is $n - 2$ for all $n \geq 2$ (and of course the height of T_1 is 0).

48. Let T be a tree with n vertices, having height h. If there are any internal vertices in T at levels less than $h - 1$ that do not have two children, take a leaf at level h and move it to be such a missing child. This only lowers the average depth of a leaf in this tree, and since we are trying to prove a lower bound on the average depth, it suffices to prove the bound for the resulting tree. Repeat this process until there are no more internal vertices of this type. As a result, all the leaves are now at levels $h - 1$ and h. Now delete all vertices at level h. This changes the number of vertices by at most (one more than) a factor of two and so has no effect on a big-Omega estimate (it changes $\log n$ by at most 1). Now the tree is complete, and by Exercise 28 it has 2^{h-1} leaves, all at depth $h - 1$, where now $n = 2^h - 1$. The desired estimate follows.

SECTION 9.2   Applications of Trees

2. We make the first word the root. Since the second word follows the first in alphabetical order, we make it the right child of the root. Similarly the third word is the left child of the root. To place the next word, *ornithology*, we move right from the root, since it follows the root in alphabetical order, and then move left from *phrenology*, since it comes before that word. The rest of the tree is built in a similar manner.

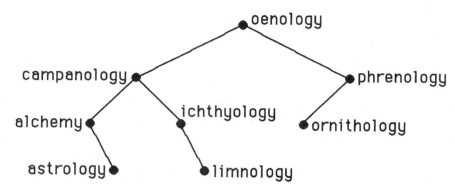

4. To find *palmistry*, which is not in the tree, we must compare it to the root (*oenology*), then the right child of the root (*phrenology*), and then the left child of that vertex (*ornithology*). At this point it is known that the word is not in the tree, since *ornithology* has no right child. Three comparisons were used. The remaining parts are similar, and the answer is 3 in each case.

6. Decision tree theory tells us that at least $\lceil \log_3 4 \rceil = 2$ weighings are needed. In fact we can easily achieve this result. We first compare the first two coins. If one is lighter, it is the counterfeit. If they balance, then we compare the other two coins, and the lighter one of these is the counterfeit.

8. Decision tree theory applied naively says that at least $\lceil \log_3 8 \rceil = 2$ weighings are needed, but in fact at least 3 weighings are needed. To see this, consider what the first weighing might accomplish. We can put one, two, or three coins in each pan for the first weighing (no other arrangement will yield any information at all). If we put one or two coins in each pan, and if the scale balances, then we only know that the counterfeit is among the six or four remaining coins. If we put three coins in each pan, and if the scale does not balance, then essentially all we know is that the counterfeit coin is among the six coins involved in the weighing. In every case we have narrowed the search to more than three coins, so one more weighing cannot find the counterfeit (there being only three possible outcomes of one more weighing).

Next we must show how to solve the problem with three weighings. Put two coins in each pan. If the scale balances, then the search is reduced to the other four coins. If the scale does not balance, then the counterfeit is among the four coins on the scale. In either case, we then apply the solution to Exercise 7 to find the counterfeit with two more weighings.

10. There are nine possible outcomes here: either there is no counterfeit, or else we need to name a coin (4 choices) and a type (lighter or heavier). Decision tree theory holds out hope that perhaps only two weighings are needed, but we claim that we cannot get by with only two. Suppose the first weighing involves two coins per pan. If the pans balance, then we know that there is no counterfeit, and subsequent weighings add no information. Therefore we have only six possible decisions (three for each of the other two outcomes of the first weighing) to differentiate among the other eight possible outcomes, and this is impossible. Therefore assume without loss of generality that the first weighing pits coin A against coin B. If the scale balances, then we know that the counterfeit is among the other two coins, if there is one. Now we must separate coins C and D on the next weighing if this weighing is to be decisive, so this weighing is equivalent to pitting C against D. If the scale does not balance, then we have not solved the problem.

We give a solution using three weighings. Weigh coin A against coin B. If they do not balance, then without loss of generality assume that coin A is lighter (the opposite result is handled similarly). Then weigh coin A against coin C. If they balance, then we know that coin B is the counterfeit and is heavy. If they do not balance, then we know that A is the counterfeit and is light. The remaining case is that in which coins A and B balance. At this point we compare C and D. If they balance, then we conclude that there is no counterfeit. If they do not balance, then one more weighing of, say, the lighter of these against A, solves the problem just as in the case in which A and B did not balance.

12. By Theorem 1 in this section, at least $\lceil \log 5! \rceil$ comparisons are needed. Since $\log_2 120 \approx 6.9$, at least seven comparisons are required. We can accomplish the sorting with seven comparisons as follows. Call the elements a, b, c, d, and e. First compare a and b; and compare c and d. Without loss of generality, let us assume that $a < b$ and $c < d$. (If not, then relabel the elements after these comparisons.) Next we compare b and d (this is our third comparison), and again relabel all four of these elements if necessary to have $b < d$. So at this point we have $a < b < d$ and $c < d$ after three comparisons. We insert e into its proper position among a, b, and d with two more comparisons using binary search, i.e., by comparing e first to b and then to either a or d. Thus we have made five comparisons and obtained a linear ordering among a, b, d, and e, as well as knowing one more piece of information about the location of c, namely either that it is less than the largest among a, b, d, and e, or that it is less than the second largest. (Drawing a diagram helps here.) In any case, it then suffices to insert c into its correct position among the three smallest members of a, b, d, and e, which requires two more comparisons (binary search), bringing the total to the desired seven.

14. The first step builds the following tree.

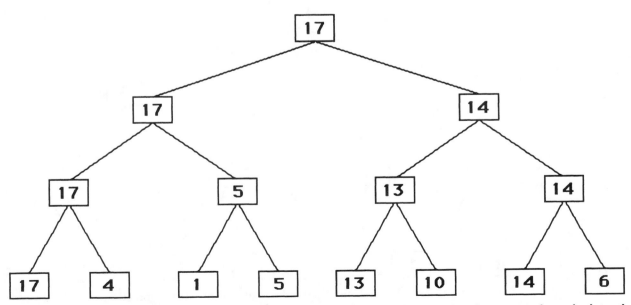

This identifies 17 as the largest element, so we replace the leaf 17 by $-\infty$ in the tree and recalculate the winner in the path from the leaf where 17 used to be up to the root. The result is as shown here.

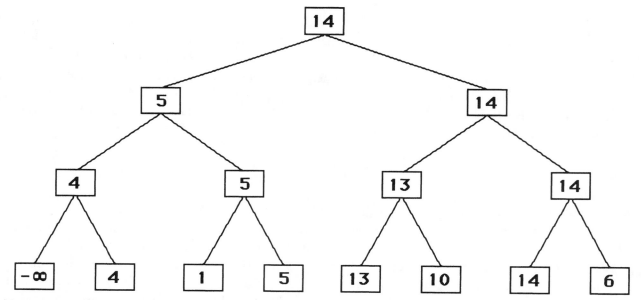

Now we see that 14 is the second largest element, so we repeat the process: replace the leaf 14 by $-\infty$ and recalculate. This gives us the following tree.

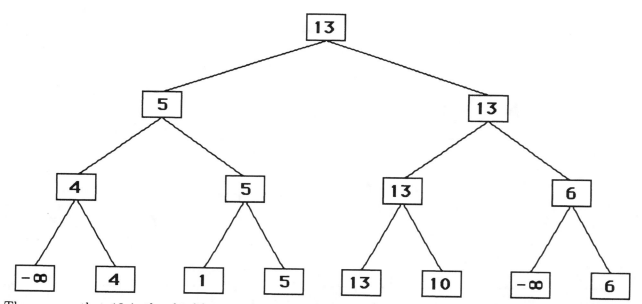

Thus we see that 13 is the third largest element, so we repeat the process: replace the leaf 13 by $-\infty$ and recalculate. The process continues in this manner. The final tree will look like this, as we determine that 1 is the eighth largest element.

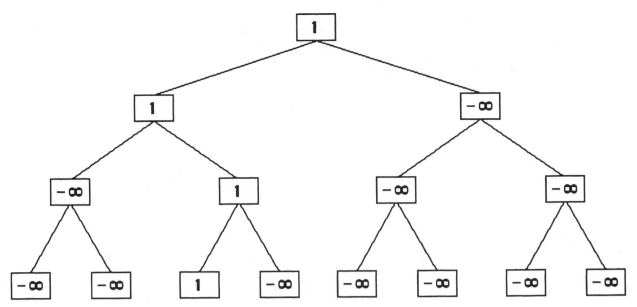

16. Each comparison eliminates one contender, and $n - 1$ contenders have to be eliminated, so there are $n - 1$ comparisons to determine the largest element.

18. Following the hint we insert enough $-\infty$ values to make n a power of 2. This at most doubles n and so will not affect our final answer in big-Theta notation. By Exercise 16 we can build the initial tree using $n - 1$ comparisons. By Exercise 17 for each round after the first it takes $k = \log n$ comparisons to identify the next largest element. There are $n - 1$ additional rounds, so the total amount of work in these rounds is $(n - 1) \log n$. Thus the total number of comparisons is $n - 1 + (n - 1) \log n$, which is $\Theta(n \log n)$.

20. The constructions are straightforward.

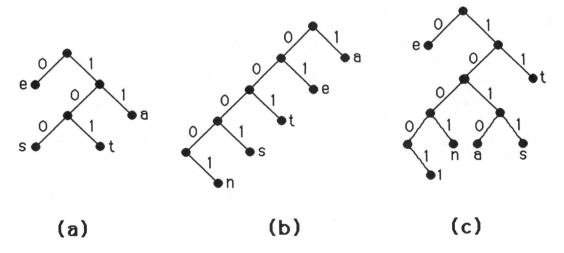

(a)   **(b)**   **(c)**

22. a) The first three bits decode as t. The next bit decodes as e. The next four bits decode as s. The last three bits decode as t. Thus the word is *test*. The remaining parts are similar, so we give just the answers.
b) *beer*   **c)** *sex*   **d)** *tax*

24. We follow Algorithm 2. Since F and C are the symbols of least weight, they are combined into a subtree, which we will call T_1 for discussion purposes, of weight $0.07 + 0.05 = 0.12$, with the larger weight symbol, F, on the left. Now the two trees of smallest weight are the single symbols A and G, and so we get a tree T_2

with left subtree A and right subtree G, of weight 0.18. The next step is to combine D and T_1 into a subtree T_3 of weight 0.27. Then B and T_2 form T_4 of weight 0.43; and E and T_3 form T_5 of weight 0.57. The final step is to combine T_5 and T_4. The result is as shown.

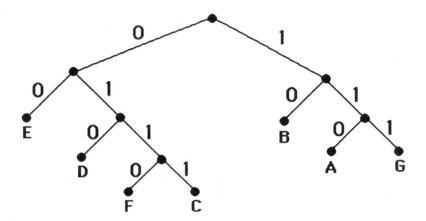

We see by looking at the tree that A is encoded by 110, B by 10, C by 0111, D by 010, E by 00, F by 0110, and G by 111. To compute the average number of bits required to encode a character, we multiply the number of bits for each letter by the weight of that latter and add. Since A takes 3 bits and has weight 0.10, it contributes 0.30 to the sum. Similarly B contributes $2 \cdot 0.25 = 0.50$. In all we get $3 \cdot 0.10 + 2 \cdot 0.25 + 4 \cdot 0.05 + 3 \cdot 0.15 + 2 \cdot 0.30 + 4 \cdot 0.07 + 3 \cdot 0.08 = 2.57$. Thus on the average, 2.57 bits are needed per character. Note that this is an appropriately weighted average, weighted by the frequencies with which the letters occur.

26. **a)** First we combine e and d into a tree T_1 with weight 0.2. Then using the rule we choose T_1 and, say, c to combine into a tree T_2 with weight 0.4. Then again using the rule we must combine T_2 and b into T_3 with weight 0.6, and finally T_3 and a. This gives codes a:1, b:01, c:001, d:0001, e:0000. For the other method we first combine d and e to form a tree T_1 with weight 0.2. Next we combine b and c (the trees with the smallest number of vertices) into a tree T_2 with weight 0.4. Next we are forced to combine a with T_1 to form T_3 with weight 0.6, and then T_3 and T_2. This gives the codes a:00, b:10, c:11, d:010, e:011.
    b) The average for the first method is $1 \cdot 0.4 + 2 \cdot 0.2 + 3 \cdot 0.2 + 4 \cdot 0.1 + 4 \cdot 0.1 = 2.2$, and the average for the second method is $2 \cdot 0.4 + 2 \cdot 0.2 + 2 \cdot 0.2 + 3 \cdot 0.1 + 3 \cdot 0.1 = 2.2$. We knew ahead of time, of course, that these would turn out to be equal, since the Huffman algorithm minimizes the expected number of bits. For variance we use the formula $V(X) = E(X^2) - E(X)^2$. For the first method, the expectation of the square of the number of bits is $1^2 \cdot 0.4 + 2^2 \cdot 0.2 + 3^2 \cdot 0.2 + 4^2 \cdot 0.1 + 4^2 \cdot 0.1 = 6.2$, and for the second method it is $2^2 \cdot 0.4 + 2^2 \cdot 0.2 + 2^2 \cdot 0.2 + 3^2 \cdot 0.1 + 3^2 \cdot 0.1 = 5.0$. Therefore the variance for the first method is $6.2 - 2.2^2 = 1.36$, and for the second method it is $5.0 - 2.2^2 = 0.16$. The second method has a smaller variance in this example.

28. The pseudocode is identical to Algorithm 2 with the following changes. First, the value of m needs to be specified, presumably as part of the input. Before the **while** loop starts, we choose the $k = ((N-1) \bmod (m-1)) + 1$ vertices with smallest weights and replace them by a single tree with a new root, whose children from left to right are these k vertices in order by weight (from greatest to smallest), with labels 0 through $k - 1$ on the edges to these children, and with weight the sum of the weights of these k vertices. Within the loop, rather than replacing the two trees of smallest weight, we find the m trees of smallest weight, delete them from the forest and form a new tree with a new root, whose children from left to right are the roots of these m trees in order by weight (from greatest to smallest), with labels 0 through $m - 1$ on the edges to these children, and with weight the sum of the weights of these m former trees.

30. a) It is easy to construct this tree using the Huffman coding algorithm, as in previous exercises. We get A:0, B:10, C:11.

b) The frequencies of the new symbols are AA:0.6400, AB:0.1520, AC:0.0080, BA:0.1520, BB:0.0361, BC:0.0019, CA:0.0080, CB:0.0019, CC:0.0001. We form the tree by the algorithm and obtain this code: AA:0, AB:11, AC:10111, BA:100, BB:1010, BC:1011011, CA:101100, CB:10110100, CC:10110101.

c) The average number of bits for part **(a)** is $1 \cdot 0.80 + 2 \cdot 0.19 + 2 \cdot 0.01 = 1.2000$ per symbol. The average number of bits for part **(b)** is $1 \cdot 0.6400 + 2 \cdot 0.1520 + 5 \cdot 0.0080 + 3 \cdot 0.1520 + 4 \cdot 0.0361 + 7 \cdot 0.0019 + 6 \cdot 0.0080 + 8 \cdot 0.0019 + 8 \cdot 0.0001 = 1.6617$ for sending two symbols, which is therefore 0.83085 bits per symbol. The second method is more efficient.

32. We prove this by induction on the number of symbols. If there are just two symbols, then there is nothing to prove, so assume the inductive hypothesis that Huffman codes are optimal for k symbols, and consider a situation in which there are $k+1$ symbols. First note that since the tree is full, the leaves at the bottom-most level come in pairs. Let a and b be two symbols of smallest frequencies, p_a and p_b. If in some binary prefix code they are not paired together at the bottom-most level, then we can obtain a code that is at least as efficient by interchanging the symbols on some of the leaves to make a and b siblings at the bottom-most level (since moving a more frequently occurring symbol closer to the root can only help). Therefore we can assume that a and b are siblings in every most-efficient tree. Now suppose we consider them to be one new symbol c, occurring with frequency equal to the sum of the frequencies of a and b, and apply the inductive hypothesis to obtain via the Huffman algorithm an optimal binary prefix code H_k on k symbols. Note that this is equivalent to applying the Huffman algorithm to the $k+1$ symbols, and obtaining a code we will call H_{k+1}. We must show that H_{k+1} is optimal for the $k+1$ symbols. Note that the average numbers of bits required to encode a symbol in H_k and in H_{k+1} are the same except for the symbols a, b, and c, and the difference is $p_a + p_b$ (since one extra bit is needed for a and b, as opposed to c, and all other code words are the same). If H_{k+1} is not optimal, let H'_{k+1} be a better code (with smaller average number of bits per symbol). By the observation above we can assume that a and b are siblings at the bottom-most level in H'_{k+1}. Then the code H'_k for k symbols obtained by replacing a and b with their parent (and deleting the last bit) has average number of bits equal to the average for H'_{k+1} minus $p_a + p_b$, and that contradicts the inductive hypothesis that H_k was optimal.

34. The first player has six choices, as shown below. In five of these cases, the analysis from there on down has already been done, either in Figure 9 of the text or in the solution to Exercise 33, so we do not show the subtree in full but only indicate the value. Note that if the cited reference was to a square vertex rather than a circle vertex, then the outcome is reversed. From the fifth vertex at the second level there are four choices, as shown, and again they have all been analyzed previously. The upshot is that since all the vertices on the second level are wins for the second player (value -1), the value of the root is also -1, and the second player can always win this game.

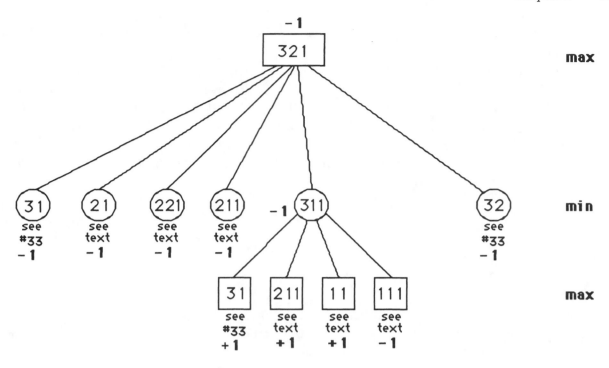

36. The game tree is too large to draw in its entirety, so we simplify the analysis by noting that a player will never want to move to a situation with two piles, one of which has one stone, nor to a single pile with more than one stone. If we omit these suicide moves, the game tree looks like this.

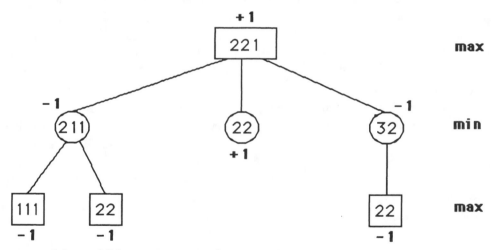

Note that a vertex with no children except suicide moves is a win for whoever is not moving at that point. The first player wins this game by moving to the position 2 2.

38. **a)** First player wins by moving in the center at this point. This blocks second player's threat and creates two threats, only one of which can the second player block.

b) This game will end in a draw with optimal play. The first player must first block the second player's threat, and then as long as the second player makes his third and fourth moves in the first and third columns, the first player cannot win.

c) The first player can win by moving in the right-most square of the middle row. This creates two threats, only one of which can the second player block.

d) As long as neither player does anything stupid (fail to block a threat), this game must end in a draw, since the next three moves are forced and then no file can contain three of the same symbol.

40. If the smaller pile contains just one stone, then the first player wins by removing all the stones in the other pile. Otherwise the smaller pile contains at least two stones and the larger pile contains more stones than that, so the first player can remove enough stones from the larger pile to make two piles with the same number of stones, where this number is at least 2. By the result of Exercise 39, the resulting game is a win for the second player when played optimally, and our first player is now the second player in the resulting game.

42. We need to record how many moves are possible from various positions. If the game currently has piles with stones in them, we can take from one to all of the stones in any pile. That means the number of possible moves is the sum of the pile sizes. However, by symmetry, moves from piles of the same size are equivalent, so the actual number of moves is the sum of the distinct pile sizes. The one exception is that a position with just one pile has one fewer move, since we cannot take all the stones.

a) From $5\,4$ the possible moves are to $5\,3$, $5\,2$, $5\,1$, $4\,4$, $4\,3$, $4\,2$, $4\,1$, 5, and 4, so there are nine children. A similar analysis shows that the number of children of these children are 8, 7, 6, 4, 7, 6, 5, 4, and 3, respectively, so the number of grandchildren is the sum of these nine numbers, namely 50.

b) There are three children with just two piles left, and these lead to 18 grandchildren. There are six children with three piles left, and these lead to 37 grandchildren. So in all there are nine children and 55 grandchildren.

c) A similar analysis shows that there are 10 children and 70 grandchildren.

d) A similar analysis shows that there are 10 children and 82 grandchildren.

44. This recursive procedure finds the value of a game. It needs to keep track of which player is currently moving, so the value of the variable *player* will be either "First" or "Second." The variable P is a position of the game (for example, the numbers of stones in the piles for nim).

```
procedure value(P, player)
if P is a leaf then value(P, player) := payoff to first player
else if player = First then
begin {compute maximum of values of children}
        v := -∞
        for each legal move m for First
        begin {compute value of game at resulting position}
                Q := (P followed by move m)
                v' := value(Q, Second)
                if v' > v then v := v'
        end
        value(P, player) := v
end
else { player = Second }
begin {compute minimum of values of children}
        v := ∞
        for each legal move m for Second
        begin {compute value of game at resulting position}
                Q := (P followed by move m)
                v' := value(Q, Second)
                if v' < v then v := v'
        end
        value(P, player) := v
end
```

SECTION 9.3   Tree Traversal

2. See the comments for the solution to Exercise 1. The order is $0 < 1 < 1.1 < 1.1.1 < 1.1.1.1 < 1.1.1.2 < 1.1.2 < 1.2 < 2$.

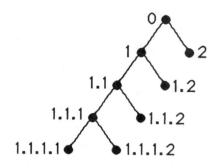

4. a) The vertex is at level 5; it is clear that an address (other than 0) of length l gives a vertex at level l.

b) We obtain the address of the parent by deleting the last number in the address of the vertex. Therefore the parent is 3.4.5.2.

c) Since v is the fourth child, it has at least three siblings.

d) We know that v's parent must have at least 1 sibling, its grandparent must have at least 4, its great-grandparent at least 3, and its great-great-grandparent at least 2. Adding to this count the fact that v has 5 ancestors and 3 siblings (and not forgetting to count v itself), we obtain a total of 19 vertices in the tree.

e) The other addresses are 0 together with all prefixes of v and the all the addresses that can be obtained from v or prefixes of v by making the last number smaller. Thus we have 0, 1, 2, 3, 3.1, 3.2, 3.3, 3.4, 3.4.1, 3.4.2, 3.4.3, 3.4.4, 3.4.5, 3.4.5.1, 3.4.5.2, 3.4.5.2.1, 3.4.5.2.2, and 3.4.5.2.3.

6. a) The following tree has these addresses for its leaves. We construct it by starting from the beginning of the list and drawing the parts of the tree that are made necessary by the given leaves. First of course there must be a root. Then since the first leaf is labeled 1.1.1, there must be a first child of the root, a first child of this child, and a first child of this latter child, which is then a leaf. Next there must be the second child of the root's first grandchild (1.1.2), and then a second child of the first child of the root (1.2). We continue in this manner until the entire tree is drawn.

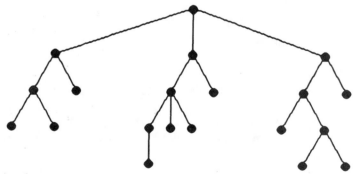

b) If there is such a tree, then the address 2.4.1 must occur since the address 2.4.2 does (the parent of 2.4.2.1). The vertex with that address must either be a leaf or have a descendant that is a leaf. The address of any such leaf must begin 2.4.1. Since no such address is in the list, we conclude that the answer to the question is no.

c) No such tree is possible, since the vertex with address 1.2.2 is not a leaf (it has a child 1.2.2.1 in the list).

8. See the comments in the solution to Exercise 7 for the procedure. The only difference here is that some vertices have more than two children: after listing such a vertex, we list the vertices of its subtrees, in preorder, from left to right. The answer is $a, b, d, e, i, j, m, n, o, c, f, g, h, k, l, p$.

10. The left subtree of the root comes first, namely the tree rooted at b. There again the left subtree comes first, so the list begins with d. After that comes b, the root of this subtree, and then the right subtree of b, namely (in order) f, e, and g. Then comes the root of the entire tree and finally its right child. Thus the answer is d, b, f, e, g, a, c.

12. This is similar to Exercise 11. The answer is $k, e, l, m, b, f, r, n, s, g, a, c, o, h, d, i, p, j, q$.

14. The procedure is the same as in Exercise 13, except that some vertices have more than two children here: before listing such a vertex, we list the vertices of its subtrees, in postorder, from left to right. The answer is $d, i, m, n, o, j, e, b, f, g, k, p, l, h, c, a$.

16. a) We build the tree from the top down while analyzing the expression by identifying the outermost operation at each stage. The outermost operation in this expression is the final subtraction. Therefore the tree has $-$ at its root, with the two operands as the subtrees at the root. The right operand is clearly 5, so the right child of the root is 5. The left operand is the result of a multiplication, so the left subtree has $*$ as its root. We continue recursively in this way until the entire tree is constructed.

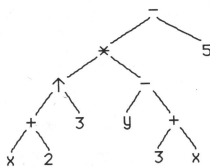

b) We can read off the answer from the picture we have just drawn simply by listing the vertices of the tree in preorder: First list the root, then the left subtree in preorder, then the right subtree in preorder. Therefore the answer is $- * \uparrow + x\, 2\, 3 - y + 3\, x\, 5$.

c) We can read off the answer from the picture we have just drawn simply by listing the vertices of the tree in postorder: $x\, 2 + 3 \uparrow y\, 3\, x + - * 5 -$.

d) The infix expression is just the given expression, fully parenthesized: $((((x + 2) \uparrow 3) * (y - (3 + x))) - 5)$. This corresponds to traversing the tree in inorder, putting in a left parenthesis whenever we go down to a left child and putting in a right parenthesis whenever we come up from a right child.

18. a) This exercise is similar to the previous few exercises. The only difference is that some portions of the tree represent the unary operation of negation ($\neg$). In the first tree, for example, the left subtree represents the expression $\neg(p \wedge q)$, so the root is the negation symbol, and the only child of this root is the tree for the expression $p \wedge q$.

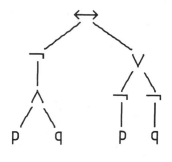
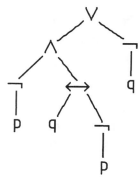

Since this exercise is similar to previous exercises, we will not go into the details of obtaining the different expressions. The only difference is that negation ($\neg$) is a unary operator; we show it preceding its operand in infix notation, even though it would follow it in an inorder traversal of the expression tree.

b) $\leftrightarrow \neg \wedge p q \vee \neg p \neg q$ and $\vee \wedge \neg p \leftrightarrow q \neg p \neg q$

c) $p q \wedge \neg p \neg q \neg \vee \leftrightarrow$ and $p \neg q p \neg \leftrightarrow \wedge q \neg \vee$

d) $((\neg(p \wedge q)) \leftrightarrow ((\neg p) \vee (\neg q)))$ and $(((\neg p) \wedge (q \leftrightarrow (\neg p))) \vee (\neg q))$

20. This requires fairly careful counting. Let us work from the outside in. There are four symbols that can be the outermost operation: the first $\neg$, the $\wedge$, the $\leftrightarrow$, and the $\vee$. Let us first consider the cases in which the first $\neg$ is the outermost operation, necessarily applied, then, to the rest of the expression. Then there are three possible choices for the outermost operation of the rest: the $\wedge$, the $\leftrightarrow$, and the $\vee$. Let us assume first that it is the $\wedge$. Then there are two choices for the outermost operation of the rest of the expression: the $\leftrightarrow$ and the $\vee$. If it is the $\leftrightarrow$, then there are two ways to parenthesize the rest—depending on whether the second $\neg$ applies to the disjunction or only to the p. Backing up, we next consider the case in which the $\vee$ is outermost operation among the last seven symbols, rather than the $\leftrightarrow$. In this case there are no further choices. We then back up again and assume that the $\leftrightarrow$, rather than the $\wedge$, is the second outermost operation. In this case there are two possibilities for completing the parenthesization (involving the second $\neg$). If the $\vee$ is the second outermost operation, then again there are two possibilities, depending on whether the $\wedge$ or the $\leftrightarrow$ is applied first. Thus in the case in which the outermost operation is the first $\neg$, we have counted 7 ways to parenthesize the expression:

$$(\neg(p \wedge (q \leftrightarrow (\neg(p \vee (\neg q))))))$$
$$(\neg(p \wedge (q \leftrightarrow ((\neg p) \vee (\neg q)))))$$
$$(\neg(p \wedge ((q \leftrightarrow (\neg p)) \vee (\neg q))))$$
$$(\neg((p \wedge q) \leftrightarrow (\neg(p \vee (\neg q)))))$$
$$(\neg((p \wedge q) \leftrightarrow ((\neg p) \vee (\neg q))))$$
$$(\neg((p \wedge (q \leftrightarrow (\neg p))) \vee (\neg q)))$$
$$(\neg(((p \wedge q) \leftrightarrow (\neg p)) \vee (\neg q)))$$

The other three cases are similar, giving us 3 possibilities if the $\wedge$ is the outermost operation, 4 if the $\leftrightarrow$ is, and 5 if the $\vee$ is. Therefore the answer is $7 + 3 + 4 + 5 = 19$.

22. We work from the beginning of the expression. In part **(a)** the root of the tree is necessarily the first $+$. We then use up as much of the rest of the expression as needed to construct the left subtree of the root. The root of this left subtree is the $*$, and its left subtree is as much of the rest of the expression as is needed. We continue in this way, making our way to the subtree consisting of root $-$ and children 5 and 3. Then the 2 must be the right child of the second $+$, the 1 must be the right child of the $*$, and the 4 must be the right child of the root. The result is shown here.

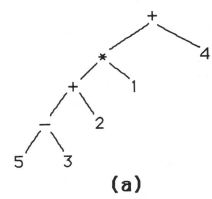

(a)

In infix form we have $((((5-3)+2)*1)+4)$. The other two trees are constructed in a similar manner.

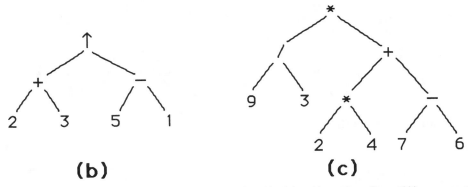

(b)   **(c)**

The infix expressions are therefore $((2+3) \uparrow (5-1))$ and $((9/3) * ((2*4) + (7-6)))$, respectively.

24. We exhibit the answers by showing with parentheses the operation that is applied next, working from left to right (it always involves the first occurrence of an operator symbol).
    a) $5\,(2\,1\,-)-3\,1\,4\,+\,+\,* = (5\,1\,-)\,3\,1\,4\,+\,+\,* = 4\,3\,(1\,4\,+)\,+\,* = 4\,(3\,5\,+)\,* = (4\,8\,*) = 32$
    b) $(9\,3\,/)\,5\,+\,7\,2\,-\,* = (3\,5\,+)\,7\,2\,-\,* = 8\,(7\,2\,-)\,* = (8\,5\,*) = 40$
    c) $(3\,2\,*)\,2\,\uparrow\,5\,3\,-\,8\,4\,/\,*\,- = (6\,2\,\uparrow)\,5\,3\,-\,8\,4\,/\,*\,- = 36\,(5\,3\,-)\,8\,4\,/\,*\,- = 36\,\,2\,(8\,4\,/)\,*\,- = 36\,(2\,2\,*)\,- = (36\,\,4\,-) = 32$

26. We prove this by induction on the length of the list. If the list has just one element, then the statement is trivially true. For the inductive step, consider the beginning of the list. There we find a sequence of vertices, starting with the root and ending with the first leaf (we can recognize the first leaf as the first vertex with no children), each vertex in the sequence being the first child of its predecessor in the list. Now remove this leaf, and decrease the child count of its parent by 1. The result is the preorder and child counts of a tree with one fewer vertex. By the inductive hypothesis we can uniquely determine this smaller tree. Then we can uniquely determine where the deleted vertex goes, since it is the first child of its parent (whom we know).

28. It is routine to see that the list is in alphabetical order in each case. In the first tree, vertex b has two children, whereas in the second, vertex b has three children, so the statement in Exercise 26 is not contradicted.

30. **a)** This is not well-formed by the result in Exercise 31.
    b) This is not well-formed by the result in Exercise 31.
    c) This is not well-formed by the result in Exercise 31.
    d) This is well-formed. Each of the two subexpressions $\circ xx$ is well-formed. Therefore the subexpression $+\circ xx \circ xx$ is well-formed; call it A. Thus the entire expression is $\times Ax$, so it is well-formed.

32. The definition is word-for-word the same as that given for prefix expressions, except that "postfix" is substituted for "prefix" throughout, and $*XY$ is replaced by $XY*$.

34. We replace the inductive step (ii) in the definition with the statement that if $X_1, X_2, \ldots, X_n$ are well-formed formulae and $*$ is an n-ary operator, then $*X_1 X_2 \ldots X_n$ is a well-formed formula.

SECTION 9.4   Spanning Trees

2. Since the edge $\{a, b\}$ is part of a simple circuit, we can remove it. Then since the edge $\{b, c\}$ is part of a simple circuit that still remains, we can remove it. At this point there are no more simple circuits, so we have a spanning tree. There are many other possible answers, corresponding to different choices of edges to remove.

4. We can remove these edges to produce a spanning tree (see comments for Exercise 2): $\{a, i\}$, $\{b, i\}$, $\{b, j\}$, $\{c, d\}$, $\{c, j\}$, $\{d, e\}$, $\{e, j\}$, $\{f, i\}$, $\{f, j\}$, and $\{g, i\}$.

6. There are many, many possible answers. One set of choices is to remove edges $\{a, e\}$, $\{a, h\}$, $\{b, g\}$, $\{c, f\}$, $\{c, j\}$, $\{d, k\}$, $\{e, i\}$, $\{g, l\}$, $\{h, l\}$, and $\{i, k\}$.

8. We can remove any one of the three edges to produce a spanning tree. The trees are therefore the ones shown below.

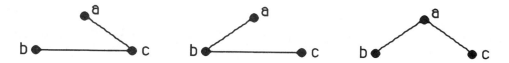

10. We can remove any one of the four edges in the middle square to produce a spanning tree, as shown.

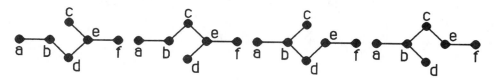

12. This is really the same problem as Exercises 11a, 12a, and 13a in Section 9.1, since a spanning tree of K_n is just a tree with n vertices. The answers are restated here for convenience.
   a) 1   **b)** 2   **c)** 3

14. The tree is shown in heavy lines. It is produced by starting at a and continuing as far as possible without backtracking, choosing the first unused vertex (in alphabetical order) at each point. When the path reaches vertex l, we need to backtrack. Backtracking to h, we can then form the path all the way to n without further backtracking. Finally we backtrack to vertex i to pick up vertex m.

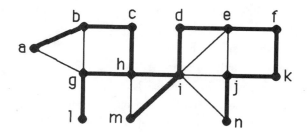

16. If we start at vertex a and use alphabetical order, then the breadth-first search spanning tree is unique. Consider the graph in Exercise 13. We first fan out from vertex a, picking up the edges $\{a, b\}$ and $\{a, c\}$. There are no new vertices from b, so we fan out from c, to get edge $\{c, d\}$. Then we fan out from d to get edges $\{d, e\}$ and $\{d, f\}$. This process continues until we have the entire tree shown in heavy lines below.

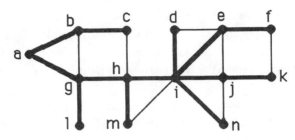

The tree for the graph in Exercise 14 is shown in heavy lines. It is produced by the same fanning-out procedure as described above.

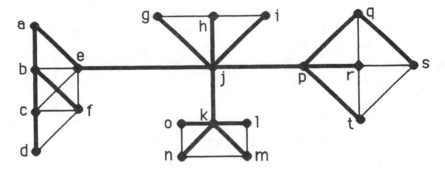

The spanning tree for the graph in Exercise 15 is shown in heavy lines.

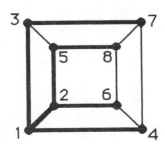

18. a) We start at the vertex in the middle of the wheel and visit all its neighbors—the vertices on the rim. This forms the spanning tree $K_{1,6}$ (see Exercise 19 for the general situation).

b) We start at any vertex and visit all its neighbors. Thus the resulting spanning tree is therefore $K_{1,4}$.

c) See Exercise 21 for the general result. We get a "double star": a $K_{1,3}$ and a $K_{1,2}$ with their centers joined by an edge.

d) By the symmetry of the cube, the result will always be the same (up to isomorphism), regardless of the order we impose on the vertices. We start at a vertex and fan out to its three neighbors. From one of them we fan out to two more, and pick up one more vertex from another neighbor. The final vertex is at a distance 3 from the root. In this figure we have labeled the vertices in the order visited.

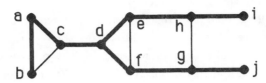

20. Since every vertex is connected to every other vertex, the breadth-first search will construct the tree $K_{1,n-1}$, with every vertex adjacent to the starting vertex. The depth-first search will produce a simple path of length $n-1$ for the same reason.

22. We construct a tree using one of these search methods. We color the first vertex red, and whenever we add a new vertex to the tree, we color it blue if we reach it from a red vertex, and we color it red if we reach it from a blue vertex. When we encounter a vertex that is already in the tree (and therefore will not be added to the tree), we compare its color to that of the vertex we are currently processing. If the colors are the same, then we know immediately that the graph is not bipartite. If we get through the entire process without finding such a clash, then we conclude that the graph is bipartite.

24. If the edge is a cut edge, then it provides the unique simple path between its endpoints. Therefore it must be in every spanning tree for the graph. Conversely, if an edge is not a cut edge, then it can be removed without disconnecting the graph, and every spanning tree of the resulting graph will be a spanning tree of the original graph not containing this edge. Thus we have shown that an edge of a connected simple graph must be in every spanning tree for this graph if and only if the edge is a cut edge—i.e., its removal disconnects the graph.

26. We can order the vertices of the graph in the order in which they are first encountered in the search processes. Note, however, that we already need an order (at least locally, among the neighbors of a vertex) to make the search processes well-defined. The resulting orders given by depth-first search or breadth-first search are not the same, of course.

28. In each case we will call the colors red, blue, and green. Our backtracking plan is to color the vertices in alphabetical order. We first try the color red for the current vertex, if possible, and then move on to the next vertex. When we have backtracked to this vertex, we then try blue, if possible. Finally we try green. If no coloring of this vertex succeeds, then we erase the color on this vertex and backtrack to the previous vertex. For the graph in Exercise 7, no backtracking is required. We assign red, blue, red, and green to the vertices in alphabetical order. For the graph in Exercise 8, again no backtracking is required. We assign red, blue, blue, green, green, and red to the vertices in alphabetical order. And for the graph in Exercise 9, no backtracking is required either. We assign red, blue, red, blue, and blue to the vertices in alphabetical order.

30. a) The largest number that can possibly be included is 19. Since the sum of 19 and any smaller number in the list is greater than 20, we conclude that no subset with sum 20 contains 19. Then we try 14 and reach the same conclusion. Finally, we try 11, and note that after we have included 8, the list has been exhausted and the sum is not 20. Therefore there is no subset whose sum is 20.
b) Starting with 27 in the set, we soon find that the subset $\{27, 14\}$ has the desired sum of 41.
c) First we try putting 27 into the subset. If we also include 24, then no further additions are possible, so we backtrack and try including 19 with 27. Now it is possible to add 14, giving us the desired sum of 60.

32. a) We begin at the starting position. At each position, we keep track of which moves we have tried, and we try the moves in the order up, down, right, and left. (We also assume that the direction from which we entered this position has been tried, since we do not want our solution to retrace steps.) When we try a move, we then proceed along the chosen route until we are stymied, at which point we backtrack and try the next possible move. Either this will eventually lead us to the exit position, or we will have tried all the possibilities and concluded that there is no solution.
b) We start at position X. Since we cannot go up, we try going down. At the next intersection there is only one choice, so we go left. (All directions are stated in terms of our view of the picture.) This lead us to a dead end. Therefore we backtrack to position X and try going right. This leads us (without choices) to the

opening about two thirds of the way from left to right in the second row, where we have the choice of going left or down. We try going down, and then right. No further choices are possible until we reach the opening just above the exit. Here we first try going up, but that leads to a dead end, so we try going down, and that leads us to the exit.

34. There is one tree for each component of the graph.

36. The algorithm is identical to the algorithm for obtaining spanning trees by deleting edges in simple circuits. While circuits remain, we remove an edge of a simple circuit. This does not disconnect any connected component of the graph, and eventually the process terminates with a forest of spanning trees of the components.

38. We apply breadth-first search, starting from the first vertex. When that search terminates, i.e., when the list is emptied, then we look for the first vertex that has not yet been included in the forest. If no such vertex is found, then we are done. If v is such a vertex, then we begin breadth-first search again from v, constructing the second tree in the forest. We continue in this way until all the vertices have been included.

40. First notice that the order in which vertices are put into (and therefore taken out of) the list L is level-order. In other words, the root of the resulting tree comes first, then the vertices at level 1 (put into the list while processing the root), then the vertices at level 2 (put into the list while processing vertices at level 1), and so on. (A formal proof of this is given in Exercise 43.) Now suppose that uv is an edge not in the tree, and suppose without loss of generality that the algorithm processed u before it processed v. (In other words, u entered the list L before v did.) Since the edge uv is not in the tree, it must be the case that v was already in the list L when u was being processed. In order for this to happen, the parent p of v must have already been processed before u. Note that p's level in the tree is one less than v's level. Therefore u's level is greater than or equal to p's level but less than or equal to v's level, and the proof is complete.

42. Assume that the connected simple graph G does not have a simple path of length at least k. Consider the longest path in the depth-first search tree. Since each edge connects an ancestor and a descendant, we can bound the number of edges by counting the total number of ancestors of each descendant. But if the longest path is shorter than k, then each descendant has at most $k-1$ ancestors. Therefore there can be at most $(k-1)n$ edges.

44. We modify the pseudocode given in Algorithm 1 by initializing a global variable m to be 0 at the beginning of the algorithm, and adding the statements "$m := m+1$" and "assign m to vertex v" as the first line of procedure *visit*. To see that this numbering corresponds to the numbering of the vertices created by a preorder traversal of the spanning tree, we need to show that each vertex has a smaller number than its children, and that the children have increasing numbers from left to right (assuming that each new child added to the tree comes to the right of its siblings already in the tree). Clearly the children of a vertex get added to the tree only after that vertex is added, so their number must exceed that of their parent. And if a vertex's sibling has a smaller number, then it must have already been visited, and therefore already have been added to the tree.

46. Note that a "lower" level is further down the tree, i.e., further from the root and therefore having a larger value. (So "lower" really means "greater than"!) This is similar to Exercise 40. Again notice that the order in which vertices are put into (and therefore taken out of) the list L is level-order. In other words, the root of the resulting tree comes first, then the vertices at level 1 (put into the list while processing the root), then the vertices at level 2 (put into the list while processing vertices at level 1), and so on. Now suppose that uv is a directed edge not in the tree. First assume that the algorithm processed u before it processed v. (In other words, u entered the list L before v did.) Since the edge uv is not in the tree, it must be the case that

v was already in the list L when u was being processed. In order for this to happen, the parent p of v must have already been processed before u. Note that p's level in the tree is one less than v's level. Therefore u's level is greater than or equal to p's level but less than or equal to v's level, so this directed edge goes from a vertex at one level to a vertex either at the same level or one level below. Next suppose that the algorithm processed v before it processed u. Then v's level is at or above u's level, and there is nothing else to prove.

48. Maintain a global variable c, initialized to 0. At the end of procedure *visit*, add the statements "$c := c + 1$" and "assign c to v." We need to show that each vertex has a larger number than its children, and that the children have increasing numbers from left to right (assuming that each new child added to the tree comes to the right of its siblings already in the tree). A vertex v is not numbered until its processing is finished, which means that all of the descendants of v must have finished their processing. Therefore each vertex has a larger number than all of its children. Furthermore, if a vertex's sibling has a smaller number, then it must have already been visited, and therefore already have been added to the tree. (Note that listing the vertices by number gives a postorder traversal of the tree.)

50. Suppose that T_1 contains a edges that are not in T_2, so that the distance between T_1 and T_2 is $2a$. Suppose further that T_2 contains b edges that are not in T_3, so that the distance between T_2 and T_3 is $2b$. Now at worst the only edges that are in T_1 and not in T_3 are those $a + b$ edges that are in T_1 and not in T_2, or in T_1 and T_2 but not in T_3. Therefore the distance between T_1 and T_3 is at most $2(a + b)$.

52. Following the construction of Exercise 51, we reduce the distance between spanning trees T_1 and T_2 by 2 when we remove edge e_1 from T_1 and add edge e_2 to it. Thus after applying this operation d times, we can convert any tree T_1 into any other spanning tree T_2 (where d is half the distance between T_1 and T_2).

54. By Exercise 16 in Section 8.5 there is an Euler circuit C in the directed graph. We follow C and delete from the directed graph every edge whose terminal vertex has been previously visited in C. We claim that the edges that remain in C form a rooted tree. Certainly there is a directed path from the root to every other vertex, since we only deleted edges that allowed us to reach vertices we could already reach. Furthermore, there can be no simple circuits, since we removed every edge that would have completed a simple circuit.

56. Since this is an "if and only if" statement, we have two things to prove. First, suppose that G contains a circuit $v_1, v_2, \ldots, v_k, v_1$, and without loss of generality, assume that v_1 is the first vertex visited in the depth-first search process. Since there is a directed path from v_1 to v_k, vertex v_k must have been visited before the processing of v_1 is completed. Therefore v_1 is an ancestor of v_k in the tree, and the edge $v_k v_1$ is a back edge. Now we have to prove the converse. Suppose that T contains a back edge uv from a vertex u to its ancestor v. Then the path in T from v to u, followed by this edge, is a circuit in G.

58. Clearly if G contains a back edge uv (i.e., u is a descendant of v), then it contains a circuit: follow the tree from v to u and then return to v along this edge. Conversely, suppose that G contains a circuit (without loss of generality, assume that no vertex is repeated until the circuit closes), and let u be the first vertex of that circuit visited by the depth-first search algorithm. Let v be the vertex on the circuit preceding u. Since all the other vertices of the circuit can be reached from u, the processing of u will not be complete until all of them have been visited. In particular, v must be a descendant of u in the tree, and therefore vu will be a back edge.

SECTION 9.5   Minimum Spanning Trees

2. We start with the minimum weight edge $\{a, b\}$. The least weight edge incident to the tree constructed so far is edge $\{a, e\}$, with weight 2, so we add it to the tree. Next we add edge $\{d, e\}$, and then edge $\{c, d\}$. This completes the tree, whose total weight is 6.

4. The edges are added in the order $\{a, b\}$, $\{a, e\}$, $\{a, d\}$, $\{c, d\}$, $\{d, h\}$, $\{a, m\}$, $\{d, p\}$, $\{e, f\}$, $\{e, i\}$, $\{g, h\}$, $\{l, p\}$, $\{m, n\}$, $\{n, o\}$, $\{f, j\}$, and $\{k, l\}$, for a total weight of 28.

6. With Kruskal's algorithm, we add at each step the shortest edge that will not complete a simple circuit. Thus we pick edge $\{a, b\}$ first, and then edge $\{c, d\}$ (alphabetical order breaks ties), followed by $\{a, e\}$ and $\{d, e\}$.The total weight is 6.

8. The edges are added in the order $\{a, b\}$, $\{a, e\}$, $\{c, d\}$, $\{d, h\}$, $\{a, d\}$, $\{a, m\}$, $\{d, p\}$, $\{e, f\}$, $\{e, i\}$, $\{g, h\}$, $\{l, p\}$, $\{m, n\}$, $\{n, o\}$, $\{f, j\}$, and $\{k, l\}$, for a total weight of 28.

10. One way to do this is simply to apply the algorithm of choice to each component. In practice it is not clear what that means, since we would have to determine the components first. More to the point, we can implement the procedures as follows. For Prim's algorithm, start with the first vertex and repeatedly add to the tree the shortest edge adjacent to it that does not complete a simple circuit. When no such edges remain, we find a vertex that is not yet in the spanning forest and grow a new tree from this vertex. We repeat this process until no new vertices remain. Kruskal's algorithm is even simpler to implement. We keep choosing the shortest edge that does not complete a simple circuit, until no such edges remain. The result is a spanning forest of minimum weight.

12. If we simply replace the word "smallest" with the word "largest" (and replace the word "minimum" in the comment with the word "maximum") in Algorithm 2, then the resulting algorithm will find a maximum spanning tree.

14. The answer is unique. It uses edges $\{d, h\}$, $\{d, e\}$, $\{b, f\}$, $\{d, g\}$, $\{a, b\}$, $\{b, e\}$, $\{b, c\}$, and $\{f, i\}$.

16. We follow the procedure outlined in the solution to Exercise 17. Recall that the minimum spanning tree uses the edges Atlanta–Chicago, Atlanta–New York, Denver–San Francisco, and Chicago–San Francisco. First we delete the edge from Atlanta to Chicago. The minimum spanning tree for the remaining graph has cost \$3900. Next we delete the edge from Atlanta to New York (and put the previously deleted edge back). The minimum spanning tree now has cost \$3800. Next we look at the graph with the edge from Denver to San Francisco deleted. The minimum spanning tree has cost \$4000. Finally we look at the graph with the edge from Chicago to San Francisco deleted. The minimum spanning tree has cost \$3700. This last tree is our answer, then; it consists of the links Atlanta–Chicago, Atlanta–New York, Denver–San Francisco, and Chicago–Denver.

18. Suppose that an edge e with smallest weight is not included in some minimum spanning tree; in other words, suppose that the minimum spanning tree T contains only edges with weights larger than that of e. If we add e to T, then we will obtain a graph with exactly one simple circuit, which contains e. We can then delete some other edge in this circuit, resulting in a spanning tree with weight strictly less than that of T (since all the other edges have larger weight than e has). This is a contradiction to the fact that T is a minimum spanning tree. Therefore an edge with smallest weight must be included in T.

20. We start with the New York to Denver link and then form a spanning tree by successively adding the cheapest edges that do not form a simple circuit. In fact the three cheapest edges will do: Atlanta–Chicago, Atlanta–New York, and Denver–San Francisco. This gives a cost of \$4000.

22. The algorithm is the same as Kruskal's, except that instead of starting with the empty tree, we start with the given set of edges. (If there is already a simple circuit among these edges, then there is no solution.)

24. We prove this by contradiction. Suppose that there is a simple circuit formed after the addition of edges at some stage in the algorithm. The circuit will contain some edges that were added at that stage and perhaps some edges that were already present. Let e_1, e_2, ..., e_r be the edges that are new, in the order they are traversed in the circuit. Thus the circuit can be thought of as the sequence e_1, T_1, e_2, T_2, ..., e_r, T_r, e_1, where each T_i is a tree that existed before the addition of new edges. Each edge in this sequence was the edge picked by the tree containing one of its two endpoints, so since there are the same number of trees as there are edges in this sequence, each tree must have picked a different edge. However, let e be the shortest edge (after tie-breaking) among $\{e_1, e_2, \ldots, e_r\}$. Then the tree at both of its ends necessarily picked e to add to the tree, a contradiction. Therefore there are no simple circuits.

26. The actual implementation of this algorithm is more difficult than this pseudocode shows, of course.

> **procedure** $Sollin(G : \text{simple graph})$
> initialize the set of trees to be the set of vertices
> **while** |set of trees| > 1 **do**
> **begin**
>   **for** each tree T_i in the set of trees
> $e_i :=$ the shortest edge from a vertex in T_i to a vertex not in T_i
>   add all the e_i's to the trees already present and
>   reorganize the resulting graph into a set of trees
> **end**

28. This is a special case of Exercise 29, with r equal to the number of vertices in the graph (each vertex is a tree by itself at the beginning of the algorithm); see the solution to that exercise.

30. As argued in the solution to Exercise 29, each stage in the algorithm reduces the number of trees by a factor of at least 2. Therefore after k stages at most $n/2^k$ trees remain. Since the number of trees is an integer, the number must be less than or equal to $\lfloor n/2^k \rfloor$.

32. Let G be a connected weighted graph. Suppose that the successive edges chosen by Kruskal's algorithm are e_1, e_2, ..., e_{n-1}, in that order, so that the tree S containing these edges is the tree constructed by the algorithm. Let T be a minimum spanning tree of G containing e_1, e_2, ..., e_k, with k chosen as large as possible (possibly 0). If $k = n - 1$, then we are done, since $S = T$. Otherwise $k < n - 1$, and in this case we will derive a contradiction by finding a minimum spanning tree T' which gives us a larger value of k. Consider $T \cup \{e_{k+1}\}$. Since T is a tree, this graph has a simple circuit which must contain e_{k+1}. Some edge e in this simple circuit is not in S, since S is a tree. Furthermore, e was available to be chosen by Kruskal's algorithm at the point at which e_{k+1} was chosen, since there is no simple circuit among $\{e_1, e_2, \ldots, e_k, e\}$ (these edges are all in T). Therefore the weight of e_{k+1} is less than or equal to the weight of e (otherwise the algorithm would have chosen e instead of e_{k+1}). Now add e_{k+1} to T and delete e; call the resulting tree T'. The weight of T' cannot be any greater than the weight of T. Therefore T' is also a minimum spanning tree, which contains the edges e_1, e_2, ..., e_k, e_{k+1}. This contradicts the choice of T, and our proof is complete.

SUPPLEMENTARY EXERCISES FOR CHAPTER 9

2. There are 20 such trees. We can organize our count by the height of the tree. There is just 1 rooted tree on 6 vertices with height 5. If the height is 4 (so that there is a path from the root containing 5 vertices), then there are 4 choices as to where to attach the sixth vertex. If the height is 3, fix a path of length three from the root. Two more vertices need to be added. If they are both attached directly to the original path, then there are $C(3 + 2 - 1, 2) = 6$ ways to attach them (since there are three possible points of attachment). On the other hand if they form a path of length 2 from their point of attachment, then there are 2 choices. Next suppose the height is 2. If there are not two disjoint paths of length 2 from the root, then there are 4 ways that the other 3 vertices can be attached to a given path of length 2 from the root (0, 1, 2, or 3 of them can be attached to the root). If there are two disjoint paths, then there are 2 choices for the sixth vertex. Finally, there is 1 tree of height 1. Thus we have $1 + 4 + 6 + 2 + 4 + 2 + 1 = 20$ trees in all.

4. We know that the sum of the degrees must be $2(n - 1)$. The $n - 1$ pendant vertices account for $n - 1$ in this sum, so the degree of the other vertex must be $n - 1$. This vertex is one part of $K_{1,n-1}$, therefore, and the pendant vertices are the other part.

6. We prove this by induction on n. The problem is trivial if $n \le 2$, so assume that the inductive hypothesis holds and let $n \ge 3$. First note that at least one of the positive integers d_i must equal 1, since the sum of n numbers each greater than or equal to 2 is greater than or equal to $2n$. Without loss of generality assume that $d_n = 1$. Now it is impossible for all the remaining d_i's to equal 1, since $2n - 2 > n$ (we are assuming that $n > 2$); without loss of generality assume that $d_1 > 1$. Now apply the inductive hypothesis to the sequence $d_1 - 1, d_2, d_3, \ldots, d_{n-1}$. There is a tree with these degrees. Add an edge from the vertex with degree $d_1 - 1$ to a new vertex, and we have the desired tree with degrees $d_1, d_2, \ldots, d_n$.

8. We consider the tree as a rooted tree. One part is the set of vertices at even-numbered levels, and the other part is the set of vertices at odd-numbered levels.

10. The following pictures show some B-trees with the desired height and degree. The root must have either 2 or 3 children, and the other internal vertices must have between 2 and 4 children, inclusive. Note that our first example is a complete binary tree.

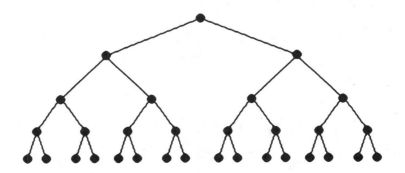

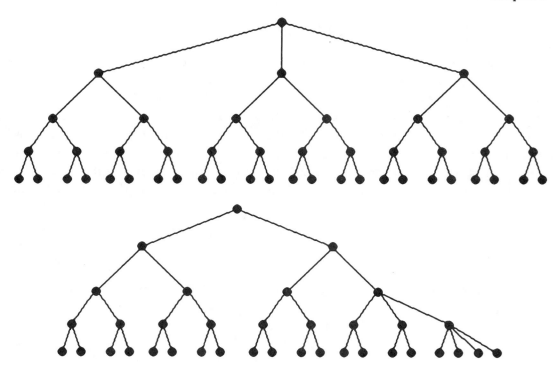

12. The lower bound for the height of a B-tree of degree k with n leaves comes from the upper bound for the number of leaves in a B-tree of degree k with height h, obtained in Exercise 11. Since there we found that $n \leq k^h$, we have $h \geq \log_k n$. The upper bound for the height of a B-tree of degree k with n leaves comes from the lower bound for the number of leaves in a B-tree of degree k with height h, obtained in Exercise 11. Since there we found that $n \geq 2\lceil k/2 \rceil^{h-1}$, we have $h \leq 1 + \log_{\lceil k/2 \rceil}(n/2)$.

14. Since B_{k+1} is formed from two copies of B_k, the number of vertices doubles as k increases by 1. Since B_0 had $1 = 2^0$ vertices, it follows by induction that B_k has 2^k vertices.

16. Looking at the pictures for B_k leads one to conjecture that the number of vertices at depth j is $C(k,j)$. For example, in B_4 the number of vertices at the various levels form the sequence 1, 4, 6, 4, 1, which are exactly $C(4,0)$, $C(4,1)$, $C(4,2)$, $C(4,3)$, $C(4,4)$. To prove this by mathematical induction (the base case being trivial), note that by the way B_{k+1} is constructed, the number of vertices at level $j+1$ in B_{k+1} is the sum of the number of vertices at level $j+1$ in B_k and the number of vertices at level j in B_k. By the inductive hypothesis this is $C(k,j+1) + C(k,j)$, which equals $C(k+1,j+1)$ as desired, by Pascal's identity. This holds for $j = k$ as well, and at the 0th level, too, there is clearly just one vertex.

18. Our inductive hypothesis is that the root and the left-most child of the root of B_k have degree k and every other vertex has degree less than k. This is certainly true for B_0 and B_1. Consider B_{k+1}. By Exercise 17, its root has degree $k+1$, as desired. The left-most child of the root is the root of a B_k, which had degree k, and we have added one edge to connect it to the root of B_{k+1}, so its degree is now $k+1$, as desired. Every other vertex of B_{k+1} has the same degree it had in B_k, which was at most k by the inductive hypothesis, and our proof is complete.

20. That an S_k-tree has 2^k vertices is clear by induction, since an S_k-tree has twice as many vertices as an S_{k-1}-tree and an S_0-tree has $2^0 = 1$ vertex. Also by induction we see that there is a unique vertex at level k, since there was a unique vertex at level $k-1$ in the S_{k-1}-tree whose root was made a child of the root of the other S_{k-1}-tree in the construction of the S_k-tree.

22. The level order in each case is the alphabetical order in which the vertices are labeled.

24. Given the set of universal addresses, we need to check two things. First we need to be sure that no address in our list is the address of an internal vertex. This we can accomplish by checking that no address in our list is a prefix of another address in our list. (Also of course, if the list contains 0, then it must contain no other addresses.) Second we need to make sure that all the internal vertices have a leaf as a descendant. To check this, for each address $a_1.a_2. \cdots .a_r$ in the list, and for each i from 1 to r, inclusive, and for each b with $1 \le b < a_i$, we check that there is an address in the list with prefix $a_1.a_2. \cdots .a_{i-1}.b$.

26. We assume that the graph in question is connected. (If it is not, then the statement is vacuously true.) If we remove all the edges of a cut set, the resulting graph cannot still be connected. If the resulting graph contained all the edges of a spanning tree, then it would be connected. Therefore there must be at least one edge of the spanning tree in the cut set.

28. A tree is necessarily a cactus, since no edge is in any simple circuit at all.

30. Suppose G is not a cactus; we will show that G contains a very simple circuit with an even number of edges (see the solution to Exercise 27 for the definition of "very simple circuit"). Suppose instead, then, that every very simple circuit of G contains an odd number of edges. Since G is not a cactus, we can find an edge $e = \{u, v\}$ that is in two different very simple circuits. By simplifying the second circuit if necessary, we can assume that the situation is as pictured here, where x might be u and y might be v. Since the circuits $u, P_3, x, P_1, y, P_4, v, e, u$ and $u, P_3, x, P_2, y, P_4, v, e, u$ are both odd, the paths P_1 and P_2 have to have the same parity. Therefore the very simple circuit consisting of P_1 followed by P_2 backwards has even length, as desired.

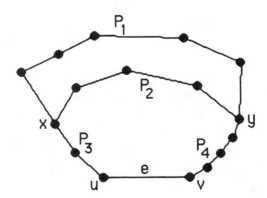

32. The only spanning tree here is the graph itself, and vertex i has degree greater than 3. Thus there is no degree-constrained spanning tree where each vertex has degree less than or equal to 3.

34. Such a tree must be a path (since it is connected and has no vertices of degree greater than 2), and since it includes every vertex in the graph, it is a Hamilton path.

36. The graphs in the first three parts are caterpillars, since every vertex is either in the horizontal path of length 3 or adjacent to a vertex in this path. In part **(d)** it is clear that there is no path that can serve as the "spine" of the caterpillar.

38. **a)** We can gracefully label the vertices in the path in the following manner. Suppose there are n vertices. We label every other vertex, starting with the first, with the numbers $1, 2, \ldots, \lceil n/2 \rceil$; we number the remaining vertices, in the same order, with n, $n-1$, ..., $\lceil n/2 \rceil + 1$. For example, if $n = 7$, then the vertices are labeled $1, 7, 2, 6, 3, 5, 4$. The successive differences are then easily seen to be $n-1$, $n-2$, ..., 2, 1, as desired.

b) We extend the idea in the solution to part **(a)**, allowing for labeling the "feet" as well as the "spine" of the caterpillar. We can assume that the first and last vertices in the spine have no feet. First we label the vertex at the beginning of the spine 1, and, as above, label the vertex adjacent to it n. If there are some feet at this vertex, then we label them 2, 3, ..., k (where the number of feet there is $k - 1$). Then we label the next vertex on the spine with the smallest available number—either 2 or $k + 1$ (if there were feet that needed labeling). If this vertex has feet, then we label them $n-1$, $n-2$, and so on. The largest available number is then used for the label of the next vertex on the spine. We continue in this manner until we have labeled the entire caterpillar. It is clear that the labeling is graceful. See the example below.

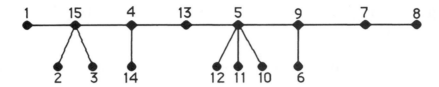

40. By Exercise 48 in Section 9.4, we can number the vertices while doing depth-first search in order of their finishing. It follows from the solution given there that this order corresponds to postorder in the spanning tree. We claim that the opposite order of these numbers gives a topological sort of the vertices in the graph. We must show that there is no directed edge uv such that u's number in this process is less than v's number (prior to reversing the order). Clearly this is true if uv is a tree edge, since the numbers of all of a vertex's descendants are less than the number of that vertex. By Exercise 56 in Section 9.4, there are no back edges in our acyclic digraph. By Exercise 47 in Section 9.4, if uv is a forward edge, then it connects a vertex to a descendant, so the number of u exceeds the number of v, and that is consistent with our given partial order. And if uv is a cross edge, then v is in a previously visited subtree, so the number on v is less than the number on u, again consistent with the given partial order.

42. We form a graph whose vertices are the allowable positions of the people and boat. Each vertex, then, contains the information as to which of the six people and the boat are on, say, the near bank (the remaining people and/or boat are on the far bank). If we label the people X, Y, Z, x, y, z (the husbands in upper case letters and the wives in the corresponding lower case letters) and the boat B, then the initial position is $XYZxyzB$ and the desired final position is the empty set. Two vertices are joined by an edge if it is possible to obtain one position from the other with one legal boat ride (where "legal" means of course that the rules of the puzzle are not violated—that no man is left alone with a woman other than his wife, and that the boat crosses the river only with one or two people in it). For example, the vertex $YZyz$ is adjacent to the vertex $XYZxyzB$, since the married couple Xx can travel to the opposite bank in the boat. Our task is to find a path in this graph from the initial position to the desired final position. Dijkstra's algorithm could be used to find such a path. The graph is too large to draw here, but with this notation (and arrows for readability), one path is $XYZxyzB \to YZyz \to YZxyzB \to YZy \to YZyzB \to Zz \to ZyzB \to Z \to ZzB \to \varnothing$.

44. We assume that what is being asked for here is not "a minimum spanning tree of the graph that also happens to satisfy the degree constraint" but rather "a tree of minimum weight among all spanning trees that satisfy the degree constraint."

a) Since b is a cut vertex we must include at least one of the two edges $\{b, c\}$ and $\{b, d\}$, and one of the other three edges incident to b. Thus the best we can do is to include edges $\{b, c\}$ and $\{a, b\}$. It is then easy to see that the unique minimum spanning tree with degrees constrained to be at most 2 consists of these two edges, together with $\{c, d\}$, $\{a, f\}$, and $\{e, f\}$.

b) Obviously we must include edge $\{a, b\}$. We cannot include edge $\{b, g\}$, because this would force some vertex to have degree greater than 2 in the spanning tree. For a similar reason we cannot include edge $\{b, d\}$. A little more thought shows that the minimum spanning tree under these constraints consists of edge $\{a, b\}$, together with edges $\{b, c\}$, $\{c, d\}$, $\{d, g\}$, $\{f, g\}$, and $\{e, f\}$.

CHAPTER 10
Boolean Algebra

SECTION 10.1   Boolean Functions

2. a) Since $x \cdot 1 = x$, the only solution is $x = 0$.

b) Since $0 + 0 = 0$ and $1 + 1 = 1$, the only solution is $x = 0$.

c) Since this equation holds for all x, there are two solutions, $x = 0$ and $x = 1$.

d) Since either x or $\overline{x}$ must be 0, no matter what x is, there are no solutions.

4. In each case, we compute the various components of the final expression and put them together as indicated. For part **(a)** we have simply

x	y	z	$\overline{z}$
1	1	1	0
1	1	0	1
1	0	1	0
1	0	0	1
0	1	1	0
0	1	0	1
0	0	1	0
0	0	0	1

For part **(b)** we have

x	y	z	$\overline{x}$	$\overline{x}\,y$	$\overline{y}$	$\overline{y}\,z$	$\overline{x}\,y + \overline{y}\,z$
1	1	1	0	0	0	0	0
1	1	0	0	0	0	0	0
1	0	1	0	0	1	1	1
1	0	0	0	0	1	0	0
0	1	1	1	1	0	0	1
0	1	0	1	1	0	0	1
0	0	1	1	0	1	1	1
0	0	0	1	0	1	0	0

For part **(c)** we have

x	y	z	$\overline{y}$	$x\,\overline{y}\,z$	xyz	$\overline{xyz}$	$x\,\overline{y}\,z + \overline{xyz}$
1	1	1	0	0	1	0	0
1	1	0	0	0	0	1	1
1	0	1	1	1	0	1	1
1	0	0	1	0	0	1	1
0	1	1	0	0	0	1	1
0	1	0	0	0	0	1	1
0	0	1	1	0	0	1	1
0	0	0	1	0	0	1	1

For part **(d)** we have

x	y	z	$\overline{x}$	$\overline{y}$	$\overline{z}$	xz	$\overline{x}\,\overline{z}$	$xz + \overline{x}\,\overline{z}$	$\overline{y}(xz + \overline{x}\,\overline{z})$
1	1	1	0	0	0	1	0	1	0
1	1	0	0	0	1	0	0	0	0
1	0	1	0	1	0	1	0	1	1
1	0	0	0	1	1	0	0	0	0
0	1	1	1	0	0	0	0	0	0
0	1	0	1	0	1	0	1	1	0
0	0	1	1	1	0	0	0	0	0
0	0	0	1	1	1	0	1	1	1

6. In each case, we note from our solution to Exercise 4 which vertices need to be blackened in the cube, as in Figure 1.

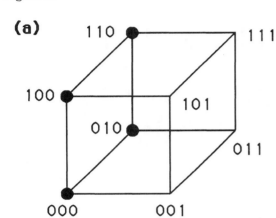

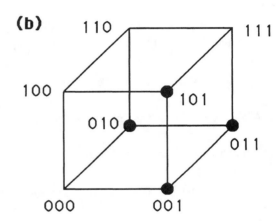

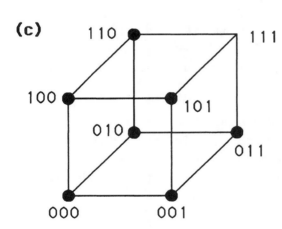

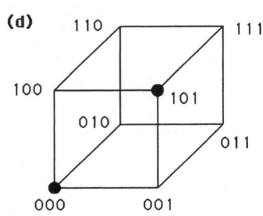

8. There are 2^{2^n} different Boolean functions of degree n, so the answer is $2^{2^7} = 2^{128} \approx 3.4 \times 10^{38}$.

10. The only way for the sum to have the value 1 is for one of the summands to have the value 1, since $0+0+0 = 0$. Each summand is 1 if and only if the two variables in the product making up that summand are both 1. The conclusion follows.

12. If $x = 0$, then $\overline{\overline{x}} = \overline{\overline{0}} = \overline{1} = 0 = x$. We obtain $\overline{\overline{1}} = 1$ by a similar calculation. The relevant table, exhibiting this calculation, has only two rows.

14. We just plug in $x = 0$ and $x = 1$ and see that the equations hold in each case. The relevant tables, exhibiting these calculations, have only two rows.

16. We can make a table to list the four possible combinations of values for x and y in each case, and check that $x + y = y + x$ and $xy = yx$. Alternatively, we simply note that $x + y = 0$ if and only if $x = y = 0$, and $xy = 1$ if and only if $x = y = 1$, and these statement are symmetric in the variables x and y.

18. We can make a table to list all the possibilities, but instead let us argue more directly. The left-hand side of this equation is 1 precisely when either $x = 1$ or both y and z are 1. In the former case, both $x + y$ and $x + z$ are 1, so their product is 1, and in the latter case both $x + y$ and $x + z$ are 1, so again their product is 1. Conversely, the left-hand side is 0 when $x = 0$ and at least one of y and z is 0. In this case, at least one of $x + y$ and $x + z$ is 0, so their product is 0.

20. The unit property states that $x + \overline{x} = 1$. There are only two things to check: $0 + \overline{0} = 0 + 1 = 1$ and $1 + \overline{1} = 1 + 0 = 1$. The relevant table, exhibiting this calculation, has only two rows.

22. a) Since $0 \oplus 0 = 0$ and $1 \oplus 0 = 1$, this expression simplifies to x.
    b) Since $0 \oplus 1 = 1$ and $1 \oplus 1 = 0$, this expression simplifies to $\overline{x}$.
    c) Looking at the definition, we see that $x \oplus x = 0$ for all x.
    d) This is similar to part (**c**); this time the expression always equals 1.

24. A glance at the definition shows that $x \oplus y = y \oplus x$ for all four possibilities for x and y.

26. In each case we simply change each 0 to a 1 and vice versa, and change all the sums to products and vice versa.
    a) xy **b)** $\overline{x} + \overline{y}$ **c)** $(x + y + z)(\overline{x} + \overline{y} + \overline{z})$ **d)** $(x + \overline{z})(x + 1)(\overline{x} + 0)$

28. By Exercise 27, what we are asked to show is equivalent to the statement that for all values of $x_1, x_2, \ldots, x_n$, we have $\overline{F(\overline{x}_1, \ldots, \overline{x}_n)} = \overline{G(\overline{x}_1, \ldots, \overline{x}_n)}$. Now this is clearly equivalent to $F(\overline{x}_1, \ldots, \overline{x}_n) = G(\overline{x}_1, \ldots, \overline{x}_n)$. But the value of the n-tuple $(\overline{x}_1, \ldots, \overline{x}_n)$ ranges over all n-tuples of 0's and 1's as the value of $(x_1, \ldots, x_n)$ ranges over all n-tuples of 0's and 1's (albeit in a different order). Since we are given that $F = G$, the desired conclusion follows.

30. Suppose that you specify $F(0,0,0)$. Then the equations determine $F(\overline{0}, \overline{0}, 0) = F(1,1,0)$ and $F(\overline{0}, 0, \overline{0}) = F(1,0,1)$. It also therefore determines $F(\overline{1}, 1, \overline{0}) = F(0,1,1)$, but nothing else. If we now also specify $F(1,1,1)$ (and there are no restrictions imposed so far), then the equations tell us, in a similar way, what $F(0,0,1)$, $F(0,1,0)$, and $F(1,0,0)$ are. This completes the definition of F. Since we had two choices in specifying $F(0,0,0)$ and two choices in specifying $F(1,1,1)$, the answer is $2 \cdot 2 = 4$.

32. To prove that the complement of x is unique, we suppose that y is a complement (i.e., $x \vee y = 1$ and $x \wedge y = 0$) and play with the symbols (using the axioms in Definition 1) until we have $y = \overline{x}$. The reason for each step in this proof is just one (or more) of these axioms.

$$y = y \wedge 1 = y \wedge (x \vee \overline{x})$$
$$= (y \wedge x) \vee (y \wedge \overline{x})$$
$$= (x \wedge y) \vee (y \wedge \overline{x})$$
$$= 0 \vee (y \wedge \overline{x})$$
$$= y \wedge \overline{x}$$
$$= (y \wedge \overline{x}) \vee 0$$
$$= (y \wedge \overline{x}) \vee (x \wedge \overline{x})$$

$$= (\overline{x} \wedge y) \vee (\overline{x} \wedge x)$$
$$= \overline{x} \wedge (y \vee x)$$
$$= \overline{x} \wedge (x \vee y)$$
$$= \overline{x} \wedge 1 = \overline{x}$$

34. This follows from Exercise 32, where we showed that the complement of an element z is that unique element y such that $z \vee y = 1$ and $z \wedge y = 0$. For this exercise, we just need to show that $y = x$ fits this definition if we choose $z = \overline{x}$. In other words, this will show that x is the complement of $\overline{x}$. But plugging into our equations we have simply $\overline{x} \vee x = 1$ and $\overline{x} \wedge x = 0$, which follow from the axioms (including commutativity).

36. We start with the left-hand side and try to obtain the right-hand side. We freely use the axioms from Definition 1 as well as the result in Exercise 31. For the first identity,

$$x \wedge (y \vee (x \wedge z)) = (x \wedge y) \vee (x \wedge x \wedge z)$$
$$= (x \wedge y) \vee (x \wedge z).$$

The second proof is dual (interchange the roles of $\wedge$ and $\vee$).

38. Since all the axioms come in dual pairs, any proof of an identity can be transformed into a proof of the dual identity by interchanging $\vee$ with $\wedge$ and interchanging 0 with 1. Hence if an identity is valid, so is its dual.

SECTION 10.2   Representing Boolean Functions

2. a) We can rewrite this as $F(x, y) = \overline{x} \cdot 1 + \overline{y} \cdot 1 = \overline{x}(y + \overline{y}) + y(x + \overline{x})$. Expanding and using the commutative and idempotent laws, this simplifies to $\overline{x}\, y + \overline{x}\,\overline{y} + x\, y$.
 b) This is already in sum-of-products form.
 c) We need to write the sum of all products; the answer is $x\, y + x\,\overline{y} + \overline{x}\, y + \overline{x}\,\overline{y}$.
 d) As in part **(a)**, we have $F(x, y) = 1 \cdot \overline{y} = (x + \overline{x})y = x\, y + \overline{x}\, y$.

4. a) We need to write all the terms that have $\overline{x}$ in them. Thus the answer is $\overline{x}\, y\, z + \overline{x}\, y\, \overline{z} + \overline{x}\, \overline{y}\, z + \overline{x}\, \overline{y}\, \overline{z}$.
 b) We need to write all the terms that include either $\overline{x}$ or $\overline{y}$. Thus the answer is $x\, \overline{y}\, z + x\, \overline{y}\, \overline{z} + \overline{x}\, y\, z + \overline{x}\, y\, \overline{z} + \overline{x}\, \overline{y}\, z + \overline{x}\, \overline{y}\, \overline{z}$.
 c) We need to include all the terms that have both $\overline{x}$ and $\overline{y}$. Thus the answer is $\overline{x}\, \overline{y}\, z + \overline{x}\, \overline{y}\, \overline{z}$.
 d) We need to include all the terms that have at least one of $\overline{x}$, $\overline{y}$, and $\overline{z}$. This is all the terms except $x\, y\, z$, so the answer is $x\, y\, \overline{z} + x\, \overline{y}\, z + x\, \overline{y}\, \overline{z} + \overline{x}\, y\, z + \overline{x}\, y\, \overline{z} + \overline{x}\, \overline{y}\, z + \overline{x}\, \overline{y}\, \overline{z}$.

6. We need to include all terms that have three or more of the variables in their uncomplemented form. This will give us a total of $1 + 5 + 10 = 16$ terms. The answer is

$$x_1 x_2 x_3 x_4 x_5 + x_1 x_2 x_3 x_4 \overline{x}_5 + x_1 x_2 x_3 \overline{x}_4 x_5 + x_1 x_2 \overline{x}_3 x_4 x_5 + x_1 \overline{x}_2 x_3 x_4 x_5 + \overline{x}_1 x_2 x_3 x_4 x_5$$
$$+ x_1 x_2 x_3 \overline{x}_4 \overline{x}_5 + x_1 x_2 \overline{x}_3 x_4 \overline{x}_5 + x_1 x_2 \overline{x}_3 \overline{x}_4 x_5 + x_1 \overline{x}_2 x_3 x_4 \overline{x}_5 + x_1 \overline{x}_2 x_3 \overline{x}_4 x_5$$
$$+ x_1 \overline{x}_2 \overline{x}_3 x_4 x_5 + \overline{x}_1 x_2 x_3 x_4 \overline{x}_5 + \overline{x}_1 x_2 x_3 \overline{x}_4 x_5 + \overline{x}_1 x_2 \overline{x}_3 x_4 x_5 + \overline{x}_1 \overline{x}_2 x_3 x_4 x_5.$$

8. We follow the hint and form the product $(\overline{x} + \overline{y} + z)(x + y + z)(x + \overline{y} + z)$. It will have the value 0 as long as one of the factors has the value 0.

10. We follow the hint and include one maxterm in this product for each combination of variables for which the function has the value 0 (see Exercise 9). Since a product is 0 if and only if at least one of the factors is 0, this sum has the desired value.

12. We need to use De Morgan's law to replace each occurrence of $s+t$ by $\overline{(\overline{s}\,\overline{t})}$, simplifying by use of the double complement law if possible.

    a) $(x+y)+z = \overline{(\overline{(x+y)}\,\overline{z})} = \overline{(\overline{x}\,\overline{y}\,\overline{z})}$ **b)** $x+\overline{y}\,(\overline{x}+z) = \overline{(\overline{x}\,(\overline{\overline{y}\,(\overline{x}+z)}))} = \overline{(\overline{x}\,(\overline{y}\,(x\,\overline{z})))}$

    c) In this case we can just apply De Morgan's law directly, to obtain $\overline{x}\,\overline{y} = \overline{x}\,y$.

    d) The second factor is changed in a manner similar to part **(a)**. Thus the answer is $\overline{x}(\overline{x}\,y\,z)$.

14. a) We use the definition of $\mid$. If $x=1$, then $x\mid x=0$; and if $x=0$, then $x\mid x=1$. These are precisely the corresponding values of $\overline{x}$.

    b) We can construct a table to look at all four cases, as follows. Since the fourth and fifth columns are equal, the expressions are equivalent.

x	y	$x\mid y$	$(x\mid y)\mid(x\mid y)$	xy
1	1	0	1	1
1	0	1	0	0
0	1	1	0	0
0	0	1	0	0

    c) We can construct a table to look at all four cases, as follows. Since the fifth and sixth columns are equal, the expressions are equivalent.

x	y	$x\mid x$	$y\mid y$	$(x\mid x)\mid(y\mid y)$	$x+y$
1	1	0	0	1	1
1	0	0	1	1	1
0	1	1	0	1	1
0	0	1	1	0	0

16. Since we already know that complementation, sum and product together are functionally complete, and since Exercise 15 tells us how to write all of these operations totally in terms of $\downarrow$, we can write every Boolean function totally in terms of $\downarrow$.

18. We use the results of Exercise 15.

    a) $(x+y)+z = ((x+y)\downarrow z)\downarrow((x+y)\downarrow z) = (((x\downarrow y)\downarrow(x\downarrow y))\downarrow z)\downarrow(((x\downarrow y)\downarrow(x\downarrow y))\downarrow z)$

    b) $(x+z)y = ((x+z)\downarrow(x+z))\downarrow(y\downarrow y) = (((x\downarrow z)\downarrow(x\downarrow z))\downarrow((x\downarrow z)\downarrow(x\downarrow z)))\downarrow(y\downarrow y)$

    c) This is already in the desired form, since it has no operators.

    d) $x\overline{y} = (x\downarrow x)\downarrow(\overline{y}\downarrow\overline{y}) = (x\downarrow x)\downarrow((y\downarrow y)\downarrow(y\downarrow y))$

20. We assume here that the constants 0 and 1 cannot be used (the answers to parts **(a)** and **(c)** are different if constants are allowed).

    a) Note that $0+0 = 0\oplus 0 = 0$. This means that every function that uses only these two operations must have the value 0 when the inputs are all 0. Therefore using only these two operations, we cannot construct the Boolean function that is 1 for all inputs.

    b) This set is not functionally complete. Note first that $\overline{(x\oplus y)} = \overline{x}\oplus y$. Thus every expression involving these two operations and x and y can be reduced to an *XOR* of the literals x, $\overline{x}$, y, and $\overline{y}$. Note that $\oplus$ is commutative and associative, so that we can rearrange such expressions to group things conveniently. Also, since $x\oplus x = 0$, $x\oplus\overline{x} = 1$, $x\oplus 1 = \overline{x}$ and $x\oplus 0 = x$, and similarly for y (see Exercise 22 in Section 10.1), we can reduce all such expressions to one of the expressions 0, 1, x, y, $\overline{x}$, $\overline{y}$, $x\oplus y$, $x\oplus\overline{y}$, $\overline{x}\oplus y$, or $\overline{x}\oplus\overline{y}$. Since none of these has the same table of values as $x+y$, we conclude that the set is not functionally complete.

c) This is similar to part **(a)**. This time we note that $0 \cdot 0 = 0 \oplus 0 = 0$. Again this means that every function that uses only these two operations must have the value 0 when the inputs are all 0. Therefore using only these two operations, we cannot construct the Boolean function that is 1 for all inputs.

SECTION 10.3   Logic Gates

2. The inputs to the *AND* gate are $\overline{x}$ and $\overline{y}$. The output is then passed through the inverter. Therefore the final output is $\overline{(\overline{x}\,\overline{y})}$. Note that there is a simpler way to form a circuit equivalent to this one, namely $x + y$.

4. This is similar to the previous three exercises. The output is $\overline{(\overline{x}\,y\,z)}(\overline{x} + y + \overline{z})$.

6. We build these circuits up exactly as the expressions are built up. In part **(b)**, for example, we use an *AND* gate to join the outputs of the inverter (which was applied to the output of the *OR* gate applied to x and y) and x.

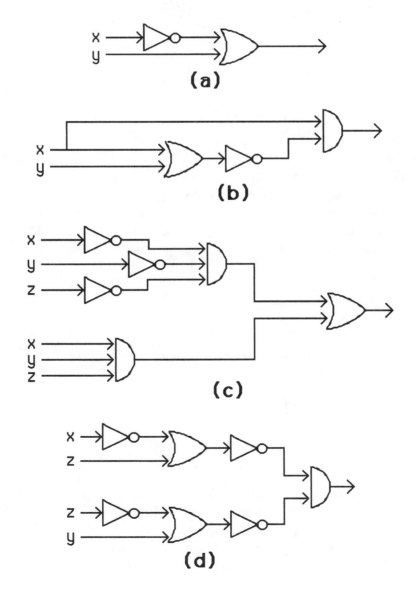

8. In analogy to the situation with three switches in Example 3, we write down the expression we want the circuit to implement: $w\,x\,y\,z + w\,x\,\overline{y}\,\overline{z} + w\,\overline{x}\,y\,\overline{z} + w\,\overline{x}\,\overline{y}\,z + \overline{w}\,x\,y\,\overline{z} + \overline{w}\,x\,\overline{y}\,z + \overline{w}\,\overline{x}\,y\,z + \overline{w}\,\overline{x}\,\overline{y}\,\overline{z}$. The circuit will have 32 inputs, combined by *AND* gates in groups of four, with inverters where necessary, to produce outputs corresponding to the eight minterms in this expression. These outputs are combined with one big *OR* gate. The circuit is shown below, with the picture rotated for ease of display on the page.

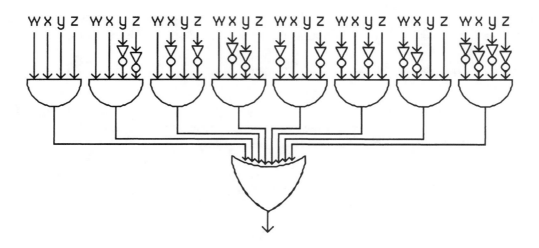

10. First we must determine what the outputs are to be. Let x and y be the input bits, where we want to compute $x - y$. There are two outputs: the difference bit z and the borrow bit b. The borrow will be 1 if a borrow is necessary, which happens only when $x = 0$ and $y = 1$. Thus $b = \overline{x}\,y$. The difference bit will be 1 when $x = 1$ and $y = 0$, and when $x = 0$ and $y = 1$; and it will be 0 in the cases in which $x = y$. Therefore we have $z = \overline{x}\,y + x\,\overline{y}$, which is the same as $b + x\,\overline{y}$. Thus we can draw the half subtractor as shown below. In analogy with Figure 8, we represent the circuit with two inputs and two outputs.

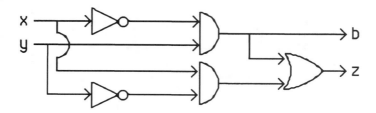

12. We need to combine half subtractors and full subtractors in much the same way that half adders and full adders were combined to produce a circuit to add binary numbers. The first bit of the answer (z_0) is the difference bit between the first two bits of the input (x_0 and y_0), obtained using the half subtractor. The borrow bit output from the half subtractor (b_0) is then the borrow bit input to the full subtractor for determining the second bit of the answer, and so on. Note that the final borrow b_3 must be 0 and is not used.

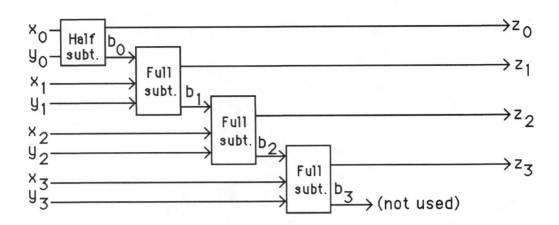

14. Let $(s_3 s_2 s_1 s_0)_2$ be the product. We need to write down Boolean expressions for each of these bits. Clearly $s_0 = x_0 y_0$. The bit s_1 is a 1 if one, but not both, of the products $x_0 y_1$ and $x_1 y_0$ are 1. Therefore we have $s_1 = (x_0 y_1 + x_1 y_0)\overline{(x_0 x_1 y_0 y_1)}$. A similar analysis will show that $s_2 = x_1 y_1 (\overline{x}_0 + \overline{y}_0)$, and that $s_3 = x_0 x_1 y_0 y_1$. The circuit we want has one circuit for each of these bits.

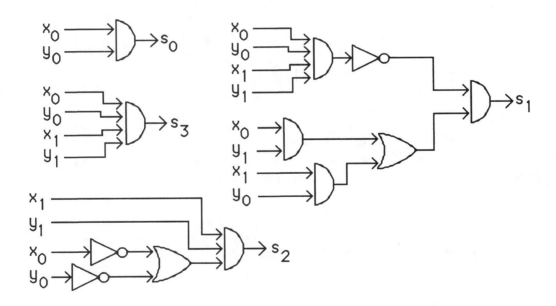

16. The answers here are duals to the answers for Exercise 15. Note that the usual symbol $\downarrow$ represents the *NOR* operation.

a) The circuit is the same as in Exercise 15a, with a *NOR* gate in place of a *NAND* gate, since $\overline{x} = x \mid x = x \downarrow x$.

$x \longrightarrow$ ⟩○ $\longrightarrow \overline{x}$

b) Since $x + y = (x \downarrow y) \downarrow (x \downarrow y)$, the answer is as shown.

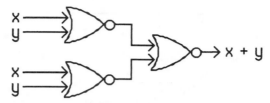

c) Since $xy = (x \downarrow x) \downarrow (y \downarrow y)$, the answer is as shown.

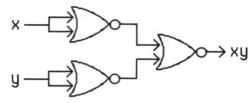

d) We use the representation $x \oplus y = (x+y)\overline{(xy)} = \overline{(\overline{(x+y)} + xy)} = (x \downarrow y) \downarrow (xy) = (x \downarrow y) \downarrow ((x \downarrow x) \downarrow (y \downarrow y))$, obtaining the following circuit.

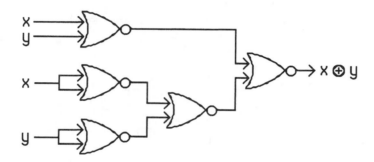

18. We know that the sum bit in the half adder is $s = x \oplus y = x\overline{y} + \overline{x}y$. The answer to Exercise 16d shows precisely this gate constructed from *NOR* gates, so it gives us this part of the answer. Also, the carry bit in the half adder is $c = xy$. The answer to Exercise 16c shows precisely this gate constructed from *NOR* gates, so it gives us this part of the answer.

20. a) The initial inputs have depth 0. Therefore the three *AND* gates all have depth 1, as do their outputs. Therefore the *OR* gate has depth 2, which is the depth of the circuit.

b) The *AND* gate at the top of Figure 6 and the two *NOT* gates have depth 1, so the *AND* gate at the bottom has depth 2. Therefore the inputs to the *OR* gate have depth 1 or 2, so its depth is 3 (one more than the maximum of these), which is the depth of the circuit.

c) The maximum of the depths of the gates is 3, for the final *AND* gate, since the *NOT* gate feeding it has depth 2. Therefore the depth of the circuit is 3.

d) We have to be careful here, since the outputs of the half-adder are 3 for the sum but 1 for the carry. So the depth of the half adder at the top of this full adder is 6 for its sum output and 4 for its carry output. The carry output goes through one more gate, giving a total depth of 5 for the *OR* gate, but the depth of the circuit is 6, because of the output at the upper right.

SECTION 10.4   Minimization of Circuits

2. We just write down the minterms for which there is a 1 in the corresponding box, and join them with $+$.

a) $xy + \bar{x}y + \bar{x}\bar{y}$ b) $xy + x\bar{y}$ c) $xy + x\bar{y} + \bar{x}y + \bar{x}\bar{y}$

4. a) The K-map is shown here. The two 1's combine into the larger block representing the expression $\bar{x}$. Therefore the answer is $\bar{x}$.

b) The K-map is as shown here. The two 1's combine into the larger block representing the expression x. Therefore the answer is x.

c) All four 1's combine to form the larger block which represents the term 1; this is the answer.

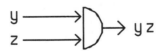

6. a) The function is already presented in its sum-of-products form, so we easily draw the following K-map.

The grouping shown here tells us that the simplest Boolean expression is just yz. Therefore the circuit shown below answers this exercise.

b) This is similar to part **(a)**. The K-map is as shown here.

One large block suffices, so the simplest Boolean expression is just $\bar{z}$. Therefore the circuit shown below answers this exercise.

$$z \longrightarrow \text{\textcircled{$\triangleright$}} \longrightarrow \bar{z}$$

c) First we must put the expression in its sum-of-products form, by "multiplying out." We have

$$\bar{x}\,y\,z\,\big((x+\bar{z})+(\bar{y}+\bar{z})\big) = \bar{x}\,y\,z\,(x+\bar{y}+\bar{z})$$
$$= \bar{x}\,x\,y\,z + \bar{x}\,y\,\bar{y}\,z + \bar{x}\,y\,z\,\bar{z}$$
$$= 0+0+0 = 0\,.$$

This tells us that the circuit always has the output 0. In some sense the simplest circuit is the one with no gates, but if we insist on using some gates, then we can use the fact that $x\,\bar{x} = 0$ and construct the following circuit.

$$x \longrightarrow \cdots \longrightarrow x\,\bar{x} = 0$$

8. In the figure below we have drawn the K-map. For example, since one of the terms was xz, we put a 1 in each cell whose address contained x and z. Note that this meant two cells, one for y and one for $\bar{y}$. Each cell with a 1 in it is an implicant, as are the pairs of cells that form blocks, namely xy, xz, and yz. Since each cell by itself is contained in a block with two cells, none of them is prime. Each of the mentioned blocks with two cells is prime, since none is contained in a larger block. Furthermore, each of these blocks is essential, since each contains a cell that no other prime implicant contains: xy contains $xy\bar{z}$, xz contains $x\bar{y}z$, and yz contains $\bar{x}yz$.

	yz	yz̄	ȳz̄	ȳz
x	1	1		1
x̄	1			

10. The figure below shows the 3-cube Q_3, labeled as requested. Compare with Figure 1 in Section 10.1. A complemented Boolean variable corresponds to 0, and an uncomplemented Boolean variable corresponds to 1. The top face 2-cube corresponds to x, since all of its vertices are labeled x. Similarly, the back face 2-cube represents y, and the right face 2-cube represents z. The opposing faces—bottom, front, and left—represent $\bar{x}$, $\bar{y}$, and $\bar{z}$, respectively.

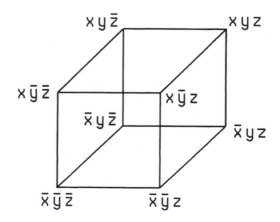

12. In each case the K-map is shown, together with all the maximal groupings and the minimal expansion. Note that in parts **(c)** and **(d)** the answer is not unique, since there is more than one minimal covering of all the squares with 1's in them.

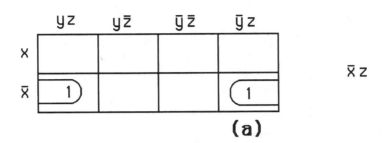

(a)

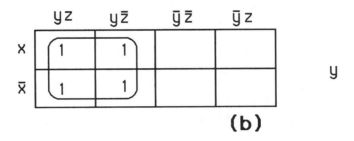

(b)

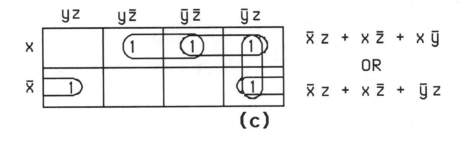

(c)

(d)

14. In each case the K-map is shown, together with the grouping that gives the answer, and the minimal expansion.

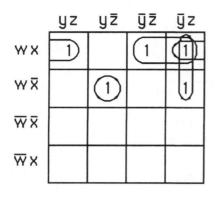

$$w\,\bar{x}\,y\,\bar{z} \;+\; w\,x\,z \;+\; w\,x\,\bar{y} \;+\; w\,\bar{y}\,z$$

(a)

$$w\,x\,y\,\bar{z} \;+\; w\,\bar{x}\,y\,z \;+\; \bar{w}\,\bar{x}\,y\,\bar{z} \;+$$
$$+\; \bar{w}\,\bar{y}\,z \;+\; x\,\bar{y}\,z$$

(b)

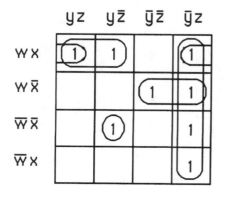

$$\bar{y}\,z \;+\; w\,\bar{x}\,\bar{y} \;+\; w\,x\,y \;+\; \bar{w}\,\bar{x}\,y\,\bar{z}$$

(c)

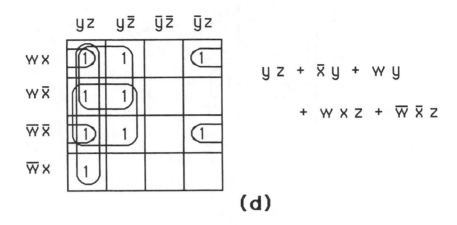

(d)

16. To represent x_1, we need to use half the cells—half correspond to x_1 and half correspond to $\overline{x}_1$. SInce there are $2^6 = 64$ cells in all, we need to use $2^5 = 32$ of them. In fact, the general statement (made formal in Exercise 33 below) is that a term that involves k literals corresponds to an $(n - k)$-dimensional subcube of the n-cube, and so will have 1's in 2^{n-k} cells. Thus we see that $\overline{x}_1 x_6$ needs $2^{6-2} = 16$ cells, $\overline{x}_1 x_2 \overline{x}_6$ needs $2^{6-3} = 8$ cells, $x_2 x_3 x_4 x_5$ needs $2^{6-4} = 4$ cells, and $x_1 \overline{x}_2 x_4 \overline{x}_5$ also needs 4 cells.

18. See the K-map shown for five variables given in the solution for Exercise 15. Minterms that differ only in their treatment of x_1 are adjacent cells in the second and third rows, or in the top and bottom rows (which are to be considered adjacent). Minterms that differ only in their treatment of x_2 are adjacent cells in the first and second rows, or in the third and fourth rows. Minterms that differ only in their treatment of x_3 are adjacent cells in the fourth and fifth columns, or in the first and eighth columns (which are to be considered adjacent), or in the second and seventh columns (which are to be considered adjacent), or in the third and sixth columns (which are to be considered adjacent). Minterms that differ only in their treatment of x_4 are adjacent cells in the second and third columns, or in the sixth and seventh columns, or in the first and fourth columns (which are to be considered adjacent), or in the fifth and eighth columns (which are to be considered adjacent). Minterms that differ only in their treatment of x_5 are adjacent cells in the first and second columns, or in the third and fourth columns, or in the fifth and sixth columns, or in the seventh and eighth columns.

20. In each case we draw the K-map, with the required squares marked by a 1 and the don't care conditions marked with a d. The required expansion is shown.

	yz	yz̄	ȳz̄	ȳz
w x	d	d	d	d
w x̄	d	d		1
w̄ x̄	1			1
w̄ x	1			1

z

(a)

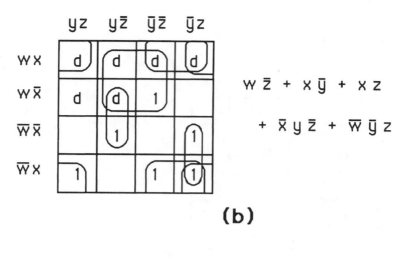

(b)

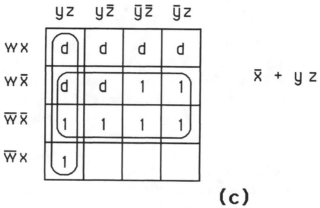

(c)

22. We organize our work as in the text.

a)

	Term	String	Term	String
			Step 1	
1	$x\,y\,\overline{z}$	110	$(1,3)\,x\,\overline{z}$	1–0
2	$\overline{x}\,y\,z$	011	$(3,4)\,\overline{y}\,\overline{z}$	–00
3	$x\,\overline{y}\,\overline{z}$	100		
4	$\overline{x}\,\overline{y}\,\overline{z}$	000		

The products in the last column, together with minterm #2, are the products that are to be used to cover the four minterms. Each is required: $x\,\overline{z}$ to cover minterm #1, $\overline{y}\,\overline{z}$ to cover minterm #4, and minterm #2 to cover itself. Therefore the answer is $x\,\overline{z}+\overline{y}\,\overline{z}+\overline{x}\,y\,z$.

b)

	Term	String	Term	String	Term	String
			Step 1		Step 2	
1	$x\,\overline{y}\,z$	101	$(1,3)\,x\,\overline{y}$	10–	$(1,3,4,5)\,\overline{y}$	–0–
2	$\overline{x}\,y\,z$	011	$(1,4)\,\overline{y}\,z$	–01		
3	$x\,\overline{y}\,\overline{z}$	100	$(2,4)\,\overline{x}\,z$	0–1		
4	$\overline{x}\,\overline{y}\,z$	001	$(3,5)\,\overline{y}\,\overline{z}$	–00		
5	$\overline{x}\,\overline{y}\,\overline{z}$	000	$(4,5)\,\overline{x}\,\overline{y}$	00–		

The product $\overline{y}$ in the last column covers all the minterms except #2, and the third product in Step 1 $(\overline{x}\,z)$ covers it. Thus the answer is $\overline{y}+\overline{x}\,z$.

c)

	Term	String		Step 1			Step 2	
	Term	String	Term	String		Term	String	
1	$x\,y\,z$	111	$(1,2)\,x\,y$	11–		$(1,2,3,5)\,x$	1––	
2	$x\,y\,\overline{z}$	110	$(1,3)\,x\,z$	1–1		$(1,3,4,6)\,z$	––1	
3	$x\,\overline{y}\,z$	101	$(1,4)\,y\,z$	–11		$(3,5,6,7)\,\overline{y}$	–0–	
4	$\overline{x}\,y\,z$	011	$(2,5)\,x\,\overline{z}$	1–0				
5	$x\,\overline{y}\,\overline{z}$	100	$(3,5)\,x\,\overline{y}$	10–				
6	$\overline{x}\,\overline{y}\,z$	001	$(3,6)\,\overline{y}\,z$	–01				
7	$\overline{x}\,\overline{y}\,\overline{z}$	000	$(4,6)\,\overline{x}\,z$	0–1				
			$(5,7)\,\overline{y}\,\overline{z}$	–00				
			$(6,7)\,\overline{x}\,\overline{y}$	00–				

All three products in the last column are necessary and sufficient to cover the minterms. Sufficiency is seen by noticing that all the numbers from 1 to 7 are included in the 4-tuples for these terms. Necessity is seen by noticing that only the first of them covers #2, only the second covers #4, and only the third covers #7. Thus the answer is $x + \overline{y} + z$.

d)

	Term	String		Step 1	
	Term	String	Term	String	
1	$x\,y\,\overline{z}$	110	$(1,2)\,x\,\overline{z}$	1–0	
2	$x\,\overline{y}\,\overline{z}$	100	$(3,4)\,\overline{x}\,\overline{y}$	00–	
3	$\overline{x}\,\overline{y}\,z$	001			
4	$\overline{x}\,\overline{y}\,\overline{z}$	000			

Clearly both products in the last column are necessary and sufficient to cover the minterms. Thus the answer is $x\,\overline{z} + \overline{x}\,\overline{y}$.

24. We follow the procedure and notation given in the text.

a)

	Term	String		Step 1	
	Term	String	Term	String	
1	$w\,x\,y\,z$	1111	$(1,2)\,w\,x\,y$	111–	
2	$w\,x\,y\,\overline{z}$	1110	$(1,3)\,w\,y\,z$	1–11	
3	$w\,\overline{x}\,y\,z$	1011	$(2,4)\,w\,x\,\overline{z}$	11–0	
4	$w\,x\,\overline{y}\,\overline{z}$	1100	$(3,5)\,w\,\overline{x}\,z$	10–1	
5	$w\,\overline{x}\,\overline{y}\,z$	1001	$(3,7)\,\overline{x}\,y\,z$	–011	
6	$\overline{w}\,x\,\overline{y}\,z$	0101	$(4,8)\,w\,\overline{y}\,\overline{z}$	1–00	
7	$\overline{w}\,\overline{x}\,y\,z$	0011	$(5,8)\,w\,\overline{x}\,\overline{y}$	100–	
8	$w\,\overline{x}\,\overline{y}\,\overline{z}$	1000	$(7,9)\,\overline{w}\,\overline{x}\,y$	001–	
9	$\overline{w}\,\overline{x}\,y\,\overline{z}$	0010			

The eight products in the last column as well as minterm #6 are possible products in the desired expansion, since they are not contained in any other product. We make a table of which products cover which of the original minterms.

	1	2	3	4	5	6	7	8	9
$w\,x\,y$	X	X							
$w\,y\,z$	X		X						
$w\,x\,\overline{z}$		X		X					
$w\,\overline{x}\,z$			X		X				
$\overline{x}\,y\,z$			X				X		
$w\,\overline{y}\,\overline{z}$				X				X	
$w\,\overline{x}\,\overline{y}$					X			X	
$\overline{w}\,\overline{x}\,y$							X		X
$\overline{w}\,x\,\overline{y}\,z$						X			

Since only the last of these terms covers minterm #6, it must be included. Similarly, the next to last product must be included, since it is the only one that covers minterms #9. At this point no other minterm is covered by a unique product, so we have to figure out a minimum covering. There are six minterms left to be covered, and each product covers only two of them. Therefore we need at least three products. In fact three products will suffice, if, for instance, we take the first, fourth, and sixth rows. Therefore one possible answer is $w\,x\,y + w\,\overline{x}\,z + w\,\overline{y}\,\overline{z} + \overline{w}\,\overline{x}\,y + \overline{w}\,x\,\overline{y}\,z$.

b)

	Term	String	Step 1 Term	String	Step 2 Term	String
1	$w\,\overline{x}\,y\,z$	1011	$(1,3)\ w\,\overline{x}\,y$	101–	$(2,4,5,7)\ \overline{y}\,\overline{z}$	––00
2	$w\,x\,\overline{y}\,\overline{z}$	1100	$(2,4)\ w\,\overline{y}\,\overline{z}$	1–00	$(3,4,6,7)\ \overline{x}\,\overline{z}$	–0–0
3	$w\,\overline{x}\,y\,\overline{z}$	1010	$(2,5)\ x\,\overline{y}\,\overline{z}$	–100		
4	$w\,\overline{x}\,\overline{y}\,\overline{z}$	1000	$(3,4)\ w\,\overline{x}\,\overline{z}$	10–0		
5	$\overline{w}\,x\,\overline{y}\,\overline{z}$	0100	$(3,6)\ \overline{x}\,y\,\overline{z}$	–010		
6	$\overline{w}\,\overline{x}\,y\,\overline{z}$	0010	$(4,7)\ \overline{x}\,\overline{y}\,\overline{z}$	–000		
7	$\overline{w}\,\overline{x}\,\overline{y}\,\overline{z}$	0000	$(5,7)\ \overline{w}\,\overline{y}\,\overline{z}$	0–00		
			$(6,7)\ \overline{w}\,\overline{x}\,\overline{z}$	00–0		

The two products in the last column, as well as the first product in Step 1 are possible products in the desired expansion, since they are not contained in any other product. Furthermore they are necessary and sufficient to cover all the minterms (they are necessary because of minterms #2, #6, and #1, respectively). Therefore the answer is $\overline{y}\,\overline{z} + \overline{x}\,\overline{z} + w\,\overline{x}\,y$.

c) This problem requires three steps, rather than just two, and there is not enough room across the page to show all the work. Suffice it to say that there are 11 minterms, 16 products of three literals, 7 products of two literals, and one "product" of one literal, namely $\overline{z}$. The products that are not superseded by other products are $\overline{z}$, $\overline{w}\,x$, and $w\,\overline{x}\,y$, and all of them are necessary and sufficient to cover the literals. Therefore the answer is $\overline{z} + \overline{w}\,x + w\,\overline{x}\,y$.

26. We use the same picture as for the sum-of-products expansion with three variables, except that the labels across the top are sums, rather than products: $y + z$, $y + \overline{z}$, $\overline{y} + \overline{z}$, and $\overline{y} + z$. We put a 0 in each square that corresponds to a maxterm in the expansion. For example, if the maxterm $x + y + z$ is present, we put a 0 in the upper left-hand corner. Then we combine the squares to produce larger blocks, exactly as in the usual K-map procedure. The product of enough corresponding sums to cover all the 0's is the desired product-of-sums expansion. See the solution to Exercise 27 for a worked example.

28. It would be hard to see the picture in three-dimensional perspective, so we content ourselves with a planar view. The usual drawing (see Figure 8) *is* a torus, if we think of the left-hand edge as wrapped around and glued to the right-hand edge, and simultaneously the top edge wrapped around and glued to the bottom edge.

30. We need to find blocks that cover all the 1's, and we do not care whether the d's are covered. It is clear that we want to include a large rectangular block covering the entire middle two columns of the K-map; its minterm is $\overline{z}$. The only other 1 needing coverage is in the upper right-hand corner, and the largest block covering it would be the entire first row, whose minterm is $w\,x$. Therefore the answer is $\overline{z} + w\,x$. It happened that all the d's were covered as well.

32. We need to find blocks that cover all the 1's, and we do not care whether the d's are covered. The best way to cover the 1's in the bottom row is to take the entire bottom row, whose minterm is $\overline{w}\,x$. To cover the remaining 1's, the largest block would be the upper right-hand quarter of the diagram, whose minterm is $w\,\overline{y}$. Therefore the minimal sum-of-products expansion is $\overline{w}\,x + w\,\overline{y}$. It did not matter that some of the d's remained uncovered.

SUPPLEMENTARY EXERCISES FOR CHAPTER 10

2. a) If $z = 0$, then the equation is the true statement $0 = 0$, independent of x and y. Hence the answer is no.
  b) This is dual to part (**a**), so the answer is again no (take $z = 1$ this time).
  c) Here the answer is yes. If we take this equation and take the exclusive *OR* of both sides with z, then, since $z \oplus z = 0$ and $s \oplus 0 = s$ for all s, the equation reduces to $x = y$.
  d) If we take $z = 1$, then both sides equal 0, so the answer is no.
  e) This is dual to part (**d**), so again the answer is no.

4. A simple example is the function $F(x, y, z) = x$. Indeed $\overline{F(\overline{x}, \overline{y}, \overline{z})} = \overline{\overline{x}} = x = F(x, y, z)$.

6. a) Since $x + y$ is certainly 1 whenever $x = 1$, we see that $F \leq G$. Clearly the reverse relationship does not hold, since we could have $x = 0$ and $y = 1$.
  b) If $G(x, y) = 1$, then necessarily $x = y = 1$, whence $F(x, y) = 1 + 1 = 1$. Thus $G \leq F$. It is not true that $F \leq G$, since we can take $x = 1$ and $y = 0$.
  c) Neither $F \leq G$ nor $G \leq F$ holds. For the first, take $x = y = 0$, and for the second take $x = y = 1$.

8. First suppose that $F + G \leq H$. We must show that $F \leq H$ and $G \leq H$. By symmetry it is enough to show that $F \leq H$. So suppose that $F(x_1, \ldots, x_n) = 1$. Then clearly $(F + G)(x_1, \ldots, x_n) = 1$ as well. Now since we are given $F + G \leq H$, we conclude that $H(x_1, \ldots, x_n) = 1$, as desired.

  For the converse, assume that $F \leq H$ and $G \leq H$. We want to show that $F + G \leq H$. Suppose that $(F + G)(x_1, \ldots, x_n) = 1$. This means that either $F(x_1, \ldots, x_n) = 1$ or $G(x_1, \ldots, x_n) = 1$. In either case, by the assumption we conclude that $H(x_1, \ldots, x_n) = 1$, and the proof is complete.

10. The picture is the 4-cube.

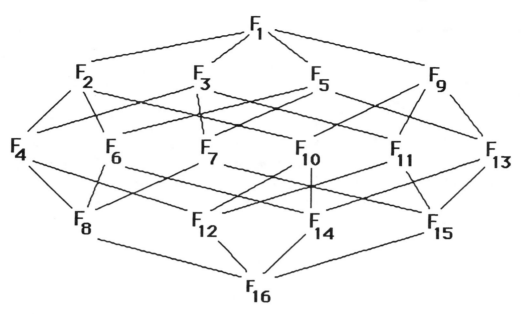

12. From the definition, it is obvious that the value is 1 if and only if either x and y are both 1 or x and y are both 0. This is exactly what $xy + \overline{x}\,\overline{y}$ says, so the identity holds.

14. a) This is clear from looking at the definition in the two cases $x = 0$ and $x = 1$.
   b) This is clear from looking at the definition in the two cases $x = 0$ and $x = 1$.
   c) This is clear from the symmetry of the definition.

16. It is not functionally complete. Every expression involving just x and the operator must have the value 1 when $x = 1$; thus we cannot achieve $\overline{x}$ with just this operator.

18. a) The first *XOR* gate has input $\overline{x}$ and y, so its output is $\overline{x} \oplus y$. Thus the output of the entire circuit is $(\overline{x} \oplus y) \oplus x$. Note that by the properties of $\oplus$, this simplifies to $1 \oplus y = \overline{y}$.
   b) This is similar to part **(a)**. The answer is $((x \oplus y) \oplus (\overline{x} \oplus z)) \oplus (\overline{y} \oplus \overline{z})$, which simplifies to 1.

20. We use four *AND* gates, the outputs of which are joined by an *OR* gate.

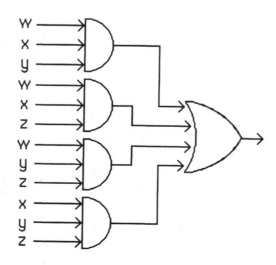

22. In each case we need to give the weights and the threshold.

   a) Let the weight on x be -1, and let the threshold be $-1/2$. If $x = 1$, then the value is -1, which is not greater than the threshold; if $x = 0$, then the value is 0, which is greater than the threshold. Thus the value is greater than the threshold if and only if $\overline{x} = 1$.

   b) We can take the weights on x and y to be 1 each, and the threshold to be $1/2$. Then the weighted sum is greater than the threshold if and only if $x = 1$ or $y = 1$, as desired.

   c) We can take the weights on x and y to be 1 each, and the threshold to be $3/2$. Then the weighted sum is greater than the threshold if and only if $x = y = 1$, as desired.

   d) We can take the weights on x and y to be -1 each, and the threshold to be $-3/2$. Then the weighted sum is greater than the threshold if and only if $x = 0$ or $y = 0$, as desired.

   e) We can take the weights on x and y to be -1 each, and the threshold to be $-1/2$. Then the weighted sum is greater than the threshold if and only if $x = y = 0$, as desired.

   f) In this case we can take the weight on x to be 2, and the weights on y and z to be 1 each. The threshold is $3/2$. In order for the weighted sum to be greater than the threshold, we need either $x = 1$ or $y = z = 1$, which is precisely what we need for $x + yz$ to have the value 1.

   g) This is similar to part (**f**). Take the weights on w, x, y, and z to be 2, 1, 1, and 2, respectively, and the threshold to be $3/2$.

   h) Note that the function is equivalent to $xz(w + \overline{y})$. Thus we want weights and a threshold that requires x and z to be 1 in order to get past the threshold, but in addition requires either $w = 1$ or $y = 0$. A little thought will convince one that letting the weights on x and z be 1, the weight on w be $1/2$, and the weight on y be $-1/2$ will do the job, if the threshold is $9/4$.

24. We prove this by contradiction, assuming that this is a threshold function. Suppose that the weights on w, x, y, and z are a, b, c, and d, respectively, and let the threshold be T. Since $w = x = 1$ and $y = z = 0$ gives a value of 1, we need $a + b \geq T$. Similarly we need $c + d \geq T$. On the other hand, since $w = y = 1$ and $x = z = 0$ gives a value of 0, we need $a + c < T$. Similarly we need $b + d < T$. Adding the first two inequalities shows that $a + b + c + d \geq 2T$; adding the last two shows that $a + b + c + d < 2T$. This contradiction tells us that $wx + yz$ is not a threshold function.

CHAPTER 11
Modeling Computation

SECTION 11.1   Languages and Grammars

2. There are of course a large number of possible answers. Five of them are *the sleepy hare runs quickly*, *the hare passes the tortoise*, *the happy hare runs slowly*, *the happy tortoise passes the hare*, and *the hare passes the happy hare*.

4. a) There is only one terminal string possible here, namely *abbb*. Therefore the language is {*abbb*}.

b) This time there are only two possible strings, so the answer is {*aba, aa*}.

c) Note that A must eventually turn into *ab*. Therefore the answer is {*abb, abab*}.

d) If the rule $S \to AA$ is applied first, then the string that results must be N a's, where N is an even number greater than or equal to 4, since each A becomes a positive even number of a's. If the rule $S \to B$ is applied first, then a string of one or more b's results. Therefore the language is $\{\, a^{2n} \mid n \geq 2 \,\} \cup \{\, b^n \mid n \geq 1 \,\}$.

e) The rules imply that the string will consist of some a's, followed by some b's, followed by some more a's ("some" might be none, though). Furthermore, the total number of a's equals the total number of b's. Thus we can write the answer as $\{\, a^n b^{n+m} a^m \mid m, n \geq 0 \,\}$.

6. If we apply the rule $S \to 0S1$ n times, followed by the rule $S \to \lambda$, then the string $0^n 1^n$ results. On the other hand, no other derivations are possible, since once the rule $S \to \lambda$ is used, the derivation stops. This proves the given statement.

8. a) It follows by induction that unless the derivation has stopped, the string generated by any sequence of applications of the rules must be of the form $0^n S 1^m$ for some nonnegative integers n and m. Conversely, every string of this form can be obtained. Since the only other rule is $S \to \lambda$, the only terminal strings generated by this grammar are $0^n 1^m$.

b) A derivation consists of some applications of the rules until the S disappears, followed, perhaps, by some more applications of the rules. First let us see what can happen up to the point at which the S disappears. The first rule adds 0's to the left of the S. The last rule makes the S disappear, whereas rules two and three turn the S into $1A$ or 1. Therefore the possible strings generated at the point the S disappears are 0^n, $0^n 1$, and $0^n 1A$, where n is a nonnegative integer. By rules four and five, the A eventually turns into one or more 1's. Therefore the possible strings are $0^n 1^m$ for nonnegative integers n and m.

10. By following the pattern given in the solution to Exercise 9, we can certainly generate all the strings $0^n 1^n 2^n$, for $n \geq 0$. We must show that no other terminal strings are possible. First, the number of 0's, A's, and B's must be equal at the point at which S disappears, with all the 0's on the left (where they must stay). The rule $BA \to BA$ tells us the A's can only move left across the B's, not conversely. Furthermore, A's turn into 1's, but only if connected by 1's to a 0; therefore the only way to get rid of the A's is for them all to move to the left of the B's and then turn into 1's. Finally, the B's can only turn into 2's, and they are all on the right.

12. a) We want exactly one 0 and an even number of 1's to its right. Thus we can use the rules $S \to 0A$, $A \to 11A$, and $A \to \lambda$.

b) We can have the new symbols grow out from the center, using the rules $S \to 0S11$ and $S \to \lambda$.

c) We can have the 0's grow out from the center, and then have the center turn into a 1-making machine. The rules we propose are $S \to 0S0$, $S \to A$, $A \to 1A$, and $A \to \lambda$.

14. We can simply have identical symbols grow out from the center, with an optional final symbol in the center itself. Thus we use the rules $S \to 0S0$, $S \to 1S1$, $S \to \lambda$, $S \to 0$, and $S \to 1$. Note that this grammar is context-free since each left-hand side is a single nonterminal symbol.

16. a) The string is the leaves of the tree, read from left to right. Thus the string is "a large mathematician hops wildly."

b) Again, the string is the leaves from left to right, namely $+987$.

18. a) If we look at the beginning of the string, we see that we can use the rule $S \to bcS$ first. Then since the remainder of the string (after the initial bc) starts with bb, we can use the rule $S \to bbS$. Finally, we can use the rule $S \to a$. We therefore obtain the first tree shown below.

b) This is similar to part **(a)**, using three rules to take care of the first six characters, two by two.

c) Again we work two by two from the left, producing the tree shown.

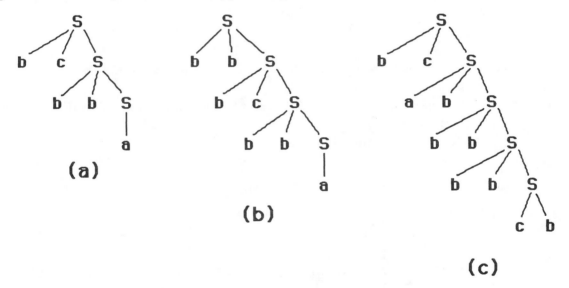

20. a) Since the string starts with a b, we might have either $Baba \Rightarrow baba$ or $Caba \Rightarrow baba$ as the last step in the derivation. The latter looks more hopeful, since the Ca could have come from the rule $A \to Ca$, meaning that the derivation ended $Aba \Rightarrow Caba \Rightarrow baba$. Now we see that since $B \to Ba$ and $B \to b$ are rules, the derivation could have been $S \Rightarrow AB \Rightarrow ABa \Rightarrow Aba \Rightarrow Caba \Rightarrow baba$.

b) There is no way to have obtained an a on the left, since every rule has every a preceded by another symbol (which does not ever turn into λ).

c) This is just like part **(a)**, since we could have used the rule $C \to cb$ instead of the rule $C \to b$, obtaining the extra c on the left. Thus the derivation is $S \Rightarrow AB \Rightarrow ABa \Rightarrow Aba \Rightarrow Caba \Rightarrow cbaba$.

d) The only way for the symbol c to have appeared is through the rule $C \to cb$. Thus we may assume (without loss of generality) that the last step in the derivation was $bbbCa \Rightarrow bbbcba$. Now the only way for Ca to have occurred is from the rule $A \to Ca$. Thus we can assume that the derivation ends $bbbA \Rightarrow bbbCa \Rightarrow bbbcba$. But there is no way for the A to appear at the end (the only rule producing an A puts a B after it). Therefore this string is not in the language.

22. a) We just translate mechanically from the Backus-Naur form to the productions. Let us use E for $\langle expression \rangle$ (which we assume is the starting symbol), and V for $\langle variable \rangle$ for convenience. The rules are $E \to (E)$, $E \to E + E$, $E \to E * E$, and $E \to V$ (from the first form), together with $V \to x$ and $V \to y$ (from the second).

b) The tree is easy to construct. The outermost operation is $+$, so the top part of the tree shows E becoming $E + E$. The right E now is the variable x. The left E is an expression in parentheses, which is itself the product of two variables.

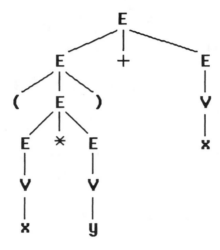

24. a) We first incorporate all the rules from the solution to Exercise 23a except the first two. Then we simply add the rule $S \to \langle sign \rangle \langle integer \rangle / \langle positive\ integer \rangle$.

b) We incorporate all of the solution to Exercise 23b except for the first line, together with a rule $\langle fraction \rangle ::= \langle sign \rangle \langle integer \rangle / \langle positive\ integer \rangle$.

c) The tree practically draws itself from the rules.

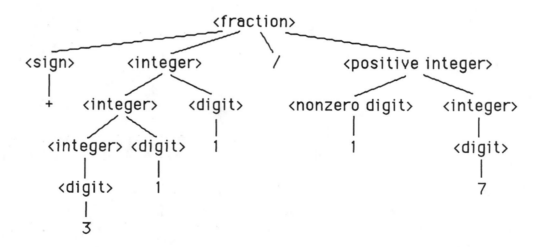

26. We ignore the need for spaces between the names, and we assume that names need to be nonempty. We also do not assume anything more than was given in the statement of the exercise.

$\langle person \rangle ::= \langle firstname \rangle \langle middleinitial \rangle \langle lastname \rangle$

$\langle lastname \rangle ::= \langle letterstring \rangle$

$\langle middleinitial \rangle ::= \langle letter \rangle$

$\langle firstname \rangle ::= \langle ucletter \rangle \mid \langle ucletter \rangle letterstring$

$\langle letterstring \rangle ::= \langle letter \rangle \mid \langle letterstring \rangle \langle letter \rangle$

$\langle letter \rangle ::= \langle lcletter \rangle \mid \langle ucletter \rangle$

$\langle lcletter \rangle ::= a \mid b \mid c \mid \ldots \mid z$

$\langle ucletter \rangle ::= A \mid B \mid C \mid \ldots \mid Z$

28. a) Strings in this set consist of one or more letters followed by an optional binary digit, followed by one or more letters. Only the letters a, b, and c are used, however.

b) Strings in this set consist of an optional plus or minus sign followed by one or more digits.

c) Strings in this set consist of any number of letters, followed by any number of binary digits, followed by any number of letters. "Any number" includes 0, so the string could consist of letters only or of binary digits only, and it could also be empty. Only the letters x and y are used, however. Note that $(D+)?$ is equivalent to $D*$.

30. This is straightforward, using the conventions. We assume that the string gives the sandwich from top to bottom. Note that words in roman font are constants here, and words in italics are variables.

$sandwich ::= \text{bread } dressing \text{ lettuce?tomato?} meat+ \text{ cheese}* \text{ bread}$

$dressing ::= \text{mustard} \mid \text{mayonnaise}$

$meat \ ::= \text{turkey} \mid \text{chicken} \mid \text{beef}$

32. The cosmetic change is to put angled brackets around the variables used for nonterminal symbols. The substantive changes are to replace uses of $+$, $*$, and $?$ with rules that have the same effect. For the plus sign, we replace $x+$, where x is a symbol by a new symbol, let's call it $\langle xplus \rangle$, and the new rule

$\langle xplus \rangle ::= x \mid \langle xplus \rangle x$

Similarly, we replace $x*$, where x is a symbol by a new symbol, let's call it $\langle xstar \rangle$, and the new rule

$\langle xstar \rangle ::= \lambda \mid \langle xstar \rangle x$

where λ is the empty string. Finally, we replace each occurrence of $x?$ by a new symbol, let's call it $\langle xquestion \rangle$, and the new rule

$\langle xquestion \rangle ::= \lambda \mid x$

where x is a symbol; and we replace each occurrence of $(junk)?$ by a new symbol, let's call it $\langle junkquestion \rangle$, and the new rule

$\langle junkquestion \rangle ::= \lambda \mid junk$

where $junk$ is a string of symbols.

34. This is very similar to the preamble to Exercise 33. The only difference is that the operators are placed between their operands, rather than behind them, and parentheses are required in expressions used as factors. Thus we have the following Backus–Naur form:

$\langle expression \rangle ::= \langle term \rangle \mid \langle term \rangle \langle addOperator \rangle \langle term \rangle$

$\langle addOperator \rangle ::= + \mid -$

$\langle term \rangle ::= \langle factor \rangle \mid \langle factor \rangle \langle mulOperator \rangle \langle factor \rangle$

$\langle mulOperator \rangle ::= * \mid /$

$\langle factor \rangle ::= \langle identifier \rangle \mid (\langle expression \rangle)$

36. The definition of "derivable from" says that it is the reflexive, transitive closure of the relation "directly derivable from." Indeed, taking $n = 0$ in that definition gives us the fact that every string is derivable from itself; and the existence of a sequence $w_0 \Rightarrow w_1 \Rightarrow \cdots \Rightarrow w_n$ for $n \geq 1$ means that (w_0, w_n) is in the transitive closure of the relation $\Rightarrow$ (see Theorem 2 in Section 7.4).

SECTION 11.2   Finite-State Machines with Output

2. In each case we need to write down, in a table, all the information contained in the arrows in the diagram. In part (**a**), for example, there are arrows from state s_1 to s_1 labeled $1, 0$ and from s_1 to s_2 labeled $0, 0$. Therefore the row of our table for this machine that gives the information for transitions from s_1 shows that on input 1 the transition is to state s_1 and the output is 0, and on input 0 the transition is to state s_2 and the output is 0.

a)

State	Next State 0	Next State 1	Output 0	Output 1
s_0	s_1	s_2	0	1
s_1	s_2	s_1	0	0
s_2	s_2	s_0	1	0

b)

State	Next State 0	Next State 1	Output 0	Output 1
s_0	s_1	s_2	1	0
s_1	s_0	s_3	1	0
s_2	s_3	s_0	0	0
s_3	s_1	s_2	1	1

c)

State	Next State 0	Next State 1	Output 0	Output 1
s_0	s_3	s_1	0	1
s_1	s_0	s_1	0	1
s_2	s_3	s_1	0	1
s_3	s_1	s_3	0	0

4. a) The machine starts in state s_0. On input 0 it moves to state s_1 and outputs 1. On the next three inputs it stays in state s_1 and outputs 1. Therefore the output is 1111.

b) The machine starts in state s_0. On input 1 it moves to state s_3 and outputs 0. Then on the next input, which is 0, it moves to state s_1 and outputs 0. The next four moves are to states s_2, s_3, s_0, and s_1, with outputs 1001. Thus the answer is 001001.

c) The idea is the same as in the other parts. The answer is 00110000110.

6. We need 9 states. The middle row of states in our picture correspond to no quarters or nickels having been deposited. The top row takes care of the cases in which a nickel has been deposited, and the bottom row handles the cases in which a quarter has been deposited. The columns record the number of dimes (0, 1, or 2). The transitions back to state s_0 are shown as leading off into open space to avoid clutter. Furthermore to avoid clutter we have not drawn six loops, namely loops at states s_3, s_4, and s_5 on input N (since additional nickels are not recorded), and loops at states s_6, s_7, and s_8 on input Q (since additional quarters are not recorded). We do not show the output, since there is none except for all the transitions back to state s_0; there the output is "unlock the door." The letters stand for the obvious coins.

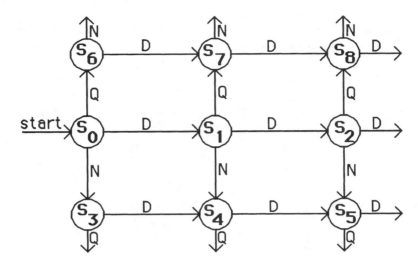

8. We need only two states, since the action depends only on the parity of the number of bits we have read in so far. Transitions from state s_0 to state s_1 are made on the odd-numbered bits, so there we output the same bit as the input. The transitions back to s_0 are made on the even-numbered bits, and there we make the output opposite to the input.

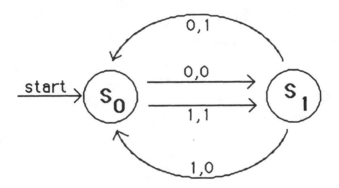

10. To avoid having the machine being too complex, we will keep the model very simple, assuming that the lock opens if and only if the input is $(10, R, 1)(8, L, 2)(37, R, 1)$. In our picture, the "input" A stands for all the inputs other than the inputs shown leading elsewhere. The output 0 means nothing happens; the output U means the lock is unlocked. If we wished to make our model more realistic, we could, for instance, allow the input $(10, R, 1)(8, L, 1)(8, L, 1)(37, R, 1)$ to open the lock, as well as, say, $(10, R, 1)(8, L, 2)(30, R, 1)(37, R, 1)$ (assuming the numbers on the dial are arranged counterclockwise).

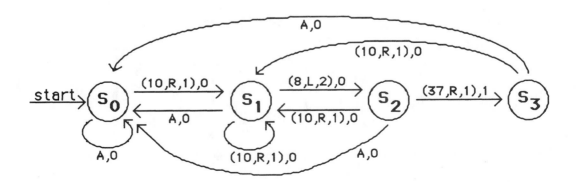

12. We need just three states, to keep track of the remainder when the number of bits read so far is divided by 3. We output 1 when we enter the state s_0 (remainder equals 0).

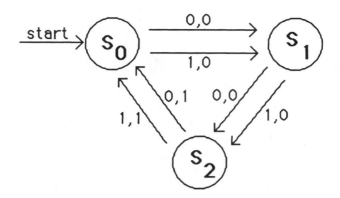

14. Here we just need to keep track of the number of consecutive 1's most recently encountered.

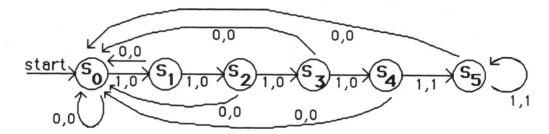

16. We draw the diagram just as we draw diagrams for finite-state machines with output, except that the transitions are labeled with just an input (since no outputs are associated with the transitions), and each state is labeled with an output. For example, since the table tells us that the output of state s_2 is 1, we write a 1 next to state s_2; and since the transition from state s_3 on input 1 is to state s_0, we draw an arrow from s_3 to s_0 labeled 1.

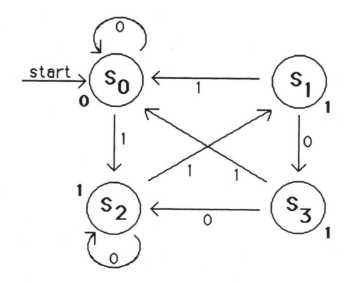

18. Note that the output for a Moore machine is one bit longer than the input: it always starts with the output for state s_0 (which is 0 for this machine).

a) The state that are encountered, after s_0, are s_0, s_2, s_2, and s_1, in that order. Therefore the output is 00111.

b) The states visited are s_2, s_1, s_0, s_2, s_1, s_0, in that order (after the initial state). Therefore the output is 0110110.

c) The procedure is similar to the other parts. The answer is 011001100110.

20. The machine is shown here. Note that state s_i represents the condition that the number of symbols read in so far is congruent to i modulo 4. Thus we make the output 1 at state s_0 and 0 for each of the other states. Each arrow, labeled $0, 1$, stands for two arrows with the same beginning and end, one labeled 0 and one labeled 1.

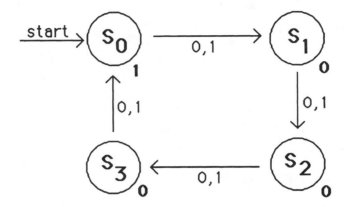

SECTION 11.3   Finite-State Machines with No Output

2. By definition $A\emptyset = \{xy \mid x \in A \land y \in \emptyset\}$. Since there are no elements of the empty set, this set is empty. Similarly $\emptyset A = \emptyset$. (This result is also a corollary of Exercise 6, since a set is empty if and only if its cardinality is 0.)

4. a) If we concatenate any number of copies of the empty string, then we get the empty string.

b) Clearly $A^* \subseteq (A^*)^*$, since $B \subseteq B^*$ for all sets B. To show that $(A^*)^* \subseteq A^*$, let w be an element of $(A^*)^*$. Then $w = w_1 w_2 \ldots w_k$ for some strings $w_i \in A^*$. This means that each $w_i = w_{i1} w_{i2} \ldots w_{in_i}$ for some strings $w_{ij} \in A$. But then $w = w_{11} w_{12} \ldots w_{1n_1} w_{21} w_{22} \ldots w_{2n_2} \ldots w_{k1} w_{k2} \ldots w_{kn_k}$, a concatenation of elements of A, so $w \in A^*$.

6. At most, AB contains one element for each element in $A \times B$, namely $uv \in AB$ when $(u, v) \in A \times B$. (It might contain fewer elements than this, since the same string in AB may arise in two different ways, i.e., from two different ordered pairs.) Therefore $|AB| \leq |A \times B| = |A||B|$.

8. a) This is false; take $A = \{1\}$, so that $A^2 = \{11\}$.

b) This is not true if we take $A = \emptyset$. If we exclude that possibility, then the length of every string in A^2 would be greater than the length of the shortest string in A if $\lambda \notin A$. Thus the statement is true for $A \neq \emptyset$.

c) This is true since $w\lambda = w$ for all strings.

d) This was Exercise 4b.

e) This is false if $\lambda \notin A$, since then the right-hand side contains the empty string but the left-hand side does not.

f) This is false. Take $A = \{0, \lambda\}$. Then $A^2 = \{\lambda, 0, 00\}$, so $|A^2| = 3 \neq 4 = |A|^2$.

10. a) The first input keeps the machine in state s_0. The second input drives it to state s_1. The third input drives it back to state s_0. Since this state (s_0) is final, the string is accepted.

b) The input string drives the machine to states s_1, s_2, s_0, and s_1, respectively. Since s_1 is not a final state, this string is not accepted.

c) The input string drives the machine to states s_1, s_2, s_0, s_1, s_2, s_0, and s_1, respectively. Since s_1 is not a final state, this string is not accepted.

d) The input string drives the machine to states s_0, s_1, s_0, s_1, s_0, s_1, s_0, s_1, and s_0, respectively. Since s_0 is a final state, this string is accepted.

12. Since s_0 is a final state, the empty string is in the language recognized by this machine; note that no other string leads to s_0. The only other final state is s_1, and it is clear that it can be reached if the input string is $1\{0,1\}^*$ or by $01^*0\{0,1\}^*$. Therefore the answer can be summarized as $\{\lambda\} \cup 1\{0,1\}^* \cup 01^*0\{0,1\}^*$.

14. Since state s_0 is final, the empty string is accepted. The only other strings that are accepted are those that drive the machine to state s_1, namely a 0 followed by any number of 1's. Therefore the answer is $\{\lambda\} \cup \{01^n \mid n \geq 0\}$.

16. We need to write down the strings that drive the machine to states s_1 or s_3. It is not hard to see that the answer is $\{1\}^*\{0\}\{0\}^* \cup \{1\}^*\{0\}\{0\}^*\{10,11\}\{0,1\}^*$.

18. The empty string is accepted, since the start state is final. No other string drives the machine to state s_0, so the only other accepted strings are the ones that can drive the machine to state s_1. Clearly the strings 0 and 1 do so. Also, every string of one or more 1's can drive the machine to state s_2, after which a 0 will take it to state s_1. Therefore all the strings of the form 1^n0 for $n \geq 1$ are also accepted. Thus the answer is $\{\lambda, 0, 1\} \cup \{1^n0 \mid n \geq 1\}$. (This can also be written as $\{\lambda, 1\} \cup \{1^n0 \mid n \geq 0\}$, since $0 = 1^00$.)

20. We can end up at state s_0 by doing nothing, and we can end up at state s_1 by reading a 1. We can also end up at these final states by reading $10\{0,1\}$ first, any number of times. Therefore the answer is $(10\{0,1\})^*\{\lambda, 1\}$.

22. One way to do Exercises 22–26 is to construct a machine following the proof of Theorem 1. Rather than do that, we construct the machines in an ad hoc way, using the answers obtained in Exercises 17–21. As we saw in the solution to Exercise 17, the language recognized by this machine is $\{0, 01, 11\}$. A deterministic machine to recognize this language is shown below. Note that state s_5 is a graveyard state.

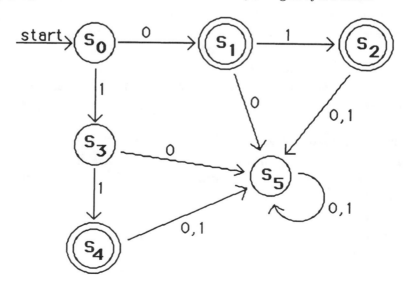

24. This is similar to Exercise 18.

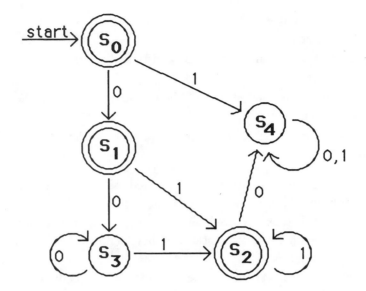

26. This one is fairly simple, since the nondeterministic machine is almost deterministic. In fact, all we need to do is to eliminate the transition from s_1 to the graveyard state s_2 on input 0, and the transition from s_3 to s_2 on input 0.

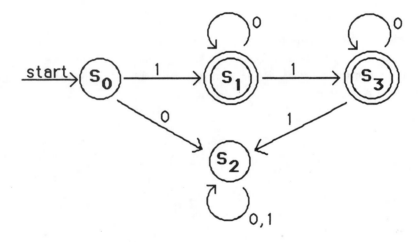

28. The machines in the solutions to Exercise 27, with the graveyard state removed, satisfy the requirements of this exercise.

SECTION 11.4   Language Recognition

2. a) The string is in the set, since it is $10^1 1^2$.

b) The string is in the set, since it is $(10)(11)$.

c) The string is in the set, since it is $1(01)1$.

d) The string is in the set: take the first $*$ to be 1, and take the 1 in the union.

e) The string is in the set, since it is $(10)(11)$.

f) The strings in this set must have odd length, so the given string is not in the set.

g) The string is in the set: take $*$ to be 0.

h) The string is in the set: choose 1 from the first group, 01 from the second, and take $* = 1$.

4. a) Since we want to accept no strings, we will have no final states. We need only one state, the start state, and there is a transition from this state to itself on all inputs.

b) This is just like part **(a)**, except that we want to accept the empty string. Our machine will have two states. The start state will be final, the other state will not be final. On all inputs, there is a transition from each of the states to the nonfinal state.

c) This time we need three states, s_0 (the start state), s_1, and s_2. Only s_1 is final. On input a, there is a transition from s_0 to s_1: this will make sure that a is accepted. All other transitions are to s_2, which serves as a graveyard state: from s_0 on all inputs except a, and from s_1 and s_2 on all inputs. (It is not clear from the exercise whether a is meant to be one fixed element of I, as we have assumed, or rather whether we are to accept all strings of length 1. If the latter is intended, then we have a transition from state s_0 to state s_1 for every $a \in I$.)

6. It is not specified whether our automaton in each case needs to be deterministic; we will build nondeterministic ones and remark that it is easy enough to convert them to deterministic ones (simply add transitions to a graveyard state for all the transitions missing from these machines). The construction is straightforward in each case: we just lead to final states on the desired inputs.

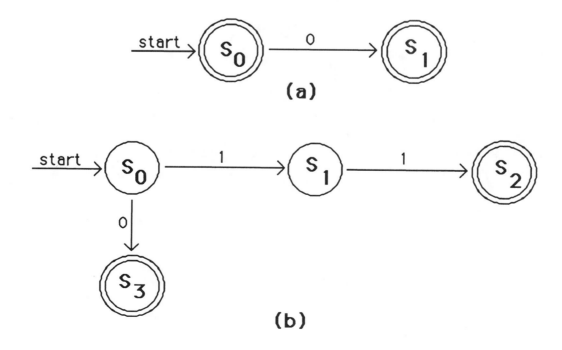

(a)

(b)

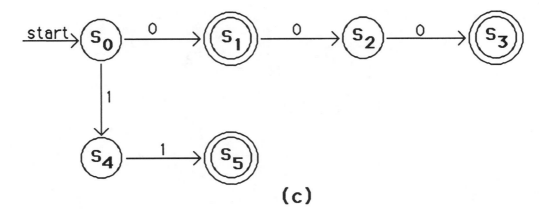

(c)

8. In each case we follow the construction inherent in the proof of Theorem 2. There is one state for each nonterminal symbol (which we have denoted with the name of the symbol), and there is one more state—the only final one unless $S \to \lambda$ is a transition—which we call F.

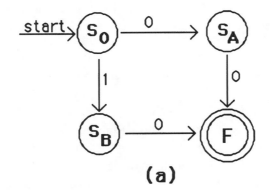

(a)

(b)

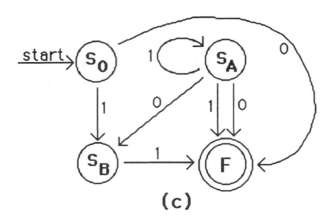

(c)

10. The transitions between states cause us to put in the rules $S \to 0A$, $S \to 1B$, $A \to 0B$, $A \to 1A$, $B \to 0B$, and $B \to 1A$. The transitions to final states cause us to put in the rules $S \to 0$, $A \to 1$, and $B \to 1$. Finally, since s_0 is a final state, we add the rule $S \to \lambda$.

12. This is clear, since the unique derivation of every terminal string in the grammar is exactly reflected in the operation of the machine. Precisely those nonempty strings that are generated drive the machine to its final state, and the empty string is accepted if and only if it is in the language.

14. We construct a new nondeterministic finite-state automaton from a given one as follows. A new state s_0' is added (but s_0 is still the start state). The new state is final if and only if s_0 is final. All transitions into s_0 are redirected so that they end at s_0'. Then all transitions out of s_0 are copied to become transitions out of s_0'. It is clear that s_0 can never be revisited, since all the transitions into it were redirected. Furthermore, s_0' is playing the same role that s_0 used to play (after one or more symbols of input have been read), so exactly the same set of strings is accepted.

16. Let the states that were encountered on input x be, in order, s_0, s_{i_1}, s_{i_2}, ..., s_{i_n}, where $n = l(x)$. Since we are given that $n \geq |S|$, this list of $n+1$ states must, by the pigeonhole principle, contain a repetition; suppose that the first repeated state is s_r. Let v be that portion of x that caused the machine to move from s_r on its first encounter back to s_r for the second encounter. Let u be the portion of x before v, and let w be the portion of x after v. In particular $l(v) \geq 1$ and $l(uv) \leq |S|$ (since all the states appearing before the second encounter with s_r are different). Furthermore, the string uv^iw, for each nonnegative integer i, must drive the machine to exactly the same final state as $x = uvw$ did, since the v^i part of the string simply drives the machine around and around in a loop starting and ending at s_r (the loop is traversed i times). Therefore all these strings are accepted (since x was accepted), and so all of them are in the language.

18. Assume that this set is regular, accepted by a deterministic finite-state automaton with state set S. Let $x = 1^{n^2}$ for some $n \geq \sqrt{|S|}$. By the pumping lemma, we can write $x = uvw$ with v nonempty, so that uv^iw is in our set for all i. Since there is only one symbol involved, we can write $u = 1^r$, $v = 1^s$ and $w = 1^t$, so that the statement that uv^iw is in our set is the statement that $(r+t) + si$ is a perfect square. But this cannot be, since successive perfect squares differ by increasing large amounts as they grow larger, whereas the terms in the sequence $(r+t) + si$ have a constant difference for $i = 0, 1, \ldots$. This contradiction tells us that the set is not regular.

20. This (far from easy) proof is similar in spirit to Warshall's algorithm. The interested reader should consult a reference in computation theory, such as *Elements of the Theory of Computation* by H. R. Lewis and C. H. Papadimitriou (Prentice-Hall, 1981).

SECTION 11.5   Turing Machines

2. We will indicate the configuration of the Turing machine using a notation such as $0[s_2]1B1$, as described in the solution to Exercise 1. (This means that the machine is in state s_2, the tape is blank except for a portion that reads $01B1$, and the tape head points to the left-most 1.) We indicate the successive configurations with arrows.

a) Initially the configuration is $[s_0]0101$. Using the first five-tuple, the machine next enters configuration $0[s_1]101$. Thereafter it proceeds as follows: $0[s_1]101 \to 01[s_1]01 \to 011[s_2]1$. Since there is no five-tuple for this combination (in state s_2 reading a 1), the machine halts. Thus (the nonblank portion of) the final tape reads 0111.

b) $[s_0]111 \to [s_1]B011 \to 0[s_2]011 \to$ halt; final tape 0011

c) $[s_0]00B00 \to 0[s_1]0B00 \to 01[s_2]B00 \to 010[s_3]00 \to$ halt; final tape 01000

d) $[s_0]B \to 1[s_1]B \to 10[s_2]B \to 100[s_3]B \to$ halt; final tape 100

4. This machine does several things. First, it looks at the first symbol on the tape and erases it (changes it to a blank) if it is a 0 but leaves it alone if it is a 1. Next it moves to the second square and starts scanning to the right, skipping over any 0's it encounters (leaving them unchanged), until it comes to a 1. (If it does not come to a 1, then it halts when reaching the end of the input.) On encountering a 1, it leaves it alone and looks at the next symbol. If that symbol is a 0, then this process repeats (i.e., blocks of 0's are skipped over until the next 1 is encountered). If it is a blank (i.e., if the input consisted of just 11 or ends in 01), then the machine just halts at this point. If it a 1, however (so that the machine has now seen a pair of consecutive 1's), then both of these final two 1's are changed to 0's and the machine halts.

6. We can do this with just one state. The five-tuples are $(s_0, 0, s_0, 1, R)$ and $(s_0, 1, s_0, 1, R)$. When the input is exhausted, the machine just halts.

8. We need to have the machine look for a pair of consecutive 1's. The following five-tuples will do that: $(s_0, 0, s_0, 0, R)$, $(s_0, 1, s_1, 1, R)$, $(s_1, 0, s_0, 0, R)$, and $(s_1, 1, s_2, 0, L)$. Once the machine is in state s_2, it has just replaced the second 1 in the first pair of consecutive 1's with a 0 and backed up to the first 1 in this pair. Thus the five-tuple $(s_2, 1, s_3, 0, R)$ will complete the job.

10. We can stay in state s_0 until we have hit the first 1; then stay in state s_1 until we have hit the second 1. At that point we can enter state s_2 which will be an accepting state. If we come to the final blank while still in states s_0 or s_1, then we will not accept. The five-tuples are simply $(s_0, 0, s_0, 0, R)$, $(s_0, 1, s_1, 1, R)$, $(s_1, 0, s_1, 0, R)$, and $(s_1, 1, s_2, 1, R)$.

12. We use the notation mentioned in the solution to Exercise 2. The tape contents are the symbols shown in each configuration, without the state.

a) $[s_0]0011 \to M[s_1]011 \to M0[s_1]11 \to M01[s_1]1 \to M011[s_1]B \to M01[s_2]1 \to M0[s_3]1M \to M[s_3]01M \to$ $[s_4]M01M \to M[s_0]01M \to MM[s_1]1M \to MM1[s_1]M \to MM[s_2]1M \to M[s_3]MMM \to MM[s_5]MM \to$ $MMM[s_6]M \to$ halt and accept

b) $[s_0]00011 \to M[s_1]0011 \to M0[s_1]011 \to M00[s_1]11 \to M001[s_1]1 \to M0011[s_1]B \to M001[s_2]1 \to$ $M00[s_3]1M \to M0[s_3]01M \to M[s_4]001M \to [s_4]M001M \to M[s_0]001M \to MM[s_1]01M \to MM0[s_1]1M \to$ $MM01[s_1]M \to MM0[s_2]1M \to MM[s_3]0MM \to M[s_4]M0MM \to MM[s_0]0MM \to MMM[s_1]MM \to$ $MM[s_2]MMM \to$ halt and reject

c) $[s_0]101100 \to$ halt and reject

d) $[s_0]000111 \to M[s_1]00111 \to M0[s_1]0111 \to M00[s_1]111 \to M001[s_1]11 \to M0011[s_1]1 \to M00111[s_1]B \to$ $M0011[s_2]1 \to M001[s_3]1M \to M00[s_3]11M \to M0[s_3]011M \to M[s_4]0011M \to [s_4]M0011M \to$

$M[s_0]0011M \rightarrow MM[s_1]011M \rightarrow MM0[s_1]11M \rightarrow MM01[s_1]1M \rightarrow MM011[s_1]M \rightarrow MM01[s_2]1M \rightarrow$
$MM0[s_3]1MM \rightarrow MM[s_3]01MM \rightarrow M[s_4]M01MM \rightarrow MM[s_0]01MM \rightarrow MMM[s_1]1MM \rightarrow$
$MMM1[s_1]MM \rightarrow MMM[s_2]1MM \rightarrow MM[s_3]MMMM \rightarrow MMM[s_5]MMM \rightarrow MMMM[s_6]MM \rightarrow$
halt and accept

14. This task is similar to the task accomplished in Example 3. There is one sense in which it is simpler: since we are allowing $n = 0$, we do not need to make any special efforts to reject the empty string. There is one sense, of course, in which it is harder, namely the need to change two 0's to M's at the left for every one 1 changed to an M at the right. The following five-tuples should accomplish the job: $(s_0, 0, s_1, M, R)$, (s_0, B, s_5, B, R), (s_0, M, s_5, M, R), $(s_1, 0, s_2, M, R)$, $(s_2, 0, s_2, 0, R)$, $(s_2, 1, s_2, 1, R)$, (s_2, M, s_3, M, L), (s_2, B, s_3, B, L), $(s_3, 1, s_4, M, L)$, $(s_4, 0, s_4, 0, L)$, $(s_4, 1, s_4, 1, L)$, (s_4, M, s_0, M, R).

16. This is pretty simple, since all we need to do is to put in two extra 1's. The following five-tuples will do the job: $(s_0, 1, s_1, 1, L)$, $(s_1, B, s_2, 1, L)$, $(s_2, B, s_3, 1, L)$.

18. We want to erase 1's in sets of three, as long as there are at least four 1's left. We can accomplish this by first checking for the presence of the four 1's, then erasing them, and then repositioning the tape head to repeat this task. The following five-tuples will do the job: $(s_0, 1, s_1, 1, R)$, $(s_1, 1, s_2, 1, R)$, $(s_2, 1, s_3, 1, R)$, $(s_3, 1, s_4, 1, L)$, $(s_4, 1, s_5, B, L)$, $(s_5, 1, s_6, B, L)$, $(s_6, 1, s_7, B, R)$, (s_7, B, s_8, B, R), (s_8, B, s_0, B, R).

20. We need to erase the first input, then replace the asterisk by a 1 and write one more 1. This straightforward task can be done with the following five-tuples: $(s_0, 1, s_0, B, R)$, $(s_0, *, s_1, 1, L)$, $(s_1, B, s_2, 1, L)$.

22. Since the number n is represented by $n + 1$ 1's, we need to be a little careful here. The most straightforward approach is to replace the middle asterisk by a 1 and erase one 1 from each end of the input. The following five-tuples will do the job: $(s_0, 1, s_1, B, R)$, $(s_1, 1, s_1, 1, R)$, $(s_1, *, s_2, 1, R)$, $(s_2, 1, s_2, 1, R)$, (s_2, B, s_3, B, L), $(s_3, 1, s_4, B, R)$.

24. The technical details here are rather messy. The reader should consult the article on the busy beaver problem in A. K. Dewdney's *The New Turing Omnibus: 66 Excursions in Computer Science* (Freeman, 1993); further references are given there.

SUPPLEMENTARY EXERCISES FOR CHAPTER 11

2. We will construct a grammar that will initially generate a string of the form $DD\ldots D0E$, with zero or more D's on the left, a 0 in the middle, and an E on the right. The D's will migrate across the 0's in the middle, each one doubling the number of 0's present. When the D reaches the E on the right, it is absorbed. Thus our grammar has the following rules. The rules $S \rightarrow A0E$, $A \rightarrow AD$, and $A \rightarrow \lambda$ create the strings of the formed mentioned above. The rule $D0 \rightarrow 00D$ causes the doubling. The rule $DE \rightarrow E$ absorbs the D's. Finally, we need to add the rule $E \rightarrow \lambda$ to finish off every derivation.

4. It can be proved by induction on the length of the derivation that every terminal string derivable from A or B is a well-formed string of parentheses. It follows that the language generated by this grammar is contained in the set of well-formed strings of parentheses. Conversely, it can be proved by induction on the length of the string that every well-formed string of parentheses is derivable from this grammar.

6. There is only one derivation of length n, for each n, namely $S \Rightarrow 0S \Rightarrow 00S \Rightarrow \cdots \Rightarrow 0^{n-1}S \Rightarrow 0^n$. Therefore derivation trees are unique.

8. a) This is true: $A(B \cup C) = \{ ax \mid a \in A \land x \in B \cup C \} = \{ ax \mid a \in A \land (x \in B \lor x \in C) \} = \{ ax \mid (a \in A \land x \in B) \lor (a \in A \land x \in C) \} = \{ ax \mid a \in A \land x \in B \} \cup \{ ax \mid a \in A \land x \in C \} = AB \cup AC$.

b) This is also true; the proof is similar to that in part **(a)**.

c) This is true: $(AB)C = \{ xc \mid x \in AB \land c \in C \} = \{ abc \mid a \in A \land b \in B \land c \in C \}$ and $A(BC)$ equals the same set.

d) This is not true. Let $A = \{0\}$ and $B = \{1\}$. Then 01 is in the left-hand side but not the right-hand side.

10. Clearly the strings generated by this regular expression have no 0 immediately preceding a 2. Conversely, we can take any string with this property and, by grouping the 2's together, view it as coming from this regular expression (we need to imagine a group of no 2's between every pair of consecutive 1's).

12. a) This regular expression is equivalent to $(0 \cup 1)^*$, whose star height is 1. Clearly we cannot find an equivalent expression with star height 0.

b) It is always true that $(\mathbf{AB}^*)^*$ is equivalent to $\mathbf{A}^* \cup \mathbf{A}(\mathbf{A} \cup \mathbf{B})^*$. Thus we can replace the given expression (which has star height 3) by one with star height 2, namely $\mathbf{0}^* \cup \mathbf{0}(\mathbf{0} \cup \mathbf{01}^*\mathbf{0})^*$. Now since the substrings of consecutive 0's and 1's can be arbitrarily long, and yet not all strings are in the language (since each two maximal substrings of 1's must be separated by at least two 0's), it is not possible to reduce the star height to 1.

c) This regular expression is equivalent to $(0 \cup 1)^*$, whose star height is 1. Clearly we cannot find an equivalent expression with star height 0.

14. We draw only the deterministic finite-state automaton for this problem. The finite-state machine with output is identical, except that the output is 1 if and only if the transition is to the final state in our picture. The idea here is simply that state s_i corresponds to having just seen i consecutive 1's.

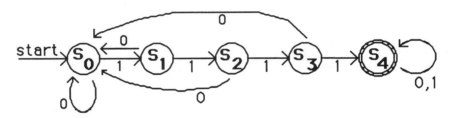

16. If x is a string and s is a state, then $f(s, x)$ means the state that string x drives the machine to if the machine is currently in state s.

a) It is clear that by following the appropriate arrows, we can reach all the states except s_3 from state s_0; for example, $f(s_0, 01) = s_5$ and $f(s_0, \lambda) = s_0$. Clearly we cannot reach state s_3 from any other state.

b) Clearly only states s_2 and s_5 are reachable from state s_2.

c) A transient state s is one for which there is no path from s to itself. Clearly, once we leave state s_0 or s_1 or s_3 or s_6, we cannot return, so these are the transient states. Because of the loops, the other states are not transient. (Note, however, that a state does not need to have a loop at it in order to be nontransient.)

d) Clearly only s_4 and s_5 are the sinks, since the other states all have arrows leaving them.

18. a) To specify a deterministic automaton, we need to pick a start state (n ways to do this), we need to pick a set of final states (2^n ways to do this), and for each pair (state, input) (and there are nk such pairs) we need to choose a state for the transition (n^{nk} ways to do this). Therefore the answer is $n2^n n^{nk} = 2^n n^{nk+1}$.

b) This is the same as part **(a)**, except that we need to choose one of the 2^n subsets of states for each pair (state, input). Therefore the answer is $n2^n(2^n)^{nk} = n2^{n+kn^2}$.

20. No states are final, so no strings are accepted. Therefore the language recognized by this machine is $\emptyset$.

22. a) An even number (we assume that "positive even number" is implied here) of 1's is represented by $11(11)^*$. An odd number of 0's is similarly represented by $0(00)^*$. If we interpret "interspersed" in a positive sense (insisting that the string start and end with 1's), then our answer is

$$11(11)^*(0(00)^*11(11)^*)^*.$$

b) This one is straightforward: $(1 \cup 0)^*(00 \cup 111)(1 \cup 0)^*$.

c) The middle of this expression must be $(1(0 \cup 00))^*$, so as to guarantee the desired interspersing. The beginning may allow up to two 0's, and the end may allow up to one 1. Therefore the answer is $(\emptyset^* \cup 0 \cup 00)(1(0 \cup 00))^*(\emptyset^* \cup 1)$.

24. It is clear from the definition of the sets generated by regular expressions that the union of two regular sets is regular. From Exercise 23 we know that the complement of a regular set is regular. Now $A \cap B = \overline{(\overline{A} \cup \overline{B})}$; therefore if A and B are regular, so is their intersection.

26. The proof is essentially identical to the solution of Exercise 18 in Section 11.4, since the gaps between successive powers of 2, like the gaps between successive squares, grow as the numbers get larger.

28. Suppose that there were a context-free grammar generating this set, and apply the analog of the pumping lemma to obtain strings u, v, w, x, and y such that not both v and x are empty and uv^iwx^iy is of the form $0^n1^n2^n$ for all i. Now if either v or x contains two or three different symbols, then uv^2wx^2y has the symbols out of order. Therefore at least one symbol (say the 0) is missing from vx. On the other hand at least one symbol (say the 1) appears in vx (since $vx \neq \lambda$). But then uv^iwx^iy must have more 1's than 0's for large i, a contradiction. Therefore there is no such context-free grammar.

APPENDIXES

APPENDIX 1   Exponential and Logarithmic Functions

2. a) Since $1024 = 2^{10}$, we know that $\log_2 1024 = 10$.

b) Since $1/4 = 2^{-2}$, we know that $\log_2(1/4) = -2$.

c) Note that $4 = 2^2$ and $8 = 2^3$. Therefore $2 = 4^{1/2}$, so $8 = (4^{1/2})^3 = 4^{3/2}$. Therefore $\log_4 8 = 3/2$.

4. We show that each side is equal to the same quantity.

$$a^{\log_b c} = \left(b^{\log_b a}\right)^{\log_b c} = b^{(\log_b a)(\log_b c)}$$

$$c^{\log_b a} = \left(b^{\log_b c}\right)^{\log_b a} = b^{(\log_b c)(\log_b a)}$$

6. Each graph looks *exactly* like Figure 2, with the scale on the x-axis changed so that the point $(b, 1)$ is on the curve in each case.

APPENDIX 2   Pseudocode

2. We need three assignment statements to do the interchange, in order not to lose one of the values.

procedure *interchange*(x, y)
temp $:= x$
$x := y$
$y :=$ *temp*

Suggested Syllabi

The text has been designed to be flexible. It can used in a variety of courses, including one-term or two-term courses, at either a basic or a more advanced level. I suggest that all instructors cover the core material as described in the preface of the text. Instructors can choose additional topics based on their specific interests or the needs of their students. In particular, extra topics for courses with a computer science slant and with a mathematics slant are presented in the preface of the text. Instructors who follow any of my suggested syllabi, treating topics in the order they are listed, can offer a course that integrates and unifies the basic themes of a discrete mathematics course.

Instructors should also consult the Instructor Resources section of the Rosen/Discrete Mathematics website (`http://www.mhhe.com/rosen`) for additional syllabi, including those used by instructors at different schools. Instructors may find it valuable to look at the syllabi used at other institutions since they may find a syllabus for a course that has similar goals as their own.

The following syllabi give the suggested number of one-hour lectures required for each chapter for several different types of courses, including

- a basic course covering both logic and algorithms
- a basic course concentrating on logic and proofs, and covering some Boolean algebra
- a basic course covering logic and assuming students are familiar with the basic notions concerning algorithms
- a course for well-prepared students with a computer science emphasis
- a course for well-prepared students with a mathematics emphasis
- a two-term course.

Each semester is assumed to consist of 45 periods of approximately 50 minutes to one hour. Instructors should be able to create their own custom syllabus by picking and choosing the sections that are important to achieve their goals.

BASIC COURSE WITH COVERAGE OF BOTH LOGIC AND ALGORITHMS

This course covers the core material carefully. Students in such a course need a complete treatment of logic and proof, sets, and functions, as well as algorithms and mathematical reasoning. From this basis, counting techniques and discrete structures can be studied effectively. Key topics involving relations, graphs, and trees are covered in this course.

Chapter	Sections	Lectures
1	1.1–1.8	9
2	2.1–2.5	6
3	3.1–3.5	8
4	4.1–4.5	6
5	5.1	1
6	6.1, 6.5	3
7	7.1, 7.3, 7.5	5
8	8.1–8.5	5
9	9.1	2

BASIC COURSE CONCENTRATING ON LOGIC AND PROOF, COVERING SOME BOOLEAN ALGEBRA

This course first covers logic, followed by treatment of the basic notions of Boolean algebra. It then continues by covering proof methods, followed by sets and functions. Algorithms and their complexity are studied. Basic notions of number theory, including number bases, primes, and the Euclidean algorithm, are covered. Stress is given to mathematical induction and recursion. Using this basis, counting techniques and discrete structures can be studied effectively.

Chapter	Sections	Lectures
1	1.1–1.8	9
10	10.1–10.2	2
2	2.1–2.5	5
3	3.1–3.4	7
4	4.1–4.5	7
6	6.1–6.3	3
7	7.1–7.3, 7.5–7.6	5
8	8.1–8.5	5
9	9.1	2

BASIC COURSE WITH COVERAGE OF BOTH LOGIC AND PROOF, BUT WITHOUT BASIC COVERAGE OF ALGORITHMS

At some schools, students taking a course in discrete mathematics already are familiar with the notion of an algorithm and complexity of algorithms. However, these students need a careful treatment of logic and proof. This course provides a complete treatment of logic and proof, sets, functions, and mathematical reasoning. From this basis, counting techniques and discrete structures can be studied effectively.

Chapter	Sections	Lectures
1	1.1–1.8	9
2	2.4–2.6	5
3	3.1–3.4	7
4	4.1–4.5	7
6	6.1, 6.3	3
7	7.1–7.3, 7.5–7.6	5
8	8.1–8.5	7
9	9.1	2

COURSE WITH A COMPUTER SCIENCE ORIENTATION

This course includes the topics in the text of the greatest interest for computer science, assuming that students have already studied the basic concepts of algorithms and complexity. The first three chapters are covered at a more advanced rate than in the basic course. (*Note*: The coverage of Chapter 11 is quite rapid, permitting only a survey of the important material of that chapter. Some instructors may prefer to omit Boolean algebra, covered in Chapter 10, and spend eight lectures on Chapter 11.)

Chapter	Sections	Lectures
1	1.1–1.8 (as needed)	5
2	2.4–2.6	3
3	3.1–3.6	6
4	4.1–4.4, 4.6	5
5	5.1–5.3	3
6	6.1–6.3	3
7	7.1–7.3, 7.5	4
8	8.1–8.5	4
9	9.1–9.4	4
10	10.1–10.4	3
11	11.1–11.5	5

COURSE WITH A MATHEMATICS ORIENTATION

This course covers topics of interest to mathematics majors and omits some of the topics that are directed toward computer science. There is a more rapid treatment of core material than in the basic course.

Chapter	Sections	Lectures
1	1.1–1.8 (as needed)	5
2	2.1–2.6	6
3	3.1–3.4	6
4	4.1–4.6	6
5	5.1, 5.2, 5.4–5.6	6
6	6.1, 6.3–6.6	5
7	7.1–7.8	7
8	8.1, 8.5, 8.6	4

TWO-TERM COURSE

In two terms all the material in the text can be covered in a thorough manner. Here is how I suggest the material should be divided.

First Term:

The first term covers the foundations: logic and proofs, sets, functions, algorithms, some number theory, matrices, mathematical reasoning, mathematical induction and recursion, basic counting techniques, probability theory, and advanced counting techniques.

Chapter	Sections	Lectures
1	1.1–1.8, Appendix 1	9
2	2.1–2.6, Appendix 2	7
3	3.1–3.6	8
4	4.1–4.7	8
5	5.1–5.3	5
6	6.1–6.6	8

Second Term:

The second term begins with relations (including closures, equivalence relations, and partial orders), introduces graph theory, studies trees and their applications, covers basic Boolean algebra, and provides a self-contained introduction to formal languages and automata theory.

Chapter	Sections	Lectures
7	7.1–7.6	8
8	8.1–8.8	12
9	9.1–9.5	10
10	10.1–10.4	6
11	11.1–11.5	9

Migrating from the Fourth Edition to the Fifth Edition

This section provides tables showing the location in the fifth edition of *Discrete Mathematics and Its Applications* of material that appeared in the fourth edition. The first table deals with the text itself, and the second deals with the exercises.

MAP OF SECTIONS

The following table shows how material in the fourth edition has been reorganized in the fifth edition. For the most part, material covered in the fourth edition can still be found in the fifth edition. However, there are many additions to the fifth edition, as explained in the preface.

fourth edition	fifth edition
1.1	1.1
1.2	1.2
1.3	1.3, 1.4
1.4	1.6
1.5	1.7
1.6	1.8
1.7	3.2
1.8	2.2
2.1	2.1
2.2	2.3
2.3	2.4
2.4	2.5
2.5	2.6
2.6	2.7
3.1	1.5, 3.1
3.2	3.3
3.3	3.4
3.4	3.5
3.5	3.6
4.1	4.1
4.2	4.2
4.3	4.3, 4.4
4.4	5.1
4.5	5.2, 5.3
4.6	4.5
4.7	4.6
5.1	6.1
5.2	6.2
5.3	6.3
5.4	6.4
5.5	6.5
5.6	6.6
6.1	7.1
6.2	7.2
6.3	7.3
6.4	7.4
6.5	7.5
6.6	7.6

(section map, continued)

fourth edition	fifth edition
7.1	8.1
7.2	8.2
7.3	8.3
7.4	8.4
7.5	8.5
7.6	8.6
7.7	8.7
7.8	8.8
8.1	9.1
8.2	9.2
8.3	9.3
8.4	2.1, 2.3, 3.5
8.5	9.4
8.6	9.5
9.1	10.1
9.2	10.2
9.3	10.3
9.4	10.4
10.1	11.1
10.2	11.2
10.3	11.3
10.4	11.4
10.5	11.5
A.1	A.1
A.2	A.2

MAP OF EXERCISES

Almost all of the exercises in the fourth edition appear in the fifth edition, but in most cases the section numbers and exercise numbers have changed. In almost every case parity has been maintained (note that the odd-numbered exercises have answers in the text and solutions in the *Student Solutions Guide*, whereas even-numbered exercises have solutions in this *Instructor's Resource Guide*). In addition, there are about 600 new exercises in the fifth edition (those whose numbers do not appear in the table below).

The following table shows where exercises from the fourth edition appear in the fifth edition. In a few cases, the exercises have been modified slightly. The notation *a.b.c* means exercise *c* in section *a.b*. The letter "s" stands for "supplementary exercise."

fourth edition	fifth edition
1.1.1–1.1.4	1.1.1–1.1.4
1.1.5–1.1.8	1.1.7–1.1.10
1.1.9–1.1.11	1.1.13–1.1.15
1.1.12–1.1.14	1.1.40–1.1.42
1.1.15–1.1.21	1.1.17–1.1.23
1.1.22–1.1.34	1.1.26–1.1.38
1.1.35	1.1.45
1.1.36–1.1.38	1.1.48–1.1.50
1.1.39–1.1.42	1.1.57–1.1.60
1.2.1–1.2.19	1.2.1–1.2.19
1.2.20–1.2.41	1.2.30–1.2.51

fourth edition	fifth edition	(exercise map, continued)
1.3.1–1.3.5	1.3.1–1.3.5	
1.3.6–1.3.8	1.4.4–1.4.6	
1.3.9	1.3.9	
1.3.10–1.3.18	1.4.8–1.4.16 (fourth edition 1.3.16–1.3.17 slightly modified)	
1.3.19	1.3.11	
1.3.20–1.3.24	1.4.26–1.4.30 (most parts)	
1.3.25–1.3.28	1.4.33–1.4.36 (most parts)	
1.3.29–1.3.30	1.4.39–1.4.40	
1.3.31–1.3.34	1.3.55–1.3.58	
1.3.35	1.4.43	
1.3.36–1.3.41	1.3.42–1.3.47	
1.3.42–1.3.43	1.4.44–1.4.45	
1.3.44–1.3.46	1.3.48–1.3.50	
1.3.47	1.4.49	
1.3.48–1.3.50	1.4.46–1.4.48	
1.3.51	(covered in Example 1.4.13)	
1.3.52–1.3.55	1.4.50–1.4.53	
1.4.1–1.4.6	1.6.1–1.6.6	
1.4.7–1.4.24	1.6.9–1.6.26	
1.4.25–1.4.27	1.6.29–1.6.31	
1.5.1–1.5.7	1.7.1–1.7.7	
1.5.8–1.5.51	1.7.10–1.7.53	
1.6.1–1.6.5	1.8.1–1.8.5	
1.6.6–1.6.11	1.8.8–1.8.13	
1.6.12–1.6.15	1.8.16–1.8.19	
1.6.16–1.6.38	1.8.22–1.8.44	
1.6.39	(covered in Example 1.8.24; see also 1.8.68)	
1.6.40–1.6.58	1.8.46–1.8.64	
1.6.59–1.6.60	1.8.69–1.8.70	
1.7.1–1.7.37	3.2.1–3.2.37	
1.7.38	(covered in Example 3.2.19)	
1.7.39–1.7.43	3.2.39–3.2.43	
1.8.1–1.8.63	2.2.1–2.2.63	
1.s.1–1.s.5	1.s.1–1.s.5	
1.s.6–1.s.7	1.s.10–1.s.11	
1.s.8–1.s.15	1.s.14–1.s.21	
1.s.16–1.s.32	1.s.34–1.s.50	
1.s.33–1.s.35	(omitted)	
1.s.36–1.s.40	2.s.14–2.s.18	
2.1.1–2.1.3	2.1.1–2.1.3	
2.1.4–2.1.27	2.1.10–2.1.33	
2.2.1–2.2.21	2.3.1–2.3.21	
2.3.1–2.3.9	2.4.1–2.4.9	
2.3.10–2.3.14	2.4.12–2.4.16	
2.3.15–2.3.24	2.4.19–2.4.28	
2.3.25–2.3.52	2.4.33–2.4.60	
2.4.1	2.5.21 (part of)	
2.4.2–2.4.4	2.5.22–2.5.24	
2.4.5–2.4.8	2.5.1–2.5.4	
2.4.9–2.4.10	(covered on page 172 of text)	
2.4.11	2.5.5	
2.4.12	2.5.8	
2.4.13–2.4.41	2.5.25–2.5.53	

fourth edition	fifth edition	(exercise map, continued)
2.5.1–2.5.17	2.6.1–2.6.17	
2.5.18–2.5.25	2.6.22–2.6.29	
2.5.26–2.5.37	2.6.36–2.6.47	
2.5.38–2.5.46	2.6.52–2.6.60	
2.6.1–2.6.37	2.7.1–2.7.37	
2.s.1–2.s.4	2.s.1–2.s.4	
2.s.5–2.s.13	2.s.19–2.s.27	
2.s.14	(essentially covered in Example 3.5.2)	
2.s.15–2.s.29	2.s.29–2.s.43	
3.1.1–3.1.10	1.5.1–1.5.10	
3.1.11	1.5.13 (partly)	
3.1.12	(omitted)	
3.1.13–3.1.19	1.5.17–1.5.23	
3.1.20	(covered in Example 1.5.18)	
3.1.21–3.1.24	1.5.25–1.5.28	
3.1.25–3.1.28	3.1.15–3.1.18	
3.1.29	1.5.33	
3.1.30	3.1.20	
3.1.31	1.5.35	
3.1.32	3.1.32	
3.1.33	1.5.34	
3.1.34–3.1.36	1.5.38–1.5.40	
3.1.37–3.1.38	3.1.21–3.1.22	
3.1.39	1.5.41	
3.1.40	3.1.24	
3.1.41	(essentially covered in Example 1.5.29)	
3.1.42	3.1.38	
3.1.43–3.1.45	1.8.65–1.8.67	
3.1.46–3.1.48	3.1.34–3.1.36	
3.1.49–3.1.51	1.5.71–1.5.73	
3.1.52	(omitted)	
3.1.53–3.1.54	3.1.25–3.1.26	
3.1.55–3.1.56	1.5.75–1.5.76	
3.1.57–3.1.58	3.1.27–3.1.28	
3.1.59	(covered in Example 3.1.5)	
3.1.60	(omitted)	
3.1.61	1.5.67	
3.1.62	1.5.64	
3.1.63	(covered in Example 1.5.27)	
3.1.64–3.1.66	1.5.68–1.5.70	
3.1.67	1.5.77	
3.1.68	(omitted)	
3.2.1–3.2.33	3.3.1–3.3.33	
3.2.34–3.2.36	3.3.36–3.3.38	
3.2.37–3.2.45	3.3.41–3.3.49	
3.2.46	(omitted)	
3.2.47	3.3.51	
3.2.48–3.2.57	3.3.54–3.3.63	
3.2.58–3.2.69	3.3.66–3.3.77	
3.3.1–3.3.4	3.4.1–3.4.4	
3.3.5–3.3.23	3.4.7–3.4.25	
3.3.24	(essentially covered in Example 3.4.13)	
3.3.25	3.4.31	
3.3.26–3.3.34	3.4.34–3.4.42	
3.3.35–3.3.53	3.4.47–3.4.65	
3.3.54–3.3.66	3.s.68–3.s.80	

<u>fourth edition</u>   <u>fifth edition</u>   (exercise map, continued)

fourth edition	fifth edition
3.4.1–3.4.9	3.5.1–3.5.9
3.4.10–3.4.25	3.5.16–3.5.31
3.5.1–3.5.13	3.6.1–3.6.13
3.s.1	1.5.24
3.s.2	3.s.4
3.s.3–3.s.5	(omitted)
3.s.6	3.s.6
3.s.7	(omitted)
3.s.8–3.s.20	3.s.8–3.s.20
3.s.21–3.s.28	3.s.25–3.s.32
3.s.29–3.s.44	3.s.41–3.s.56
3.s.45–3.s.49	3.s.59–3.s.63
3.s.50	3.s.64 (slightly changed)
3.s.51–3.s.52	3.s.65–3.s.66
4.1.1–4.1.51	4.1.1–4.1.51
4.1.52–4.1.56	4.1.54–4.1.58
4.2.1–4.2.14	4.2.1–4.2.14
4.2.15	4.2.17
4.2.16–4.2.17	4.2.40–4.2.41
4.2.18–4.2.24	4.2.20–4.2.26
4.2.25–4.2.29	4.2.29–4.2.33
4.2.30–4.2.33	4.2.36–4.2.39
4.2.34–4.2.35	4.2.18–4.2.19
4.2.36–4.2.37	4.2.42–4.2.43
4.3.1–4.3.10	4.3.1–4.3.10
4.3.11–4.3.15	4.3.13–4.3.17
4.3.16	4.3.20
4.3.17–4.3.32	4.3.25–4.3.40
4.3.33–4.3.34	4.4.23–4.4.24
4.3.35	4.4.3 (slightly changed)
4.3.36–4.3.45	4.4.4–4.4.13
4.3.46	(incorporated in 4.4.14)
4.3.47	4.4.19
4.3.48	4.4.22
4.3.49–4.3.59	4.4.27–4.4.37
4.3.60–4.3.62	4.3.42–4.3.44
4.3.63	4.4.39
4.4.1–4.4.30	5.1.1–5.1.30
4.4.31–4.4.36	5.1.35–5.1.40
4.5.1–4.5.5	5.2.1–5.2.5
4.5.6–4.5.11	5.2.12–5.2.17
4.5.12–4.5.13	(covered in Example 5.2.13)
4.5.14–4.5.27	5.2.22–5.2.35
4.5.28–4.5.35	5.3.2–5.3.9
4.5.36	5.3.32
4.5.37	(covered in Example 5.3.10)
4.5.38	(essentially 5.3.14)
4.5.39	(essentially 5.3.15)
4.5.40	(covered in Example 5.3.10)
4.5.41	(covered in Example 5.3.6)
4.5.42–4.5.46	5.3.22–5.3.26
4.5.47–4.5.49	5.3.29–5.3.31
4.5.50–4.5.52	5.3.36–5.3.38
4.6.1–4.6.20	4.5.1–4.5.20
4.6.21–4.6.52	4.5.25–4.5.56
4.7.1	4.6.1
4.7.2–4.7.14	4.6.4–4.6.16

fourth edition	fifth edition	(exercise map, continued)
4.s.1–4.s.21	4.s.1–4.s.21	
4.s.22–4.s.23	5.s.1–5.s.2	
4.s.24–4.s.26	4.s.22–4.s.24	
4.s.27	(covered in second proof of Corollary 4.3.1)	
4.s.28–4.s.30	4.s.26–4.s.28	
4.s.31	(covered in Corollary 4.4.3)	
4.s.32–4.s.33	4.s.30–4.s.31	
4.s.34	5.s.4	
4.s.35	5.s.3	
4.s.36–4.s.38	5.s.12–5.s.14	
4.s.39–4.s.43	5.s.23–5.s.27	
4.s.44	5.s.30	
4.s.45–4.s.56	4.s.33–4.s.44	
5.1.1	6.1.1	
5.1.2–5.1.4	6.1.4–6.1.6	
5.1.5–5.1.10	6.1.9–6.1.14	
5.1.11–5.1.62	6.1.17–6.1.68	
5.2.1–5.2.52	6.2.1–6.2.52	
5.3.1–5.3.16	6.3.1–6.3.16	
5.3.17–5.3.25	6.3.29–6.3.37	
5.4.1–5.4.60	6.4.1–6.4.60	
5.5.1–5.5.29	6.5.1–6.5.29	
5.6.1–5.6.27	6.6.1–6.6.27	
5.s.1–5.s.35	6.s.1–6.s.35	
6.1.1–6.1.4	7.1.1–7.1.4	
6.1.5–6.1.8	7.1.7–7.1.10	
6.1.9	7.1.13	
6.1.10–6.1.11	7.1.16–7.1.17	
6.1.12	7.1.20	
6.1.13–6.1.21	7.1.23–7.1.31	
6.1.22–6.1.24	7.1.40–7.1.42	
6.1.25–6.1.37	7.1.45–7.1.57	
6.2.1–6.2.5	7.2.1–7.2.5	
6.2.6–6.2.11	7.2.14–7.2.19	
6.3.1	7.3.1	
6.3.2	7.3.3	
6.3.3	(omitted)	
6.3.4	7.3.7	
6.3.5–6.3.9	7.3.11–7.3.15	
6.3.10	7.3.18	
6.3.11	7.3.20	
6.3.12–6.3.13	7.3.22–7.3.23	
6.3.14–6.3.15	7.3.26–7.3.27	
6.3.16	7.3.30	
6.3.17	(parts of 7.3.31–7.3.32)	
6.3.18	7.3.36	
6.3.19	7.3.35	
6.4.1–6.4.35	7.4.1–7.4.35	
6.5.1–6.5.10	7.5.1–7.5.10	
6.5.11–6.5.25	7.5.15–7.5.29	
6.5.26	7.5.32	
6.5.27	7.5.37	
6.5.28–6.5.43	7.5.40–7.5.55	

<u>fourth edition</u>   <u>fifth edition</u>   (exercise map, continued)

fourth edition	fifth edition
6.6.1–6.6.14	7.6.1–7.6.14
6.6.15–6.6.45	7.6.17–7.6.47
6.6.46–6.6.50	7.6.54–7.6.58
6.s.1–6.s.26	7.s.1–7.s.26
6.s.27	7.6.59
6.s.28–6.s.33	7.s.28–7.s.33
6.s.34–6.s.35	(covered in Example 3.4.15)
6.s.36–6.s.48	7.s.36–7.s.48
7.1.1–7.1.13	8.1.1–8.1.13
7.1.14–7.1.17	8.1.16–8.1.19
7.1.18–7.1.21	8.1.26–8.1.29
7.2.1–7.2.11	8.2.1–8.2.11
7.2.12–7.2.20	8.2.18–8.2.26
7.2.21–7.2.45	8.2.29–8.2.53
7.3.1–7.3.69	8.3.1–8.3.69
7.4.1–7.4.6	8.4.1–8.4.6
7.4.7–7.4.38	8.4.15–8.4.46
7.5.1–7.5.7	8.5.1–8.5.7 (these ask about circuits *and* paths)
7.5.8–7.5.14	8.5.1–8.5.7 (these ask about circuits *and* paths)
7.5.15–7.5.23	8.5.9–8.5.17
7.5.24–7.5.28	8.5.18–8.5.22 (these ask about circuits *and* paths)
7.5.29–7.5.33	8.5.18–8.5.22 (these ask about circuits *and* paths)
7.5.34–7.5.56	8.5.24–8.5.46
7.5.57–7.5.72	8.5.49–8.5.64
7.6.1–7.6.30	8.6.1–8.6.30
7.7.1–7.7.7	8.7.1–8.7.7
7.7.8–7.7.35	8.7.10–8.7.37
7.8.1–7.8.2	8.8.1–8.8.3 (differently organized)
7.8.3–7.8.31	8.8.5–8.8.33
7.s.1–7.s.52	8.s.1–8.s.52
8.1.1	9.1.2
8.1.2	9.1.4
8.1.3	9.1.6
8.1.4	9.1.8
8.1.5	9.1.10
8.1.6–8.1.7	9.1.11–9.1.13 (reorganized)
8.1.8–8.1.40	9.1.14–9.1.46
8.2.1–8.2.10	9.2.1–9.2.10
8.2.11–8.2.14	9.2.19–9.2.22
8.3.1–8.3.15	9.3.1–9.3.15
8.3.16–8.3.23	9.3.16–9.3.19 (reorganized)
8.3.24–8.3.38	9.3.20–9.3.34
8.4.1–8.4.3	2.1.35–2.1.37
8.4.4–8.4.8	3.5.32–3.5.36
8.4.9–8.4.10	2.1.41–2.1.42
8.4.11	2.3.24
8.4.12–8.4.18	3.5.38–3.5.44
8.4.19	(discussed in Section 3.5)
8.5.1–8.5.16	9.4.1–9.4.16
8.5.17–8.5.20	9.4.23–9.4.26
8.5.21–8.5.22	(discussed in Section 9.4)
8.5.23–8.5.34	9.4.27–9.4.38
8.5.35–8.5.41	9.4.49–9.4.55
8.6.1–8.6.32	9.5.1–9.5.32

	fourth edition	fifth edition	(exercise map, continued)

(exercise map, continued)

fourth edition	fifth edition
8.s.1–8.s.12	9.s.1–9.s.12
8.s.13–8.s.19	9.s.19–9.s.25
8.s.20	(essentially 2.1.38)
8.s.21	(discussed in Section 2.1)
8.s.22	(covered in Example 2.3.6)
8.s.23	(omitted)
8.s.24–8.s.36	9.s.26–9.s.38
8.s.37	9.2.38 (part of)
8.s.38	9.s.42
8.s.39	9.s.41
8.s.40	9.s.43
8.s.41	9.s.44
9.1.1–9.1.2	10.1.1–10.1.2
9.1.3–9.1.15	10.1.7–10.1.19
9.1.16–9.1.33	10.1.22–10.1.39
9.2.1–9.2.20	10.2.1–10.2.20
9.3.1–9.3.19	10.3.1–10.3.19
9.4.1–9.4.7	10.4.1–10.4.7
9.4.8–9.4.10	10.4.12–10.4.14
9.4.11	10.4.17 (slightly modified)
9.4.12–9.4.24	10.4.20–10.4.32
9.s.1–9.s.24	10.s.1–10.s.24
10.1.1–10.1.24	11.1.1–11.1.24
10.1.25	11.1.36
10.2.1–10.2.21	11.2.1–11.2.21
10.3.1–10.3.29	11.3.1–11.3.29
10.4.1–10.4.20	11.4.1–11.4.20
10.5.1–10.5.24	11.5.1–11.5.24
10.s.1–10.s.28	11.s.1–11.s.28
A.1.1–A.1.6	A.1.1–A.1.6
A.2.1–A.2.3	A.2.1–A.2.3

Teaching Suggestions

In this part of the *Instructor's Guide*, I suggest how this text can be used effectively to teach an introductory course in discrete mathematics. These views are based on my personal experience teaching in the classroom as well as on those of some of the many instructors who have used this text in previous editions.

In the following material I provide an overview of each chapter of the text. Along with a description of the contents of that chapter, I describe its importance in an introductory course. After this overview, I give detailed information about each section of the chapter. First, I state the section goals and identify the prerequisites for that section. Then, I give my suggestions on how to teach from the section. In particular, I identify troublesome concepts and suggest how to handle them. I point out particularly useful examples and important concepts. Finally, I describe exercises that I feel are noteworthy, especially those that tie together diverse concepts or introduce new ideas. I hope this information makes teaching from the text easier and more rewarding for you.

CHAPTER 1
The Foundations: Logic and Proof, Sets, and Functions

Overview: Chapter 1 presents an introduction to both propositional and predicate logic and rules of inference and basic proof methods, as well as to sets and functions. The material on logic and proof provides the foundations needed throughout higher mathematics and computer science. Without a firm foundation in logic, students have a great deal of difficulty with the course and subsequent courses. Since much of this material may be review, quickly cover, or do not cover at all, material that your students already know.

The first four sections deal with logic; propositional logic is covered in Sections 1.1 and 1.2, and predicate logic is covered in Sections 1.3 and 1.4. I feel that this is the best way to start a course in discrete mathematics, since students must be able to think logically and carry out precise reasoning. Section 1.5 introduces proof methods and begins the discussion of proof strategy. The proof methods discussed in this section are used in the coverage of sets and functions in Sections 1.6–1.8, and in the coverage of algorithms and number theory in Chapter 2. We return to the study of proof strategies in Chapter 3, where we will also study mathematical induction and its variants.

SECTION 1.1 **Logic**

Goals: To introduce the basic terminology of propositional logic, including logical connectives, to show how to construct truth tables, to illustrate the importance of logic with applications, and to motivate the study of logic through logic puzzles.

Prerequisites: None.

Advice: The material on logical connectives is straightforward. Most difficulties with this material involve confusion between common English usage and precise mathematical definitions. In particular, students have trouble with inclusive versus exclusive *or*; make sure the distinction is clear. Stress the definition of an implication, especially when the premise is false.

Emphasize that $p \rightarrow q$ is false only when p is true and q is false. This material is used extensively in Sections 1.5 and 3.2 when methods of proving implications and mathematical induction are discussed. Go over the different ways implications are expressed; these are listed after Definition 5. Define the converse, contrapositive, and inverse of an implication (see Example 7); these terms are often confused with each other. The subsection on translating English sentences into logical statements should be covered; students often need help with this important task. The subsection on system specifications is of particular appeal to students in computer science and engineering; it shows that logic is of immediate practical importance. Computer science students are usually familiar with logical operators from their use in programming, so make the connection between the material in this section and logical operators used in programming languages. (In fact almost everyone has been forced to understand logical operations from doing Boolean searches on the Web—see Example 14.) You may want to spend time covering the subsection on logical puzzle; many people find these puzzles fascinating—in particular, see Example 15 which introduces one of Raymond Smullyan's knights and knaves puzzles.

Exercises: Exercises 41–42 and 51–61 are logical puzzles that can challenge students; of these, Exercises 51–55 are puzzles involving Smullyan's knights and knaves. Exercises 35–37 introduce fuzzy logic, which is used in expert systems and artificial intelligence. Exercises 43–48 are devoted to system specifications. Exercises 38–40 cover some logical paradoxes.

SECTION 1.2 Propositional Equivalences

Goals: To show how propositional equivalences are established and to introduce the most important such equivalences.

Prerequisites: Section 1.1.

Advice: Table 5 presents basic propositional equivalences. We will see similar tables for set identities in Section 1.7 and for Boolean algebra in Section 10.1. Mention that these properties hold in a wide variety of settings that all fit into one abstract form. Many students have the tendency to just memorize the properties, so stress that it is more important to understand their meaning and why they are true. Explain the different ways that such propositional equivalences can be established, including by the use of truth tables, by showing the propositions are true (or false) for precisely the same sets of values, and by using previously proved equivalences, including those in Tables 5–7. (Note: We discuss proofs formally in Section 1.5. Some practice with straightforward proofs here will help motivate the in-depth coverage that will follow.)

Exercises: The exercise set introduces some new topics, including duality, disjunctive normal form, and functional completeness. Students can learn about duality by doing Exercises 30–33. Exercises 34–36 develop the concept of disjunctive normal form. Exercises 37–39 introduce the concept of functional completeness, and Exercises 40–48 introduce the operators *NAND* ($|$) and *NOR* ($\downarrow$) and show that the sets $\{\,|\,\}$ and $\{\downarrow\}$ are both functionally complete. The notion of a satisfiable compound proposition is studied in Exercises 54–55.

SECTION 1.3 Predicates and Quantifiers

Goals: To introduce predicate logic, especially existential and universal quantification. Moreover, to explain how to translate between English sentences (or mathematical statements) and logical expressions.

Prerequisites: Sections 1.1–1.2.

Advice: This section is important since students often have trouble proving statements that involve quantification, including the inductive step in mathematical induction. Make sure they have a clear idea what the truth values of existential and universal quantifications mean. Mention that showing that a statement of the form $\forall x\, P(x)$ can be shown to be false with a counterexample. Explain how to negate existential and universal quantifications (see Table 2). We will need this in Section 1.5 when we discuss how to prove theorems that involve quantification (in particular, with existence proofs and counterexamples). Discuss the different ways to express universal and existential quantifications in English.

Devote special attention to the subsection on translating English sentences into logical statements; this is a particularly difficult task for many students. Be sure to stress that there is more than one way to translate a particular English sentence into a logical statement; see Examples 17 and 18. Examples 19 and 20, taken from Lewis Carroll, illustrate the subtleties of translating English sentences into correct statements involving predicate and propositional logic. The subsection on logic programming shows that the material in this section is important in computer programming and AI.

Exercises: Exercises 21–26 provide a wide variety of examples of how quantifiers are used when English sentences are translated into logical statements. Exercises 30–32 deal with negations involving quantified statements. Exercises 36–40 cover the use of quantifiers to express system specifications. Exercises 48–50 introduce the uniqueness quantifier. Exercises 51–54 deal with Prolog. Exercises 55–58 are questions based on work by Lewis Carroll.

SECTION 1.4   Nested Quantifiers

Goals: This section explains how to work with nested quantifiers and makes clear that the order of quantification matters. This section helps students gain maturity working with complicated logical expressions involving multiple quantifiers.

Prerequisites: Sections 1.1–1.3.

Advice: Explain the meaning of statements involving nested quantifiers—see Examples 1–4. Cover the process of translating complicated statements in English into logical expressions involving nested quantifiers—see Examples 5–9. Describe how nested quantifiers work (see Table 1); you may find the analogy to nested loops useful. Show students who have studied the definition of limit how to express this definition using quantifiers (Example 10). Do some examples that show that order of quantification is important when several different quantifications occur in the same statement (see Example 15). Example 13 shows how to use quantifiers and predicates to express that a limit does not exist.

Exercises: Exercises 14–16 involve translating English sentences into logical expressions involving nested quantifiers. Exercises 17–18 involve translating system specifications into logical expressions involving nested quantifiers. Exercises 19–23 involve translating mathematical statements into expressions involving nested quantifiers. Negations of statements involving nested quantifiers are the subject of Exercises 34–36. Prenex normal form is introduced in Exercises 46–47. Exercises 50–53 involve expressing definitions from calculus (and real analysis) using quantifiers.

SECTION 1.5   Methods of Proof

Goals: To introduce rules of inference for propositional and predicate calculus and methods of proof. Furthermore, to learn how to distinguish between correct and incorrect arguments, and to understand and construct different types of proofs.

Prerequisites: Sections 1.1–1.4.

Advice: Begin with definitions of important terms, including theorem, proof, corollary, lemma, conjecture, and so on. A key goal is for students to understand what constitutes a valid proof; they need to be able to understand existing proofs and create their own. Let them know that axioms and previously proven results can be used and that arguments must follow correct rules of inference for propositions and for predicates. Spend time showing how to prove implications; this will pay off when you discuss mathematical induction and whenever you prove theorems that are implications. Contrast indirect proofs with the fallacies of affirming the conclusion and denying the hypothesis. Mention begging the question; students will think this is not likely to occur, but you can show them examples from their own "proofs."

Introduce the basic rules of inference for propositional calculus—see Table 1. Describe the rules of inference for quantified statements—see Table 2. Cover the various ways to prove an implication, including direct and indirect proofs. Introduce some proof strategy, describing when to try a direct proof and when to try an indirect proof. Introduce proofs by contradiction and go over an example of such a proof, such as Example 20 and 21. Discuss proof by cases and proofs of equivalences. Introduce existence proofs, and discuss the difference between constructive and nonconstructive existence proofs. Explain what is needed in a uniqueness proof. Students usually benefit from a discussion of mistakes in proofs; cover some of Examples 31–35.

Exercises: Exercises 23–32 require students to use direct proofs, indirect proofs, and proofs by contradiction. Exercises 33–37 involve proofs by cases. Exercises 48–52 require constructive and nonconstructive existence proofs. Uniqueness proofs are the subject of Exercises 54–59.

SECTION 1.6   Sets

Goals: To introduce the basic terminology of set theory.

Prerequisites: Sections 1.1–1.5.

Advice: Make sure students understand that when specifying the elements of sets the number of times an element is listed and the order in which the elements are listed do not matter. These facts are illustrated by Example 5. Students have trouble distinguishing between the sets $\emptyset$ and $\{\emptyset\}$, so explain that the empty set is the set with no elements and that it is a subset of every set. I like to start with the empty set and take the power set and then the power set again to force students to see the difference between the empty set, the set containing the empty set, and other confusing sets. You may want to present the proof of Theorem 1, which shows that every nonempty set has at least two subsets, the set itself and the empty set, especially since this is an excellent illustration of proof methods covered in Section 1.5

Exercises: Russell's paradox is described in Exercise 30. This is a difficult exercise for students, but it is important since it shows that a consistent set of axioms is needed for set theory. Exercise 29 shows how to define ordered pairs in terms of sets.

SECTION 1.7   Set Operations

Goals: To show how set identities are established and to introduce the most important such identities.

Prerequisites: Sections 1.1–1.6.

Advice: The relationship between set identities and logical equivalences becomes clear when set operations are expressed using set builder notation and logical operators. Show students several different ways to prove a set identity, namely by showing each side is a subset of the other, by a membership table, by the use of logical equivalences, or by using set identities that have already been established. Explain that the set identities in Table 1 are analogous to the propositional equivalences in Section 1.2 and to Boolean identities that will be given in Chapter 10. We touch briefly on how to count elements in the union of two sets, foreshadowing the treatment of inclusion–exclusion in Chapter 6.

Exercises: The notion of the symmetric difference of two sets is introduced in the exercise set and studied in Exercises 24–35. Fuzzy sets, used in expert systems and artificial intelligence, are the subject of Exercises 51–53. You can ask your creative students to make the connection between fuzzy logic, introduced in Section 1.1, and fuzzy sets. Multisets are dealt with in Exercises 49–50; multisets are sometimes used when combinations with repetition allowed are studied. The successor of a set is defined in Exercise 47.

SECTION 1.8 **Functions**

Goals: To introduce the concept of a function, the notion of one-to-one functions, onto functions, and the floor and ceiling functions.

Prerequisites: Sections 1.1–1.7.

Advice: We define functions as assignments and their graphs as the sets of ordered pairs determined by these assignments. As such, the graph of a function is a type of relation, a topic we cover in Chapter 7. Although functions are discussed in a general setting, most of the examples deal with functions from one discrete set to another, as is appropriate for a course in discrete mathematics. Sometimes students have trouble with the definitions of one-to-one and onto functions. Use Figure 5 to help make these concepts clear. Show students how to express the definitions of one-to-one and onto in terms of quantifiers. Make sure your students have a clear understanding of the floor and ceiling functions; there is often confusion about their values at negative real numbers. Examples 22 and 23 show how these functions are applied in basic problems in data communications. Table 1 displays useful properties of the floor and ceiling functions. Make sure students are familiar with these properties. Proving results about the floor and ceiling functions provides more practice with methods of proof. The section concludes with the definition of the factorial function; be sure to cover this if your students are not already familiar with factorials.

Exercises: Exercises 38–46 give students the opportunity to work with the properties of the floor and ceiling functions, and Exercises 50–53 involve application of these functions to simple calculations in data communications. Exercise 64 asks students to show that the notions of one-to-one and onto are equivalent when the domain and codomain are finite sets of the same cardinality. The notion of a partial function, important in the study of Turing machines (see Section 11.5), is introduced in Exercises 69–70. The result in Exercise 71 shows that the set of ordered pairs of positive integers is countable, a topic studied in Section 3.2

CHAPTER 2
The Fundamentals: Algorithms, the Integers, and Matrices

Overview: Sections 2.1 introduces the concept of an algorithm. The purpose of this material is to ensure that students understand what an algorithm is and the different ways algorithms are expressed. The section illustrates the concept of an algorithm by covering searching and sorting algorithms. The notion of a greedy algorithm is also introduced. Section 2.2 introduces asymptotic notations used to describe the growth of functions, including big-O, big-Omega, and big-Theta notations. Section 2.3 describes how to express the complexity of an algorithm. This is important since later chapters discuss a variety of algorithms and their complexity. This material may be omitted if your students already have mastered these concepts in a computer science course. Section 2.4 presents some fundamental material on number theory, including base b expansions, congruences, and greatest common divisors. In Section 2.5 we study several important algorithms from number theory, including the Euclidean algorithm. The goal of Section 2.6 is to introduce two applications of number theory—arithmetic with large integers and public key cryptography. Section 2.7 presents all the material on matrices and matrix operations needed for the rest of the book.

SECTION 2.1   Algorithms

Goals: To introduce the concept and basic properties of an algorithm.

Prerequisites: Chapter 1.

Advice: The algorithm for finding the largest element in a finite sequence of integers provides a good example of an algorithm since it is simple and it solves a useful problem. Students should understand the steps used in actually solving a problem. First we find an algorithm, which is first expressed in English and then in pseudocode. Next, we study the complexity of the algorithm. Then we construct a computer program to implement it. Finally we verify the correctness of the program. We concentrate on the mathematical portions of the study of algorithms in this text, namely, how to solve problems using algorithms (in this section), how to study their complexity (in Section 2.3), and how to prove them correct (in Sections 3.4 and 3.5).

Introduce the problems of searching and sorting and present the linear and binary searches and one or both of the bubble sort and the insertion sort. (We will study the complexity of these algorithms later on.) This may be a good time to introduce the notion of a greedy algorithm. The change-making algorithm presented here provides an easy introduction to this topic and the question of whether a particular greedy algorithm produces optimal solutions.

Exercises: A variant of the binary search algorithm is introduced in Exercise 26. This version of the algorithm stops if the middle term at any stage equals the desired integer. The ternary search algorithm is introduced in Exercise 27; this exercise gives students the opportunity to develop a search algorithm on their own, generalizing the binary search algorithm. The selection sort is introduced and studied in Exercises 41–42 and the binary insertion sort in Exercises 47–49. A greedy algorithm for scheduling talks in a lecture hall is introduced in Exercise 57.

SECTION 2.2   The Growth of Functions

Goals: To introduce big-O and related notation (Ω, Θ) and to show how to estimate the size of functions using this notation.

Prerequisites: Chapter 1.

Advice: Students have trouble with big-O notation. Often they cannot decide how to choose the witnesses C and k in the definition. Show them how different pairs of constants can be used as witnesses. Give several different examples to illustrate the concept. Show how the definition of this notation involves the use of existential and universal quantifiers. Cover Examples 4 and 5, which give estimates for the sum of the n smallest positive integers and for $n!$. (Note that we have avoided using summation notation since it is not formally introduced until Section 3.2. If your students are already familiar with this notation, you may want to use it when discussing these estimates.) Indicate the importance of big-O in estimating the complexity of algorithms. We will study this formally in Section 2.3.

Exercises: Another type of asymptotic notation is introduced in the exercise set—little-o notation, which depends on the notion of a limit. If your students have a satisfactory background working with limits you may want to assign some of Exercises 51–59, which deal with this concept. We will use the result in Exercise 62 when we use trees to study the complexity of sorting algorithm in Section 9.2.

SECTION 2.3   Complexity of Algorithms

Goals: To introduce computational complexity analysis.

Prerequisites: Chapter 1 and Sections 2.1–2.2.

Advice: This section deals with complexity of algorithms. This an important mathematical part of computer science. We define different types of complexity, but concentrate on time complexity. Explain the distinction between worst case and average case complexity. Tell students the merits and drawbacks of using big-O estimates. Explain how the witnesses C and k in a big-O estimate have practical implications. Since average case complexity depends on notions of probability, a topic not formally studied until Chapter 5, tell students in an informal way how average case analysis depends on the distribution of input values. Explain to students the notions of tractable, intractable, solvable, unsolvable, NP, and NP-complete problems.

Exercises: You may want to assign Exercise 8, which deals with Horner's method for evaluating polynomials. Have students compare the complexity of this algorithm with the conventional method described in Exercise 7.

SECTION 2.4   The Integers and Division

Goals: To introduce some fundamental concepts from number theory, including the division algorithm, prime factorization, and congruences.

Prerequisites: Chapter 1.

Advice: Students often do not see that when factoring an integer it is necessary to do trial divisions only by integers less than or equal to the square root of the integer being factored. This is emphasized in Examples 5 and 6. Be sure to prove that there are infinitely many primes (Theorem 4). Discussing the search for new Mersenne primes (which can be monitored on the Web) illustrates that discrete mathematics is an active field of study. Be sure you mention that what is called the division algorithm is not really an algorithm, since this is quite confusing. (We will present an algorithm that finds the quotient and remainder in Section 2.5.) Make it clear that using prime factorizations to find greatest common divisors is easy once these factorizations are known, but that factoring integers is extremely time consuming. Mention that the Euclidean algorithm, which will be discussed in Section 2.5, is a much more efficient algorithm for finding greatest common divisors.

Explain the difference between congruence notation and the **mod** function. Cover the basic properties of congruences; we will need this material in Chapter 7 when we discuss congruence modulo m as an equivalence relation. You may want to introduce hashing functions and/or pseudorandom numbers, covered in Examples 18 and 19, respectively; these are easy and important applications of number theory to computer science. I recommend that you cover the discussion of cryptography using modular arithmetic in this section; students particularly enjoy this. More cryptography will be covered in Section 2.5.

Exercises: Exercise 15 asks for a proof that $\log_2 3$ is irrational; it is a simple, but challenging, exercise that follows from the fundamental theorem of arithmetic. Exercises 21–22 establish the relationship between the congruence notation and the **mod** function. Your students may enjoy learning some extra topics in number theory by doing Exercises 20 and 25–27, which deal with perfect numbers and the Euler phi function, respectively. Exercises 42–47 ask that certain results pertaining to congruences be established. These exercises give students some practice working with the notion of a congruence. Exercises 55–57 involve the idea of a check digit used in ISBNs. Exercises 59–60 ask students to conjecture a formula or rule for generating the terms of sequences that are related to prime numbers.

SECTION 2.5   Integers and Algorithms

Goals: To cover representations of integers in different bases, including binary, octal, and hexadecimal representations and to introduce algorithms involving integers, including the Euclidean algorithm and algorithms for arithmetic.

Prerequisites: Chapter 1 and Sections 2.1–2.3.

Advice: If your students do not have practice using different bases for representing integers, spend some time on the discussion of such representations in this section. Show students how to convert from one base to another (see Algorithm 1). The algorithms for addition, subtraction, and multiplication of integers were the first procedures to be called algorithms. Students need to understand this type of algorithm to understand how computers perform arithmetic. (Note: We will introduce a more efficient algorithm for multiplication in Section 6.3.) Performing modular exponentiation is important in cryptography; it is presented as Algorithm 5.

Be sure to cover the Euclidean algorithm. Besides being one of the oldest algorithms invented, it is an excellent illustration of the concept of an algorithm. We will study the complexity of the Euclidean algorithm in Section 3.4. (We defer the complexity analysis to that section since we will need an estimate for the size of Fibonacci numbers, which we will establish in that section.)

Exercises: The exercise set introduces other ways to represent integers, including those important in computer arithmetic. In particular, balanced ternary expansions are described in Exercise 26, one's complement representations are defined in the preamble to Exercise 30, two's complement representations are defined in the preamble to Exercise 36, binary coded decimal expansions are discussed in Exercise 43, and Cantor expansions are introduced in the preamble to Exercise 44. The simple conversions between binary and hexadecimal notations are the subject of Exercises 11 and 12. The complexity of modular exponentiation is the subject of Exercise 54.

SECTION 2.6   Applications of Number Theory

Goals: To cover two important applications of number theory after first developing several key results. The key results are the fact that the greatest common divisor of two integers can be expressed as a linear combination of these integers and the Chinese Remainder Theorem. The two important applications are computer arithmetic with large integers and public key cryptography.

Prerequisites: Chapter 1 and Sections 2.4–2.5.

Advice: After showing that the greatest common divisor of two positive integers can be expressed as a linear combination of these integers, you can show that the prime factorization of an integer is unique (up to the order of the factors); the fact that every positive integer has a prime factorization is proved in Section 3.3. The Chinese Remainder Theorem is introduced using an ancient Chinese puzzle as motivation. Computer arithmetic with large integers is then developed using the Chinese Remainder Theorem. You may want to briefly discuss pseudoprimes and probabilistic primarily testing before covering public key cryptography, one of the most interesting and important applications covered in this text.

Exercises: To have students work through some important theorems from elementary number theory, assign Exercises 16 and 17, which develop Wilson's theorem and Fermat's Little Theorem, respectively. The notion of strong pseudoprimes is the subject of Exercises 31–32. (The remark in the preamble to Exercise 30 is important when probabilistic primality testing is discussed in Chapter 5.) The extended Euclidean algorithm, which can be used to express greatest common divisors as linear combinations, is addressed in Exercises 48–51. Quadratic residues and the Legendre symbol are discussed in Exercises 52–58.

SECTION 2.7   Matrices

Goals: To introduce basic properties of matrices and matrix arithmetic, including Boolean operations on zero-one matrices.

Prerequisites: Chapter 1 and Sections 2.1–2.3.

Advice: This section presents a brief review of the material on matrices needed in later sections of the text. Students should understand how matrix multiplication is defined and know that it is not commutative. We discuss the complexity of matrix multiplication in this section. (We will return to this topic in Chapter 6.) I suggest covering Example 6, which deals with the question of determining the most efficient order to compute the product of many matrices. The material on zero-one matrices and Boolean operations on them will be new to most students. This material is used only in Section 7.4, when the transitive closure of relations is discussed, and it may be omitted if you do not intend to cover that section.

Exercises: Make sure students know what a diagonal matrix is (see Exercise 14). You may want to assign Exercises 18–21, which deal with the notion of the inverse of a matrix.

CHAPTER 3
Mathematical Reasoning, Induction, and Recursion

Overview: This chapter is devoted to mathematical reasoning, a main focus of the course, induction, and recursion. A basic introduction to proof methods, such as that provided in Section 1.5, does not give students an understanding how proofs are actually constructed. In Section 3.1 we describe some useful strategies for proving theorems and for studying conjectures. Section 3.2 introduces material on sequences and summations that arise throughout discrete mathematics and which are needed to understand examples of proof by mathematical induction, which is covered in Section 3.3. In Section 3.3 we show how to prove a variety of theorems using various forms of mathematical induction and equivalent techniques. In particular, we study the basic form of mathematical induction (sometimes called weak induction), strong induction (sometimes called the second principle of mathematical induction), and how proofs can be based on the well-ordering property of the set of positive integers. Section 3.4 discusses recursive definitions of functions, sequences, and sets and introduces the notion of structural induction, which is used to prove results about recursively defined sets. In Section 3.5 we deal with recursive algorithms and illustrate how to prove them correct and study their complexity. Finally, Section 3.6 ties together some important concepts, namely algorithms and proofs, with a discussion of program correctness.

SECTION 3.1	**Proof Strategy**
Goals:	To learn various strategies for proving theorems, to understand the roles of conjectures and counterexamples, and to learn about some important open problems.
Prerequisites:	Chapter 1 and Sections 2.1 and 2.4.
Advice:	The material presented here provides students with a window into what mathematics is really about. Explain some of the strategies used to find proofs of theorems. Explain that the proof methods studied in Chapter 1 provide the tool kit, but the art of finding proof is something altogether different. You can illustrate this by covering Examples 1 and 2, which illustrate working backwards, Examples 3 and 4, which show how using proof by cases can be useful, and Example 5, which illustrates how leveraging an existing proof can provide a good starting point for constructing a new proof.

Discuss the role of conjectures and how to approach them. Examples 6 and 7 provide good illustrations how conjectures are formulated and proved, and Examples 8 and 9 illustrate how counterexamples can be used to settle conjectures that turn out to be false. Devote some time to discussing the role of open problems. Students will find the story behind Fermat's Last Theorem compelling. Learning about easily understood conjectures that remain unsolved also motivates many students.

The subsection on the famous halting problem, which computer science majors should see again in a Theory of Computation course, is optional. It is a beautiful example of proof by contradiction, but the argument is subtle (and gives students difficulties), partly because of its self-referential nature.

Exercises:	Working the exercises in this section provides students with some experience figuring out which proof methods to use and how to settle conjectures. Exercise 14 is an excellent example of working backwards. Exercises 23–24 involve some important properties of the **mod** function that are used later in the book. Exercise 29 provides an opportunity for students to adapt an existing proof. The famous three jug problem is the subject of Exercise 47, which asks students to prove or disprove that you can solve this problem.

SECTION 3.2	**Sequences and Summations**
Goals:	To introduce terminology used for sequences and summations and to introduce the concept of countability.
Prerequisites:	Chapter 1.
Advice:	The first part of this section deals with sequences and is straightforward, except for the material on special integer sequences, which requires more critical and creative thinking than the other material. Examples 5–8 involve conjecturing a formula or rule for generating the terms of a sequence when only the first few terms are known. Encourage students to try the on-line *Encyclopedia of Integer Sequences*, mentioned on page 228.

The second part of the section introduces summation notation. Make sure students can work with the different forms of this notation and with shifting indices in summations. In particular, this will be helpful later when we prove summation formulae using mathematical induction. Students should also understand that sequences and strings are just special types of functions.

The final subsection addresses the cardinality of sets. Be sure to show that the set of positive rational numbers is countable via the Cantor diagonalization method; this is covered in Example 19. The proof given in Example 20—that the set of real numbers is uncountable—is elegant and quite subtle. Motivate this by using a numerical example for the construction of a real number that was not listed.

Exercises: Exercises 9–10 ask students to conjecture the formula or rule for generating the terms of a sequence from the first few terms; these exercises are more challenging than Exercises 5–6, which ask students to list the terms of sequences defined in different ways. Exercises 7–8 are interesting since they point out that there are many different naturally arising sequences that have the same initial terms. Telescoping sums are defined in Exercise 19 and are used to find the sums of the first k positive integers and the squares of these integers in Exercises 21 and 22, respectively. Product notation is introduced in the exercise set. Assign Exercise 27 if you wish to cover this. Exercises 44 and 45 provide alternative methods of proving that the set of positive rational numbers is countable.

SECTION 3.3   Mathematical Induction

Goals: To explain how to construct proofs of a variety of theorems using various forms of mathematical induction.

Prerequisites: Chapter 1 and Sections 2.4 and 3.1–3.2.

Advice: Mathematical induction may be the most important topic in the text. Carefully explain the steps that make up a proof by mathematical induction. Explain why the basis step can begin at any integer. I find that it helps to structure proofs by induction. Write out the proposition $P(n)$, prove the basis step $P(n_0)$, specifying the integer n_0, then give a complete proof of the inductive step, beginning by explicitly stating the goal, that is, to prove that the universal quantification $\forall k(P(k) \rightarrow P(k+1))$ is true. (It helps to write down both $P(k)$ and $P(k+1)$ before writing this quantification out.) Sometimes students think proofs by induction are circular reasoning. Make sure they know why this is not the case. Indicate that the basis step often turns out to be a vacuous or trivial proof.

Tell students that mathematical induction cannot be used to find formulae or to formulate theorems, but can be used to prove that a formula or theorem is correct. This can be emphasized by following the introductory remarks in the text and in Example 1. First conjecture a formula for the sum of the first n odd positive integers from evidence provided by the smallest cases. Then prove that the guess is correct using mathematical induction.

Students should see inductive proofs of different types of theorems. Show them how to prove one or two inequalities. (See Example 2 and Example 9, for instance. Surprisingly, students have trouble taking the inequality in the inductive hypothesis and establishing the corresponding inequality for the next largest integer.) Illustrate how to prove a result about divisibility (see Example 3), how to prove that a set with n elements has 2^n subsets (see Example 7), or how to prove a set identity (see Example 10). I particularly like Example 11, which shows how to use mathematical induction to prove a result about tiling chessboards. Students who have studied infinite series may relate to Example 6, since this shows that the harmonic series diverges.

Show students how to prove theorems using strong induction. Example 13 provides a good illustration of strong induction. Go over Example 14, which proves that every positive integer is the product of primes (students will find the basis step difficult to understand if the basis case is for the integer 1; you may want to begin with the integer 2). Example 15 shows how a result can be proved in two ways, one using the principle of mathematical induction and the other using the second principle of mathematical induction.

Present the well-ordering property and show how it can used directly to prove results such as that in Example 17. You may want to also cover the method of infinite descent and illustrate its use in Example 18 to show that $\sqrt{2}$ is irrational. Be sure to describe why mathematical induction is a valid proof technique. The final subsection explains how mathematical induction follows from the well-ordering property.

Exercises: Exercises 1 and 2 ask for a formula and proof of this formula for the sum of the first n even integers. Some other exercises I recommend include: Exercises 5 and 6, guess a formula and prove it; Exercise 10, prove a summation formula involving factorials; Exercise 12, prove an inequality; Exercise 19, prove a result about postage stamps; Exercise 21, prove a divisibility result; Exercise 41, prove a result from calculus; and Exercise 45, prove a generalized distributive law for sets. Exercises 34, 35, and 40 require strong induction. Exercises 50–54 asks students to find the flaw in incorrect inductive proofs. Exercise 66 uses the well-ordering property to show that the greatest common divisor of two positive integers can be written as a linear combination of these integers. Exercise 77 presents a challenging paradox involving the well-ordering principle.

SECTION 3.4   Recursive Definitions and Structural Induction

Goals: To show how functions, sequences, and sets can be defined recursively and to show how to use various forms of induction, including structural induction, to prove properties of such entities.

Prerequisites: Chapter 1 and Sections 2.4 and 3.1–3.3.

Advice: Make it clear why recursively defined functions and sequences are well-defined as a consequence of mathematical induction. Cover Example 2, which gives an inductive definition of the factorial function. Go over Example 5, which introduces the Fibonacci numbers. Example 6 illustrates the use of an inductive definition to prove a result about the sequence defined by that definition. Use Example 6 to prove Lamé's Theorem, which establishes the complexity of the Euclidean algorithm. This theorem was an early result in computational complexity, pre-dating by a century the modern interest in this subject.

Describe how sets and structures can be recursively defined and illustrate this with Example 7. Explain how sets of strings are defined recursively and cover Example 9, which shows how the length of a string can be recursively defined. Cover Example 10 or Example 11, which illustrate how well-formed formulae are defined. You can further illustrate the importance of recursive definitions of sets by explaining how the set of rooted trees and the sets of extended binary and full binary trees are defined (Definitions 4–6).

Introduce the technique of structural induction and provide some examples of how it is used to prove results about recursively defined sets. Useful illustrations of proofs using structural induction are provided by Example 13, which proves a result about well-formed formulae, Example 14, which proves that the length of the concatenation of two strings is the sum of the lengths of the two strings, and Theorem 2, which proves a result about full binary trees.

This section concludes with coverage of a generalized form of mathematical induction and the illustration of how generalized induction can be used to prove a result about ordered pairs of nonnegative integers (Example 15).

Exercises: Assign some exercises on the Fibonacci numbers (see Exercises 12–19). For some challenging exercises have students work with the number of partitions of an integer (see Exercise 47) or the Ackermann function (see Exercises 48–55). Exercises 23–29 and 31 ask for recursive definitions of sets and strings, and Exercise 40 asks for a recursive definition of the set of bit strings with more zeros than ones. For exercises involving structural induction see Exercises 32–33, 36, and 43–44. Exercises 45–46 involve generalized induction.

SECTION 3.5   Recursive Algorithms

Goals: To introduce the concept of a recursive algorithm, to construct recursive versions of some algorithms, and to illustrate how to prove that a recursive algorithm is correct.

Prerequisites: Chapter 1 and Sections 2.1–2.4 and 3.1–3.3.

Advice: The concept of a recursive algorithm is extremely important but difficult for students to master. Your students may have studied this topic in computer science courses, so here we concentrate on how recursion relates to some of the algorithms we have studied and the complexity of using recursion versus iteration. Go over Example 3, which illustrates how to show that the recursive algorithm for modular exponentiation is correct. Cover Example 4, which gives a recursive version of the Euclidean algorithm, and Example 6, which gives a recursive version of the binary search algorithm. Spend some time explaining the difference between an iterative algorithm and a recursive algorithm. Then compare and contrast the iterative and recursive approaches for computing Fibonacci numbers; this shows that recursion can be considerably less efficient than iteration. Recursive algorithms can be simple to specify once the concept is understood, but can be computational quagmires.

Be sure to introduce the merge sort algorithm and if you have time, explain how to estimate its computational complexity (Theorem 1).

Exercises: Exercise 11 involves an interesting recursive algorithm for multiplying nonnegative integers. Exercises 10 and 12–15 ask students to prove that algorithms are correct. Exercises 16–19 involve evaluating powers iteratively and recursively. Exercises 21–23 give students the chance to work through the recursion versus iteration question for a sequence similar to the Fibonacci numbers. Exercises 29–30 ask for recursive algorithms to find the reversal and n^{th} power of a string. The quick sort is introduced and studied in Exercises 38–43.

SECTION 3.6   Program Correctness

Goals: To introduce the concept of program correctness and to demonstrate how to prove that programs are correct.

Prerequisites: Chapter 1 and Sections 2.1 and 3.1–3.5.

Advice: Drawing a connection between algorithms and proofs gives students who are interested in computer science but scornful of the value of proofs an appreciation of why mathematical reasoning is important. In this section we present one scheme for proving that programs are correct. This scheme is based on the concept of initial and final assertions. Some basic rules of inference for showing that programs are correct are presented. The examples are simple, but they illustrate the major ideas of the subject. We introduce the concept of a loop invariant, and in Example 4 we use mathematical induction to show how to verify a loop invariant. In Example 5 we show how to verify the correctness of a program using a combination of the various rules of inference.

Exercises: Exercises 1–4 ask for proofs that some simple programs are correct. Exercise 5 asks students to devise a rule of inference for conditional statements with one or more **else ... if** clauses; Exercise 6 asks that this rule of inference be used to verify a program. Exercise 7 asks students to use a loop invariant to verify the correctness of a program.

CHAPTER 4
Counting

Overview: The goal of Chapter 4 is to present a rich set of basic counting techniques. We begin with the product and sum rules; most counting methods are based on these fundamental principles. We stress throughout the chapter that finding an appropriate technique and model is the substantial part of the solution of a counting problem; applying the appropriate formula once this has been done is the easy part. We introduce the pigeonhole principle and show how it can be used to prove a variety of results. Permutations and combinations are studied formally in Section 4.3, with Section 4.4 devoted specifically to the binomial coefficients. We generalize to counting problems with repetitions allowed in Section 4.5. Finally, in the concluding section of the chapter, we discuss algorithms for generating some of the combinatorial objects we have studied.

SECTION 4.1   **The Basics of Counting**

Goals: To introduce basic counting rules and to show how they are used to solve a variety of counting problems.

Prerequisites: Chapter 1 and Sections 2.1–2.4 and 3.1–3.4.

Advice: This section contains a discussion of the product rule and the sum rule. Discuss Example 5 to illustrate the use of the product rule; this example counts the number of functions from a set with m elements to a set with n elements. Similarly, Example 6 uses the product rule to count the number of one-to-one functions from a set with m elements to a set with n elements, and Example 7 uses the product rule to count telephone numbers.

The sum and product rules provide the foundation for a large number of sophisticated enumeration methods. Show how counting problems (such as enumerating valid passwords on a computer system, discussed in Example 14, or counting Internet addresses, discussed in Example 15) can be solved using a combination of the two rules. Briefly introduce the inclusion–exclusion principle; this will be studied in more depth in Chapter 6. Explain how tree diagrams can be used in counting by considering the number of outcomes of a playoff series, as is done in Example 18 (it is amusing when the World Series, basketball, or Stanley Cup playoffs are taking place when you cover this).

Exercises: Exercises 46–47 are solved using both the product rule and the sum rule. Exercise 37 asks for the number of bit strings of length n that are palindromes. Tree diagrams can be used to solve Exercises 48–53. Exercise 58 asks for the number of different strings of data that can be transmitted using an IP datagram.

SECTION 4.2   **The Pigeonhole Principle**

Goals: To introduce the pigeonhole principle and show how to use it in enumeration and in proofs.

Prerequisites: Chapter 1 and Sections 2.4–2.5 and 4.1.

Advice: Students have trouble drawing valid conclusions from the pigeonhole principle. You can clarify this using Figure 1, which illustrates what you can and cannot conclude from the pigeonhole principle, namely that if there are more pigeons than pigeonholes, some pigeonhole contains more than one pigeon, but some pigeonholes may contain no pigeons, and others may contain many pigeons. Example 4 provides an interesting application of the pigeonhole principle.

Describe the generalized pigeonhole principle. Make sure students understand how to solve problems such as that posed in Example 8. Often they will give answers that are too large because they do not understand the use of the ceiling function in the generalized pigeonhole principle.

Students have trouble with subtle types of arguments using the pigeonhole principle. Anticipate confusion if you cover any of Examples 10, 11, or 12. I suggest covering Example 13, which solves the puzzle about three mutual friends or enemies in a group of six people. This application of the pigeonhole principle is the simplest result of Ramsey theory.

Exercises: Assign Exercise 8, which relates the pigeonhole principle to the fact that a function cannot be one-to-one if its domain has more elements than its codomain. Exercises 24–28 develop further results from Ramsey theory.

SECTION 4.3   **Permutations and Combinations**

Goals: To introduce permutations and combinations, to solve counting problems using them, and to show how theorems are proved by combinatorial arguments.

Prerequisites: Chapter 1 and Sections 2.4, 3.1–3.3, and 4.1.

Advice: Students need to understand clearly that a combination involves an unordered selection of objects from a set with no repetition allowed, while a permutation involves an ordered selection of objects from a set with no repetition allowed. (We will consider the cases when repetition is allowed in Section 4.5.)

Exercises: The questions asked in Exercises 8–39 require students to use permutations and combinations to solve counting problems. You may want to assign Exercise 40, which deals with the number of circular arrangements of objects. Exercises 41–43 require careful reasoning to count the number of ways races can end when ties are allowed.

SECTION 4.4   **Binomial Coefficients**

Goals: To introduce the binomial theorem and to show how combinatorial identities can be proved by combinatorial arguments.

Prerequisites: Chapter 1 and Sections 2.4, 3.1–3.3, 4.1, and 4.3.

Advice: Note that we use $C(n, r)$ and $\binom{n}{r}$ interchangeably to denote the number of r-combinations of a set with n elements. Present the combinatorial proofs of Pascal's identity and the binomial theorem. Since students are uncomfortable with proofs of this ilk, explain carefully how counting arguments really can be used to prove theorems.

Exercises: Exercise 14–17 ask students to prove inequalities involving binomial coefficients. (The result of Exercise 17 is used later in the text.) Combinatorial proofs are required in Exercises 21–22, 27–30, and 38. Exercise 32 asks for a proof by mathematical induction of the binomial theorem. Compared to the combinatorial proof, this alternative approach is substantially more complicated. Exercise 39 asks students to conjecture a formula or rule that generates the terms of a sequence from its initial terms; the intended answers here involve binomial coefficients.

SECTION 4.5   Generalized Permutations and Combinations

Goals: To solve counting problems involving permutations and combinations with repetition allowed and permutations where objects may be indistinguishable.

Prerequisites: Chapter 1 and Sections 2.1–2.4, 3.1–3.4, 4.1, and 4.3–4.4.

Advice: This section is devoted to permutations and combinations with repetition allowed. To motivate the discussion, it helps to discuss a variety of counting problems with students, determining whether you are enumerating combinations or permutations, with or without repetition allowed. Stress that determining the appropriate model is more important than memorizing the formulae. Students often have trouble with combinations with repetition allowed. Give lots of simple examples to motivate this and show the connection with determining nonnegative integer solutions to equations of the form $\sum_{j=1}^{r} x_j = n$. The "stars and bars" proof of the formula for combinations with repetition allowed is subtle and requires careful explanation.

Work through Example 8, which asks for the number of different strings that can be formed by reordering the characters in *SUCCESS*. Make sure that students see that the position of the individual *S*'s doesn't matter and only where there are *S*'s does. (One way to show this is to label the individual letters with subscripts—S_1, S_2, and S_3—and show that different permutations of the letters lead to the same string when subscripts are removed.) Once this point is clear, you will find that the proof of Theorem 3 is easy for students to understand.

Exercises: Exercises 1–13 involve counting problems where repetition is allowed. Exercises 30–37 involve counting permutations with indistinguishable objects. Assign some of Exercises 14–16, which ask for the number of solutions in integers to equations of the form $\sum_{j=1}^{r} x_j = n$ where some constraints are present. You may want to assign Exercise 53, which asks for a proof of the multinomial theorem.

SECTION 4.6   Generating Permutations and Combinations

Goals: To introduce algorithms for generating permutations and combinations.

Prerequisites: Chapter 1 and Sections 2.1–2.3, 3.1–3.4, 4.1, and 4.3–4.4.

Advice: There are many occasions when we need to generate the combinations or permutations of a set. Explain that there are many possible procedures for generating permutations and combinations, so that the ones in the text are not the only such algorithms. It helps to work through some small examples to see how an algorithm generates permutations or combinations.

Exercises: Exercises 10–13 develop another algorithm, based on Cantor expansions, for generating permutations. This set of exercises is challenging, but quite interesting.

CHAPTER 5
Discrete Probability

Overview: The goal of Chapter 5 is to develop basic concepts of discrete probability, including conditional probability and expected values, and we show how to use these concepts to study the average case complexity of an algorithm.

SECTION 5.1   An Introduction to Discrete Probability

Goals: To introduce discrete probability theory.

Prerequisites: Chapter 1 and Sections 2.3, 3.1–3.2, 4.1, and 4.3–4.4.

Advice: Students in a first course in discrete mathematics should be exposed to the concept of probability. There are many reasons why probability is important for all students, but it is particularly important for computer science students, who need to understand the concept of the average-case complexity of an algorithm, a topic to be covered in Section 5.3.

Probability can be illustrated in an appealing way by discussing how it applies to lotteries and to card games. Students enjoy learning how to compute the odds of winning the "pick six" lottery by picking six correct numbers out of the first n positive integers where n is between 40 and 50. If you calculate probabilities from poker, make sure that all your students know the contents of a standard deck of cards, what the 13 kinds of cards are, and what the four suits are. Finding the probability of a full house involves some careful counting; it is done in Example 7. Subtle aspects of probabilistic reasoning are illustrated by the notorious Monty Hall Three Door Puzzle (Example 11). Exploring correct and incorrect lines of reasoning involving this puzzle can be quite instructive.

Exercises: Exercises 8–20 ask for the probability of various kinds of poker hands. Exercise 35 asks for an analysis of different bets in roulette. Exercise 38 introduces the concept of independent events.

SECTION 5.2   Probability Theory

Goals: To introduce important concepts from discrete probability, including conditional probability, independence, random variables, and the binomial distribution. To introduce the notions of probabilistic algorithms and the probabilistic method.

Prerequisites: Chapter 1 and Sections 2.2–2.4, 3.1–3.3, 4.1, 4.3–4.4, and 5.1.

Advice: Describe the rules that probabilities of finitely many outcomes must obey. Then show how these rules are met by probabilities determined using Laplace's definition. Examples 3 and 4 determine the conditional probabilities of events, and Examples 5, 6, and 7 deal with independence of events.

Be sure to cover the famous birthday problem (Example 13) and its extension to computing the probability of collisions in hashing functions (Example 14). You may want to introduce probabilistic algorithms; Example 16, which covers probabilistic primality testing, is important for generating large primes for cryptographic applications.

You may want to introduce the probabilistic method, which shows how probability theory can be used in nonconstructive existence proofs. Theorem 4 illustrates how this method can be used to establish a lower bound on some Ramsey numbers.

Exercises: Exercises 19–22 involve variations of the birthday problem. Exercises 36–37 establish a formula for the probability of the union of pairwise disjoint events. Exercises 39 provides another example of how the probabilistic method is used. Exercise 40 describes a probabilistic algorithm for determining whether a permutation of the integers 1 through n has already been sorted.

SECTION 5.3 **Expected Value and Variance**

Goals: To introduce the concept of the expected value of a random variable. To show how the linearity of expectations can be used to solve a variety of problems. To show how expected values and their properties can be used to find the average case complexity of algorithms. To introduce the notion of the variance of a random variable and to introduce Chebyshev's inequality.

Prerequisites: Chapter 1 and Sections 2.2–2.3, 3.1–3.2, 4.1, 4.3–4.4 and 5.1–5.2.

Advice: Describe how expected values are found; be sure to cover Theorem 1 and illustrate how it is used to compute expected values with Example 3 and in the proof of Theorem 2, which gives the expected number of success in n Bernoulli trials. Make sure to cover the linearity of expectations and illustrate the usefulness of this property by covering Examples 6 and 7, which find the expected number of hats returned correctly in the famous hatcheck problem and the expected number of inversions in a permutation.

Explain how the properties of expected values are used in average-case complexity analysis. Cover Example 8, which finds the average-case complexity of linear search, or Example 9, which finds the average-case complexity of the insertion sort.

Introduce the geometric distribution, which provides an example of an infinite sample space, and find its expectation (Theorem 4). Cover independence of random variables and Theorem 5, which states that the expected value of the product of independent random variables is the product of their expected values. Introduce the notion of the variance of a random variable and explain how it is used in Chebyshev's inequality.

Instructors should note that probability generating functions and how they are used for calculating expected values and variances are introduced in the exercise set of Section 6.4.

Exercises: Markov's inequality is introduced in Exercise 29. The average-case complexity of a variant of bubble sort and the quick sort are studied in Exercises 33 and 34, respectively. The variance in the number of fixed elements in a random permutation is studied in Exercise 35. Covariance is introduced in Exercises 36–38.

CHAPTER 6
Advanced Counting Techniques

Overview: We introduce several important counting techniques in this chapter. In particular, we show how to use recurrence relations to solve counting problems, and we show how to solve a variety of counting problems using the principle of inclusion–exclusion.

The first three sections of the chapter are devoted to recurrence relations. Section 6.1 shows how recurrence relations can be used to solve counting problems and shows how to solve some recurrence relations using iteration. Section 6.2 develops the methodology for solving linear recurrence relations with constant coefficients. Section 6.3 is devoted to divide-and-conquer algorithms and the recurrence relations used to study their complexity. Another advanced technique, the use of generating functions to solve counting problems, is introduced in Section 6.4. The final two sections of the chapter cover the principle of inclusion–exclusion and its many applications. Specifically, Section 6.5 introduces this principle and presents its proof, and Section 6.6 shows how to apply this principle by showing how it can be used to count such things as the number of primes not exceeding a positive integer, the number of onto functions from one finite set to another, and the number of derangements of a set.

SECTION 6.1	**Recurrence Relations**
Goals:	To show how counting problems can be modeled using recurrence relations.
Prerequisites:	Chapter 1 and Sections 2.1–2.4, 3.1–3.4, 4.1, and 4.3–4.4.
Advice:	Explain that a recurrence relation is a type of recursive definition, so that initial conditions are required, as well as the rule for obtaining subsequent terms of the sequence. Students should be given a clear idea of what it means for a sequence to solve a particular recurrence relation. In Example 5 we determine the number of moves required to solve the famous Tower of Hanoi puzzle. This example introduces the use of iteration to solve recurrence relations. Students will find it interesting that the generalization of the Tower of Hanoi problem to four pegs (known as the Reve's puzzle) still contains open questions. Cover Example 6, which shows how recurrence relations can be used to find bit strings of a particular length that do have two consecutive 0's. If time permits, cover Example 8, which introduces the Catalan numbers in the enumeration of ways to insert parentheses into the product of numbers to determine the order of multiplications.
Exercises:	Exercises 10–16 give students the opportunity to set up some relatively simple recurrence relations. I suggest assigning some of Exercises 23–26 and 40–41. These provide some good examples of constructing recurrence relations for the number of bit strings with certain properties. Exercises 49–53 provide a set of challenging exercises concerning the Josephus problem, and Exercises 54–61 involve the generalization of the Tower of Hanoi puzzle to four pegs (the Reve's puzzle). Exercises 62–68 introduce the concept of a backward difference and relate recurrence relations to difference equations. You may want to assign some of these exercises.
SECTION 6.2	**Solving Recurrence Relations**
Goals:	To solve linear recurrence relations with constant coefficients.
Prerequisites:	Section 6.1 and its prerequisites.
Advice:	We state and prove methods for solving linear recurrence relations with constant coefficients. We start with the simplest case (homogeneous without repeated roots of the characteristic equation) and advance to the general case (Theorems 4 and 6). Show students what it means for a recurrence relation to be linear, to be homogeneous, and to have constant coefficients, using examples where such properties occur and other examples where they do not. Make sure the concept of the degree of such a recurrence relation is clear (e.g., $a_n = a_{n-1} + a_{n-8}$ has degree 8). You may need to review briefly how to factor polynomials. Students who have studied differential equations will recognize the analogy between the methods presented here and those used to solve linear differential equations. If time permits, cover the case of repeated roots for homogeneous recurrence relations. Explain how nonhomogeneous linear recurrence relations are solved, including the case where the right-hand side is a product of a power of a constant and a polynomial.

It might be advisable to discuss the use of computer algebra systems (such as maple or Mathematica), which can solve recurrence relations as easily as a pocket calculator can perform long division. In fact these systems have a variety of powerful features important to discrete mathematics.

You may want to cover Example 4, which provides an explicit formula for the Fibonacci numbers, Example 5, which illustrates what needs to be done when the characteristic equation has repeated roots, and Example 6, which shows how to solve a linear homogeneous recurrence relation of degree greater than two.

Exercises: Exercises 38–39 involve solving linear homogeneous recurrence relations with complex roots. We have avoided this situation in most other places since many students will not be comfortable working with complex numbers. Exercises 48–50 introduce the case of nonconstant coefficients.

SECTION 6.3   Divide-and-Conquer Algorithms and Recurrence Relations

Goals: To study the complexity of divide-and-conquer algorithms with functions that satisfy a special kind of recurrence relation.

Prerequisites: Chapter 1, Chapter 2 (especially Section 2.2), and Sections 3.1–3.4, 4.1, and 6.1.

Advice: Go over different divide-and-conquer algorithms, including binary searching, finding the maximum and minimum of a set of integers, the merge sort, and fast multiplication of integers. Such algorithms are described in Examples 1–4. Student often have trouble with divide-and-conquer recurrence relations, which are the recurrence relations arising in the complexity analysis of divide-and-conquer algorithms. State and show how to use Theorem 1, and perhaps Theorem 2 (the master theorem), which give big-O estimates for the values of functions that satisfy divide-and-conquer recurrence relations of the form $f(n) = af(n/b) + g(n)$ with $g(n) = c$ or $g(n) = cn^d$. Mention that the proof of Theorem 1 produces a formula for $f(n)$ when n is a power of b. Show how to apply the master theorem to give big-O estimates for the complexity of various algorithms (see Examples 9–11). If time permits, describe the closest-pairs algorithm described in Example 12 and explain how to estimate its complexity using the master theorem.

Exercises: Exercises 14, 17, 18, 23, and 28 give students the opportunity to analyze divide-and-conquer algorithms not discussed in the text.

SECTION 6.4   Generating Functions

Goals: To introduce the notion of a generating function, to show how generating functions can be used to model and solve counting problems, and to show how generating functions can be used to solve recurrence relations.

Prerequisites: Section 6.2 and its prerequisites and familiarity with infinite series.

Advice: Students find generating functions more difficult to understand and appreciate than the other counting topics covered in the text. This is a pity, since generating functions provide very powerful tools for enumeration. Stress how to model counting problems using generating functions and thereby obtain a mechanical means of solving them. Students will find Table 1 invaluable in doing the exercises in this section; in fact they will certainly want to learn some of these generating functions well enough not to need to refer to the table or work them out each time.

It might be advisable to discuss the use of computer algebra systems (such as maple or Mathematica), which are powerful tools when working with generating functions. The *Student Solutions Guide* and the *Instructor's Resource Guide* give some details of the use of maple in the solutions of relevant exercises in this chapter. (They also give details on using maple to solve recurrence relations.)

We also illustrate how generating functions can be used to solve recurrence relations—see Examples 16–17. A brief optional final subsection shows that generating functions can be used to prove identities.

Exercises: Exercises 13–29 get at the heart of the issue—using generating functions to model and solve counting problems. Exercises 32–39 ask students to solve recurrence relations using generating functions, including producing an explicit formula for the Fibonacci numbers; the algebra can get a little overwhelming at times, and you might wish to encourage students to use a computer algebra system. Exercises 42–43 ask for proofs of combinatorial identities using generating functions. Exercise 46 outlines a way to derive an explicit formula for the sum of the first n squares. Exponential generating functions are introduced in the preamble to Exercise 45, and probability generating functions are introduced in the preamble to Exercise 57.

SECTION 6.5   Inclusion–Exclusion

Goals: To introduce the principle of inclusion–exclusion and show how it is used to solve some simple counting problems.

Prerequisites: Chapter 1 and Sections 2.4, 3.1–3.4, 4.1, and 4.3–4.5.

Advice: Motivate the proof of the principle of inclusion–exclusion using the case of three sets. Show that elements in one, two, or all three of the sets are counted just once. Cover the proof of inclusion–exclusion carefully. Show that each element in the union of the sets is counted exactly once. This principle can also be proved by mathematical induction (see Exercise 22). You may wish to cover Example 2, which deals with divisibility of integers. This example foreshadows the treatment of the sieve of Eratosthenes in Section 6.6.

Exercises: Exercise 12 is a good thought question; it asks students to determine the number of positive integers not exceeding 1000 that are either squares or cubes. There are $2^n - 1$ terms in the expansion given by the principle of inclusion–exclusion; Exercises 18, 19, and 21 give students the opportunity to make sure that they understand this general theorem.

SECTION 6.6   Applications of Inclusion–Exclusion

Goals: To use inclusion–exclusion to solve complicated counting problems, such as determining the number of onto functions, the number of primes less than a specified integer, and the number of derangements of a finite set of objects.

Prerequisites: Section 6.5 and its prerequisites.

Advice: Make sure that the alternative formulation of inclusion–exclusion in terms of properties is clear. Illustrate the use of this formulation with Example 1, which counts the number of solutions in nonnegative integers of a linear equation with constraints. I suggest that you cover the application to the sieve of Eratosthenes, counting primes less than 100 using inclusion–exclusion (be sure to adjust the number of integers not divisible by 2, 3, 5, or 7 to exclude the integer 1, but to include these four primes). Example 2 illustrates how to count functions from a finite set onto another finite set. Example 3 shows how certain enumeration problems can be solved by counting onto functions. If you have time, go over the hatcheck problem; this can be very entertaining to students. For students who know about infinite series it is worthwhile explaining how the probability that no one receives the correct hat tends extremely rapidly to $1/e$ as $n \to \infty$.

Exercises: I suggest you assign Exercises 6 and 7; these require students to do a little thinking besides just setting up inclusion–exclusion formulae. Exercises 9–11 are enumeration problems solved by counting onto functions. Exercise 15 is a good thought question; it asks students to count permutations with various properties, including derangements. Exercise 23 asks for a formula for the number of integers not exceeding n that are relatively prime to n, i.e., $\phi(n)$. This is an excellent application of inclusion–exclusion. (My enthusiasm for number theory seems to be showing here.)

CHAPTER 7
Relations

Overview: We study an important discrete structure in this chapter, namely the relation. We first define binary relations and relations on a set. We show how to use zero-one matrices and directed graphs to represent relations on a set. We study the different properties of binary relations and discuss in detail two important classes of binary relations: equivalence relations and partial orderings. We show how to find closures of binary relations with respect to various properties, devoting considerable attention to algorithms for constructing the transitive closure of a relation. We briefly study n-ary relations and describe the applications of these relations to models for data bases. The material in this chapter is straightforward with the exception of the material on transitive closures, some properties of equivalence relations, and some results concerning partial orderings.

SECTION 7.1   **Relations and Their Properties**

Goals: To introduce the concept of a relation and basic properties of relations, including the reflexive, symmetric, antisymmetric, and transitive properties.

Prerequisites: Chapter 1 and Sections 2.4, 3.1–3.3, 4.1, and 4.3–4.4.

Advice: Explain that the graph of a function is a relation, whereas relations can express more general correspondences between elements of two sets. Students have trouble verifying properties of relations when the conditions to check are vacuous, such as showing that the relation $\{(0,1),(0,2)\}$ on the set $\{0,1,2\}$ is transitive since there are no pairs of the form (a,b) and (b,c) in this relation. There is often confusion concerning the relationship between the terms *symmetric* and *antisymmetric*; make sure students know that there are relations that are both symmetric and antisymmetric and relations that are neither symmetric nor antisymmetric.

You may want to cover Examples 6 and 16, which determine the number of relations and reflexive relations, respectively, on a set with n elements.

Exercises: Assign Exercise 8, which asks for examples of relations that are both symmetric and antisymmetric and others that are neither symmetric nor antisymmetric. Be sure to assign some exercises that involve the inverse relation R^{-1} of a relation R; this is defined in the preamble to Exercise 24, and arises in Exercises 24–27. Counting the relations with a particular property is a way to review counting techniques and reinforce students' understanding of the property (students will find such exercises difficult). Example 16 computes the number of reflexive relations on a set with n elements, and Exercise 45 asks for a similar computation involving other properties. You may want to assign some of Exercises 9–13; these deal with irreflexive relations, defined in the preamble to Exercise 9.

SECTION 7.2   *n*-ary Relations and Their Applications

Goals: To introduce the concept of *n*-ary relations and show how these relations are used to represent data bases.

Prerequisites: Chapter 1 and Sections 2.1, 2.4, 3.1–3.3, 4.1, and 7.1.

Advice: Students like seeing an application of relations, an abstract subject, to computer science, so this material goes over quite well. I suggest describing how operations on *n*-ary relations relate to operations of practical interest on large data bases, such as student records or employee data bases. The material in this section is straightforward. However, make sure students understand that different records can collapse to the same record when projections are applied and that the join of two relations can contain more than one record, or no records, for each record in each of the relations being joined. Stress that a domain of an *n*-ary relation is a key if and only if its value is never the same in two different records *that ever appear* in the data base. Give examples of the selection operator and explain how logical connectives can be used to define the condition that *n*-tuples must satisfy to be selected. You may want to briefly discuss the database query language SQL and how it is used to carry out the operations discussed in this section.

Exercises: Exercises 10–13 involve the selection operator. Properties of the selection operator are covered in Exercises 20–24; properties of the projection operator are covered in Exercises 25–27. Exercise 19 illustrates the various things that can happen when a join of two relations is formed. Exercises 28–29 deal with SQL.

SECTION 7.3   Representing Relations

Goals: To show how relations can be represented using zero-one matrices and directed graphs.

Prerequisites: Sections 2.7 and 7.1 and their prerequisites.

Advice: This section discusses two ways to represent relations on a set: zero-one matrices and directed graphs. Some of the material in this section and later sections depends on arithmetic with zero-one matrices, which was covered in Section 2.7. Relate properties of relations with the corresponding properties of the zero-one matrices that represent them.

We introduce directed graphs in this section, and use them throughout the chapter to represent relations. Again, you should relate properties of relations to the corresponding properties of the directed graphs that represent them. Giving the directed graph interpretation of the transitive property is quite helpful, since students can readily see whether there is always an edge between two vertices that are connected by a path of length 2. (Don't forget about missing loops!) Directed graphs will be studied in greater depth in Chapter 8.

Exercises: Exercises 31–32 ask students to use the directed graph of several relations to determine whether these relations are reflexive, symmetric, antisymmetric, and/or transitive.

SECTION 7.4   Closures of Relations

Goals: To introduce the concept of the closure of a relation with respect to a property, and to develop algorithms for constructing transitive closures.

Prerequisites: Section 7.3 and its prerequisites.

Advice: This is the most difficult section of the chapter, since constructing transitive closures can be complicated. There is no particular difficulty constructing the reflexive and symmetric closures of a relation. Students are tempted to construct the transitive closure of a relation by just adding the pairs that are missing, i.e., pairs not in the relation of the form (a, c) where (a, b) and (b, c) are in the relation. Show them that this is not sufficient with an example (e.g., a path of length 3). They also sometimes forget to add (a, a) and (b, b) when (a, b) and (b, a) are in the relation.

The concept of an interior vertex of a path and how this concept is used in Warshall's algorithm is confusing. Make sure to give at least one example of this before embarking on the development of Warshall's algorithm, as is done in the text. Be sure to give a careful exposition of Lemma 2.

Exercises: You may want to assign Exercises 15 and 35, which show that there are some properties for which the closure of a relation does not exist.

SECTION 7.5 Equivalence Relations

Goals: To study equivalence relations and their equivalence classes.

Prerequisites: Section 7.3 and its prerequisites.

Advice: This section introduces the concept of an equivalence relation. Students often have trouble with the notion of an equivalence class. Make sure you cover Example 4, which shows that congruence modulo m, where m is a positive integer, is an equivalence relation. Emphasize that two different elements can be representatives of the same equivalence class. It helps to show that $[1]_4 = [5]_4 = [-3]_4$, and so on. Spend sufficient time showing that the equivalence classes of an equivalence relation form a partition. Students find this confusing. Also be careful when showing that a partition of a set determines an equivalence relation. Students find this very subtle.

Exercises: Exercise 5 presents an important way to establish that a relation is an equivalence relation. It can be used in many of the subsequent exercises, including Exercises 7 and 8. Refinements of partitions are the subject of Exercises 37–38.

SECTION 7.6 Partial Orderings

Goals: To study partial orderings and their properties and applications. You may want to cover topological sorting and scheduling. You may also want to discuss lattices and their application to information flow.

Prerequisites: Section 7.3 and its prerequisites.

Advice: This section introduces the concept of a partial ordering. I find that students find it difficult to think of partial orderings (other than the usual less than or equal relation), such as divisibility of positive integers and set inclusion, as ways to order elements of a set. Also, make it clear that the notation for a partial order (the curly less than or equal sign, $\preceq$) is general, and refers to more than just the less than or equal relation ($\leq$). Show how to extend lexicographic ordering to strings. This concept is important in computer science. Hasse diagrams can be confusing. Much of the information they contain must be inferred. Carefully go through the process of constructing a Hasse diagram at least once, such as is done in Examples 11 and 12.

A lot of terminology about posets is presented here. Make sure students understand the distinction between minimal and least elements and maximal and greatest elements. The concepts of greatest lower bounds and least upper bounds also require careful explaining. Once these topics are covered, you can define a lattice. Cover Example 24, which describes the lattice model of information flow; this concrete example helps motivate the definition of a lattice and shows how lattices can be used in applications. The application of topological sorting to project scheduling is something that most students find interesting.

Exercises: Exercises 6 and 7 introduce the concept of the dual of a poset. I suggest assigning Exercise 34, which asks students to show that there is at most one greatest and one least element of a poset. Exercises 58 and 59 ask for scheduling the tasks required in building a house and carrying out the tasks in a software project; this can be done using topological sorting.

CHAPTER 8
Graphs

Overview: This chapter provides an introduction to graph theory and its applications. Sections 8.1–8.4 cover the basics of the subject, including graph terminology, how graphs are represented, isomorphism, and connectivity. The remaining sections cover particular topics that are treated independently. These topics are Euler and Hamilton paths and circuits, shortest-path problems in weighted graphs, planarity, and coloring. Cover any or all these as time permits.

The graph theoretic terminology used in this book is based on one of the most commonly used sets of such terminology. It is consistent and mostly self-explanatory. However, there are many other ways to define the terms used in graph theory. Pay careful attention to the precise definitions given here and warn your students that there is no standard terminology in graph theory.

SECTION 8.1   **Introduction to Graphs**

Goals: To introduce different types of graphs and to show how they are used in modeling.

Prerequisites: Chapter 1.

Advice: This section introduces different types of graphs. The use of computer networks to motivate the definitions goes over well. Rigorous definitions of multigraphs and pseudographs are given. However, these rigorous definitions are used only sparingly in subsequent sections, since we are concerned with basic properties and applications of graphs, and not with obtaining the most general and most detailed results.

A variety of graph models are introduced. These demonstrate the wide range of subjects to which graph theory can be applied. Cover some or all of Examples 1–9, which involve applications to ecology, acquaintanceships, psychology, films, game theory, collaboration, telephone calls, the Internet, and parallel processing. Students in your class may have interests in a variety of other disciplines, so stress that discrete mathematics has applications to almost every (and maybe every) discipline. References listed in the Suggested Readings section of the text will help you direct students to applications in their particular areas of interest.

Exercises: Intersection graphs are introduced in Exercise 11.

SECTION 8.2   **Graph Terminology**

Goals: To introduce the basic terminology of graph theory, basic results about graphs, and important families of graphs.

Prerequisites: Chapter 1 and Sections 3.1, 4.1–4.2, 7.3, 7.5, and 8.1.

Advice: The material in this section presents no particular difficulties. When showing that the sum of the degrees of the vertices of an undirected graph is even, make the analogy between people shaking hands and vertices being adjacent (that is why this result is called the "handshaking" theorem). Make sure to cover the families of graphs introduced in this section: complete graphs, complete bipartite graphs, cycles, wheels, and cubes. They are used extensively as examples in subsequent sections. Students have difficulty with the notion of a bipartite graph. When explaining this you might want to use the language of partitions of sets.

You may want to cover Examples 12 and 13, which show how graphs are used to model local area networks and interconnection networks for parallel computers, respectively.

Exercises: Assign Exercises 28–29, since they involve several concepts covered in the section; they deal with the problem of determining whether a graph with a given degree sequence exists. You may want to discuss Exercises 35–37 , which introduce and use the concept of a regular graph.

SECTION 8.3   Representing Graphs and Graph Isomorphism

Goals: To show how to represent graphs and to study isomorphism of graphs.

Prerequisites: Chapter 1 and Sections 2.7, 3.1, 4.1, and 8.1–8.2.

Advice: We describe several ways to represent graphs: adjacency lists, adjacency matrices, and incidence matrices. This material is straightforward, although it does require familiarity with matrices. You may want to discuss the circumstances under which each of these different ways to represent graphs is preferable.

The last part of this section is devoted to isomorphism of graphs. Stress how invariants of graphs can be used to show that two graphs are not isomorphic, but cannot show that two graphs are isomorphic. It is useful to give students a "shopping list" of invariants to examine: number of vertices, number of edges, degree sequence, and so on. In the text we discuss isomorphism only for simple graphs. We give a nontrivial example of determining whether two graphs are isomorphic in Example 11.

Exercises: Exercises 34–44 ask students to determine whether pairs of graphs are isomorphic. Be sure to assign a variety of these exercises. You should assign Exercise 60, which asks students to define isomorphism for directed graphs, and then have them do Exercises 61–64, which ask whether pairs of directed graphs are isomorphic.

SECTION 8.4   Connectivity

Goals: To introduce the notions of paths and circuits in graphs and to define connectivity of graphs.

Prerequisites: Section 8.3 and its prerequisites.

Advice: The material in this section presents no particular difficulties. Make sure that the definitions of paths, circuits, and simple paths and circuits are clear. (Unfortunately the terminology for the concepts discussed in this section varies in discussions by different authors.) Discuss the meaning of paths in acquaintanceship graphs, collaboration graphs, and the Hollywood graph—see Examples 2–4. Explain the difference between strongly connected and weakly connected directed graphs, since the difference between these concepts is sometimes confusing. Introduce the notions of connected components in undirected graphs and strongly connected components in directed graphs; illustrate these notions with the connected components of the telephone call graph (Example 7) and the strongly connected components of the Web graph (Example 11), respectively. You may want to show how paths are used to help determine whether two graphs are isomorphic. This is illustrated in Example 13. Go over the proof of Theorem 2, which works for all types of graphs.

Exercises: You may want to assign Exercises 32–33, which introduce the concept of a vertex basis. Cover Exercise 43 if you plan to discuss trees, since the result in this exercise is used in Chapter 9.

SECTION 8.5   Euler and Hamilton Paths

Goals: To develop necessary and sufficient conditions for the existence of Euler circuits and paths, to give algorithms for constructing them, and to study Hamilton paths and circuits.

Prerequisites: Section 8.4 and its prerequisites.

Advice: We introduce the famous Königsberg bridge problem here. It is something every mathematics student should see. Algorithm 1 presents one procedure for constructing Euler circuits based on the idea used in the proof that every simple graph with all vertices of even degree has such a circuit. Tell students that the situation for Hamilton paths and circuits is different from that for Euler paths and circuits: there are no known simple necessary and sufficient conditions for their existence. However, you may want to state some sufficient conditions for the existence of Hamilton circuits, such as Theorem 3 (Dirac's Theorem) and Theorem 4 (Ore's Theorem).

Exercises: Exercises 24–25 ask for necessary and sufficient conditions for the existence of Euler paths and circuits in directed graphs. Exercises 50–53 develop Fleury's algorithm for constructing Euler circuits. Exercises 56–64 involve the application of Hamilton paths and circuits to the knight's tour problem. The proof of Ore's theorem is outlined in Exercise 65.

SECTION 8.6   Shortest-Path Problems

Goals: To present an algorithm for finding a shortest path in a weighted graph, and to discuss the traveling salesman problem.

Prerequisites: Chapter 1 and Sections 2.1–2.3, 3.1–3.4, 4.1, and 8.1–8.4.

Advice: We define weighted graphs in this section and describe one problem involving such graphs, namely the determination of shortest paths. We present Dijkstra's algorithm for determining shortest paths. Students have a tendency to solve shortest-path problems by inspection. Make sure they work through all steps of the algorithm.

  The traveling salesman problem is a famous example of a problem for which no known algorithm can produce the optimum solution efficiently. It is worth covering if time permits.

Exercises: It may help to assign Exercise 4, which is difficult to do by inspection. I recommend that you have students work through some or all of Exercises 21–23, which deal with Floyd's algorithm for finding a shortest path between all pairs of vertices in a graph. Assigning exercises on the traveling salesman problem (such as Exercise 27) will convince students that the lack of an efficient algorithm for this problem is a serious issue.

SECTION 8.7   Planar Graphs

Goals: To introduce the concept of planarity of graphs and to develop tools to decide whether a graph is planar.

Prerequisites: Section 8.3 and its prerequisites.

Advice: The three house–three utility problem provides a good introduction to the concept of planarity; almost everyone finds this puzzle captivating. Sometimes students are confused that a graph can be planar even though the standard way of drawing it has crossings, such as K_4 or $K_{2,3}$. Cover Example 3, which gives an ad hoc proof that $K_{3,3}$ is not planar. Students often make the mistake of using Corollary 1, which states that a connected planar simple graph with e edges and $v \geq 3$ vertices satisfies $e \leq 3v-6$, to show that graphs are planar. Cover Example 5, which shows that this cannot be done.

If you cover Kuratowski's theorem, explain how to use it to show that graphs are nonplanar, such as is done in Examples 7 and 8. Make sure that students understand how difficult it is to use this theorem to show that a graph is planar, however. Mention that planarity of graphs is an important topic for circuit design; this will perk the interest of electrical engineering students.

Exercises: Exercise 9 asks for a proof that K_5 is nonplanar, which can be constructed in a similar way to the proof given in the text for the nonplanarity of $K_{3,3}$. Exercise 16 asks for a proof that a connected bipartite planar simple graph satisfies $e \leq 2v - 4$, where e is the number of edges and $v \geq 3$ is the number of vertices. The concepts of the crossing number and the thickness of a graph are introduced in the preambles to Exercises 26 and 30, respectively. These are important concepts for applications of graph theory to VLSI. Exercises 36–37 ask about drawing graphs on a torus without edges crossing.

SECTION 8.8   Graph Coloring

Goals: To introduce the concept of the coloring of a graph and give applications of graph colorings.

Prerequisites: Section 8.3 and its prerequisites.

Advice: Make sure students understand the connection between coloring maps and coloring graphs. Since students sometimes try to apply the four color theorem to nonplanar graphs, show them that the chromatic number of a graph can be arbitrarily large by using K_n as an example. Also, show that bipartite graphs are the graphs with a chromatic number of at most 2. Sometimes students do not immediately see that the chromatic number of $K_{m,n}$ is 2. I suggest covering the application of graph coloring to scheduling final exams; since you may cover this section near the end of your term, finals may be near.

Exercises: You may want to have students study the coloring algorithm described in the preamble to Exercise 27; emphasize that this algorithm may use too many colors and tell students that no one has found an efficient algorithm that colors graphs using the fewest possible colors. Exercises 34 and 35 ask for proofs of the Six Color Theorem and the Five Color Theorem, respectively. These proofs are considerable easier than the proof of the Four Color Theorem!

CHAPTER 9
Trees

Overview: Trees have a tremendous variety of applications. They are used extensively throughout computer science to build data structures, to perform encoding, to study formal languages, and in searching and sorting. This chapter introduces the terminology used to describe trees, their basic properties, and some of their important applications.

In Section 9.1 we cover basic terminology and establish relationships between the number of vertices of different types and the number of edges in trees. In Section 9.2 we introduce applications of trees to decision problems, to coding, to binary searching, and to studying games. We introduce tree traversal algorithms in Section 9.3; these are used extensively when compilers evaluate expressions. We discuss various ways to construct spanning trees, such as breadth-first searching and backtracking, and give applications of backtracking for solving a variety of problems in Section 9.4. Finally, in Section 9.5 we give algorithms for constructing minimum spanning trees. I recommend covering Section 9.1 in all courses. Cover the other sections that interest you as time permits.

SECTION 9.1   Introduction to Trees

Goals: To introduce the concept of a tree, to present basic terminology for trees, and to develop relationships among the number of vertices of different kinds and the number of edges in trees.

Prerequisites: Chapter 1 and Sections 3.1–3.4, 4.1, 4.3–4.4, and 8.1–8.4.

Advice: A large amount of terminology is presented in this section, but almost all the terms are self-explanatory. We begin by defining unrooted trees; then we define rooted trees and show how an unrooted tree can be rooted by choosing any vertex as the root. You should show how additional structure can be placed on a rooted tree by ordering the children of each internal vertex. This is a good place to tell students that in many applications of binary trees each vertex except the root is specified to be either a right child or a left child (we will need this when discussing binary search trees). Go over one or two uses of trees in modeling, such as those discussed in Examples 5, 6, 7, and 8. These involve chemistry, business, and computer science.

The relationships between the number of vertices, internal vertices, and leaves of a full m-ary tree are straightforward. Explain that the equalities $n = mi + 1$ and $n = l + i$ can be used to solve for each of n, l, and i in terms of the other two. Students sometimes find the application of these equations difficult. It helps to go carefully through Example 9, which describes one such application to chain letters, emphasizing how the model is set up. Be sure to cover Theorem 5 and Corollary 1; they will be needed in our study of the complexity of sorting algorithms.

Exercises: I recommend Exercises 11–13, which ask how many nonisomorphic rooted trees there are with particular numbers of vertices. This is a question whose solution involves synthesizing different concepts, such as the definition of a rooted tree, the concept of isomorphism, and the usefulness of invariants. Exercise 48, which establishes a big-Omega estimate for the average depth of a leaf in a binary tree with n vertices, is needed later in the chapter when trees are used to study the complexity of sorting.

SECTION 9.2   Applications of Trees

Goals: To introduce several applications of trees, including binary search trees, decision trees, prefix codes, and game trees.

Prerequisites: Section 9.1 and its prerequisites.

Advice: We introduce four applications of trees in this section. We begin with binary search trees. Explain the algorithm for locating and adding items to a binary search tree with some examples, such as that given in the text. Go over the complexity analysis for this algorithm; mention that there are procedures for balancing binary search trees to make this algorithm as efficient as possible.

Decision trees are introduced here. Example 2, which shows how to use a decision tree to find a counterfeit coin, gives a good preview of how such trees are used. We show how to use decision trees to study the complexity of sorting algorithms; we provide big-Omega estimates for the worst-case and average-case complexity of sorting algorithms based on binary comparisons.

Next, we introduce the use of binary trees to represent prefix codes. Since students sometimes have trouble with the concept of a prefix code, go over the definition and examples carefully. We introduce Huffman coding for producing optimal prefix codes, a key technique of data compression. Example 4 illustrates how to use this algorithm.

Finally, we show how trees can be used to study games. We introduce the minmax strategy and illustrate how nim and tic-tac-toe are analyzed using game trees.

Exercises: Exercises 6–10 deal with finding a counterfeit coin among a set of coins, where it may not be known whether the counterfeit coin is lighter or heavier than the genuine coins. The tournament sort, which uses ordered binary trees, is studied in Exercises 13–18. Exercise 26 illustrates that there can be more than one Huffman code for the same set of symbols and frequencies, depending on how ties are broken. Exercise 27 asks for the construction of a Huffman code for the letters of English using their frequencies in typical English text. Exercise 31 develops a connection between the Fibonacci numbers and Huffman coding. Games trees are used to study nim and tic-tac-toe in Exercises 33–43.

SECTION 9.3   Tree Traversal

Goals: To introduce tree traversal algorithms and prefix and postfix notation.

Prerequisites: Chapter 1 and Sections 2.1–2.3, 3.1–3.4, and 9.1–9.2.

Advice: Tree traversal is used extensively in computer science. In this section we present different traversal algorithms. First, I recommend performing these traversal algorithms directly from the recursive definitions, as illustrated in Examples 2, 3, and 4. Then explain how these traversals can be quickly performed by drawing a curve around the tree and listing vertices by how many times they are passed (see Figure 9). Show how expression trees are constructed. Define the infix, prefix, and postfix form of an expression, obtained by traversing this expression tree.

Exercises: Exercises 26–27 ask for proofs that expressions in postfix and prefix notation are well-defined. Well-formed formulae in prefix notation are introduced in the preamble to Exercise 30 and are studied in Exercises 30–31.

SECTION 9.4   Spanning Trees

Goals: To introduce the concept of a spanning tree, to give algorithms for constructing such trees, and to show how to solve problems using backtracking.

Prerequisites: Chapter 1 and Sections 2.1–2.3, 3.1–3.4, and 9.1–9.2.

Advice: Explain that a simple graph may have many different spanning trees, as is demonstrated in Example 1. Show how to produce spanning trees by removing edges that form circuits. Then show students how to use breadth-first and depth-first searches to produce spanning trees. Define the notion of tree edges and back edges in spanning trees constructed using depth-first search; these concepts are illustrated in Example 4. Give an example to show how backtracking can be used to solve a problem such as coloring a graph, placing n queens on a chessboard so that no queen can attack another, and finding elements of a subset having a specified sum, covered in Examples 6, 7, and 8, respectively. Introduce the notion of depth-first search in directed graphs and introduce the application of depth-first and breadth-first searching by Web spiders (Example 10).

Exercises: Exercise 32 gives another application of backtracking to the solution of mazes. Spanning forests are introduced in Exercises 33–38. You may want to cover rooted spanning trees; they are introduced in Exercises 53–55. The classification of the edges of a directed graph relative to a spanning tree constructed via depth-first search is introduced in Exercise 47.

SECTION 9.5   Minimum Spanning Trees

Goals: To study minimum spanning trees and produce algorithms for generating them.

Prerequisites: Section 9.4 and its prerequisites.

Advice: The construction of minimum spanning trees is required for many applications, so algorithms for their construction have been studied extensively. We present the two best known such algorithms, Prim's algorithm and Kruskal's algorithm. It is useful to go over both Prim's and Kruskal's algorithms to illustrate that the same problem can be solved in different ways. Proving that Prim's algorithm produces a spanning tree is rather subtle, so go over the proof slowly.

Exercises: Exercises 11–15 are concerned with maximum spanning trees. Working through variants of Kruskal's algorithm and Prim's algorithm for maximum spanning trees helps students understand these algorithms. You may be interested in having students work through the development of Sollin's algorithm given in Exercises 24–31; this is an example of an algorithm designed for parallel processing.

CHAPTER 10
Boolean Algebra

Overview: This chapter presents a brief introduction to Boolean algebra. We do not study Boolean algebra in a general setting, but rather we study the set $\{0, 1\}^n$ and Boolean functions on this set. In Section 10.1 we prove some fundamental identities satisfied by Boolean functions. We show in Section 10.2 how to represent Boolean functions using sum-of-products expansions. We show that certain sets of operators are functionally complete, that is, can be used to represent all Boolean expressions. Next, in Section 10.3 we show how to build circuits to perform some simple tasks using the rules of Boolean algebra. Finally, in Section 10.4 we show how to minimize sum-of-products expansions using K-maps and the Quine–McCluskey method.

SECTION 10.1   Boolean Functions

Goals: To introduce Boolean functions and important identities involving these functions.

Prerequisites: Chapter 1 and Sections 3.1–3.4 and 4.1.

Advice: The distinction between Boolean expressions and functions is subtle. It is hard for students to see that there are 2^{2^n} Boolean functions of degree n. Example 5 shows that this is true. When discussing the identities of Boolean algebra, explain that these rules are analogous to those for propositional equivalences and to those for set identities. If you are so inclined, cover the subsection on the abstract definition of a Boolean algebra. You may also want to mention how lattices are used to define Boolean algebras.

Exercises: Exercise 9 asks for a proof of one of the absorption laws. Exercise 10 will be used to design a circuit in Example 2 of Section 9.3. The Boolean operator *XOR* is introduced in the preamble to Exercise 22 and studied in Exercises 22–25.

SECTION 10.2 **Representing Boolean Functions**

Goals: To represent Boolean functions with sum-of-products expansions and to find functionally complete sets of operators.

Prerequisites: Section 10.1 and its prerequisites.

Advice: This section shows how to represent Boolean functions using sum-of-products expansions. This presents students with no particular difficulties. We also discuss functional completeness in this section. We use De Morgan's laws to show that $\{+, ^-\}$ and $\{\cdot, ^-\}$ are functionally complete. We then show that there is a functionally complete set of just one operator, namely $\{\,|\,\}$.

Exercises: Exercises 7–11 develop another way to represent Boolean expressions, namely by product-of-sums expansions. Exercises 15–16 show that $\{\downarrow\}$ is functionally complete.

SECTION 10.3 **Logic Gates**

Goals: To introduce logic gates and to build circuits using these gates.

Prerequisites: Section 10.2 and its prerequisites.

Advice: Point out that there are different ways to draw the same circuit, as Figure 3 demonstrates. Go over one or both of Examples 2 and 3, which show how logic gates can be used to build voting circuits and light switch circuits. Be sure to go over half adders and full adders; this shows how logic gates can be used to do computer arithmetic.

Exercises: You may want to assign Exercises 10–11, which ask for circuits to perform subtraction. I suggest assigning some of Exercises 15–18, which deal with circuits built from *NAND* or *NOR* gates. Multiplexers are defined in the preamble to Exercise 19. You may want to assign Exercise 19 so that students have some exposure to this important element in circuit design.

SECTION 10.4 **Minimization of Circuits**

Goals: To simplify sum-of-products expansions using K-maps and the Quine–McCluskey method.

Prerequisites: Section 10.3 and its prerequisites.

Advice: This section presents procedures for producing the simplest possible Boolean sums of products to represent Boolean expressions. We first present K-maps for sum-of-products expressions in two, three, and four variables. Make sure students understand all the ways to combine terms by combining adjacent cells in K-maps. This is illustrated in Figures 6 and 9. Emphasize that the largest combinations of squares should be used first. Do Example 8, which illustrates *don't care* conditions, where certain cells in a K-map can be arbitrarily included or excluded. Finally, go over the Quine–McCluskey method. Emphasize that it is an algorithm that can be mechanized, as opposed to the technique of K-maps, which depends on visual inspection, and that more than one final answer is possible, depending on how the covering of terms is produced. This covering is the difficult part of the procedure; it can be done using backtracking.

Exercises: You may wish to assign Exercise 20, which involves *don't care* conditions. The simplification of product-of-sums expansions using K-maps is the subject of Exercise 26.

CHAPTER 11
Modeling Computation

Overview: This chapter is an introduction to the theory of computation. Phrase-structure grammars and finite-state automata are introduced and the connection between them demonstrated. There are several reasons for covering the topics of this chapter. First, they illustrate how discrete mathematics and discrete structures are used in computer science. Second, they introduce students to a fascinating area that is worthy of extensive further study. And third, they form an attractive set of topics, leading to one central result: Kleene's theorem. This chapter concludes with a section on Turing machines, which provide a model for essentially all computing machines. This chapter, including this last section, provides a gateway to further studies in the theory of computation.

SECTION 11.1   Languages and Grammars

Goals: To introduce phrase-structure grammars and the Chomsky classification of these grammars. To introduce Backus–Naur from.

Prerequisites: Chapter 1 and Sections 2.4, 3.1–3.4, and 9.1.

Advice: We introduce formal languages and grammars through the use of an example that involves a subset of English. This helps motivate the more abstract definitions that follow. It is worthwhile to explain the difference between a natural language, like English, and a formal language, and to mention that this material is used in linguistics and in computer science (especially in the area of compilers).

Students have trouble distinguishing between different types of phrase-structure grammars. Be sure to cover Examples 8, 9, and 10 in the text; they provide useful illustrations of different types of grammars, but more importantly, they will be used later in the chapter.

Backus–Naur form is important in specifying languages. Illustrate its use with Example 13, which shows how it was used to define an identifier in ALGOL 60. Example 15, which shows how to use Backus–Naur form to describe the signed integers, is also worth covering.

Exercises: Exercise 13 gives students the opportunity to distinguish between different types of grammars. Exercises 22–27 involve Backus–Naur form, and extended Backus–Naur form is defined and used in Exercises 28–32.

SECTION 11.2   Finite State Machines with Output

Goals: To introduce the concept of a finite-state machine with output and to model different types of machines using them.

Prerequisites: Chapter 1 and Sections 3.1–3.4 and 8.1–8.3.

Advice: We discuss finite-state machines with output in this section. The example of a vending machine described in this section helps students understand the different elements that make up a finite-state machine. The finite-state machines we discuss in the text are known as Mealy machines; they have an output associated with each transition. Moore machines, a variant of finite-state machines with output, have an output associated with each state; these are covered in the exercise set.

Make sure that students understand how a Mealy machine produces an output string from an input string. Examples 5, 6, and 7 provide other good illustrations of Mealy machines.

Example 7 is also an example of a language recognizer, a topic we will develop further for finite-state machines without output in the next two sections of the chapter.

Exercises: Exercises 16–21 deal with Moore machines. Good discussion questions you can raise for students are: When is it easier to use a Moore machine and when is it easier to use a Mealy machine? What would it mean for two finite-state machines, which may be a Mealy machine and a Moore machine, to be equivalent? How can equivalent Mealy and Moore machines be constructed?

SECTION 11.3   Finite State Machines with No Output

Goals: To show how to perform operations with sets of strings, to introduce deterministic and non-deterministic finite-state automata, and to show how they recognize sets of strings.

Prerequisites: Section 11.2 and its prerequisites.

Advice: Make sure that students understand how to form concatenations of sets of strings, as is done in Example 1, and Kleene closures of sets of strings, as is done in Example 3. Students confuse the empty string λ, the set $\{\lambda\}$ containing the empty string, the empty set $\emptyset$, and the set $\{\emptyset\}$ containing the empty set, so make sure the distinction between these objects is clear.

Next we discuss finite-state machines with no output. We begin with deterministic finite-state automata, where the transition from each state on each input is well-defined. Later in the section we introduce nondeterministic finite-state automata, where there can be any number, including zero, of possible transitions from a state on an input. Make sure that students have a clear understanding of what it means for a deterministic automaton to recognize a string and what the language recognized by a machine is. Example 5 illustrates this. Students have trouble understanding what it means for nondeterministic automata to recognize a string, so you may want to devote extra time to Example 8.

Stress the constructive aspect of Theorem 1, which shows how to find a deterministic finite automaton that recognizes the same language as a given nondeterministic finite automaton. Example 9 illustrates this procedure.

Exercises: Assign some of Exercises 1–8 so that students get some practice working with concatenations and Kleene closures of sets of strings.

SECTION 11.4   Language Recognition

Goals: To define regular sets, to show that they are the sets recognized by finite-state automata, and to show that they are the languages generated by regular grammars.

Prerequisites: Section 11.3 and its prerequisites.

Advice: The difference between regular expressions and the regular sets that they represent is subtle; I suggest going over Example 1 carefully. Kleene's theorem is the central result of the chapter. It states that regular sets, that is, those sets represented by regular expressions, are precisely those sets recognized by finite-state automata. The proof of Kleene's theorem is complicated, but it is modular, so that you can, if so desired, cover only some of the parts in detail or split the proof into manageable pieces. Example 2 illustrates the constructive nature of this proof, but obviously produces an overly complicated automaton, as is shown in Figure 3.

We also show that regular sets are precisely those sets that are generated by regular grammars. This tells us that a language is generated by a regular grammar if and only if it is recognized by a finite-state automaton. Example 5 shows that nonregular sets exist; it illustrates the idea behind the pumping lemma (see Exercise 16).

This section concludes with brief hints at more powerful types of machines, such as pushdown automata and Turing machines (covered in Section 11.5). Students who have developed an interest in the theory of computation will look forward to learning more about these machines in their subsequent studies.

Exercises: Exercise 16 formally introduces the pumping lemma, generalizing the idea used in Example 5.

SECTION 11.5 **Turing Machines**

Goals: To define Turing machines, to explain how Turing machines can be used to recognize languages, to describe how Turing machines can be used to compute number-theoretic functions, and to introduce the Church–Turing thesis.

Prerequisites: Section 11.4 and its prerequisites.

Advice: This section presents the definition of a Turing machine. The definition given here is perhaps the simplest and the least technical of many equivalent definitions of Turing machines. The important point to make is that the capabilities of Turing machines are essentially independent of the way they are defined. When Turing machines are studied in greater depth, different variations of Turing machines are employed to carry out particular tasks and these variations are shown to have equivalent capabilities.

Next, this section covers the use of Turing machines to recognize strings. There are also various ways to define what it means for a Turing machine to recognize a string. Again, we introduce perhaps the simplest, and least technical, way. However, it is important to stress that this is one of many possible ways to do this.

Then the section shows how to use Turing machines to compute number-theoretic functions. The example included is extremely simple; building Turing machines to compute more complicated number-theoretic functions can be complex and technical.

Finally, the section concludes with a discussion of the Church–Turing thesis, which plays a key role in the theory of computation. Essentially it states that Turing machines can simulate any computations that a computer can perform. And that is a good place to end the book.

Exercises: The busy beaver problem is described in the preamble to Exercise 23. Starred Exercise 23, which involves the busy beaver problem for $n = 2$, should prove interesting for students who want a computational challenge.

Appendixes

APPENDIX 1 **Exponential and Logarithmic Functions**

Goals: To review basic properties of logarithmic and exponential functions.

Prerequisites: None.

Advice: Most students will have some facility working with logarithmic and exponential functions, but others will need a brief review. Make sure that students are aware of the result given in Theorem 3, which shows how to convert bases in logarithms. Note that in the text "$\log x$" always refers to the base 2 logarithm of x.

Exercises: Exercise 4 should be assigned since it contains a result used in big-O estimates of the complexity of divide-and-conquer algorithms.

APPENDIX 2   Pseudocode

Goals: To introduce the rules for the pseudocode used in the text.

Prerequisites: None.

Advice: This appendix is designed as a reference for the pseudocode used in the book. Point out that pseudocode is designed to be flexible and serves as a compromise between English and a programming language.

Exercises: Exercise 3 illustrates that we could make do with a smaller set of commands, since **for** loops can be simulated by **while** loops.

Sample Tests

This section of the *Instructor's Guide* contains sample tests for an introductory course in discrete mathematics. Two tests are included for each chapter of the text. The problems on these tests were used on examinations given in discrete mathematics courses at various schools, or are similar to such questions. The first test contains straightforward problems and is easier than the second test. Some of the problems from these second tests are moderately difficult. I have also included two sample final examinations. Each of these contains problems from each chapter of the text. The second of these is the more challenging examination.

You may want to use these tests as a source of questions for your own examinations, rather than using them exactly as they are. If you do so, select questions primarily from the first of the two examinations for straightforward questions, and from the second for more challenging questions. Also, for a much richer set of questions, consult the extensive test bank also included in this *Guide*.

These sample tests are an attempt to efficiently test students. Wherever appropriate, problems with numerical or short answers are given. However, there are many places in the course where it is not possible to adequately assess students without requiring longer answers. You will find that there are several problems where I have asked students to prove or disprove a statement. I find questions of this sort test whether students can think mathematically and write correct mathematical arguments.

On my examinations I give explicit directions to students to provide complete answers, including reasons for the steps of proofs; I advise you to do the same.

Each sample test has been printed on its individual page. Solutions are provided immediately following the test.

Chapter 1—Test 1

1. What is the truth value of $(p \vee q) \rightarrow (p \wedge q)$ when both p and q are false?

2. What are the converse and contrapositive of the statement "If it is sunny, then I will go swimming"?

3. Show that $\neg(p \vee \neg q)$ and $q \wedge \neg p$ are equivalent

   (a) using a truth table.

   (b) using logical equivalences.

4. Suppose that $Q(x)$ is the statement "$x + 1 = 2x$." What are the truth values of $\forall x\, Q(x)$ and $\exists x\, Q(x)$?

5. Let $A = \{a, c, e, h, k\}$, $B = \{a, b, d, e, h, i, k, l\}$, and $C = \{a, c, e, i, m\}$. Find each of the following sets.

   (a) $A \cap B$

   (b) $A \cap B \cap C$

   (c) $A \cup C$

   (d) $A \cup B \cup C$

   (e) $A - B$

   (f) $A - (B - C)$

6. Prove or disprove that if A, B, and C are sets then $A - (B \cap C) = (A - B) \cap (A - C)$.

7. Let $f(n) = 2n + 1$. Is f a one-to-one function from the set of integers to the set of integers? Is f an onto function from the set of integers to the set of integers? Explain the reasons behind your answers.

8. Suppose that f is the function from the set $\{a, b, c, d\}$ to itself with $f(a) = d$, $f(b) = a$, $f(c) = b$, $f(d) = c$. Find the inverse of f.

9. Prove each of the following statements.

   (a) The sum of two even integers is always even.

   (b) The sum of an even integer and an odd integer is always odd.

Chapter 1—Test 1 Solutions

1. When p and q are both false, so are $(p \vee q)$ and $(p \wedge q)$. Hence $(p \vee q) \to (p \wedge q)$ is true.

2. The converse of the statement is "If I go swimming, then it is sunny." The contrapositive of the statement is "If I do not go swimming, then it is not sunny."

3. (a) We have the following truth table.

p	q	$\neg q$	$p \vee \neg q$	$\neg(p \vee \neg q)$	$\neg p$	$q \wedge \neg p$
T	T	F	T	F	F	F
T	F	T	T	F	F	F
F	T	F	F	T	T	T
F	F	T	T	F	T	F

Since the fifth and seventh columns agree, we conclude that $\neg(p \vee \neg q)$ and $q \wedge \neg p$ are equivalent.

(b) By De Morgan's law $\neg(p \vee \neg q)$ and $\neg p \wedge \neg\neg q$ are equivalent. By the double negation law, this is equivalent to $\neg p \wedge q$, which is equivalent to $q \wedge \neg p$ by the commutative law. We conclude that $\neg(p \vee \neg q)$ and $q \wedge \neg p$ are equivalent.

4. Since $x + 1 = 2x$ is true if and only if $x = 1$, we see that $Q(x)$ is true if and only if $x = 1$. It follows that $\forall x\, Q(x)$ is false and $\exists x\, Q(x)$ is true.

5. (a) $\{a, e, h, k\}$

   (b) $\{a, e\}$

   (c) $\{a, c, e, h, i, k, m\}$

   (d) $\{a, b, c, d, e, h, i, k, l, m\}$

   (e) $\{c\}$

   (f) $A - \{b, d, h, k, l\} = \{a, c, e\}$

6. This is false. For a counterexample take $A = \{1, 2\}$, $B = \{1\}$, and $C = \{2\}$. We have $A - (B \cap C) = \{1, 2\} - \varnothing = \{1, 2\}$, while $(A - B) \cap (A - C) = \{2\} \cap \{1\} = \varnothing$.

7. If $f(n) = f(m)$, then $2n + 1 = 2m + 1$. It follows that $n = m$. Hence f is one-to-one. Since $f(n) = 2n + 1$ is odd for every integer n, it follows that $f(n)$ is not onto; for example, 2 is not in its range.

8. The inverse is $f^{-1}(a) = b$, $f^{-1}(b) = c$, $f^{-1}(c) = d$, $f^{-1}(d) = a$.

9. (a) Suppose that m and n are even integers. Then there are integers j and k such that $m = 2j$ and $n = 2k$. It follows that $m + n = 2j + 2k = 2(j + k) = 2l$, where $l = j + k$. Hence $m + n$ is even.

   (b) Suppose that m is even and n is odd. Then there are integers j and k such that such that $m = 2j$ and $n = 2k + 1$. It follows that $m + n = 2j + (2k + 1) = 2(j + k) + 1 = 2l + 1$, where $l = j + k$. Hence $m + n$ is odd.

Chapter 1—Test 2

1. Prove or disprove that $(p \rightarrow q) \rightarrow r$ and $p \rightarrow (q \rightarrow r)$ are equivalent.

2. Let $P(m, n)$ be "n is greater than or equal to m" where the universe of discourse is the set of nonnegative integers. What are the truth values of $\exists n \forall m\, P(m, n)$ and $\forall m \exists n\, P(m, n)$?

3. Let A, B, and C be sets. Prove or disprove that $A - (B \cap C) = (A - B) \cup (A - C)$.

4. Consider the function $f(n) = 2\lfloor n/2 \rfloor$ from $\mathbf{Z}$ to $\mathbf{Z}$. Is this function one-to-one? Is this function onto? Justify your answers.

5. Prove that all the solutions to the equation $x^2 = x + 1$ are irrational.

Chapter 1—Test 2 Solutions

1. Suppose that p is false, q is true, and r is false. Then $(p \to q) \to r$ is false since its premise $p \to q$ is true while its conclusion r is false. On the other hand, $p \to (q \to r)$ is true in this situation since its premise p is false. Therefore $(p \to q) \to r$ and $p \to (q \to r)$ are not equivalent.

2. For every positive integer n there is an integer m such that $n < m$ (take $m = n + 1$ for instance). Hence $\exists n \forall m \, P(m, n)$ is false. For every integer m there is an integer n such that $n \geq m$ (take $n = m + 1$ for instance). Hence $\forall m \exists n \, P(m, n)$ is true.

3. We see that $A - (B \cap C) = A \cap \overline{B \cap C} = A \cap (\overline{B} \cup \overline{C}) = (A \cap \overline{B}) \cup (A \cap \overline{C}) = (A - B) \cup (A - C)$. These equalities follow from the definition of the difference of two sets, De Morgan's law, the distributive law for intersection over union, and the definition of the difference of two sets, respectively.

4. Note that $f(0) = 2\lfloor 0/2 \rfloor = 0$ and $f(1) = 2\lfloor 1/2 \rfloor = 0$. Hence f is not one-to-one. Note that $f(n)$ is even for every integer n. Hence f is not onto.

5. This equation is equivalent to (and therefore has the same solutions as) $x^2 - x - 1 = 0$. By the quadratic formula, the solutions are exactly $(1 \pm \sqrt{5})/2$. If either of these were a rational number r, then we would have $\sqrt{5} = \pm(2r - 1)$. Since the rational numbers are closed under the arithmetic operations, this would tell us that $\sqrt{5}$ was rational, which we know from this chapter it is not.

Chapter 2—Test 1

1. Describe an algorithm for finding the smallest integer in a finite sequence of integers.

2. Determine the worst case complexity in terms of the number of comparisons used for the algorithm you described in problem 1.

3. Decide whether $175 \equiv 22 \pmod{17}$.

4. Find the prime factorization of 45617.

5. Use the Euclidean algorithm to find

   (a) $\gcd(203, 101)$.

   (b) $\gcd(34, 21)$.

6. The binary expansion of an integer is $(110101)_2$. What is the base 10 expansion of this integer?

7. Let $\mathbf{A} = \begin{bmatrix} 1 & 2 & 3 \\ 0 & 1 & 4 \end{bmatrix}$ and $\mathbf{B} = \begin{bmatrix} 1 & 2 \\ 0 & 1 \\ 2 & 3 \end{bmatrix}$. Find $\mathbf{AB}$ and $\mathbf{BA}$. Are they equal?

8. Let $\mathbf{A} = \begin{bmatrix} 1 & 0 & 1 \\ 0 & 1 & 1 \\ 1 & 1 & 0 \end{bmatrix}$ and $\mathbf{B} = \begin{bmatrix} 0 & 1 & 0 \\ 0 & 1 & 1 \\ 1 & 0 & 0 \end{bmatrix}$. Find the join, meet, and Boolean product of these two zero-one matrices.

9. Let $f(n) = 3n^2 + 8n + 7$. Show that $f(n)$ is $O(n^2)$. Be sure to specify the values of the witnesses C and k.

Chapter 2—Test 1 Solutions

1. Suppose the terms of the sequence are a_1, a_2, ..., a_n. First, assign $min := a_1$. Then successively compare a_i with min for $i = 2, 3, \ldots, n$, assigning the value of a_i to min if $a_i < min$. After all the terms have been examined, the value of min will be the smallest integer in the sequence.

2. There are $n - 1$ comparisons used by the algorithm in problem 1, ignoring the bookkeeping. Hence this is a $O(n)$ algorithm in both the worst and average cases.

3. We have $175 - 22 = 153$ and $17 \mid 153$ since $153 = 17 \cdot 9$. Hence $175 \equiv 22 \pmod{17}$.

4. We see that neither 2, 3, 5, nor 7 divides 45617. Dividing by 11, we find that $45617/11 = 4147$. We divide by 11 again to find that $4147/11 = 377$. We find that 377 is not divisible by 11. We divide by 13 and find that $377 = 13 \cdot 29$. Hence the prime factorization of 45617 is $45617 = 11 \cdot 11 \cdot 13 \cdot 29$.

5. (a) We have $203 = 2 \cdot 101 + 1$ and $101 = 101 \cdot 1$. It follows that $\gcd(203, 101) = 1$.

   (b) We have $34 = 1 \cdot 21 + 13$, $21 = 1 \cdot 13 + 8$, $13 = 1 \cdot 8 + 5$, $8 = 1 \cdot 5 + 3$, $5 = 1 \cdot 3 + 2$, $3 = 1 \cdot 2 + 1$, $2 = 2 \cdot 1$ Hence $\gcd(34, 21) = 1$.

6. We have $(110101)_2 = 1 \cdot 2^5 + 1 \cdot 2^4 + 0 \cdot 2^3 + 1 \cdot 2^2 + 0 \cdot 2^1 + 1 \cdot 2^0 = 32 + 16 + 4 + 1 = 53$.

7. We have $\mathbf{AB} = \begin{bmatrix} 7 & 13 \\ 8 & 13 \end{bmatrix}$ and $\mathbf{BA} = \begin{bmatrix} 1 & 4 & 11 \\ 0 & 1 & 4 \\ 2 & 7 & 18 \end{bmatrix}$. Obviously $\mathbf{AB} \neq \mathbf{BA}$ since they are not even the same size.

8. The join of $\mathbf{A}$ and $\mathbf{B}$ is $\begin{bmatrix} 1 & 1 & 1 \\ 0 & 1 & 1 \\ 1 & 1 & 0 \end{bmatrix}$. The meet of $\mathbf{A}$ and $\mathbf{B}$ is $\begin{bmatrix} 0 & 0 & 0 \\ 0 & 1 & 1 \\ 1 & 0 & 0 \end{bmatrix}$. The Boolean product of $\mathbf{A}$ and $\mathbf{B}$ is $\begin{bmatrix} 1 & 1 & 0 \\ 1 & 1 & 1 \\ 0 & 1 & 1 \end{bmatrix}$.

9. We have $f(n) = 3n^2 + 8n + 7 \leq 3n^2 + 8n^2 + 7n^2 = 18n^2$ whenever $n \geq 1$. It follows that $f(n)$ is $O(n^2)$, since we can take $C = 18$ and $k = 1$ in the definition.

Chapter 2—Test 2

1. (a) Describe an algorithm for finding the second largest integer in a sequence of distinct integers.

    (b) Give a big-O estimate of the number of comparison used by your algorithm.

2. Find the prime factorization of 111111.

3. Find each of the following values.

    (a) $18 \bmod 7$

    (b) $-88 \bmod 13$

    (c) $289 \bmod 17$

4. Let m be a positive integer, and let a, b, and c be integers. Show that if $a \equiv b \pmod{m}$, then $a - c \equiv b - c \pmod{m}$.

5. Use the Euclidean algorithm to find

    (a) $\gcd(201, 302)$.

    (b) $\gcd(144, 233)$.

6. What is the hexadecimal expansion of the $(\text{ABC})_{16} + (\text{2F5})_{16}$?

7. Prove or disprove that $\mathbf{AB} = \mathbf{BA}$ whenever $\mathbf{A}$ and $\mathbf{B}$ are 2×2 matrices.

8. Show that $1^3 + 2^3 + 3^3 + \cdots + n^3$ is $O(n^4)$.

9. Show that the function $f(x) = (x + 2) \log(x^2 + 1) + \log(x^3 + 1)$ is $O(x \log x)$.

Chapter 2—Test 2 Solutions

1. (a) We first compare the first and second integers in the sequence $a_1, a_2, \ldots, a_n$, setting the value of the variable *firstmax* equal to the larger, and the value of the variable *secondmax* equal to the smaller. For each successive integer a_i in the sequence, $i = 3, 4, \ldots, n$, we first compare it to *firstmax*. If $a_i > firstmax$, then we make the assignments *secondmax* := *firstmax* and *firstmax* := a_i. Otherwise, we compare a_i to *secondmax*, and if $a_i > secondmax$, then we make the assignment *secondmax* := a_i. At the end of this procedure the value of *secondmax* will be the second largest integer in the sequence.

   (b) We do one comparison at the beginning of the algorithm to determine whether a_1 or a_2 is larger. Then for each successive term, for $i = 3, 4, \ldots, n$, we carry out at most two comparisons. Hence the largest number of comparisons used is $2(n-2) + 1 = 2n - 3$, ignoring bookkeeping. This is $O(n)$.

2. We see that 2 does not divide 111111, but that 3 does divide 111111, with $111111/3 = 37037$. We see that 3 does not divide 37037, and that 5 does not divide it either. We see that 7 does divide 37037 with $37037/7 = 5291$. We see that 7 does not divide 5291, but 11 does divide 5291 with $5291 = 11 \cdot 481$. We find that 11 does not divide 481, but 13 does, with $481 = 13 \cdot 37$. Since 37 is prime, it follows that the prime factorization of 111111 is $111111 = 3 \cdot 7 \cdot 11 \cdot 13 \cdot 37$.

3. (a) We have $18 = 2 \cdot 7 + 4$. Hence $18 \bmod 7 = 4$.

   (b) We have $-88 = -7 \cdot 13 + 3$. Hence $-88 \bmod 13 = 3$.

   (c) We have $289 = 17 \cdot 17$. Hence $289 \bmod 17 = 0$.

4. Since $a \equiv b \pmod m$ we have $m \mid a - b$. Hence there is an integer k such that $a - b = mk$. It follows that $(a - c) - (b - c) = a - b = mk$, so $a - c \equiv b - c \pmod m$.

5. (a) We see that $302 = 1 \cdot 201 + 101$, $201 = 1 \cdot 101 + 100$, $101 = 1 \cdot 100 + 1$, and $100 = 100 \cdot 1$. Hence $\gcd(302, 201) = 1$.

   (b) We see that $233 = 1 \cdot 144 + 89$, $144 = 1 \cdot 89 + 55$, $89 = 1 \cdot 55 + 34$, $55 = 1 \cdot 34 + 21$, $34 = 1 \cdot 21 + 13$, $21 = 1 \cdot 13 + 8$, $13 = 1 \cdot 8 + 5$, $8 = 1 \cdot 5 + 3$, $5 = 1 \cdot 3 + 2$, $3 = 1 \cdot 2 + 1$, $2 = 2 \cdot 1$. Hence $\gcd(233, 144) = 1$.

6. Working from right to left in base 16, we have $C + 5 = 11$, so the rightmost digit of the sum is 1 and the carry is 1. We have $B + F + 1 = 1B$, so the second digit from the right is B and the carry is 1. We have $A + 2 + 1 = D$. Hence the sum is $(DB1)_{16}$.

7. This is false. Counterexamples are easy to find. For instance, let $\mathbf{A} = \begin{bmatrix} 0 & 0 \\ 2 & 0 \end{bmatrix}$ and $\mathbf{B} = \begin{bmatrix} 1 & 0 \\ 1 & 0 \end{bmatrix}$. Then $\mathbf{AB} = \begin{bmatrix} 0 & 0 \\ 2 & 0 \end{bmatrix}$ while $\mathbf{BA} = \begin{bmatrix} 0 & 0 \\ 0 & 0 \end{bmatrix}$.

8. We have $1^3 + 2^3 + 3^3 + \cdots + n^3 \le n^3 + n^3 + n^3 + \cdots + n^3 = n \cdot n^3 = n^4$ whenever n is a positive integer. It follows that $1^3 + 2^3 + 3^3 + \cdots + n^3$ is $O(n^4)$, with witnesses $C = 1$ and $k = 1$.

9. We have $x + 2$ is $O(x)$ since $x + 2 \le 2x$ for all $x \ge 2$; $\log(x^2 + 1)$ is $O(\log x)$ since $\log(x^2 + 1) \le \log(2x^2) = \log 2 + 2 \log x \le 3 \log x$ whenever $x \ge 2$; and similarly $\log(x^3 + 1)$ is $O(\log x)$. It follows that $(x + 2) \log(x^2 + 1)$ is $O(x \log x)$ and consequently $f(x)$ is $O(x \log x)$.

Chapter 3—Test 1

1. Prove that there are no solutions in positive integers to the equation $x^4 + y^4 = 100$.

2. Prove or disprove that a positive integer congruent to 1 modulo 4 cannot have a prime factor congruent to 3 modulo 4.

3. Use mathematical induction to show that $\sum_{j=0}^{n}(j+1) = (n+1)(n+2)/2$ whenever n is a nonnegative integer.

4. Show that $3^n < n!$ whenever n is an integer with $n \geq 7$.

5. Suppose that the only currency were 3-dollar bills and 10-dollar bills. Show that every amount greater than 17 dollars could be made from a combination of these bills.

6. Suppose that $\{a_n\}$ is defined recursively by $a_n = a_{n-1}^2 - 1$ and that $a_0 = 2$. Find a_3 and a_4.

7. Give a recursive algorithm for computing na using addition, where n is a positive integer and a is a real number.

8. Find the values of $\sum_{j=2}^{8} 3$ and $\sum_{j=0}^{4}(2j+1)$.

Chapter 3—Test 1 Solutions

1. If $x^4 + y^4 = 100$, then both x and y must be less than 4, since $4^4 = 256$. Therefore the only possible values for x and y are 1, 2, and 3, and the fourth powers of these are 1, 16, and 81. Since none of $1 + 1$, $1 + 16$, $1 + 81$, $16 + 16$, $16 + 81$, and $81 + 81$ is 100, there can be no solution.

2. This is false, since $9 = 4 \cdot 2 + 1 = 3 \cdot 3$.

3. The basis step follows since $\sum_{j=0}^{0}(j+1) = 0 + 1 = (0+1)(0+2)/2$. For the inductive step assume that $\sum_{j=0}^{k}(j+1) = (k+1)(k+2)/2$. It follows that $\sum_{j=0}^{k+1}(j+1) = \sum_{j=0}^{k}(j+1) + [(k+1)+1] = (k+1)(k+2)/2 + [(k+1)+1] = (k+1)(k+2)/2 + (k+2) = (k+2)[(k+1)/2+1] = (k+2)(k+3)/2 = [(k+1)+1][(k+1)+2]/2$. This completes the proof by mathematical induction.

4. The basis step holds since $3^7 = 2187 < 5040 = 7!$. For the inductive step assume that $3^k < k!$ where k is a positive integer greater than or equal to 7. Using the inductive hypothesis we see that $3^{k+1} = 3 \cdot 3^k < 3 \cdot k! < (k+1)k! = (k+1)!$. This completes the proof.

5. We find that 18 dollars can be made using six 3-dollar bills. Now suppose that n dollars can be formed, where $n \geq 18$. Suppose that at least two 10-dollar bills were used. Then two 10-dollar bills can be replaced by seven 3-dollar bills to form $n+1$ dollars. Otherwise, if zero or one 10-dollar bill were used, then at least three 3-dollar bills were used. Then replace three 3-dollar bills by one 10-dollar bill to form $n+1$ dollars.

6. We have $a_0 = 2$, $a_1 = a_0^2 - 1 = 2^2 - 1 = 3$, $a_2 = a_1^2 - 1 = 3^2 - 1 = 8$, $a_3 = a_2^2 - 1 = 8^2 - 1 = 63$, and $a_4 = a_3^2 - 1 = 63^2 - 1 = 3968$.

7. We can compute na recursively using the following procedure.

    procedure $mult(a : \text{real number}, n : \text{positive integer})$
    if $n = 1$ **then** $mult(a, n) := a$
    else $mult(a, n) := a + mult(a, n - 1)$

8. We have $\sum_{j=2}^{8} 3 = 7 \cdot 3 = 21$ and $\sum_{j=0}^{4}(2j+1) = 1 + 3 + 5 + 7 + 9 = 25$.

Chapter 3—Test 2

1. Prove or disprove that there are six consecutive composite integers.

2. What is wrong with the following proof that every positive integer equals the next larger positive integer?

    "Proof." Let $P(n)$ be the proposition that $n = n + 1$. Assume that $P(k)$ is true, so that $k = k + 1$. Add 1 to both sides of this equation to obtain $k + 1 = k + 2$. Since this is the statement $P(k + 1)$, it follows that $P(n)$ is true for all positive integers n.

3. Prove that $\displaystyle\sum_{j=n}^{2n-1} (2j + 1) = 3n^2$ whenever n is a positive integer.

4. Use mathematical induction to show that n lines in the plane passing through the same point divide the plane into $2n$ parts.

5. Let $a_1 = 2$, $a_2 = 9$, and $a_n = 2a_{n-1} + 3a_{n-2}$ for $n \geq 3$. Show that $a_n \leq 3^n$ for all positive integers n.

6. Describe a recursive algorithm for computing 3^{2^n} where n is a nonnegative integer.

7. Show that the set of odd positive integers greater than 3 is countable.

8. Find the values of $\displaystyle\sum_{j=1}^{100} 2$ and $\displaystyle\sum_{j=1}^{100} (-1)^j$.

Chapter 3—Test 2 Solutions

1. We can give a constructive proof. The six consecutive integers $7! + 2$, $7! + 3$, $7! + 4$, $7! + 5$, $7! + 6$, and $7! + 7$ are all composite, since $i \mid 7! + i$ for $i = 2, 3, 4, 5, 6, 7$.

2. The error is that no basis step has been done.

3. The basis step holds since $\sum_{j=1}^{1}(2j+1) = 3 = 3 \cdot 1^2$. For the inductive step assume that $\sum_{j=k}^{2k-1}(2j+1) = 3k^2$.
   It follows that $\sum_{j=k+1}^{2(k+1)-1}(2j+1) = \sum_{j=k}^{2k-1}(2j+1) - (2k+1) + (4k+1) + (4k+3) = 3k^2 + 6k + 3 = 3(k+1)^2$.
   This completes the proof.

4. The basis step follows since one line divides the plane into $2 \cdot 1$ parts. For the inductive step assume that k lines passing through a point divide the plane into $2k$ parts. Suppose that we have $k + 1$ lines. If we take k of these lines, by the inductive hypothesis they divide the plane into $2k$ parts. Adding the $(k + 1)^{\text{th}}$ line splits exactly two of these parts in two. Hence these $k + 1$ concurrent lines split the plane into $2k + 2 = 2 \cdot (k + 1)$ parts. This completes the proof.

5. Let $P(n)$ be the proposition that $a_n \leq 3^n$. The proof uses strong induction. The basis step follows since $a_1 = 2 \leq 3 = 3^1$, and $a_2 = 9 \leq 9 = 3^2$. For the inductive step assume that $P(j)$ is true for $1 \leq j \leq k$. Then $a_j \leq 3^j$ for $1 \leq j \leq k$. Hence $a_{k+1} = 2a_k + 3a_{k-1} \leq 2 \cdot 3^k + 3 \cdot 3^{k-1} = 2 \cdot 3^k + 3^k = 3 \cdot 3^k = 3^{k+1}$. This shows that $P(k + 1)$ is also true, and our proof is complete.

6. We can use the following recursive procedure.

   procedure $x(n : \text{nonnegative integer})$
   if $n = 0$ **then** $x(n) := 3$
   else $x(n) := x(n - 1) * x(n - 1)$

7. The function $f(n) = 2n + 3$ is a one-to-one correspondence from the set of positive integers to the set of odd positive integers greater than 3. Hence this set is countable.

8. We have $\sum_{j=1}^{100} 2 = 100 \cdot 2 = 200$ and $\sum_{j=1}^{100}(-1)^j = -1 + 1 - 1 + 1 - \cdots + 1 = 0$.

Chapter 4—Test 1

1. Each locker in an airport is labeled with an uppercase letter followed by three digits. How many different labels for lockers are there?

2. There are 805 lockers in the athletic center and 4026 students who need lockers. Therefore, some students must share lockers. What is the largest number of students who must necessarily share a locker?

3. Find the value of each of the following quantities.

    (a) $C(5,4)$

    (b) $C(5,0)$

    (c) $P(5,1)$

    (d) $P(5,5)$

4. How many rows are found in a truth table involving nine different propositions?

5. What is the coefficient of $x^2 y^7$ in $(x+y)^9$?

6. How many ways are there to choose five doughnuts if there are eight varieties (and only the type of each doughnut matters)?

7. How many different string can be made using all the letters in the word *GOOGOL*?

Chapter 4—Test 1 Solutions

1. By the product rule for counting there are $26 \cdot 10 \cdot 10 \cdot 10 = 26,000$ different labels for lockers.

2. By the generalized pigeonhole principle there are at least $\lceil 4026/805 \rceil = 6$ students who must share a locker.

3. (a) $C(5,4) = \dfrac{5!}{4!1!} = 5$

   (b) $C(5,0) = \dfrac{5!}{0!5!} = 1$

   (c) $P(5,1) = 5$

   (d) $P(5,5) = 5 \cdot 4 \cdot 3 \cdot 2 \cdot 1 = 120$

4. There are $2^9 = 512$ rows in a truth table involving nine different propositions.

5. By the binomial theorem the coefficient of $x^2 y^7$ in $(x+y)^9$ is $\dbinom{9}{2} = \dfrac{9!}{7!2!} = \dfrac{9 \cdot 8}{2 \cdot 1} = 36$.

6. The number of ways to choose five doughnuts from eight different varieties equals the number of 5-combinations with repetition allowed from a set with 8 elements. This equals $C(5+8-1, 8-1) = C(12,7) = \dfrac{12!}{7!5!} = \dfrac{12 \cdot 11 \cdot 10 \cdot 9 \cdot 8}{1 \cdot 2 \cdot 3 \cdot 4 \cdot 5} = 792$.

7. There are three Os, two Gs, and one L in *GOOGOL*. The number of different strings that can be made from these letters is $\dfrac{6!}{3!2!1!} = 60$.

Chapter 4—Test 2

1. How many students must be in a class to guarantee that at least five were born on the same day of the week?

2. How many different license plates can be made if each license plate consists of three letters followed by three digits or four letters followed by two digits?

3. (a) How many functions are there from a set with three elements to a set with eight elements?

   (b) How many one-to-one functions are there from a set with three elements to a set with eight elements?

   (c) How many onto functions are there from a set with three elements to a set with eight elements?

4. What is the coefficient of x^7y^{12} in $(x+y)^{19}$ and in $(2x+3y)^{19}$?

5. Show that $C(n,r) = C(n, n-r)$ using

   (a) a combinatorial argument.

   (b) algebraic manipulation.

6. (a) How many ways are there to arrange the letters of the word *NONSENSE*?

   (b) How many of these ways start or end with the letter O?

7. (a) How many ways are there to choose 12 cookies if there are five varieties of cookies?

   (b) How many ways are there to choose 12 cookies if there are five varieties, including chocolate chip, and at least four chocolate chip cookies must be chosen?

Chapter 4—Test 2 Solutions

1. Since there are seven days of the week, to guarantee that at least five students were born on the same day requires at least $7 \cdot 4 + 1 = 29$ students.

2. There are $26^3 10^3 + 26^4 10^2 = 63{,}273{,}600$ different license plates.

3. (a) There are $8^3 = 512$ functions.

   (b) There are $8 \cdot 7 \cdot 6 = 336$ one-to-one functions.

   (c) There are obviously no onto functions.

4. The coefficient of $x^7 y^{12}$ in $(x + y)^{19}$ is $\binom{19}{7} = 50{,}388$. The coefficient of $x^7 y^{12}$ in $(2x + 3y)^{19}$ is $\binom{19}{7} \cdot 2^7 3^{12} = 3{,}427{,}615{,}885{,}824$.

5. (a) Choosing r elements from a set with n elements is equivalent to picking the $n - r$ elements not to choose.

   (b) $C(n, r) = \dfrac{n!}{r!(n - r)!} = \dfrac{n!}{(n - r)!(n - (n - r))!} = C(n, n - r)$

6. (a) There are $\dfrac{8!}{3!2!2!1!} = 1680$ ways.

   (b) Since the letter O must be in the first position or last position, the number of strings is twice the number of ways to arrange the letters *NNSENSE*. Hence there are $2 \cdot \dfrac{7!}{3!2!2!} = \dfrac{7!}{3!2!} = 420$ ways.

7. (a) The solution is the number of 12-combinations with repetition of five objects. Therefore there are $C(12 + 5 - 1, 5 - 1) = C(16, 4) = 1820$ ways.

   (b) Since at least four chocolate chip cookies must be chosen, this is equivalent to determining the number of ways to choose eight cookies from five varieties. Consequently the answer is given by the number of 8-combinations with repetition of five objects. Therefore there are $C(8 + 5 - 1, 5 - 1) = C(12, 4) = 495$ ways.

Chapter 5—Test 1

1. What is the probability that a fair coin lands heads four times out of five flips?

2. What is the probability that a positive integer less than 100 picked at random has all distinct digits?

3. Suppose that two cards are drawn without replacement from a well-shuffled deck. What is the probability that both cards have numbers and that the numbers on the cards are the same (note that only the numbers 2 through 10 are shown on cards, since aces, kings, queens, and jacks are represented by letters).

4. A fair red die and a fair blue die are rolled. What is the expected value of the sum of the number on the red die plus three times the number on the blue die?

Chapter 5—Test 1 Solutions

1. There are 2^5 possible outcomes of five flips. The number of possible ways to have the coin come up heads four times is the number of ways to pick four flips out of five. This can be done in $C(5,4) = 5$ ways. Hence the probability that the coin lands heads four times out of five flips is $5/2^5 = 5/32$.

2. There are 99 choices for the integer. Only 11, 22, 33, ..., 99 do not have distinct digits. The remaining 90 integers do have distinct digits. Therefore the answer is $90/99$.

3. The probability that the first card has a number on it is $36/52$, since $4 \cdot 9 = 36$ cards have numbers. At that point the deck has 51 remaining cards, and 3 of them have the same number as the first card drawn. Therefore the final answer is $(36/52)(3/51) = 36/884$.

4. Let X_r and X_b be the random variables for the numbers shown on the dice. We are asked for $E(X_r + 3X_b)$. Since these dice are fair, we know that $E(X_r) = E(X_b) = (1 + 2 + 3 + 4 + 5 + 6)/6 = 3.5$. By linearity of expectation, we have $E(X_r + 3X_b) = 3.5 + 3 \cdot 3.5 = 14$.

Chapter 5—Test 2

1. A computer picks out at random a sequence of six digits.

    (a) What is the probability that a person picks all six digits in their correct positions?

    (b) What is the probability that a person picks exactly five of the digits, in the correct order?

2. What is the probability that in a group of 200 random people, at least two of them have the same triple of initials (such as LMS for Laurel Marie Sandor), assuming that each triple of initials is equally likely. Give the answer as a calculation; it is not necessary to evaluate the expression.

3. Suppose that a bag contains six slips of paper: one with the number 1 written on it, two with the number 2, and three with the number 3. What is the expected value and variance of the number drawn if one slip is selected at random from the bag?

4. What is the probability that a random person who tests positive for a certain blood disease actually has the disease, if we know that 1% of the population has the disease, that 95% of those who have the disease test positive for it, and 2% of those who do not have the disease test positive for it.

Chapter 5—Test 2 Solutions

1. (a) The probability that a person chooses all six digits in the correct order is $1/10^6$.

   (b) The number of ways a person can choose exactly five digits correctly is the number of ways to choose one position to be incorrect, namely 6, times the number of ways to choose an incorrect digit for that position, namely 9, times the number of ways to choose the other digits, namely 1. Hence there are 54 ways to choose exactly five digits correctly. The probability is $54/10^6$.

2. This is like the birthday problem, except that there are $26^3 = 17{,}576$ possible triples of initials. Therefore the answer is

$$1 - \frac{17575}{17576} \cdot \frac{17574}{17576} \cdots \frac{17377}{17576}.$$

   This actually works out to about 68%.

3. The expected value is $\frac{1}{6} \cdot 1 + \frac{2}{6} \cdot 2 + \frac{3}{6} \cdot 3 = \frac{14}{6}$. To compute the variance we compute $E(X^2) - E(X)^2$, where X is the value on the slip. We have $E(X^2) = \frac{1}{6} \cdot 1 + \frac{2}{6} \cdot 4 + \frac{3}{6} \cdot 9 = \frac{36}{6} = 6$, so $V(X) = 6 - \left(\frac{14}{6}\right)^2 = \frac{5}{9}$.

4. Let H be the event that a person has the disease, and let T be the event that a person tests positive for it. We are told that $P(H) = 0.01$, that $P(T|H) = 0.95$, and that $P(T|\overline{H}) = 0.02$. We want to compute $P(H|T)$. First note that $P(T) = P(T \cap H) + P(T \cap \overline{H})$. By the definition of conditional probability, we know that $P(T \cap H) = P(H) \cdot P(T|H) = 0.01 \cdot 0.95 = 0.0095$, and $P(T \cap \overline{H}) = P(\overline{H}) \cdot P(T|\overline{H}) = 0.99 \cdot 0.02 = 0.0198$. Therefore we have, again by the definition of conditional probability and the calculations just made,

$$P(H|T) = \frac{P(H \cap T)}{P(T)} = \frac{0.0095}{0.0095 + 0.0198} = \frac{0.0095}{0.0293} \approx 32\%.$$

Chapter 6—Test 1

1. Find a recurrence relation and initial condition for the number of fruit flies in a jar if there are 12 flies initially and every week there are six times as many flies in the jar as there were the previous week.

2. Find the solution of the recurrence relation $a_n = 3a_{n-1}$, with $a_0 = 2$.

3. Find the solution of the linear homogeneous recurrence relation $a_n = 7a_{n-1} - 6a_{n-2}$ with $a_0 = -1$ and $a_1 = 4$.

4. Suppose that $f(n)$ satisfies the divide-and-conquer relation $f(n) = 2f(n/3) + 5$ and $f(1) = 7$. What is $f(81)$?

5. Suppose that $|A| = |B| = |C| = 100$, $|A \cap B| = 60$, $|A \cap C| = 50$, $|B \cap C| = 40$, and $|A \cup B \cup C| = 175$. How many elements are in $A \cap B \cap C$?

6. How many positive integers not exceeding 1000 are not divisible by either 4 or 6?

7. How many onto functions are there from a set with six elements to a set with four elements?

8. List the derangements of the set $\{1, 2, 3, 4\}$.

9. Find a generating function for the sequence $2, 3, 4, 5, \ldots$.

Chapter 6—Test 1 Solutions

1. We have $f(n) = 6f(n-1)$ whenever n is a positive integer where $f(n)$ is the number of fruit flies after n weeks, with $f(0) = 12$.

2. By iteration we find that $a_n = 3a_{n-1} = 3(3a_{n-2}) = 3^2 a_{n-2} = \cdots = 3^n a_0 = 2 \cdot 3^n$. This can be verified using mathematical induction.

3. The characteristic equation is $r^2 - 7r + 6 = (r-1)(r-6) = 0$. The characteristic roots are $r = 1$ and $r = 6$. The solutions are of the form $a_n = c_1 \cdot 1^n + c_2 \cdot 6^n = c_1 + c_2 \cdot 6^n$. Since $a_0 = -1$ and $a_1 = 4$ we have $c_1 + c_2 = -1$ and $c_1 + 6c_2 = 4$. Subtracting the first equation from the second gives $5c_2 = 5$, so $c_2 = 1$. This implies that $c_1 + 1 = -1$, so $c_1 = -2$. Hence the solution is $a_n = -2 + 6^n$.

4. Using the recurrence relation repeatedly, and simplifying when possible, we find that $f(81) = 2 \cdot f(27) + 5 = 2 \cdot (2 \cdot f(9) + 5) + 5 = 4 \cdot f(9) + 15 = 4 \cdot (2 \cdot f(3) + 5) + 15 = 8 \cdot f(3) + 35 = 8 \cdot (2 \cdot f(1) + 5) + 35 = 16 \cdot f(1) + 75 = 16 \cdot 7 + 75 = 187$.

5. By the principle of inclusion–exclusion $|A \cup B \cup C| = |A| + |B| + |C| - |A \cap B| - |A \cap C| - |B \cap C| + |A \cap B \cap C|$. Hence $175 = 100 + 100 + 100 - 60 - 50 - 40 + |A \cap B \cap C|$. Therefore $|A \cap B \cap C| = 175 - 150 = 25$.

6. The number of positive integers not exceeding 1000 that are not divisible by either 4 or 6 equals $1000 - \lfloor 1000/4 \rfloor - \lfloor 1000/6 \rfloor + \lfloor 1000/12 \rfloor = 1000 - 250 - 166 + 83 = 667$. Here we used the fact that the integers divisible by both 4 and 6 are those divisible by 12.

7. There are $4^6 - C(4,3)3^6 + C(4,2)2^6 - C(4,1)1^6 = 4096 - 4 \cdot 729 + 6 \cdot 64 - 4 = 1560$ onto functions.

8. The derangements of $\{1, 2, 3, 4\}$ are the permutations of these four integers that leave no integer in its original position. These are 2143, 2341, 2413, 3142, 3412, 3421, 4123, 4312, and 4321.

9. We know that the generating function for the sequence $1, 2, 3, 4, \ldots$ is $\dfrac{1}{(1-x)^2}$. Therefore the generating function for the sequence $0, 2, 3, 4, \ldots$ is this function with the constant term omitted, i.e., $\dfrac{1}{(1-x)^2} - 1$. It follows that the generating function for the given sequence is this last function divided by x, namely $\left(\dfrac{1}{(1-x)^2} - 1 \right) / x$. This can also be written as $\dfrac{2-x}{(1-x)^2}$.

Chapter 6—Test 2

1. (a) Find a recurrence relation for the number of ways to climb n stairs if stairs can be climbed two or three at a time.

    (b) What are the initial conditions?

    (c) How many ways are there to climb eight stairs?

2. What is the solution to the recurrence relation $a_n = 8a_{n-1} + 9a_{n-2}$ if $a_0 = 3$ and $a_1 = 7$?

3. Suppose that $f(n)$ satisfies the divide-and-conquer recurrence relation $f(n) = 3f(n/4) + n^2/8$ with $f(1) = 2$. What is $f(64)$?

4. How many positive integers not exceeding 1000 are not divisible by 4, 6, or 9?

5. How many ways are there to assign six jobs to four employees so that every employee is assigned at least one job?

6. How many permutations are there of the digits in the string 12345 that leave 3 fixed but leave no other integer fixed? (For instance, 24351 is such a permutation.)

7. Use generating functions to solve the recurrence relation $a_k = 5a_{k-1}$ for $k = 1, 2, 3, \ldots$, with initial condition $a_0 = 3$.

Chapter 6—Test 2 Solutions

1. (a) Let a_n be the number of ways to climb n stairs. Suppose that $n \geq 4$. Then $a_n = a_{n-2} + a_{n-3}$, since n stairs can be climbed by going up $n-2$ stairs followed by a step of 2 stairs or by going up $n-3$ stairs followed by a step of 3 stairs.

   (b) We see that $a_1 = 0$, $a_2 = 1$, and $a_3 = 1$.

   (c) Note that $a_4 = a_2 + a_1 = 1 + 0 = 1$, $a_5 = a_3 + a_2 = 1 + 1 = 2$, $a_6 = a_4 + a_3 = 1 + 1 = 2$, $a_7 = a_5 + a_4 = 2 + 1 = 3$, and $a_8 = a_6 + a_5 = 2 + 2 = 4$.

2. The characteristic equation of this linear homogeneous recurrence relation is $r^2 - 8r - 9 = (r-9)(r+1) = 0$. The characteristic roots are $r = 9$ and $r = -1$. Hence the solutions are of the form $a_n = c_1 \cdot 9^n + c_2(-1)^n$, where c_1 and c_2 are constants. Since $a_0 = 3$ and $a_1 = 7$ we have $3 = c_1 + c_2$ and $7 = 9c_1 - c_2$. Adding these equations gives $10 = 10c_1$, so $c_1 = 1$. Substituting this value of c_1 into the first equation gives $c_2 = 2$. Hence the solution is given by $a_n = 9^n + 2(-1)^n$.

3. We have $f(64) = 3f(16) + 64^2/8 = 3f(16) + 512 = 3(3f(4) + 16^2/8) + 512 = 9f(4) + 608 = 9(3f(1) + 4^2/8) + 608 = 27f(1) + 626 = 27 \cdot 2 + 626 = 680$.

4. By the principle of inclusion–exclusion, the number of positive integers not exceeding 1000 that are divisible by 4, 6, or 9 equals $\lfloor 1000/4 \rfloor + \lfloor 1000/6 \rfloor + \lfloor 1000/9 \rfloor - \lfloor 1000/12 \rfloor - \lfloor 1000/36 \rfloor - \lfloor 1000/18 \rfloor + \lfloor 1000/36 \rfloor = 250 + 166 + 111 - 83 - 27 - 55 + 27 = 389$. Hence there are $1000 - 389 = 611$ positive integers not exceeding 1000 that are not divisible by either 4, 6, or 9.

5. The number of ways to assign six jobs to four employees so that every employee is assigned at least one job equals the number of onto functions from a set with six elements to a set with four elements. This equals $4^6 - C(4,3)3^6 + C(4,2)2^6 - C(4,1)1^6 = 4096 - 2916 + 384 - 4 = 1560$.

6. The number of permutations of 12345 that leave 3 but no other integer fixed equals the number of derangements of 4 integers, namely 1, 2, 4, and 5. This equals $D_4 = 4!(1 - 1/1! + 1/2! - 1/3! + 1/4!) = 24(1 - 1 + 1/2 - 1/6 + 1/24) = 9$.

7. Let $G(x)$ be the generating function for the sequence $\{a_k\}$, i.e., $G(x) = \sum_{k=0}^{\infty} a_k x^k$. Then $xG(x) = \sum_{k=0}^{\infty} a_k x^{k+1} = \sum_{k=1}^{\infty} a_{k-1} x^k$. It follows that $G(x) - 5xG(x) = \sum_{k=0}^{\infty} a_k x^k - 5\sum_{k=1}^{\infty} a_{k-1} x^k = a_0 + \sum_{k=1}^{\infty} (a_k - 5a_{k-1})x^k = 3$, because of the given recurrence relation and initial condition. Thus $G(x) - 5xG(x) = (1-5x)G(x) = 3$, so $G(x) = 3/(1-5x)$. It follows from an identity in Table 1 of Section 5.4 that $G(x) = 3\sum_{k=0}^{\infty} 5^k x^k$. Consequently $a_k = 3 \cdot 5^k$.

Chapter 7—Test 1

1. Which ordered pairs are in the relation $\{(x, y) \mid x > y + 1\}$ on the set $\{1, 2, 3, 4\}$?

2. Consider the following relations on $\{1, 2, 3\}$.

$$R_1 = \{(1,1), (1,3), (2,2), (3,1)\}$$
$$R_2 = \{(1,1), (2,2), (3,1), (3,3)\}$$
$$R_3 = \{(1,2), (2,1), (3,3)\}$$
$$R_4 = \{(1,3), (2,3)\}$$

(a) Which of these relations are reflexive? Justify your answers.

(b) Which of these relations are symmetric? Justify your answers.

(c) Which of these relations are antisymmetric? Justify your answers.

(d) Which of these relations are transitive? Justify your answers.

3. Find the reflexive closure and the symmetric closure of the relation $\{(1,2), (1,4), (2,3), (3,1), (4,2)\}$ on the set $\{1, 2, 3, 4\}$.

4. What is the transitive closure of the relation in problem 3?

5. (a) Show that the relation $R = \{(x, y) \mid x \text{ and } y \text{ are bit strings containing the same number of 0s}\}$ is an equivalence relation.

(b) What are the equivalence classes of the bit strings 1, 00, and 101 under the relation R?

6. (a) Are the sets $\{1, 3, 6\}$, $\{2, 4, 7\}$, and $\{5\}$ a partition of $\{1, 2, 3, 4, 5, 6, 7\}$?

(b) Are the sets $\{1, 2, 4, 5\}$, $\{3, 6, 7\}$, and $\{2, 3\}$ a partition of $\{1, 2, 3, 4, 5, 6, 7\}$?

7. Show that the inclusion relation, $\{(A, B) \mid A \subseteq B\}$, is a partial ordering on the set of all subsets of $\mathbf{Z}$.

8. What are the minimal and maximal elements in the poset with the following Hasse diagram? Are there least and greatest elements?

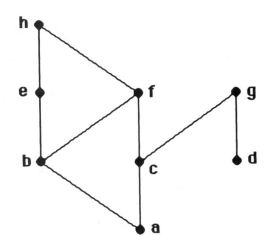

Chapter 7—Test 1 Solutions

1. The ordered pairs in this relation are $(3,1)$, $(4,1)$, and $(4,2)$.

2. (a) R_2 is reflexive since it contains $(1,1)$, $(2,2)$, and $(3,3)$. The relations R_1, R_3, and R_4 are not reflexive since they do not contain all three of these ordered pairs.

   (b) R_1 and R_3 are symmetric since they contains (i,j) whenever they contain (j,i). To check this for R_1 requires only that we note that both $(1,3)$ and $(3,1)$ are in the relation and to check this for R_3 requires only that we note that both $(1,2)$ and $(2,1)$ are in the relation. R_2 and R_4 are not symmetric since each contains one of $(3,1)$ and $(1,3)$, but not the other.

   (c) R_2 and R_4 are antisymmetric since neither contains ordered pairs (i,j) and (j,i) where $i \neq j$. To check this for R_2 requires only that we check that $(1,3)$ is not in R_2, since $(3,1)$ is the only ordered pair in the relation with different first and second elements; to check this for R_4 requires only that we check that neither $(3,1)$ nor $(3,2)$ is in the relation. We see that R_1 is not antisymmetric since both $(1,3)$ and $(3,1)$ are in R_1. We see that R_3 is not antisymmetric since both $(1,2)$ and $(2,1)$ are in R_3.

   (d) R_2 and R_4 are transitive. This is easily verified since neither relation has pairs (a,b) and (b,c) with $a \neq b$ and $b \neq c$. R_1 is not transitive since $(3,1)$ and $(1,3)$ belong to R_1 but $(3,3)$ is not in R_1. R_3 is not transitive since $(1,2)$ and $(2,1)$ belong to R_3 but $(1,1)$ does not belong to R_3.

3. The reflexive closure is obtained by adding the pairs $(1,1)$, $(2,2)$, $(3,3)$, and $(4,4)$. The symmetric closure is obtained by adding the pairs $(1,3)$, $(2,1)$, $(2,4)$, $(3,2)$, and $(4,1)$.

4. We add the pairs $(1,3)$, $(2,1)$, $(3,2)$, $(3,4)$, and $(4,3)$ at the first stage; these represent paths of length two. At the second stage we add $(1,1)$, $(2,2)$, $(2,4)$, $(3,3)$, $(4,1)$ and $(4,4)$. We conclude that the transitive closure contains all possible ordered pairs.

5. (a) Let x be a bit string. Then $(x,x) \in R$ since x has the same number of 0s as itself. Hence R is reflexive. Now suppose that $(x,y) \in R$. Then x and y have the same number of 0s. Consequently y and x have the same number of 0s. It follows that $(y,x) \in R$. Next, suppose that $(x,y) \in R$ and $(y,z) \in R$. Then x and y contain the same number of 0s, and y and z contain the same number of 0s. It follows that x and z contain the same number of 0s. Hence $(x,z) \in R$. We conclude that R is transitive.

   (b) The equivalence class of 1 is the set of all bit strings that contain no 0s; explicitly, $[1]_R = \{\lambda, 1, 11, 111, 1111, \ldots\}$. The equivalence class of 00 is the set of all bit strings that contain exactly two 0s, that is $[00]_R = \{00, 100, 010, 001, 1100, 1010, 1001, 0110, 0101, 0011, \ldots\}$. The equivalence class of 101 is the set of all bit strings that contain exactly one 0, that is, $[101]_R = \{0, 10, 01, 110, 101, 011, 1110, 1101, 1011, 0111, \ldots\}$.

6. (a) The subsets listed form a partition of $\{1,2,3,4,5,6,7\}$ since they are pairwise disjoint nonempty sets and their union is this set.

   (b) These subsets are not pairwise disjoint so they do not form a partition.

7. We see that set inclusion is reflexive since $A \subseteq A$ whenever A is a subset of $\mathbf{Z}$. Since $A \subseteq B$ and $B \subseteq A$ imply that $A = B$ whenever A and B are subsets of $\mathbf{Z}$, we see that set inclusion is antisymmetric. Now suppose that $A \subseteq B$ and $B \subseteq C$ where A, B, and C are subsets of $\mathbf{Z}$. Then $A \subseteq C$, so set inclusion is transitive.

8. The minimal elements are a and d. The maximal elements are h and g. There is no least element and there is no greatest element. If there were a least element then there would be exactly one minimal element, and if there were a greatest element then there would be exactly one maximal element.

Chapter 7—Test 2

1. Consider the following relations on the set of positive integers.

$$R_1 = \{\, (x,y) \mid x + y > 10 \,\}$$
$$R_2 = \{\, (x,y) \mid y \text{ divides } x \,\}$$
$$R_3 = \{\, (x,y) \mid \gcd(x,y) = 1 \,\}$$
$$R_4 = \{\, (x,y) \mid x \text{ and } y \text{ have the same prime divisors} \,\}$$

   (a) Which of these relations are reflexive? Justify your answers.

   (b) Which of these relations are symmetric? Justify your answers.

   (c) Which of these relations are antisymmetric? Justify your answers.

   (d) Which of these relations are transitive? Justify your answers.

2. Suppose that R_1 and R_2 are symmetric relations on a set A. Prove or disprove that $R_1 - R_2$ is also symmetric.

3. What is the join of the 3-ary relation

   {(Lewis, MS410, N507), (Rosen, CS540, N525), (Smith, CS518, N504), (Smith, MS410, N510)}

   and the 4-ary

   {(MS410, N507,Monday, 6: 00), (MS410, N507, Wednesday, 6: 00), (CS540, N525, Monday, 7: 30),

   (CS518, N504, Tuesday, 6: 00), (CS518, N504, Thursday, 6: 00)}

   with respect to the last two fields of the first relation and the first two fields of the second relation?

4. Show that the relation $R = \{(x,y) \mid x - y \text{ is an integer}\}$ is an equivalence relation on the set of rational numbers. What are the equivalence classes of 0 and $\frac{1}{2}$?

5. Consider the poset with the following Hasse diagram.

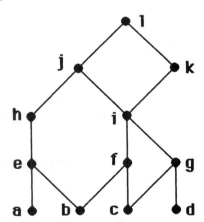

   (a) Find all maximal elements of the poset.

   (b) Find all minimal elements of the poset.

   (c) Find the least element of the poset if it exists, or show that it does not exist.

   (d) Find the greatest element of the poset if it exists, or show that it does not exist.

   (e) What is the greatest lower bound of the set $\{a, b, c\}$?

   (f) What is the least upper bound of the set $\{a, b, c\}$?

6. Use a topological sort to order the elements of the poset with the Hasse diagram given in problem 5.

Chapter 7—Test 2 Solutions

1. (a) R_1 is not reflexive since $1+1 < 10$, so $(1,1)$ is not in R_1. R_2 is reflexive since $x \mid x$ for every positive integer x, so $(x,x) \in R_2$ for all x. R_3 is not reflexive since $\gcd(2,2) = 2$, so $(2,2)$ is not in R_3. R_4 is reflexive since x and x have the same prime divisors for every positive integer x, so $(x,x) \in R_4$ for all x.

   (b) R_1 is symmetric, since $x + y > 10$ implies that $y + x > 10$. R_2 is not symmetric since since $1 \mid 2$ but $2 \nmid 1$. R_3 is symmetric since $\gcd(x,y) = 1$ implies that $\gcd(y,x) = 1$. R_4 is symmetric since x and y have the same prime divisors if and only if y and x have the same prime divisors.

   (c) R_1 is not antisymmetric since $(2,9)$ and $(9,2)$ both belong to R_1. R_2 is antisymmetric since $y \mid x$ and $x \mid y$ imply that $x = y$ if x and y are positive integers. R_3 is not antisymmetric since $\gcd(2,1) = \gcd(1,2) = 1$. R_4 is not antisymmetric since 12 and 18 have the same prime divisors, namely 2 and 3, and 18 and 12 have the same prime divisors.

   (d) R_1 is not transitive since $(2,9) \in R_1$ and $(9,3) \in R_1$ but $(2,3) \notin R_1$. R_2 is transitive since $y \mid x$ and $z \mid y$ imply that $z \mid x$. R_3 is not transitive since $\gcd(2,3) = 1$ and $\gcd(3,2) = 1$ but $\gcd(2,2) = 2$. R_4 is transitive, for if x and y have the same prime divisors and y and z have the same prime divisors, then x and z have the same prime divisors.

2. Suppose that R_1 and R_2 are symmetric. If $(a,b) \in R_1 - R_2$ then $(a,b) \in R_1$ and $(a,b) \notin R_2$. Since R_1 is symmetric it follows that $(b,a) \in R_1$. Since R_2 is symmetric it follows that $(b,a) \notin R_2$, for if $(b,a) \in R_2$ then $(a,b) \in R_2$. Hence $(b,a) \in R_1 - R_2$. It follows that $R_1 - R_2$ is symmetric.

3. The join is

$$\{(\text{Lewis}, \text{MS410}, \text{N507}, \text{Monday}, 6\!:\!00), (\text{Lewis}, \text{MS410}, \text{N507}, \text{Wednesday}, 6\!:\!00),$$
$$(\text{Rosen}, \text{CS540}, \text{N525}, \text{Monday}, 7\!:\!30), (\text{Smith}, \text{CS518}, \text{N504}, \text{Tuesday}, 6\!:\!00),$$
$$(\text{Smith}, \text{CS518}, \text{N504}, \text{Thursday}, 6\!:\!00)\}$$

4. Since $x - x = 0$ is an integer for every rational number x it follows that R is reflexive. Suppose that $(x,y) \in R$. Then $x - y$ is an integer, which implies that $y - x$ is an integer. Hence $(y,x) \in R$. It follows that R is symmetric. Now suppose that $(x,y) \in R$ and $(y,z) \in R$. Then $x - y$ and $y - z$ are integers, so $x - z = (x-y) + (y-z)$ is also an integer. It follows that R is transitive. Hence R is an equivalence relation. We have $[0]_R = \{x \in \mathbf{Q} \mid x - 0 \in \mathbf{Z}\} = \mathbf{Z}$ and $[\frac{1}{2}]_R = \{x \in \mathbf{Q} \mid x - \frac{1}{2} \in \mathbf{Z}\} = \{k + \frac{1}{2} \mid k \in \mathbf{Z}\} = \{\ldots, -\frac{5}{2}, -\frac{3}{2}, -\frac{1}{2}, \frac{1}{2}, \frac{3}{2}, \frac{5}{2}, \ldots\}$.

5. (a) The maximal element is l.

   (b) The minimal elements are a, b, c, and d.

   (c) There is no least element since there is more than one minimal element.

   (d) The greatest element is l.

   (e) There is no lower bound for the set $\{a,b,c\}$, so there is no greatest lower bound.

   (f) The upper bounds for the set $\{a,b,c\}$ are the elements j and l. Since j is less than l, j is the least upper bound.

6. One possible ordering is: $a, b, e, h, c, d, g, f, i, k, j, l$.

Chapter 8—Test 1

1. How many vertices and how many edges do each of the following graphs have?

   (a) K_5

   (b) C_4

   (c) W_5

   (d) $K_{2,5}$

2. Does a simple graph that has five vertices each of degree 3 exist? If so, draw such a graph. If not, explain why no such graph exists.

3. How many nonisomorphic simple graphs are there with three vertices? Draw examples of each of these.

4. Is there an Euler circuit in the following graph? If so, find such a circuit. If not, explain why no such circuit exists.

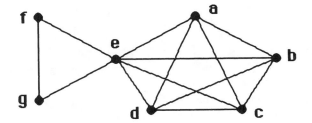

5. Is there a Hamilton circuit in the graph shown in problem 4? If so, find such a circuit. If not, prove why no such circuit exists.

6. Is the following graph planar? If so draw it without any edges crossing. If it is not, prove that it is not planar.

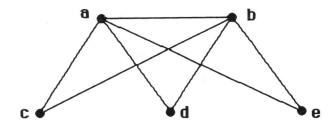

7. What is the chromatic number of each of the graphs in problem 1? Explain your answers.

Chapter 8—Test 1 Solutions

1. (a) K_5 has five vertices and $C(5,2) = 10$ edges.

(b) C_4 has four vertices and four edges.

(c) W_5 has $5 + 1 = 6$ vertices and $5 + 5 = 10$ edges.

(d) $K_{2,5}$ has $2 + 5 = 7$ vertices and $2 \cdot 5 = 10$ edges.

2. There is no simple graph with four vertices each of degree 3 since the sum of the degrees of such a graph would be 15, which is odd. This is impossible by the handshaking theorem.

3. There are four nonisomorphic simple graphs with three vertices, as shown.

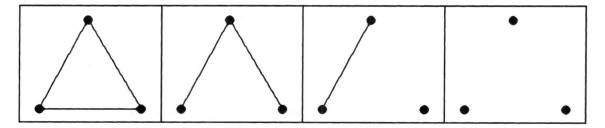

4. All vertices have even degree (the degree of each of a, b, c, and d is 4, the degree of e is 6, and the degree of each of f and g is 2). Hence the graph has an Euler circuit. One such Euler circuit is $a, b, c, a, d, c, e, d, b, e, g, f, e, a$.

5. There is no Hamilton circuit. Since the degree of each of f and g is 2, any such circuit must contain the edges $\{e, f\}$ and $\{e, g\}$, which implies that the vertex e must be visited twice.

6. The graph is planar, since it can be drawn with no crossing as follows.

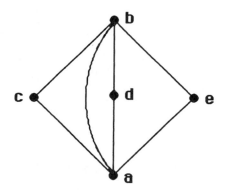

7. (a) The chromatic number of K_5 is 5. Each vertex is adjacent to all other vertices in the graph, and so must be assigned its own color.

(b) The chromatic number of C_4 is 2. Suppose that the vertices are v_1, v_2, v_3, and v_4, where the edges are $\{v_1, v_2\}$, $\{v_2, v_3\}$, $\{v_3, v_4\}$, and $\{v_4, v_1\}$. Then we can color v_1 and v_3 red and color v_2 and v_4 blue.

(c) The chromatic number of W_5 is 4. As is easily seen, three colors are needed for the vertices in the cycle with five vertices, and the central vertex must be assigned its own color.

(d) The chromatic number of $K_{2,5}$ is 2. Any bipartite graph can be colored with two colors. In particular, we can color the two vertices in one set in the partition of the vertices red, and the five vertices in the other set in the partition blue.

Chapter 8—Test 2

1. For each of the following sequences determine whether there is a simple graph whose vertices have these degrees. Draw such a graph if it exists.

   (a) $0, 1, 1, 2$

   (b) $2, 2, 2, 2$

   (c) $1, 2, 3, 4, 5$

2. Is the following graph bipartite? Justify your answer.

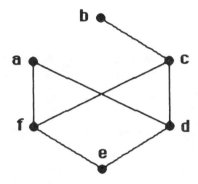

3. Decide whether the graphs G and H are isomorphic. Prove that your answer is correct.

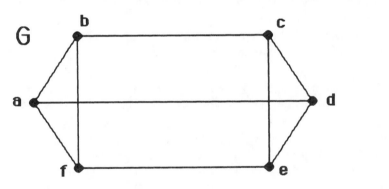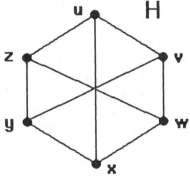

4. Consider the graphs K_5, $K_{2,3}$, and W_5. Which of these graphs have an Euler circuit? Which have an Euler path?

5. Which of the graphs in problem 4 are planar?

6. What is the chromatic number of each of the graphs in problem 4?

7. Use Dijkstra's Algorithm to find the length of the shortest path between the vertices a and z in the following weighted graph.

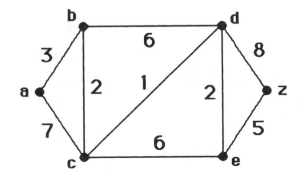

Chapter 8—Test 2 Solutions

1. (a) Yes   (b) Yes

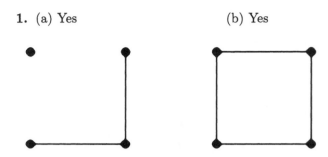

(c) There are at least two reasons why this graph cannot exist. First, the sum of degrees is odd. Second, there can be no vertex of degree 5 in a simple graph with five vertices.

2. The graph is bipartite. The vertex set can be partitioned into $\{a, c, e\}$ and $\{b, d, f\}$. There are no edges connecting a vertex in one set and a vertex in the other set.

3. These graphs are not isomorphic, since G contains a subgraph isomorphic to K_3 but H does not. (In fact, H is bipartite.)

4. K_5 has five vertices each of degree 4, so it has an Euler circuit (and an Euler path) since all its vertices have even degree. $K_{2,3}$ has two vertices of degree 3 and three vertices of degree 2, so it does not have an Euler circuit, but it does have an Euler path since it has exactly two vertices of odd degree. W_5 has five vertices of degree 3 and one vertex of degree 5, so it has neither an Euler circuit nor an Euler path since it has more than two vertices of odd degree.

5. K_5 is nonplanar. $K_{2,3}$ is planar, as can easily be seen by drawing it with no crossings, or since it has no subgraph homeomorphic to $K_{3,3}$ or K_5. W_5 is planar as is seen from the usual way of drawing it.

6. The chromatic number of K_5 is 5, since each vertex must be colored differently from all others. $K_{2,3}$ has chromatic number 2, since it is a bipartite graph. W_5 has chromatic number 4, since three colors are required to color C_5 and a fourth color must be used for the hub vertex.

7. First iteration: distinguished vertices: a; labels: $a:0$, $b:3$, $c:7$, $d:\infty$, $e:\infty$, $z:\infty$. Second iteration: distinguished vertices: a, b; labels: $a:0$, $b:3$, $c:5$, $d:9$, $e:\infty$, $z:\infty$. Third iteration: distinguished vertices: a, b, c; labels: $a:0$, $b:3$, $c:5$, $d:6$, $e:11$, $z:\infty$. Fourth iteration: distinguished vertices: a, b, c, d; labels: $a:0$, $b:3$, $c:5$, $d:6$, $e:8$, $z:14$. Fifth iteration: distinguished vertices: a, b, c, d, e; labels: $a:0$, $b:3$, $c:5$, $d:6$, $e:8$, $z:13$. Since at the next iteration z is a distinguished vertex, we conclude that the shortest path has length 13.

Chapter 9—Test 1

1. Which of the following graphs are trees? Explain your answers.

   (a)   (b)   (c)

   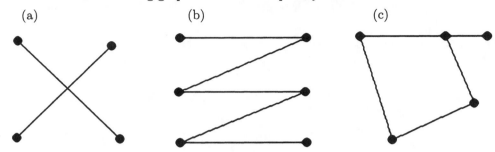

2. A tree has 99 edges. How many vertices does it have?

3. Form a binary search tree from the words of the sentence *This test is not so difficult*, using alphabetical order, inserting words in the order they appear in the sentence.

4. Is the code   A: 11, B: 10, C: 0   a prefix code?

5. Construct an expression tree for $(3 + x) - 5 \cdot y$ and write this expression is prefix form and postfix form.

6. Use a depth-first search to find a spanning tree of the following graph. Start at the vertex a, and use alphabetical order.

   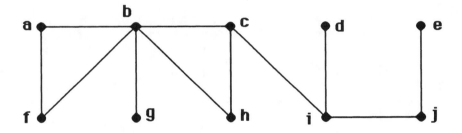

7. Use Prim's algorithm to find a minimum spanning tree for the following weighted graph. Use alphabetical order to break ties.

   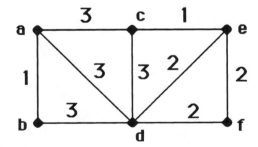

Chapter 9—Test 1 Solutions

1. The graph in part (a) is not connected, so it is not a tree. The graph in part (b) is a tree since it is connected and contains no simple circuits. The graph in part (c) is not a tree since it contains a simple circuit.

2. If a tree has e edges and n vertices, then $e = n - 1$. Hence if a tree has 99 edges, then it has 100 vertices.

3. The following binary search tree is produced.

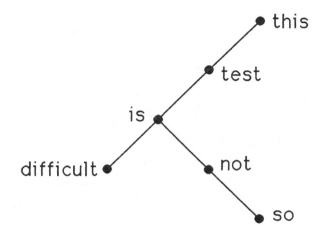

4. This is a prefix code since the code for A, 11, does not start the code for B or the code for C; the code for B, 10, does not start the code for A or the code for C; and the code for C, 0, does not start the code for A or the code for B.

5. The following tree represents the expression $(3 + x) - 5 \cdot y$

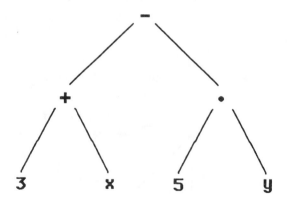

The prefix form and postfix form of this expression are obtained by carrying out a preorder and a postorder traversal, respectively. The preorder form is $- + 3\,x \cdot 5\,y$. The postorder form is $3\,x + 5\,y \cdot -$.

6. The edges produced by a depth-first search are $\{a, b\}$, $\{b, c\}$, $\{c, h\}$, $\{c, i\}$, $\{i, d\}$, $\{i, j\}$, $\{j, e\}$, $\{b, f\}$, and $\{b, g\}$.

7. Prim's algorithm adds the edges: $\{a, b\}$ of weight 1, $\{a, c\}$ of weight 3, $\{c, e\}$ of weight 1, $\{d, e\}$ of weight 2, $\{d, f\}$ of weight 2. The weight of the minimum spanning tree is 9.

Chapter 9—Test 2

1. (a) Suppose that a full 3-ary tree has 100 internal vertices. How many leaves does it have?

    (b) Suppose that a full 4-ary tree has 100 leaves. How many internal vertices does it have?

2. How many nonisomorphic trees are there with four vertices? Draw them.

3. Is the code   A: 111, B: 101, C: 011, D: 010, E: 10, F: 1101   a prefix code?

4. Perform a preorder, inorder, and postorder traversal of the rooted tree T.

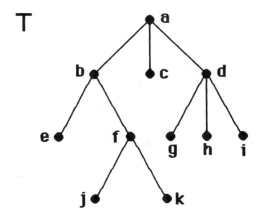

5. Use backtracking to find a sum of integers in the set $\{18, 19, 23, 25, 31\}$ that equals 44.

6. Find a minimum spanning tree in the following weighted graph using Prim's algorithm.

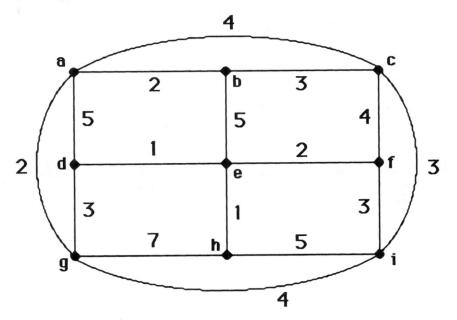

Chapter 9—Test 2 Solutions

1. (a) A full 3-ary tree with 100 internal vertices has $l = (3-1) \cdot 100 + 1 = 201$ leaves.

   (b) A full 4-ary tree with 100 leaves has $i = (100-1)/(4-1) = 33$ internal vertices.

2. There are two nonisomorphic unrooted trees with four vertices, as shown.

3. This is not a prefix code since the code for E, 10, begins the code for B, 101.

4. The preorder traversal is $a, b, e, f, j, k, c, d, g, h, i$; the inorder traversal is $e, b, j, f, k, a, c, g, d, h, i$; and the postorder traversal is $e, j, k, f, b, c, g, h, i, d, a$.

5. We build the following tree using backtracking. We find that $44 = 19 + 25$.

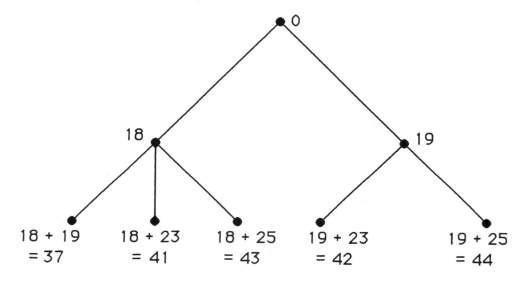

6. Prim's algorithm adds the edges $\{d, e\}$ of weight 1, $\{e, h\}$ of weight 1, $\{e, f\}$ of weight 2, $\{d, g\}$ of weight 3, $\{g, a\}$ of weight 2, $\{a, b\}$ of weight 2, $\{b, c\}$ of weight 3, and $\{c, i\}$ of weight 3. The total weight of the minimum spanning tree is 17.

Chapter 10—Test 1

1. What is the value of the Boolean function $f(x, y, z) = (\overline{x} + \overline{y})z + xyz$ when $x = 1$, $y = 0$ and $z = 1$?

2. Prove or disprove that $xy + y = y$ whenever x and y are Boolean variables.

3. How many different Boolean functions are there of degree 3?

4. Find the sum-of-products expansion of a Boolean function $f(x, y, z)$ that is 1 if and only if $x = y = 1$ and $z = 0$, or $x = 0$ and $y = z = 1$, or $x = y = 0$ and $z = 1$.

5. What is the output of the following circuit?

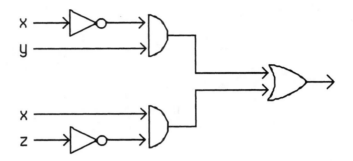

6. Use a K-map to minimize the sum-of-products expansion $xyz + x\overline{y}z + x\overline{y}\overline{z} + \overline{x}\overline{y}z$.

Chapter 10—Test 1 Solutions

1. We have $f(1,0,1) = (\overline{1} + \overline{0}) \cdot 1 + 1 \cdot 0 \cdot 1 = (0 + 1) \cdot 1 + 0 = 1 \cdot 1 + 0 = 1 + 0 = 1$.

2. When $y = 1$ we have $xy + y = x + 1 = 1 = y$. When $y = 0$ we have $xy + y = x \cdot 0 + 0 = 0 + 0 = 0 = y$. Hence $xy + y = y$ for all values of the Boolean variables x and y.

3. There are $2^{2^3} = 2^8 = 256$ Boolean functions of degree 3.

4. The sum-of-products expansion is $x y \overline{z} + \overline{x} y z + \overline{x} \overline{y} z$.

5. The output of the circuit is $\overline{x} y + x \overline{z}$.

6. We construct the following K-map.

Combining terms gives us the expansion $x \overline{y} + x z + \overline{y} z$.

Chapter 10—Test 2

1. Prove or disprove that $x + xy + xyz = x$ whenever x, y, and z are Boolean variables.

2. Find a Boolean function $f(x, y, z)$ that has the value 1 if and only if exactly two of x, y, and z have the value 1.

3. Is the set of operators $\{+, \cdot\}$ functionally complete? Justify your answer.

4. Construct a circuit using inverters, *OR* gates, and *AND* gates that gives an output of 1 if three people on a committee do not all vote the same.

5. Use a K-map to minimize the sum-of-products expansion $xyz + x\overline{y}z + \overline{x}\,\overline{y}z + x\overline{y}\,\overline{z} + \overline{x}yz + \overline{x}\,\overline{y}\,\overline{z}$.

Chapter 10—Test 2 Solutions

1. When x has the value 1, then $x + xy + xyz = 1 + 1 \cdot y + 1 \cdot yz = 1 = x$. When x has the value 0, then $x + xy + xyz = 0 + 0 \cdot y + 0 \cdot yz = 0 + 0 + 0 = 0 = x$. Hence this identity holds for all values of the Boolean variables x, y, and z.

2. We want the sum-of-products expansion that has the value 1 if and only if $x = y = 1$ and $z = 0$, or $x = z = 1$ and $y = 0$, or $y = z = 1$ and $x = 0$. Hence, this sum-of-products expansion is $x y \overline{z} + x \overline{y} z + \overline{x} y z$.

3. The set of operators $\{+, \cdot\}$ is not functionally complete. There is no way to obtain $\overline{x}$ from these two operators. To see this, note that $x + x = x$ and $x \cdot x = x$. Therefore every expression involving x and the operators in this set will be equal to x, never $\overline{x}$.

4. Let x, y, and z represent the votes of the three people on the committee with a variable taking the value 1 if the vote is affirmative and the value 0 if the vote is negative. The circuit should produce an output of 1 if and only if not all three of the variables have the same value. The function $f(x, y, z) = \overline{(x y z + \overline{x}\,\overline{y}\,\overline{z})}$ gives this output. Hence we can use the following circuit.

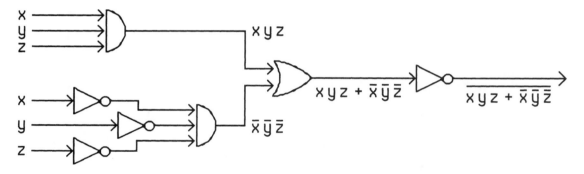

5. We construct the following K-map.

	yz	$y\overline{z}$	$\overline{y}\,\overline{z}$	$\overline{y}z$
x	1		1	1
$\overline{x}$	1		1	1

This gives us the expansion $\overline{y} + z$.

Chapter 11—Test 1

1. The productions of a phrase-structure grammar are $S \to S1$, $S \to 0A$, and $A \to 1$. Find a derivation of 0111.

2. What language is generated by the phrase-structure grammar if the productions are $S \to S11$, $S \to \lambda$ where S is the start symbol?

3. Construct a finite-state machine that models a vending machine accepting only quarters that gives a container of orange juice when 50 cents has been deposited, followed by a button being pushed. (The possible inputs are quarters and the button, and the possible outputs are nothing, orange juice, and a quarter. The machine returns any extra quarters.)

4. Suppose that $A = \{1, 11, 01\}$ and $B = \{0, 10\}$. Find AB and BA.

5. Let $A = \{1, 10\}$. Which strings belong to A^*?

6. What is the output produced by the following finite-state automaton when the input string is 11101?

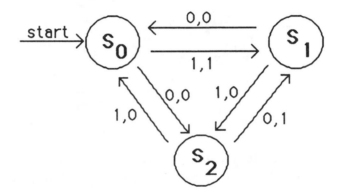

7. Which strings belong to the set represented by the regular expression $\mathbf{0^* \cup 11}$?

Chapter 11—Test 1 Solutions

1. We first apply the production $S \to S1$. Then we apply this production again to obtain $S11$. Next we apply the production $S \to 0A$ to obtain $0A11$. Next we apply the production $A \to 1$ to obtain 0111.

2. The language generated is the set of all strings consisting of an even number of 1s (and no other symbols).

3. The following finite-state machine models the vending machine.

KEY:
b = button
n = nothing
OJ = orange juice

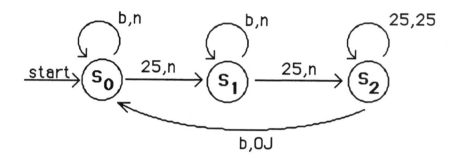

4. We find that $AB = \{10, 110, 1110, 010, 0110\}$ and $BA = \{01, 011, 001, 101, 1011, 1001\}$.

5. The strings in A^* are those for which every 0 is preceded by at least one 1.

6. The output produced is 10000.

7. The set contains strings consisting of all 0s (including the empty string) and the string 11.

Chapter 11—Test 2

1. What is the language generated by the grammar with productions $S \to SA$, $S \to 0$, $A \to 1A$, and $A \to 1$, where S is the start symbol?

2. Find a grammar for the set $\{0^{2n}1^n \mid n \geq 0\}$.

3. Construct a finite-state machine with output that produces a 1 if and only if the last three input bits read are all 0s.

4. Let $A = \{1, 10\}$. Describe the elements of A^*.

5. Construct a finite-state automaton that recognizes the set represented by the regular expression $\mathbf{10^*}$.

6. Find a deterministic finite-state automaton equivalent to the nondeterministic finite-state machine shown.

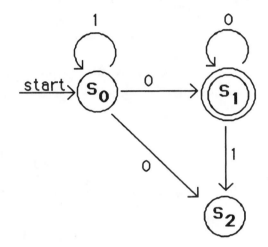

7. Which strings belong to the regular set represented by the regular expression $(\mathbf{1^*01^*0})^*$?

Chapter 11—Test 2 Solutions

1. The language is the set of all strings that consist of a 0 followed by an arbitrary number of 1s (possibly none).

2. We can use the grammar with productions $S \to 00S1$ and $S \to \lambda$ where S is the start symbol.

3. The following finite-state machine produces a 1 if and only if the last three input bits read are all 0s.

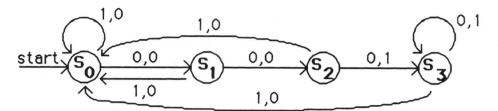

4. The strings in the set A^* are those strings where each 0 is preceded by a 1.

5. The following finite-state automaton recognizes the set represented by the regular expression **10***.

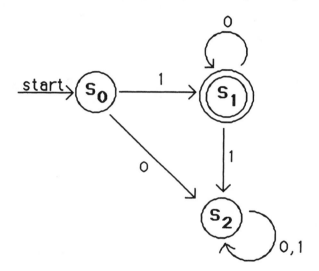

6. The following deterministic finite-state automaton is equivalent.

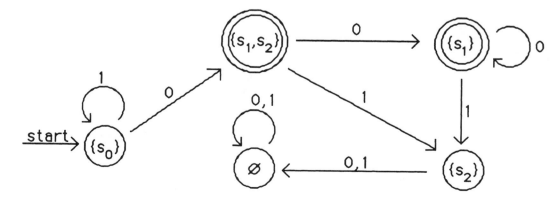

7. These are the strings containing an even number of 0s and not ending with a 1.

Final Exam 1

1. Prove or disprove that if A and B are sets then $A \cap (A \cup B) = A$.

2. Find the prime factorization of 16575.

3. (a) Prove or disprove: If $a \equiv b \pmod 5$, where a and b are integers, then $a^2 \equiv b^2 \pmod 5$.

   (b) Prove or disprove: If $a^2 \equiv b^2 \pmod 5$, where a and b are integers, then $a \equiv b \pmod 5$.

4. Use mathematical induction to prove that $n! \geq 2^{n-1}$ whenever n is a positive integer.

5. Suppose that $a_1 = 10$, $a_2 = 5$, and $a_n = 2a_{n-1} + 3a_{n-2}$ for $n \geq 3$. Prove that 5 divides a_n whenever n is a positive integer.

6. How many bit string of length 10 have at least one 0 in them?

7. (a) How many functions are there from a set with three elements to a set with four elements?

   (b) How many are one-to-one?

   (c) How many are onto?

8. A door lock is opened by pushing a sequence of buttons. Each of the three terms in the combination is entered by pushing either one button or two buttons simultaneously. If there are 5 buttons, how many different combinations are there? (Example: 1-3, 2, 2-4 is a valid combination.)

9. Find a recurrence relation and initial conditions for the number of ways to go up a flight of stairs if stairs can be climbed one, two, or three at a time.

10. How many positive integers not exceeding 1000 are not divisible by either 8 or 12?

11. (a) Show that the relation $R = \{ (x,y) \mid x - y \text{ is an even integer} \}$ is an equivalence relation on the set of real numbers.

    (b) What are the equivalence classes of 1 and $\frac{1}{2}$ with respect to R?

12. Answer the following questions about the graph $K_{3,4}$.

    (a) How many vertices and how many edges are in this graph?

    (b) Is this graph planar? Justify your answer.

    (c) Does this graph have an Euler circuit? Does it have an Euler path? Give reasons for your answers.

    (d) What is the chromatic number of this graph?

13. Find a spanning tree for the graph $K_{3,4}$ using

    (a) a depth-first search.

    (b) a breadth-first search.

14. Find the sum-of-products expansion of the Boolean function $f(x, y, z)$ that has the value 1 if and only if an odd number of the variables x, y, and z have the value 1.

15. Find the set recognized by the following deterministic finite-state machine.

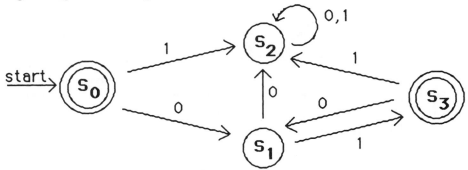

16. A fair coin is flipped until a tail first appears, at which time no more flips are made.

    (a) What is the probability that exactly five flips are made?

    (b) What is the expected number of flips?

Final Exam 1 Solutions

1. Suppose that $x \in A$. Then $x \in A \cup B$, so $x \in A \cap (A \cup B)$. Conversely, suppose that $x \in A \cap (A \cup B)$. Then $x \in A$. Hence $A \cap (A \cup B) = A$.

2. We find that 2 does not divide 16575, but 3 does with $16575/3 = 5525$. We see that 3 does not divide 5525, but 5 does with $5525/5 = 1105$. We see that 5 divides 1105 with $1105/5 = 221$. We see that neither 5, 7, nor 11 divides 221. However, 13 does, with $221/13 = 17$. Hence $16575 = 3 \cdot 5^2 \cdot 13 \cdot 17$.

3. (a) Suppose that $a \equiv b \pmod 5$. Then $5 \,|\, a - b$, so there is an integer k such that $a - b = 5k$. It follows that $a^2 - b^2 = (a + b)(a - b) = (a + b)5k$. Hence $a^2 - b^2 = 5l$, where $l = (a + b)k$. It follows that $5 \,|\, a^2 - b^2$, so $a^2 \equiv b^2 \pmod 5$.

   (b) We see that $1^2 \equiv 4^2 \pmod 5$, but $1 \not\equiv 4 \pmod 5$.

4. The basis step follows since $1! = 1 = 2^0$. For the inductive hypothesis assume that $n! \geq 2^{n-1}$. Then $(n + 1)! = (n + 1) \cdot n! \geq (n + 1) \cdot 2^{n-1} \geq 2 \cdot 2^{n-1} = 2^n$.

5. The basis step is completed by noting that $a_1 = 10$ and $a_2 = 5$ are both divisible by 5. For the inductive step assume that a_k is divisible by 5 for every positive integer k with $k < n$, where $n \geq 3$. It follows that $a_n = 2a_{n-1} + 3a_{n-2}$ is divisible by 5, since the sum of two integers divisible by 5 is also divisible by 5.

6. The number of bit strings of length 10 with at least one 0 in them is the number of all bits strings of length 10 minus the number of bits strings of length 10 with no 0s in them. This is $2^{10} - 1 = 1024 - 1 = 1023$.

7. (a) There are $4^3 = 64$ functions from a set with three elements to a set with four elements.

   (b) There are $4 \cdot 3 \cdot 2 = 24$ one-to-one functions from a set with three elements to a set with four elements.

   (c) There are no onto functions from a set with three elements to a set with four elements.

8. A push of buttons in the combinations is either the push of one of the five buttons or the simultaneous push of one of $C(5, 2) = 10$ combinations of two of the five buttons. Hence there are $15 \cdot 15 \cdot 15 = 3375$ possible combinations for the door lock.

9. Let a_n denote the number of ways to climb n stairs if stairs can be climbed one, two, or three at a time. Suppose that n is a positive integer, $n \geq 4$. A person can climb n stairs by going up $n - 1$ stairs and then climbing one stair, by going up $n - 2$ stairs and then climbing two stairs, or by going up $n - 3$ stairs and then climbing three stairs. Hence $a_n = a_{n-1} + a_{n-2} + a_{n-3}$. Note that $a_1 = 1$ since there is only one way to climb one stair, $a_2 = 2$ since two stairs can be climbed one stair at a time or two stairs at once, and $a_3 = 4$ since we can climb three stairs by taking stairs one at a time, by going up two stairs followed by one stair, by going up one stair followed by two stairs, or by taking all three stairs at once.

10. The number of integers not exceeding 1000 that are not divisible by either 8 or 12 is 1000 minus the number of these integers that are divisible by either 8 or 12. Using the principle of inclusion–exclusion, we see that there are $\lfloor 1000/8 \rfloor + \lfloor 1000/12 \rfloor - \lfloor 1000/24 \rfloor = 125 + 83 - 41 = 167$ such integers, where we used the fact that the integers divisible by both 8 and 12 are those divisible by $\operatorname{lcm}(8, 12) = 24$. Hence there are $1000 - 167 = 833$ positive integers not exceeding 1000 that are not divisible by either 8 or 12.

11. (a) Since $x - x = 0$ is an even integer for every real number x it follows that R is reflexive. If $(x, y) \in R$ then $x - y$ is an even integer. It follows that $y - x = -(x - y)$ is also an even integer. Hence R is symmetric. Now suppose that $(x, y) \in R$ and $(y, z) \in R$. Then $x - y$ and $y - z$ are even integers. Since $x - z = (x - y) + (y - z)$ and the sum of two even integers is again even, it follows that $x - z$ is also an even integer. This shows that R is transitive. We conclude that R is an equivalence relation.

    (b) We have $[1]_R = \{\, x \mid x - 1 \text{ is an even integer} \,\}$. Hence $[1]_R = \{\, x \mid x = 1 + 2k \text{ where } k \text{ is an integer} \,\}$. In other words, $[1]_R$ is the set of odd integers. Similarly, $[\frac{1}{2}]_R = \{\, x \mid x - \frac{1}{2} \text{ is an even integer} \,\}$. Hence $[\frac{1}{2}]_R = \{\, x \mid x = \frac{1}{2} + 2k \text{ where } k \text{ is an integer} \,\}$. This is the set $\{\ldots, -\frac{7}{2}, -\frac{3}{2}, \frac{1}{2}, \frac{5}{2}, \frac{9}{2}, \ldots\}$.

12. (a) The graph $K_{3,4}$ has $3 + 4 = 7$ vertices and $3 \cdot 4 = 12$ edges.

    (b) $K_{3,4}$ is not planar since it contains a subgraph isomorphic to $K_{3,3}$, which is not planar.

    (c) $K_{3,4}$ has three vertices of degree 4 and four vertices of degree 3. Since there are more than two vertices of odd degree, there is no Euler path in this graph, and therefore also no Euler circuit.

(d) The chromatic number of $K_{3,4}$ is 2 since this graph is bipartite.

13. A depth-first spanning tree of $K_{3,4}$ is shown on the left and a breadth-first spanning tree of $K_{3,4}$ is shown on the right. (Note that the first answer depends on the part of the graph you start in.)

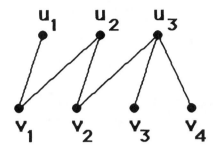 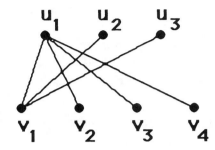

14. The sum-of-products expansion is $f(x, y, z) = x\,y\,z + x\,\overline{y}\,\overline{z} + \overline{x}\,y\,\overline{z} + \overline{x}\,\overline{y}\,z$.

15. The set recognized is the set represented by $(\mathbf{01})^*$.

16. The number of flips follows a geometric distribution with parameter $p = 1/2$.

(a) The coin must land heads four times in a row and then tails, and the probability of this is $(1/2)^5 = 1/32$.

(b) The expected number of flips in a geometric distribution is $1/p = 2$.

Final Exam 2

1. Prove or disprove that $\overline{(A - B)} = \overline{A} \cup B$ whenever A and B are sets.

2. Prove or disprove that the fourth power of an odd positive integer always leaves a remainder of 1 when divided by 16.

3. Use mathematical induction to prove that every postage of greater than 5 cents can be formed from 3-cent and 4-cent stamps.

4. How many bit strings of length 10 have at least eight 1s in them?

5. (a) How many functions are there from a set with four elements to a set with three elements?

   (b) How many of these functions are one-to-one?

   (c) How many are onto?

6. How many symmetric relations are there on a set with eight elements?

7. (a) Let m be a positive integer greater than 2. Show that the relation R consisting of those ordered pairs of integers (a, b) with $a \equiv \pm b \pmod{m}$ is an equivalence relation.

   (b) Describe the equivalence classes of this relation where $m = 4$.

8. (a) Does the graph $K_{2,5}$ have an Euler circuit? If not, does it have an Euler path?

   (b) Does the graph $K_{2,5}$ have a Hamilton path?

9. How many nonisomorphic unrooted trees are there with four vertices? Draw these trees.

10. Construct a binary search tree from the words of the sentence *This is your discrete mathematics final*, using alphabetical order, inserting words in the order they appear in the sentence.

11. Find the sum-of-products expansion for the Boolean function $x + y + z$.

12. (a) Describe the bit strings that are in the regular set represented by **0*11(0 ∪ 1)***?

    (b) Construct a nondeterministic finite-state automaton that recognizes this set.

13. A thumb tack is tossed until it first lands with its point down, at which time no more tosses are made. On each toss, the probability of the tack's landing point down is 1/3.

    (a) What is the probability that exactly five tosses are made?

    (b) What is the expected number of tosses?

Final Exam 2 Solutions

1. This set equality can be proved in several different ways. One method is to use set identities already known to hold. We find that $\overline{(A - B)} = \overline{(A \cap \overline{B})} = \overline{A} \cup \overline{(\overline{B})} = \overline{A} \cup B$, where we have used De Morgan's laws and the double complementation law.

2. Suppose that a is an odd integer. Then $a = 2k+1$. We have $a^4 = (2k+1)^4 = 16k^4 + 32k^3 + 24k^2 + 8k + 1 = 16(k^4 + 2k^3) + 8k(3k+1) + 1$. If k is even then $8k = 16l$ where $k = 2l$, so $a^4 = 16N + 1$, where N is an integer. If k is odd then $3k + 1 = 3(2l+1) + 1 = 6l + 4 = 2m$, where $m = 3l + 2$, so again $a^4 = 16N + 1$, where N is an integer. It follows that $a \equiv 1 \pmod{16}$ whenever a is an odd integer.

3. The basis step is completed by noting that postage of 6 cents can be formed using two 3-cent stamps. Now assume that postage of n cents can be formed, where n is a positive integer greater than or equal to 6. If a 3-cent stamp was used to form n cents postage, replace this stamp with a 4-cent stamp to obtain postage of $n+1$ cents. Otherwise, if only 4-cent stamps were used, then at least two of them were used, so replace two 4-cent stamps with three 3-cent stamps to obtain postage of $n+1$ cents.

4. The number of bit strings of length 10 with at least eight 1s in them equals the number with exactly eight 1s plus the number with exactly nine 1s plus the number with exactly ten 1s. There are $C(10, 8) = 10!/(2!8!) = 45$ such strings with exactly eight 1s, $C(10, 9) = 10$ such strings with exactly nine 1s, and $C(10, 10) = 1$ such string with exactly ten 1s. Hence there are $45 + 10 + 1 = 56$ bit strings of length 10 containing at least eight 1s.

5. (a) There are $3^4 = 81$ functions from a set with four elements to a set with three elements.

   (b) There are no one-to-one functions from a set with four elements to a set with three elements since $4 > 3$.

   (c) There are $3^4 - C(3, 2)2^4 + C(3, 1)1^4 = 81 - 48 + 3 = 36$ onto functions from a set with four elements to a set with three elements.

6. A symmetric relation is determined by specifying whether (i, j) and (j, i) belong to this relation for the pairs with $i \neq j$, and whether (i, i) belongs to the relation for all elements i in the set. Since there are eight elements in the set, there are $C(8, 2) = 28$ pairs (i, j) and (j, i) with $i \neq j$, and eight elements i. Hence there are $2^{28+8} = 2^{36}$ symmetric relations on a set with eight elements.

7. (a) Let a be an integer. Then $a \equiv a \pmod{m}$ since $m \mid a - a$. It follows that R is reflexive. Now suppose that $(a, b) \in R$. Then $a \equiv b \pmod{m}$ or $a \equiv -b \pmod{m}$. It is easy to see that $b \equiv a \pmod{m}$ or $b \equiv -a \pmod{m}$. Hence $(b, a) \in R$. It follows that R is symmetric. Now assume that $(a, b) \in R$ and $(b, c) \in R$. Then $a \equiv b \pmod{m}$ or $a \equiv -b \pmod{m}$, and $b \equiv c \pmod{m}$ or $b \equiv -c \pmod{m}$. We can easily see that each of the four combinations leads to $a \equiv c \pmod{m}$ or $a \equiv -c \pmod{m}$. Hence $(a, c) \in R$, and R is transitive.

   (b) Let $m = 4$. The equivalence classes of R are $[0]_R = \{ a \in \mathbf{Z} \mid a \equiv 0 \pmod 4 \} = \{\ldots, -8, -4, 0, 4, 8, \ldots\}$, $[1]_R = \{ a \in \mathbf{Z} \mid a \equiv \pm 1 \pmod 4 \} = \{\ldots, -5, -3, -1, 1, 3, 5, \ldots\}$, and $[2]_R = \{ a \in \mathbf{Z} \mid a \equiv 2 \pmod 4 \} = \{\ldots, -6, -2, 2, 6, \ldots\}$.

8. (a) The graph $K_{2,5}$ has two vertices of degree 5 and five vertices of degree 2. Hence it has an Euler path and no Euler circuit.

   (b) There is no Hamilton path in this graph since any path containing all five vertices of degree 2 must visit some of the vertices of degree 5 more than once.

9. There are two nonisomorphic unrooted trees with four vertices, as shown.

10. We construct the following binary search tree.

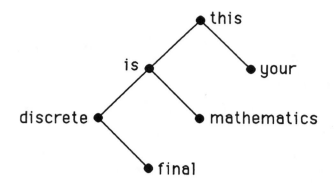

11. The Boolean function $x + y + z$ has the value 1 unless $x = y = z = 0$, so it has the value 1 for the other seven combinations of the values of these variable. Hence the sum-of-products expansion is
$f(x, y, z) = x\,y\,z + x\,y\,\overline{z} + x\,\overline{y}\,z + x\,\overline{y}\,\overline{z} + \overline{x}\,y\,z + \overline{x}\,y\,\overline{z} + \overline{x}\,\overline{y}\,z.$

12. (a) The strings in this set are those that begin with an arbitrary number of 0s followed by two consecutive 1s, followed by an arbitrary bit string.

(b) The following nondeterministic finite-state automaton recognizes this set.

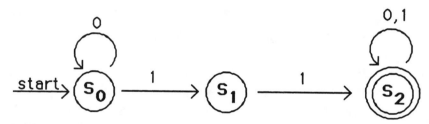

13. The number of tosses follows a geometric distribution with parameter $p = 1/3$.

(a) The tack must land point up four times in a row and then point down, and the probability of this is $(2/3)^4(1/3) = 16/243$.

(b) The expected number of tosses in a geometric distribution is $1/p = 3$.

TEST BANK

Questions for Chapter 1

In questions 1–5, determine whether the proposition is TRUE or FALSE.

1. $1 + 1 = 3$ if and only if $2 + 2 = 3$.

2. If it is raining, then it is raining.

3. If $1 < 0$, then $3 = 4$.

4. If $2 + 1 = 3$, then $2 = 3 - 1$.

5. If $1 + 1 = 2$ or $1 + 1 = 3$, then $2 + 2 = 3$ and $2 + 2 = 4$.

6. Write the truth table for the proposition $\neg(r \to \neg q) \lor (p \land \neg r)$.

7. (a) Find a proposition with the truth table at the right.
(b) Find a proposition using only $p, q, \neg$, and the connective $\lor$ that has this truth table.

p	q	?
T	T	F
T	F	F
F	T	T
F	F	F

8. Find a proposition with three variables p, q, and r that is true when p and r are true and q is false, and false otherwise

9. Find a proposition with three variables p, q, and r that is true when exactly one of the three variables is true, and false otherwise

10. Find a proposition with three variables p, q, and r that is never true.

11. Find a proposition using only $p, q, \neg$ and the connective $\lor$ with the truth table at the right.

p	q	?
T	T	F
T	F	T
F	T	T
F	F	F

12. Determine whether $p \to (q \to r)$ and $p \to (q \land r)$ are equivalent.

13. Determine whether $(p \to q) \land (\neg p \to q) \equiv q$.

14. Write a proposition equivalent to $p \lor \neg q$ that uses only $p, q, \neg$ and the connective $\land$.

15. Write a proposition equivalent to $\neg p \land \neg q$ using only $p, q, \neg$ and the connective $\lor$.

16. Prove that the proposition "if it is not hot, then it is hot" is equivalent to "it is hot".

17. Write a proposition equivalent to $p \to q$ using only $p, q, \neg$ and the connective: $\lor$.

18. Write a proposition equivalent to $p \to q$ using only $p, q, \neg$ and the connective $\land$.

19. Prove that $p \to q$ and its converse are not logically equivalent.

20. Prove that $\neg p \to \neg q$ and its inverse are not logically equivalent.

21. Determine whether the following two propositions are logically equivalent: $p \vee (q \wedge r)$, $(p \wedge q) \vee (p \wedge r)$.

22. Determine whether the following two propositions are logically equivalent: $p \to (\neg q \wedge r)$, $\neg p \vee \neg(r \to q)$.

23. Prove that $(q \wedge (p \to \neg q)) \to \neg p$ is a tautology using propositional equivalence and the laws of logic.

24. Determine whether this proposition is a tautology: $((p \to q) \wedge \neg p) \to \neg q$.

25. Determine whether this proposition is a tautology: $((p \to \neg q) \wedge q) \to \neg p$.

In 26–32, write the statement in the form "If ..., then ...."

26. x is even only if y is odd.

27. A implies B.

28. It is hot whenever it is sunny.

29. To get a good grade it is necessary that you study.

30. Studying is sufficient for passing.

31. The team wins if the quarterback can pass.

32. You need to be registered in order to check out library books.

33. Write the contrapositive, converse, and inverse of the following: If you try hard, then you will win.

34. Write the contrapositive, converse, and inverse of the following: You sleep late if it is Saturday.

In 35–37 write the negation of the statement. (Don't write "It is not true that ....")

35. It is Thursday and it is cold.

36. I will go to the play or read a book, but not both.

37. If it is rainy, then we go to the movies.

38. Explain why the negation of "Al and Bill are absent" is not "Al and Bill are present".

39. Using c for "it is cold" and d for "it is dry", write "It is neither cold nor dry" in symbols.

40. Using c for "it is cold" and r for "it is rainy", write "It is rainy if it is not cold" in symbols.

41. Using c for "it is cold" and w for "it is windy", write "To be windy it is necessary that it be cold" in symbols.

42. Using c for "it is cold", r for "it is rainy", and w for "it is windy", write "It is rainy only if it is windy and cold" in symbols.

43. A set of propositions is *consistent* if there is an assignment of truth values to each of the variables in the propositions that makes each proposition true. Is the following set of propositions consistent?
    The system is in multiuser state if and only if it is operating normally.
    If the system is operating normally, the kernel is functioning.
    The kernel is not functioning or the system is in interrupt mode.
    If the system is not in multiuser state, then it is in interrupt mode.

The system is in interrupt mode.

In 44–46 suppose that $Q(x)$ is "$x + 1 = 2x$", where x is a real number. Find the truth value of the statement.

44. $Q(2)$.

45. $\forall x\, Q(x)$.

46. $\exists x\, Q(x)$.

In 47–54 $P(x, y)$ means "$x + 2y = xy$", where x and y are integers. Determine the truth value of the statement.

47. $P(1, -1)$.

48. $P(0, 0)$.

49. $\exists y\, P(3, y)$.

50. $\forall x \exists y\, P(x, y)$.

51. $\exists x \forall y\, P(x, y)$.

52. $\forall y \exists x\, P(x, y)$.

53. $\exists y \forall x\, P(x, y)$.

54. $\neg \forall x \exists y\, \neg P(x, y)$.

In 55–56 $P(x, y)$ means "x and y are real numbers such that $x + 2y = 5$". Determine whether the statement is true.

55. $\forall x \exists y\, P(x, y)$.

56. $\exists x \forall y\, P(x, y)$.

In 57–59 $P(m, n)$ means "$n \geq m$", where the universe of discourse for m and n is the set of nonnegative integers. What is the truth value of the statement?

57. $\forall n\, P(0, n)$.

58. $\exists n \forall m\, P(m, n)$.

59. $\forall m \exists n\, P(m, n)$.

In 60–63 suppose the variable x represents students and y represents courses, and:

    $U(y)$: y is an upper-level course $M(y)$: y is a math course $F(x)$: x is a freshman
        $B(x)$: x is a full-time student $T(x, y)$: student x is taking course y.

Write the statement using these predicates and any needed quantifiers.

60. Fran is taking MTH 281.

61. All students are freshmen.

62. Every freshman is a full-time student.

63. No math course is upper-level.

In 64–66 suppose the variable x represents students and y represents courses, and:

$U(y)$: y is an upper-level course $M(y)$: y is a math course $F(x)$: x is a freshman

$A(x)$: x is a part-time student $T(x, y)$: student x is taking course y.

Write the statement using these predicates and any needed quantifiers.

64. Every student is taking at least one course.

65. There is a part-time student who is not taking any math course.

66. Every part-time freshman is taking some upper-level course.

In 67–69 suppose the variable x represents students and y represents courses, and:

$F(x)$: x is a freshman $A(x)$: x is a part-time student $T(x, y)$: x is taking y.

Write the statement in good English without using variables in your answers.

67. $F(\text{Helen})$.

68. $\neg \exists y\, T(\text{Joe}, y)$.

69. $\exists x\, (A(x) \wedge \neg F(x))$.

In 70–72 suppose the variable x represents students and y represents courses, and:

$M(y)$: y is a math course $F(x)$: x is a freshman

$B(x)$: x is a full-time student $T(x, y)$: x is taking y.

Write the statement in good English without using variables in your answers.

70. $\forall x \exists y\, T(x, y)$.

71. $\exists x \forall y\, T(x, y)$.

72. $\forall x \exists y\, [(B(x) \wedge F(x)) \rightarrow (M(y) \wedge T(x, y))]$.

In 73–75 suppose the variables x and y represent real numbers, and

$L(x, y) : x < y$ $G(x) : x > 0$ $P(x) : x$ is a prime number.

Write the statement in good English without using any variables in your answer.

73. $L(7, 3)$.

74. $\forall x \exists y\, L(x, y)$.

75. $\forall x \exists y\, [G(x) \rightarrow (P(y) \wedge L(x, y))]$.

In 76–78 suppose the variables x and y represent real numbers, and

$L(x, y) : x < y$ $Q(x, y) : x = y$ $E(x) : x$ is even $I(x) : x$ is an integer.

Write the statement using these predicates and any needed quantifiers.

76. Every integer is even.

77. If $x < y$, then x is not equal to y.

78. There is no largest real number.

In 79–80 suppose the variables x and y represent real numbers, and

$E(x) : x$ is even $G(x) : x > 0$ $I(x) : x$ is an integer.

Write the statement using these predicates and any needed quantifiers.

79. Some real numbers are not positive.

80. No even integers are odd.

In 81–82 suppose the variable x represents people, and

$$F(x): x \text{ is friendly} \qquad T(x): x \text{ is tall} \qquad A(x): x \text{ is angry.}$$

Write the statement using these predicates and any needed quantifiers.

81. Some people are not angry.

82. All tall people are friendly.

83. No friendly people are angry.

In 84–85 suppose the variable x represents people, and

$$F(x): x \text{ is friendly} \qquad T(x): x \text{ is tall} \qquad A(x): x \text{ is angry.}$$

Write the statement using these predicates and any needed quantifiers.

84. Some tall angry people are friendly.

85. If a person is friendly, then that person is not angry.

In 86–88 suppose the variable x represents people, and

$$F(x): x \text{ is friendly} \qquad T(x): x \text{ is tall} \qquad A(x): x \text{ is angry.}$$

Write the statement in good English. Do not use variables in your answer.

86. $A(\text{Bill})$.

87. $\neg \exists x \, (A(x) \wedge T(x))$.

88. $\neg \forall x \, (F(x) \rightarrow A(x))$.

In 89–91 suppose the variable x represents students and the variable y represents courses, and

$A(y): y$ is an advanced course $S(x): x$ is a sophomore $F(x): x$ is a freshman $T(x, y): x$ is taking y.

Write the statement using these predicates and any needed quantifiers.

89. There is a course that every freshman is taking.

90. No freshman is a sophomore.

91. Some freshman is taking an advanced course.

In 92–93 suppose the variable x represents students and the variable y represents courses, and

$A(y): y$ is an advanced course $F(x): x$ is a freshman $T(x, y): x$ is taking y $P(x, y): x$ passed y.

Write the statement using the above predicates and any needed quantifiers.

92. No one is taking every advanced course.

93. Every freshman passed calculus.

In 94–96 suppose the variable x represents students and the variable y represents courses, and

$$T(x, y): x \text{ is taking } y \qquad P(x, y): x \text{ passed } y.$$

Write the statement in good English. Do not use variables in your answers.

94. $\neg P(\text{Fran, MAT 100})$.

95. $\exists y \forall x\ T(x, y)$.

96. $\forall x \exists y\ T(x, y)$.

In 97–101 assume that the universe for x is all people and the universe for y is the set of all movies. Write the English statement using the following predicates any any needed quantifiers:

$\quad S(x, y)$: x saw y $L(x, y)$: x liked y $A(y)$: y won an award $C(y)$: y is a comedy.

97. No comedy won an award.

98. Lois saw *Casablanca*, but didn't like it.

99. Some people have seen every comedy.

100. No one liked every movie he has seen.

101. Ben has never seen a movie that won an award.

In 102–104 assume that the universe for x is all people and the universe for y is the set of all movies. Write the statement in good English, using the predicates

$\quad\quad\quad\quad\quad\quad S(x, y)$: x saw y $L(x, y)$: x liked y.

Do not use variables in your answer.

102. $\exists y\ \neg S(\text{Margaret}, y)$.

103. $\exists y \forall x\ L(x, y)$.

104. $\forall x \exists y\ L(x, y)$.

In 105–114 suppose the variable x represents students, y represents courses, and $T(x, y)$ means "x is taking y". Match the English statement with all its equivalent symbolic statements in this list:

1. $\exists x \forall y\ T(x, y)$
2. $\exists y \forall x\ T(x, y)$
3. $\forall x \exists y\ T(x, y)$
4. $\neg \exists x \exists y\ T(x, y)$
5. $\exists x \forall y\ \neg T(x, y)$
6. $\forall y \exists x\ T(x, y)$
7. $\exists y \forall x\ \neg T(x, y)$
8. $\neg \forall x \exists y\ T(x, y)$
9. $\neg \exists y \forall x\ T(x, y)$
10. $\neg \forall x \exists y\ \neg T(x, y)$
11. $\neg \forall x \neg \forall y\ \neg T(x, y)$
12. $\forall x \exists y\ \neg T(x, y)$

105. Every course is being taken by at least one student.

106. Some student is taking every course.

107. No student is taking all courses.

108. There is a course that all students are taking.

109. Every student is taking at least one course.

110. There is a course that no students are taking.

111. Some students are taking no courses.

112. No course is being taken by all students.

113. Some courses are being taken by no students.

114. No student is taking any course.

In 115–125 suppose the variable x represents students, $F(x)$ means "x is a freshman'," and $M(x)$ means "x is a math major". Match the statement in symbols with one of the English statements in this list:

1. Some freshmen are math majors.
2. Every math major is a freshman.
3. No math major is a freshman.

115. $\forall x \, (M(x) \rightarrow \neg F(x))$.

116. $\neg \exists x \, (M(x) \wedge \neg F(x))$.

117. $\forall x \, (F(x) \rightarrow \neg M(x))$.

118. $\forall x \, (M(x) \rightarrow F(x))$.

119. $\exists x \, (F(x) \wedge M(x))$.

120. $\neg \forall x \, (\neg F(x) \vee \neg M(x))$.

121. $\forall x \, (\neg(M(x) \wedge \neg F(x)))$.

122. $\forall x \, (\neg M(x) \vee \neg F(x))$.

123. $\neg \exists x \, (M(x) \wedge \neg F(x))$.

124. $\neg \exists x \, (M(x) \wedge F(x))$.

125. $\neg \forall x \, (F(x) \rightarrow \neg M(x))$.

In 126–129 let $F(A)$ be the predicate "A is a finite set" and $S(A, B)$ be the predicate "A is contained in B". Suppose the universe of discourse consists of all sets. Translate the statement into symbols.

126. Not all sets are finite.

127. Every subset of a finite set is finite.

128. No infinite set is contained in a finite set.

129. The empty set is a subset of every finite set.

In 130–134 write the negation of the statement in good English. Don't write "It is not true that ... ."

130. Some bananas are yellow.

131. All integers ending in the digit 7 are odd.

132. No tests are easy.

133. Roses are red and violets are blue.

134. Some skiers do not speak Swedish.

135. A student is asked to give the negation of "all bananas are ripe".

(a) The student responds "all bananas are not ripe". Explain why the English in the student's response is ambiguous.

(b) Another student says that the negation of the statement is "no bananas are ripe". Explain why this is not correct.

(c) Another student says that the negation of the statement is "some bananas are ripe". Explain why this is not correct.

(d) Give the correct negation.

136. Explain why the negation of "Some students in my class use e-mail" is not "Some students in my class do not use e-mail".

137. What is the rule of inference used in the following:

If it snows today, the university will be closed. The university will not be closed today. Therefore, it did not snow today.

138. What is the rule of inference used in the following:

If I work all night on this homework, then I can answer all the exercises. If I answer all the exercises, I will understand the material. Therefore, if I work all night on this homework, then I will understand the material.

139. Explain why an argument of the following form is not valid:
$$p \rightarrow q$$
$$\underline{\neg p}$$
$$\therefore \neg q$$

140. Determine whether the following argument is valid:
$$p \rightarrow r$$
$$q \rightarrow r$$
$$\underline{\neg(p \vee q)}$$
$$\therefore \neg r$$

141. Determine whether the following argument is valid:
$$p \rightarrow r$$
$$q \rightarrow r$$
$$\underline{q \vee \neg r}$$
$$\therefore \neg p$$

142. Show that the hypotheses "I left my notes in the library or I finished the rough draft of the paper" and "I did not leave my notes in the library or I revised the bibliography" imply that "I finished the rough draft of the paper or I revised the bibliography".

143. Determine whether the following argument is valid. Name the rule of inference or the fallacy.

If n is a real number such that $n > 1$, then $n^2 > 1$. Suppose that $n^2 > 1$. Then $n > 1$.

144. Determine whether the following argument is valid. Name the rule of inference or the fallacy.

If n is a real number such that $n > 2$, then $n^2 > 4$. Suppose that $n \leq 2$. Then $n^2 \leq 4$.

145. Determine whether the following argument is valid:
She is a Math Major or a Computer Science Major.
If she does not know discrete math, she is not a Math Major.
If she knows discrete math, she is smart.
She is not a Computer Science Major.
Therefore, she is smart.

146. Determine whether the following argument is valid.
Rainy days make gardens grow.
Gardens don't grow if it is not hot.
It always rains on a day that is not hot.
Therefore, if it is not hot, then it is hot.

147. Determine whether the following argument is valid.

If you are not in the tennis tournament, you will not meet Ed.
If you aren't in the tennis tournament or if you aren't in the play, you won't meet Kelly.
You meet Kelly or you don't meet Ed.
It is false that you are in the tennis tournament and in the play.
Therefore, you are in the tennis tournament.

148. Show that the premises "Every student in this class passed the first exam" and "Alvina is a student in this class" imply the conclusion "Alvina passed the first exam".

149. Show that the premises "Jean is a student in my class" and "No student in my class is from England" imply the conclusion "Jean is not from England".

150. Show that the premise "My daughter visited Europe last week" implies the conclusion "Someone visited Europe last week".

151. Suppose you wish to prove a theorem of the form "if p then q".
(a) If you give a direct proof, what do you assume and what do you prove?
(b) If you give an indirect proof, what do you assume and what do you prove?
(c) If you give a proof by contradiction, what do you assume and what do you prove?

152. Suppose that you had to prove a theorem of the form "if p then q". Explain the difference between a direct proof and an indirect proof.

153. Give a direct proof of the following: "If x is an odd integer and y is an even integer, then $x + y$ is odd".

154. Give a proof by contradiction of the following: "If n is an odd integer, then n^2 is odd".

155. Consider the following theorem: "if x and y are odd integers, then $x + y$ is even". Give a direct proof of this theorem.

156. Consider the following theorem: "if x and y are odd integers, then $x + y$ is even". Give a proof by contradiction of this theorem.

157. Give a proof by contradiction of the following: If x and y are even integers, then xy is even.

158. Consider the following theorem: If x is an odd integer, then $x + 2$ is odd. Give a direct proof of this theorem

159. Consider the following theorem: If x is an odd integer, then $x + 2$ is odd. Give an indirect proof of this theorem.

160. Consider the following theorem: If x is an odd integer, then $x + 2$ is odd. Give a proof by contradiction of this theorem.

161. Consider the following theorem: If n is an even integer, then $n + 1$ is odd. Give a direct proof of this theorem.

162. Consider the following theorem: If n is an even integer, then $n + 1$ is odd. Give an indirect proof of this theorem.

163. Consider the following theorem: If n is an even integer, then $n + 1$ is odd. Give a proof by contradiction of this theorem.

164. Prove that the following is true for all positive integers n: n is even if and only if $3n^2 + 8$ is even.

165. Prove the following theorem: n is even if and only if n^2 is even.

166. Prove: if m and n are even integers, then $4|mn$.

167. Prove or disprove: if p is prime and $p > 2$, then $p^2 + 4$ is prime.

168. Prove or disprove: there are six consecutive composite integers.

169. Prove or disprove: there is a prime $p > 3$ such that p, $p + 2$, and $p + 4$ are prime.

170. Show that the premises "Everyone who read the textbook passed the exam", and "Ed read the textbook" imply the conclusion "Ed passed the exam".

171. Prove or disprove: For all real numbers x and y, $\lfloor x - y \rfloor = \lfloor x \rfloor - \lfloor y \rfloor$.

172. Prove or disprove: For all real numbers x and y, $\lfloor x + \lfloor x \rfloor \rfloor = \lfloor 2x \rfloor$.

173. Prove or disprove: For all real numbers x and y, $\lfloor xy \rfloor = \lfloor x \rfloor \cdot \lfloor y \rfloor$.

174. Prove or disprove: $A - (B \cap C) = (A - B) \cup (A - C)$.

175. Prove that $\overline{A \cap B} = \overline{A} \cup \overline{B}$ by giving a containment proof (that is, prove that the left side is a subset of the right side and that the right side is a subset of the left side).

176. Prove that $\overline{A \cap B} = \overline{A} \cup \overline{B}$ by giving an element table proof.

177. Prove that $\overline{A \cap B} = \overline{A} \cup \overline{B}$ by giving a proof using logical equivalence.

178. Prove that $\overline{A \cap B} = \overline{A} \cup \overline{B}$ by giving a Venn diagram proof.

179. Prove that $A \cap (B \cup C) = (A \cap B) \cup (A \cap C)$ by giving a containment proof (that is, prove that the left side is a subset of the right side and that the right side is a subset of the left side).

180. Prove that $A \cap (B \cup C) = (A \cap B) \cup (A \cap C)$ by giving an element table proof.

181. Prove that $A \cap (B \cup C) = (A \cap B) \cup (A \cap C)$ by giving a proof using logical equivalence.

182. Prove that $A \cap (B \cup C) = (A \cap B) \cup (A \cap C)$ by giving a Venn diagram proof.

183. Prove or disprove: if A, B, and C are sets, then $A - (B \cap C) = (A - B) \cap (A - C)$.

184. Prove or disprove $A \oplus (B \oplus C) = (A \oplus B) \oplus C$.

On 185-188 use a Venn diagram to determine which relationship, $\subseteq$, $=$, or $\supseteq$, is true for the pair of sets.
185. $A \cup B$, $A \cup (B - A)$.

186. $A \cup (B \cap C)$, $(A \cup B) \cap C$.

187. $(A - B) \cup (A - C)$, $A - (B \cap C)$.

188. $(A - C) - (B - C)$, $A - B$.

In 189–193 determine whether the given set is the power set of some set. If the set is a power set, give the set of which it is a power set.
189. $\{\emptyset, \{\emptyset\}, \{a\}, \{\{a\}\}, \{\{\{a\}\}\}, \{\emptyset, a\}, \{\emptyset, \{a\}\}, \{\emptyset, \{\{a\}\}\}, \{a, \{a\}\}, \{a, \{\{a\}\}\}, \{\{a\}, \{\{a\}\}\}, \{\emptyset, a, \{a\}\}, \{\emptyset, a, \{\{a\}\}\}, \{\emptyset, \{a\}, \{\{a\}\}\}, \{a, \{a\}, \{\{a\}\}\}, \{\emptyset, a, \{a\}, \{\{a\}\}\}\}$.

190. $\{\emptyset, \{a\}\}$.

191. $\{\emptyset, \{a\}, \{\emptyset, a\}\}$.

192. $\{\emptyset, \{a\}, \{\emptyset\}, \{a, \emptyset\}\}$.

193. $\{\emptyset, \{a, \emptyset\}\}$.

194. Prove that $\overline{\overline{S} \cup \overline{T}} = S \cap T$ for all sets S and T.

In 195–205 mark each statement TRUE or FALSE. Assume that the statement applies to all sets.

195. $A - (B - C) = (A - B) - C$.

196. $(A - C) - (B - C) = A - B$.

197. $A \cup (B \cap C) = (A \cup B) \cap (A \cup C)$.

198. $A \cap (B \cup C) = (A \cup B) \cap (A \cup C)$.

199. $\overline{A \cup \overline{B}} \cup \overline{A} = \overline{A}$.

200. If $A \cup C = B \cup C$, then $A = B$.

201. If $A \cap C = B \cap C$, then $A = B$.

202. If $A \cap B = A \cup B$, then $A = B$.

203. If $A \oplus B = A$, then $B = A$.

204. There is a set A such that $|\mathcal{P}(A)| = 12$.

205. $A \oplus A = A$.

206. Find three subsets of $\{1, 2, 3, 4, 5, 6, 7, 8, 9\}$ such that the intersection of any two has size 2 and the intersection of all three has size 1.

In 207–209 fill in the blanks.

207. $\displaystyle\bigcup_{i=1}^{+\infty} [-1/i, 1/i] = $ _____.

208. If $U = \{1, 2, \ldots, 9\}$, $A = $ all multiples of 2, $B = $ all multiples of 3, and $C = \{3, 4, 5, 6, 7\}$, then $C - (B - A) = $ _____.

209. If $S = \{1, 2, 3, 4, 5\}$, then $|\mathcal{P}(S)| = $ _____.

In 210–213 suppose $A = \{x, y\}$ and $B = \{x, \{x\}\}$. Mark the statement TRUE or FALSE.

210. $x \subseteq B$.

211. $\varnothing \in \mathcal{P}(B)$.

212. $\{x\} \subseteq A - B$.

213. $|\mathcal{P}(A)| = 4$.

In 214–221 suppose $A = \{a, b, c\}$. Mark the statement TRUE or FALSE.

214. $\{b, c\} \in \mathcal{P}(A)$.

215. $\{\{a\}\} \subseteq \mathcal{P}(A)$.

216. $\varnothing \subseteq A$.

217. $\{\varnothing\} \subseteq \mathcal{P}(A)$.

218. $\varnothing \subseteq A \times A$.

219. $\{a, c\} \in A$.

220. $\{a, b\} \in A \times A$.

221. $(c, c) \in A \times A$.

In 222–229 suppose $A = \{1, 2, 3, 4, 5\}$. Mark the statement TRUE or FALSE.

222. $\{1\} \in \mathcal{P}(A)$.

223. $\{\{3\}\} \subseteq \mathcal{P}(A)$.

224. $\emptyset \subseteq A$.

225. $\{\emptyset\} \subseteq \mathcal{P}(A)$.

226. $\emptyset \subseteq \mathcal{P}(A)$.

227. $\{2, 4\} \in A \times A$.

228. $\{\emptyset\} \in \mathcal{P}(A)$.

229. $(1, 1) \in A \times A$.

In 230–232 suppose the following are fuzzy sets:
$$F = \{0.7 \, Ann, 0.1 \, Bill, 0.8 \, Fran, 0.3 \, Olive, 0.5 \, Tom\},$$
$$R = \{0.4 \, Ann, 0.9 \, Bill, 0.9 \, Fran, 0.6 \, Olive, 0.7 \, Tom\}.$$

230. Find $\overline{F}$ and $\overline{R}$.

231. Find $F \cup R$.

232. Find $F \cap R$.

In 233–242, suppose $A = \{a, b, c\}$ and $B = \{b, \{c\}\}$. Mark the statement TRUE or FALSE.

233. $c \in A - B$.

234. $|\mathcal{P}(A \times B)| = 64$.

235. $\emptyset \in \mathcal{P}(B)$.

236. $B \subseteq A$.

237. $\{c\} \subseteq B$.

238. $\{a, b\} \in A \times A$.

239. $\{b, c\} \in \mathcal{P}(A)$.

240. $\{b, \{c\}\} \in \mathcal{P}(B)$.

241. $\emptyset \subseteq A \times A$.

242. $\{\{\{c\}\}\} \subseteq \mathcal{P}(B)$.

In 243–255 determine whether the set is finite or infinite. If the set is finite, find its size.

243. $\{x \mid x \in \mathbf{Z} \text{ and } x^2 < 10\}$.

244. $\mathcal{P}(\{a, b, c, d\})$, where $\mathcal{P}$ denotes the power set.

245. $\{1, 3, 5, 7, \ldots\}$.

246. $A \times B$, where $A = \{1, 2, 3, 4, 5\}$ and $B = \{1, 2, 3\}$.

247. $\{ x \mid x \in \mathbf{N} \text{ and } 9x^2 - 1 = 0 \}$.

248. $\mathcal{P}(A)$, where A is the power set of $\{a, b, c\}$.

249. $A \times B$, where $A = \{a, b, c\}$ and $B = \emptyset$.

250. $\{ x \mid x \in \mathbf{N} \text{ and } 4x^2 - 8 = 0 \}$.

251. $\{ x \mid x \in \mathbf{Z} \text{ and } x^2 = 2 \}$.

252. $\mathcal{P}(A)$, where $A = \mathcal{P}(\{1, 2\})$.

253. $\{1, 10, \ 100, \ 1000, \dots\}$.

254. $S \times T$, where $S = \{a, b, c\}$ and $T = \{1, 2, 3, 4, 5\}$.

255. $\{ x \mid x \in \mathbf{Z} \text{ and } x^2 < 8 \}$.

256. Prove that between every two rational numbers a/b and c/d
(a) there is a rational number.   (b) there are an infinite number of rational numbers.

257. Prove that there is no smallest positive rational number.

In 258–266 determine whether the rule describes a function with the given domain and codomain.

258. $f \colon \mathbf{N} \to \mathbf{N}$ where $f(n) = \sqrt{n}$.

259. $h \colon \mathbf{R} \to \mathbf{R}$ where $h(x) = \sqrt{x}$.

260. $g \colon \mathbf{N} \to \mathbf{N}$ where $g(n) = $ any integer $> n$.

261. $F \colon \mathbf{R} \to \mathbf{R}$ where $F(x) = \dfrac{1}{x - 5}$.

262. $F \colon \mathbf{Z} \to \mathbf{R}$ where $F(x) = \dfrac{1}{x^2 - 5}$.

263. $F \colon \mathbf{Z} \to \mathbf{Z}$ where $F(x) = \dfrac{1}{x^2 - 5}$.

264. $G \colon \mathbf{R} \to \mathbf{R}$ where $G(x) = \begin{cases} x + 2 & \text{if } x \geq 0 \\ x - 1 & \text{if } x \leq 4. \end{cases}$

265. $f \colon \mathbf{R} \to \mathbf{R}$ where $f(x) = \begin{cases} x^2 & \text{if } x \leq 2 \\ x - 1 & \text{if } x \geq 4. \end{cases}$

266. $G \colon \mathbf{Q} \to \mathbf{Q}$ where $G(p/q) = q$.

267. Give an example of a function $f \colon \mathbf{Z} \to \mathbf{Z}$ that is 1-1 and not onto $\mathbf{Z}$.

268. Give an example of a function $f \colon \mathbf{Z} \to \mathbf{Z}$ that is onto $\mathbf{Z}$ but not 1-1.

269. Give an example of a function $f \colon \mathbf{Z} \to \mathbf{N}$ that is both 1-1 and onto $\mathbf{N}$.

270. Give an example of a function $f \colon \mathbf{N} \to \mathbf{Z}$ that is both 1-1 and onto $\mathbf{Z}$.

271. Give an example of a function $f \colon \mathbf{Z} \to \mathbf{N}$ that is 1-1 and not onto $\mathbf{N}$.

272. Give an example of a function $f \colon \mathbf{N} \to \mathbf{Z}$ that is onto $\mathbf{Z}$ and not 1-1.

273. Suppose $f: \mathbf{N} \to \mathbf{N}$ has the rule $f(n) = 4n + 1$. Determine whether f is 1-1.

274. Suppose $f: \mathbf{N} \to \mathbf{N}$ has the rule $f(n) = 4n + 1$. Determine whether f is onto $\mathbf{N}$.

275. Suppose $f: \mathbf{Z} \to \mathbf{Z}$ has the rule $f(n) = 3n - 1$. Determine whether f is 1-1.

276. Suppose $f: \mathbf{Z} \to \mathbf{Z}$ has the rule $f(n) = 3n - 1$. Determine whether f is onto $\mathbf{Z}$.

277. Suppose $f: \mathbf{Z} \to \mathbf{Z}$ has the rule $f(n) = 3n - 1$. Determine whether f is 1-1.

278. Suppose $f: \mathbf{N} \to \mathbf{N}$ has the rule $f(n) = 4n^2 + 1$. Determine whether f is onto $\mathbf{N}$.

279. Suppose $f: \mathbf{R} \to \mathbf{R}$ where $f(x) = \lfloor x/2 \rfloor$.
(a) Draw the graph of f.   (b) Is f 1-1?   (c) Is f onto $\mathbf{R}$?

280. Suppose $f: \mathbf{R} \to \mathbf{R}$ where $f(x) = \lfloor x/2 \rfloor$.
(a) If $S = \{\, x \mid 1 \le x \le 6 \,\}$, find $f(S)$.   (b) If $T = \{3, 4, 5\}$, find $f^{-1}(T)$.

281. Determine whether f is a function from the set of all bit strings to the set of integers if $f(S)$ is the position of a 1 bit in the bit string S.

282. Determine whether f is a function from the set of all bit strings to the set of integers if $f(S)$ is the number of 0 bits in S.

283. Determine whether f is a function from the set of all bit strings to the set of integers if $f(S)$ is the largest integer i such that the ith bit of S is 0 and $f(S) = 1$ when S is the empty string (the string with no bits).

284. Let $f(x) = \lfloor x^3/3 \rfloor$. Find $f(S)$ if S is:
(a) $\{-2, -1, 0, 1, 2, 3\}$.   (b) $\{0, 1, 2, 3, 4, 5\}$.   (c) $\{1, 5, 7, 11\}$.   (d) $\{2, 6, 10, 14\}$.

285. Suppose $f: \mathbf{R} \to \mathbf{Z}$ where $f(x) = \lceil 2x - 1 \rceil$.
(a) Draw the graph of f.   (b) Is f 1-1? (Explain)   (c) Is f onto $\mathbf{Z}$? (Explain)

286. Suppose $f: \mathbf{R} \to \mathbf{Z}$ where $f(x) = \lceil 2x - 1 \rceil$.
(a) If $A = \{x \mid 1 \le x \le 4\}$, find $f(A)$.
(b) If $B = \{3, 4, 5, 6, 7\}$, find $f(B)$.
(c) If $C = \{-9, -8\}$, find $f^{-1}(C)$.
(d) If $D = \{0.4, 0.5, 0.6\}$, find $f^{-1}(D)$.

287. Suppose $g: \mathbf{R} \to \mathbf{R}$ where $g(x) = \left\lfloor \dfrac{x-1}{2} \right\rfloor$.
(a) Draw the graph of g.   (b) Is g 1-1?   (c) Is g onto $\mathbf{R}$?

288. Suppose $g: \mathbf{R} \to \mathbf{R}$ where $g(x) = \left\lfloor \dfrac{x-1}{2} \right\rfloor$.
(a) If $S = \{x \mid 1 \le x \le 6\}$, find $g(S)$.   (b) If $T = \{2\}$, find $g^{-1}(T)$.

289. Show that $\lceil x \rceil = -\lfloor -x \rfloor$.

290. Prove or disprove: For all positive real numbers x and y, $\lfloor x \cdot y \rfloor \le \lfloor x \rfloor \cdot \lfloor y \rfloor$.

291. Prove or disprove: For all positive real numbers x and y, $\lceil x \cdot y \rceil \le \lceil x \rceil \cdot \lceil y \rceil$.

292. Suppose $g: A \to B$ and $f: B \to C$ where $A = \{1, 2, 3, 4\}$, $B = \{a, b, c\}$, $C = \{2, 7, 10\}$, and f and g are defined by $g = \{(1, b), (2, a), (3, a), (4, b)\}$ and $f = \{(a, 10), (b, 7), (c, 2)\}$. Find $f \circ g$.

293. Suppose $g: A \to B$ and $f: B \to C$ where $A = \{1, 2, 3, 4\}$, $B = \{a, b, c\}$, $C = \{2, 7, 10\}$, and f and g are defined by $g = \{(1, b), (2, a), (3, a), (4, b)\}$ and $f = \{(a, 10), (b, 7), (c, 2)\}$. Find f^{-1}.

In 294–297 suppose $g: A \to B$ and $f: B \to C$ where $A = B = C = \{1, 2, 3, 4\}$, $g = \{(1, 4), (2, 1), (3, 1), (4, 2)\}$ and $f = \{(1, 3), (2, 2), (3, 4), (4, 2)\}$.

294. Find $f \circ g$.

295. Find $g \circ f$.

296. Find $g \circ g$.

297. Find $g \circ (g \circ g)$.

In 298–301 suppose $g: A \to B$ and $f: B \to C$ where $A = \{1, 2, 3, 4\}$, $B = \{a, b, c\}$, $C = \{2, 8, 10\}$, and g and f are defined by $g = \{(1, b), (2, a), (3, b), (4, a)\}$ and $f = \{(a, 8), (b, 10), (c, 2)\}$.

298. Find $f \circ g$.

299. Find f^{-1}.

300. Find $f \circ f^{-1}$.

301. Explain why g^{-1} is not a function.

In 302–303 suppose $g: A \to B$ and $f: B \to C$ where $A = \{a, b, c, d\}$, $B = \{1, 2, 3\}$, $C = \{2, 3, 6, 8\}$, and g and f are defined by $g = \{(a, 2), (b, 1), (c, 3), (d, 2)\}$ and $f = \{(1, 8), (2, 3), (3, 2)\}$.

302. Find $f \circ g$.

303. Find f^{-1}.

304. For any function $f: A \to B$, define a new function $g: \mathcal{P}(A) \to \mathcal{P}(B)$ as follows: for every $S \subseteq A$, $g(S) = \{ f(x) \mid x \in S \}$. Prove that f is onto if and only if g is onto.

In 305–309 find the inverse of the function f or else explain why the function has no inverse.

305. $f: \mathbf{Z} \to \mathbf{Z}$ where $f(x) = x \bmod 10$.

306. $f: A \to B$ where $A = \{a, b, c\}$, $B = \{1, 2, 3\}$ and $f = \{(a, 2), (b, 1), (c, 3)\}$.

307. $f: \mathbf{R} \to \mathbf{R}$ where $f(x) = 3x - 5$.

308. $f: \mathbf{R} \to \mathbf{R}$ where $f(x) = \lfloor 2x \rfloor$.

309. $f: \mathbf{Z} \to \mathbf{Z}$ where $f(x) = \begin{cases} x + 2 & \text{if } x \geq 5 \\ x - 1 & \text{if } x \leq 4. \end{cases}$

310. Suppose $g: A \to B$ and $f: B \to C$, where $f \circ g$ is 1-1 and g is 1-1. Must f be 1-1?

311. Suppose $g: A \to B$ and $f: B \to C$, where $f \circ g$ is 1-1 and f is 1-1. Must g be 1-1?

312. Suppose $f: \mathbf{R} \to \mathbf{R}$ and $g: \mathbf{R} \to \mathbf{R}$ where $g(x) = 2x + 1$ and $g \circ f(x) = 2x + 11$. Find the rule for f.

In 313–317 for each partial function, determine its domain, codomain, domain of definition, set of values for which it is undefined or if it is a total function:

313. $f: \mathbf{Z} \to \mathbf{R}$ where $f(n) = 1/n$.

314. $f: \mathbf{Z} \to \mathbf{Z}$ where $f(n) = \lceil n/2 \rceil$.

315. $f: \mathbf{Z} \times \mathbf{Z} \to \mathbf{Q}$ where $f(m, n) = m/n$.

316. $f: \mathbf{Z} \times \mathbf{Z} \to \mathbf{Z}$ where $f(m, n) = mn$.

317. $f: \mathbf{Z} \times \mathbf{Z} \to \mathbf{Z}$ where $f(m, n) = m - n$ if $m > n$.

318. For the partial function $f: \mathbf{Z} \times \mathbf{Z} \to \mathbf{R}$ defined by $f(m, n) = \dfrac{1}{n^2 - m^2}$, determine its domain, codomain, domain of definition, and set of values for which it is undefined or whether it is a total function.

319. Let $f: \{1, 2, 3, 4, 5\} \to \{1, 2, 3, 4, 5, 6\}$ be a function.

(a) How many total functions are there?

(b) How many of these functions are one-to-one?

Answers for Chapter 1

1. True.

2. True.

3. True.

4. True.

5. False.

6.

p	q	r	$\neg(r \to \neg q) \vee (p \wedge \neg r)$
T	T	T	T
T	T	F	T
T	F	T	F
T	F	F	T
F	T	T	T
F	T	F	F
F	F	T	F
F	F	F	F

7. (a) $\neg p \wedge q$,   (b) $\neg(p \vee \neg q)$.

8. $p \wedge \neg q \wedge r$.

9. $(p \wedge \neg q \wedge \neg r) \vee (\neg p \wedge q \wedge \neg r) \vee (\neg p \wedge \neg q \wedge r)$.

10. $(p \wedge \neg p) \vee (q \wedge \neg q) \vee (r \wedge \neg r)$.

11. $\neg(\neg p \vee q) \vee \neg(p \vee \neg q)$.

12. Not equivalent. Let q be false and p and r be true.

13. Both truth tables are identical:

p	q	$(p \to q) \wedge (\neg p \to q)$	q
T	T	T	T
T	F	F	F
F	T	T	T
F	F	F	F

14. $\neg(\neg p \wedge q)$.

15. $\neg(p \vee q)$.

16. Both propositions are true when "it is hot" is true and both are false when "it is hot" is false.

17. $\neg p \vee q$.

18. $\neg(p \wedge \neg q)$.

19. Truth values differ when p is true and q is false.

20. Truth values differ when p is false and q is true.

21. No.

22. Yes.

23. $(q \land (p \to \neg q)) \to \neg p \iff (q \land (\neg p \lor \neg q)) \to \neg p \iff ((q \land \neg p) \lor (q \land \neg q)) \to \neg p \iff (q \land \neg p) \to \neg p \iff \neg(q \land \neg p) \lor \neg p \iff (\neg q \lor p) \lor \neg p \iff \neg q \lor (p \lor \neg p)$, which is always true.

24. No.

25. Yes.

26. If x is even, then y is odd.

27. If A, then B.

28. If it is sunny, then it is hot.

29. If you don't study, then you don't get a good grade (equivalently, if you get a good grade, then you study).

30. If you study, then you pass.

31. If the quarterback can pass, then the team wins.

32. If you are not registered, then you cannot check out library books (equivalently, if you check out library books, then you are registered).

33. Contrapositive: If you will not win, then you do not try hard. Converse: If you will win, then you try hard. Inverse: If you do not try hard, then you will not win.

34. Contrapositive: If you do not sleep late, then it is not Saturday. Converse: If you sleep late, then it is Saturday. Inverse: If it is not Saturday, then you do not sleep late.

35. It is not Thursday or it is not cold.

36. I will go to the play and read a book, or I will not go to the play and not read a book.

37. It is rainy and we do not go to the movies.

38. Both propositions can be false at the same time. For example, Al could be present and Bill absent.

39. $\neg c \land \neg d$.

40. $\neg c \to r$.

41. $w \to c$.

42. $r \to (w \land c)$.

43. Using m, n, k, and i, there are three rows of the truth table that have all five propositions true: the rows TTTT, FFTT, FFFT for m, n, k, i.

44. False.

45. False.

46. True.

47. True.

48. True.

49. True.

50. False.

51. False.

52. False.

53. False.

54. False.

55. True, since for every real number x we can find a real number y such that $x+2y = 5$, namely $y = (5-x)/2$.

56. False, if it were true then $y = (5 - x)/2$ for every x, which is not possible.

57. True.

58. False.

59. True.

60. T(Fran, MTH 281).

61. $\forall x\, F(x)$.

62. $\forall x\, (F(x) \to B(x))$.

63. $\forall y\, (M(y) \to \neg U(y))$.

64. $\forall x \exists y\, T(x,y)$.

65. $\exists x \forall y\, [A(x) \wedge (M(y) \to \neg T(x,y))]$.

66. $\forall x \exists y\, [(F(x) \wedge A(x)) \to (U(y) \wedge T(x,y))]$.

67. Helen is a freshman.

68. Joe is not taking any course.

69. Some part-time students are not freshmen.

70. Every student is taking a course.

71. Some student is taking every course.

72. Every full-time freshman is taking a math course.

73. $7 < 3$.

74. There is no largest number.

75. No matter what positive number is chosen, there is a larger prime.

76. $\forall x\, (I(x) \to E(x))$.

77. $\forall x \forall y\, (L(x,y) \to \neg Q(x,y))$.

78. $\forall x \exists y\, L(x,y)$.

79. $\exists x\, \neg G(x)$.

80. $\neg \exists x\, (I(x) \wedge E(x) \wedge \neg E(x)])$.

81. $\exists x\, \neg A(x)$.

82. $\forall x\, (T(x) \to F(x))$.

83. $\forall x\, (F(x) \to \neg A(x))$.

84. $\exists x\, (T(x) \wedge A(x) \wedge F(x))$.

85. $\forall x\, (F(x) \to \neg A(x))$.

86. Bill is angry.

87. No one is tall and angry.

88. Some friendly people are not angry.

89. $\exists y \forall x\, (F(x) \to T(x,y))$.

90. $\neg \exists x\, (F(x) \wedge S(x)]$.

91. $\exists x \exists y\, (F(x) \wedge A(y) \wedge T(x,y))$.

92. $\neg \exists x \forall y \ (A(y) \rightarrow T(x, y))$.

93. $\forall x \ (F(x) \rightarrow P(x, calculus))$.

94. Fran did not pass MAT 100.

95. There is a course that all students are taking.

96. Every student is taking at least one course.

97. $\forall y \ (C(y) \rightarrow \neg A(y))$.

98. $S(\text{Lois}, Casablanca) \wedge \neg L(\text{Lois}, Casablanca)$.

99. $\exists x \forall y \ [C(y) \rightarrow S(x, y)]$.

100. $\neg \exists x \forall y \ [S(x, y) \rightarrow L(x, y)]$.

101. $\neg \exists y \ [A(y) \wedge S(\text{Ben}, y)]$.

102. There is a movie that Margaret did not see.

103. There is a movie that everyone liked.

104. Everyone liked at least one movie.

105. 6.

106. 1, 10.

107. 12.

108. 2.

109. 3.

110. 7.

111. 5, 8, 11.

112. 9.

113. 7.

114. 4.

115. 3.

116. 2.

117. 3.

118. 2.

119. 1.

120. 1.

121. 2.

122. 3.

123. 2.

124. 3.

125. 1.

126. $\exists A \ \neg F(A)$.

127. $\forall A \forall B \ [(F(B) \wedge S(A, B)) \rightarrow F(A)]$.

128. $\neg \exists A \exists B \ (\neg F(A) \wedge F(B) \wedge S(A, B))$.

129. $\forall A \ (F(A) \rightarrow S(\varnothing, A))$.

130. No bananas are yellow.

131. Some integers ending in the digit 7 are not odd.

132. Some tests are easy.

133. Roses are not red or violets are not blue.

134. All skiers speak Swedish.

135. (a) Depending on which word is emphasized, the sentence can be interpreted as "all bananas are non-ripe fruit" (i.e., no bananas are ripe) or as "not all bananas are ripe" (i.e., some bananas are not ripe).
(b) Both statements can be false at the same time.
(c) Both statements can be true at the same time.
(d) Some bananas are not ripe.

136. Both statements can be true at the same time.

137. Modus tollens.

138. Hypothetical syllogism.

139. p false and q true yield true hypotheses but a false conclusion.

140. Not valid: p false, q false, r true.

141. Not valid: p true, q true, r true.

142. Use resolution on $l \vee f$ and $\neg l \vee r$ to conclude $f \vee r$.

143. Not valid: fallacy of affirming the conclusion.

144. Not valid: fallacy of denying the hypothesis.

145. Valid.

146. Valid.

147. Not valid.

148. Universal instantiation.

149. Universal instantiation.

150. Existential generalization.

151. (a) Assume p, prove q.
(b) Assume $\neg q$, prove $\neg p$.
(c) Assume $p \wedge \neg q$, show that this leads to a contradiction.

152. Direct proof: Assume p, show q. Indirect proof: Assume $\neg q$, show $\neg p$.

153. Suppose $x = 2k + 1$, $y = 2l$. Therefore $x + y = 2k + 1 + 2l = 2(k + l) + 1$, which is odd.

154. Suppose $n = 2k+1$ but $n^2 = 2l$. Therefore $(2k+1)^2 = 2l$, or $4k^2 + 4k + 1 = 2l$. Hence $2(2k^2 + 2k - l) = -1$ (even = odd), a contradiction. Therefore n^2 is odd.

155. Let $x = 2k + 1$, $y = 2l + 1$. Therefore $x + y = 2k + 1 + 2l + 1 = 2(k + l + 1)$, which is even.

156. Suppose $x = 2k + 1$ and $y = 2l + 1$, but $x + y = 2m + 1$. Therefore $(2k + 1) + (2l + 1) = 2m + 1$. Hence $2(k + l - m + 1) = 1$ (even = odd), which is a contradiction. Therefore $x + y$ is even.

157. Suppose $x = 2k$ and $y = 2l$, but $xy = 2m + 1$. Therefore $2k \cdot 2l = 2m + 1$. Hence $2(2kl - m) = 1$ (even = odd), which is a contradiction. Therefore xy is even.

158. Let $x = 2k + 1$. Therefore $x + 2 = 2k + 1 + 2 = 2(k + 1) + 1$, which is odd.

159. Suppose $x + 2 = 2k$. Therefore $x = 2k - 2 = 2(k - 1)$, which is even.

160. Suppose x is odd but $x + 2$ is even. Therefore $x = 2k + 1$ and $x + 2 = 2l$. Hence $(2k + 1) + 2 = 2l$. Therefore $2(k + 1 - l) = -1$ (even = odd), a contradiction.

161. Let $n = 2k$. Therefore $n + 1 = 2k + 1$, which is odd.

162. Suppose $n + 1$ is even. Therefore $n + 1 = 2k$. Therefore $n = 2k - 1 = 2(k - 1) + 1$, which is odd.

163. Suppose $n = 2k$ but $n + 1 = 2l$. Therefore $2k + 1 = 2l$ (even = odd), which is a contradiction.

164. If n is even, then $n = 2k$. Therefore $3n^2 + 8 = 3(2k)^2 + 8 = 12k^2 + 8 = 2(6k^2 + 4)$, which is even. If n is odd, then $n = 2k + 1$. Therefore $3n^2 + 8 = 3(2k + 1)^2 + 8 = 12k^2 + 12k + 11 = 2(6k^2 + 6k + 5) + 1$, which is odd.

165. If n is even, then $n^2 = (2k)^2 = 2(2k^2)$, which is even. If n is odd, then $n^2 = (2k+1)^2 = 2(2k^2 + 2k) + 1$, which is odd.

166. If $m = 2k$ and $n = 2l$, then $mn = 4kl$. Hence $4 \mid mn$.

167. False: $p = 11$ is a counterexample because $11^2 + 4 = 125$, which is not prime.

168. The statement is true: $7! + 2$, $7! + 3$, $\ldots$, $7! + 7$ are composite.

169. There is no such prime p since one of the three integers must be divisible by 3.

170. Let $R(x)$ be the predicate "x has read the textbook" and $P(x)$ be the predicate "x passed the exam". The following is the proof:

    1. $\forall x \, (R(x) \rightarrow P(x))$ hypothesis
    2. $R(\text{Ed}) \rightarrow P(\text{Ed})$ universal instantiation on 1
    3. $R(\text{Ed})$ hypothesis
    4. $P(\text{Ed})$ modus ponens on 2 and 3

171. False: $x = 2$ $y = 1/2$.

172. False: $x = 1/2$.

173. False: $x = 3/2$, $y = 3/2$.

174. True, since $A - (B \cap C) = A \cap \overline{B \cap C} = A \cap (\overline{B} \cup \overline{C}) = (A \cap \overline{B}) \cup (A \cap \overline{C}) = (A - B) \cup (A - C)$.

175. $\overline{A \cap B} \subseteq \overline{A} \cup \overline{B}$: Let $x \in \overline{A \cap B}$. $\therefore x \notin A \cap B$, $\therefore x \notin A$ or $x \notin B$, $\therefore x \in \overline{A}$ or $x \in \overline{B}$, $\therefore x \in \overline{A} \cup \overline{B}$. Reversing the steps shows that $\overline{A} \cup \overline{B} \subseteq \overline{A \cap B}$.

176. The columns for $\overline{A \cap B}$ and $\overline{A} \cup \overline{B}$ match: each entry is 0 if and only if A and B have the value 1.

177. $\overline{A \cap B} = \{x \mid x \in \overline{A \cap B}\} = \{x \mid x \notin A \cap B\} = \{x \mid \neg(x \in A \cap B)\} = \{x \mid \neg(x \in A \wedge x \in B)\} = \{x \mid \neg(x \in A) \vee \neg(x \in B)\} = \{x \mid x \notin A \vee x \notin B\} = \{x \mid x \in \overline{A} \vee x \in \overline{B}\} = \{x \mid x \in \overline{A} \cup \overline{B}\} = \overline{A} \cup \overline{B}$.

178.

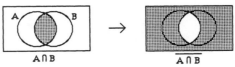

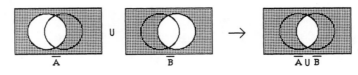

179. $A \cap (B \cup C) \subseteq (A \cap B) \cup (A \cap C)$: Let $x \in A \cap (B \cup C)$. $\therefore x \in A$ and $x \in B \cup C$, $\therefore x \in A$ and $x \in B$, or $x \in A$ and $x \in C$, $\therefore x \in (A \cap B) \cup (A \cap C)$. Reversing the steps gives the opposite containment.

180. Each set has the same values in the element table: the value is 1 if and only if A has the value 1 and either B or C has the value 1.

181. $A \cap (B \cup C) = \{x \mid x \in A \cap (B \cup C)\} = \{x \mid x \in A \wedge x \in (B \cup C)\} = \{x \mid x \in A \wedge (x \in B \vee x \in C)\} = \{x \mid (x \in A \wedge x \in B) \vee (x \in A \wedge x \in C)\} = \{x \mid x \in A \cap B \vee x \in A \cap C\} = \{x \mid x \in (A \cap B) \cup (A \cap C)\} = (A \cap B) \cup (A \cap C)$.

182.

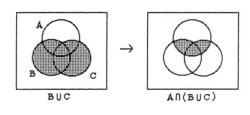

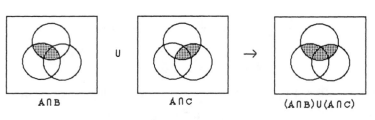

183. False. For example, let $A = \{1, 2\}$, $B = \{1\}$, $C = \{2\}$.

184. True, using either a membership table or a containment proof, for example.

185. $=$.

186. $\supseteq$.

187. $=$.

188. $\subseteq$.

189. Yes $\{\varnothing, a, \{a\}, \{\{a\}\}\}$.

190. Yes, $\{a\}$.

191. No, it lacks $\{\varnothing\}$.

192. Yes, $\{\{a, \varnothing\}\}$.

193. No, it lacks $\{a\}$ and $\{\varnothing\}$.

194. Since $\overline{S} \cup \overline{T} = \overline{S \cap T}$ (De Morgan's law), the complements are equal.

195. False.

196. False.

197. True.

198. False.

199. True.

200. False.

201. False.

202. True.

203. False.

204. False.

205. False.

206. For example, $\{1, 2, 3\}$, $\{2, 3, 4\}$, $\{1, 3, 4\}$.

207. $[-1, 1]$.

208. $\{4, 5, 6, 7\}$.

209. 32.

210. False.

211. True.

212. False.

213. True.

214. True.

215. True.

216. True.

217. True.

218. True.

219. True.

220. False.

221. True.

222. True.

223. True.

224. True.

225. True.

226. True.

227. False.

228. False.

229. True.

230. $\overline{F} = \{0.3\ Ann, 0.9\ Bill, 0.2\ Fran, 0.7\ Olive, 0.5\ Tom\}$,
$\overline{R} = \{0.6\ Ann, 0.1\ Bill, 0.1\ Fran, 0.4\ Olive, 0.3\ Tom\}$

231. $\{0.7\ Ann, 0.9\ Bill, 0.9\ Fran, 0.6\ Olive, 0.7\ Tom\}$.

232. $\{0.4\ Ann, 0.1\ Bill, 0.8\ Fran, 0.3\ Olive, 0.5\ Tom\}$.

233. True.

234. True.

235. True.

236. False.

237. False.

238. False.

239. True.

240. True.

241. True.

242. True.

243. 7.

244. 16.

245. Infinite.

246. 15.

247. 0.

248. 256.

249. 0.

250. 0.

251. 0.

252. 16.

253. Infinite.

254. 15.

255. 5.

256. (a) If $\dfrac{a}{b} \leq \dfrac{c}{d}$, then $\dfrac{a}{b} \leq \dfrac{\frac{a}{b} + \frac{c}{d}}{2} = \dfrac{ad + bc}{2bd} \leq \dfrac{c}{d}$.

(b) Assume $\dfrac{a}{b} < \dfrac{c}{d}$. Let m_1 be the midpoint of $\left[\dfrac{a}{b}, \dfrac{c}{d}\right]$. For $i > 1$ let m_i be the midpoint of $\left[\dfrac{a}{b}, m_{i-1}\right]$.

257. If $0 < \dfrac{a}{b}$, then $0 < \ldots < \dfrac{a}{4b} < \dfrac{a}{3b} < \dfrac{a}{2b} < \dfrac{a}{b}$.

258. Not a function; $f(2)$ is not an integer.

259. Function.

260. Not a function; $g(1)$ has more than one value.

261. Not a function; $F(5)$ not defined.

262. Function.

263. Not a function; $F(1)$ not an integer.

264. Not a function; the cases overlap.

265. Not a function; $f(3)$ not defined.

266. Not a function; $f(1/2) = 2$ and $f(2/4) = 4$.

267. $f(n) = 2n$.

268. $f(n) = \left\lfloor \dfrac{n}{2} \right\rfloor$.

269. $f(n) = \begin{cases} -2n, & n \leq 0 \\ 2n - 1, & n > 0. \end{cases}$

270. $f(n) = \begin{cases} \dfrac{-n}{2}, & n \text{ even} \\ \dfrac{n+1}{2}, & n \text{ odd.} \end{cases}$

271. $f(n) = \begin{cases} -2n, & n \leq 0 \\ 2n + 1, & n > 0. \end{cases}$

272. $f(n) = \begin{cases} \dfrac{-n}{2}, & n \text{ even} \\ \dfrac{n-1}{2}, & n \text{ odd.} \end{cases}$

273. Yes.

274. No.

275. Yes.

276. No.

277. Yes.

278. No.

279. (a)

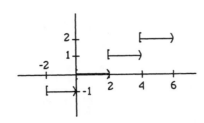

(b) No.

(c) No.

280. (a) $\{0, 1, 2, 3\}$

(b) $[6, 12)$.

281. No; there may be no 1 bits or more than one 1 bit.

282. Yes.

283. No; f not defined for the string of all 1s, for example $S = 11111$.

284. (a) $\{-3, -1, 0, 2, 9\}$.

(b) $\{0, 2, 9, 21, 41\}$.

(c) $\{0, 41, 114, 443\}$.

(d) $\{2, 72, 333, 914\}$.

285. (a)

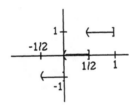

(b) No.

(c) Yes.

286. (a) $\{1, 2, 3, 4, 5, 6, 7\}$.

(b) $\{5, 7, 9, 11, 13\}$.

(c) $(-9/2, -7/2]$.

(d) $\emptyset$.

287. (a)

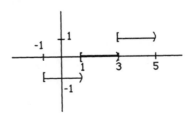

(b) No.

(c) No.

288. (a) $\{0, 1, 2\}$.

(b) $[5, 7)$.

289. Let $n = \lceil x \rceil$, so that $n - 1 < x \le n$. Multiplying by -1 yields $-n + 1 > -x \ge -n$, which means that $-n = \lfloor -x \rfloor$.

290. False: $x = y = 1.5$.

291. True: $x \le \lceil x \rceil$, $y \le \lceil y \rceil$; therefore $xy \le \lceil x \rceil \lceil y \rceil$; since $\lceil x \rceil \lceil y \rceil$ is an integer at least as great as xy, then $\lceil xy \rceil \le \lceil x \rceil \lceil y \rceil$.

292. $\{(1,7),(2,10),(3,10),(4,7)\}$.

293. $\{(2,c),(7,b),(10,a)\}$.

294. $\{(1,2),(2,3),(3,3),(4,2)\}$.

295. $\{(1,1),(2,1),(3,2),(4,1)\}$.

296. $\{(1,2),(2,4),(3,4),(4,1)\}$.

297. $\{(1,1),(2,2),(3,2),(4,4)\}$.

298. $\{(1,10),(2,8),(3,10),(4,8)\}$.

299. $\{(2,c),(8,a),(10,b)\}$.

300. $\{(2,2),(8,8),(10,10)\}$.

301. $g^{-1}(a)$ is equal to both 2 and 4.

302. $\{(a,3),(b,8),(c,2),(d,3)\}$.

303. $\{(2,3),(3,2),(8,1)\}$.

304. Suppose f is onto. Let $T \in \mathcal{P}(B)$ and let $S = \{\, x \in A \mid f(x) \in T \,\}$. Then $g(S) = T$, and g is onto. If f is not onto B, let $y \in B - f(A)$. Then there is no subset S of A such that $g(S) = \{y\}$.

305. $f^{-1}(10)$ does not exist.

306. $\{(1,b),(2,a),(3,c)\}$.

307. $f^{-1}(x) = \dfrac{5+x}{3}$.

308. $f^{-1}(\frac{1}{2})$ does not exist.

309. $f^{-1}(6)$ is not a single value.

310. No.

311. Yes.

312. $f(x) = x + 5$.

313. **Z**, **R**, **Z** $-$ $\{0\}$, $\{0\}$.

314. **Z**, **Z**, **Z**, total function.

315. **Z** $\times$ **Z**, **Q**, **Z** $\times$ (**Z** $-$ $\{0\}$), **Z** $\times$ $\{0\}$.

316. **Z** $\times$ **Z**, **Z**, **Z** $\times$ **Z**, total function.

317. **Z** $\times$ **Z**, **Z**, $\{\, (m,n) \mid m > n \,\}$, $\{\, (m,n) \mid m \le n \,\}$.

318. **Z** $\times$ **Z**, **R**, $\{\, (m,n) \mid m \ne n \text{ or } m \ne -n \,\}$, $\{\, (m,n) \mid m = n \text{ or } m = -n \,\}$.

319. (a) $6^5 = 7{,}776$.

(b) $6 \cdot 5 \cdot 4 \cdot 3 \cdot 2 \cdot 1 = 720$.

Questions for Chapter 2

1. Describe an algorithm that takes a list of n integers $a_1, a_2, \ldots, a_n$ and finds the number of integers each greater than five in the list.

2. Describe an algorithm that takes a list of integers $a_1, a_2, \ldots, a_n$ $(n \geq 2)$ and finds the second-largest integer in the sequence.

3. Describe an algorithm that takes a list of n integers $(n \geq 1)$ and finds the location of the last even integer in the list, or returns 0 if there are no even integers in the list.

4. Describe an algorithm that takes a list of n integers $(n \geq 1)$ and finds the average of the largest and smallest integers in the list.

5. Describe in words how the binary search works.

6. Show how the binary search algorithm searches for 27 in the following list: 5 6 8 12 15 21 25 31.

7. You have supplies of boards that are one foot, five feet, seven feet, and twelve feet long. You need to lay pieces end-to-end to make a molding 15 feet long and wish to do this using the fewest number of pieces possible. Explain why the greedy algorithm of taking boards of the longest length at each stage (so long as the total length of the boards selected does not exceed 15 feet) does not give the fewest number of boards possible.

8. Use the definition of big-oh to prove that $1^2 + 2^2 + \cdots + n^2$ is $O(n^3)$.

9. Use the definition of big-oh to prove that $\dfrac{3n - 8 - 4n^3}{2n - 1}$ is $O(n^2)$.

10. Use the definition of big-oh to prove that $1^3 + 2^3 + \cdots + n^3$ is $O(n^4)$.

11. Use the definition of big-oh to prove that $\dfrac{6n + 4n^5 - 4}{7n^2 - 3}$ is $O(n^3)$.

12. Use the definition of big-oh to prove that $1 \cdot 2 + 2 \cdot 3 + 3 \cdot 4 + \cdots + (n-1) \cdot n$ is $O(n^3)$.

13. Let $f(n) = 3n^2 + 8n + 7$. Show that $f(n)$ is $O(n^2)$. Find C and k from the definition.

In 14–19 find the best big-oh function for the function. Choose your answer from among the following:
$$1, \ \log_2 n, \ n, \ n \log_2 n, \ n^2, \ n^3, \ldots, 2^n, \ n!.$$

14. $f(n) = 1 + 4 + 7 + \cdots + (3n + 1)$.

15. $g(n) = 1 + 3 + 5 + 7 + \cdots + (2n - 1)$.

16. $\dfrac{3 - 2n^4 - 4n}{2n^3 - 3}$.

17. $f(n) = 1 + 2 + 3 + \cdots + (n^2 - 1) + n^2$.

18. $\lceil n + 2 \rceil \cdot \lceil n/3 \rceil$.

19. $3n^4 + \log_2 n^{8}$.

20. Show that $\displaystyle\sum_{j=1}^{n} (j^3 + j)$ is $O(n^4)$.

21. Show that $f(x) = (x + 2) \log_2(x^2 + 1) + \log_2(x^3 + 1)$ is $O(x \log_2 x)$.

22. Find the best big-O function for $n^3 + \sin n^7$.

23. Find the best big-O function for $\dfrac{x^3 + 7x}{3x + 1}$.

24. Prove that $5x^4 + 2x^3 - 1$ is $\Theta(x^4)$.

25. Prove that $\dfrac{x^3 + 7x^2 + 3}{2x + 1}$ is $\Theta(x^2)$.

26. Prove that $x^3 + 7x + 2$ is $\Omega(x^3)$.

In 27–38 find the "best" big-oh notation to describe the complexity of the algorithm. Choose your answers from the following:

$$1,\ \log_2 n,\ n,\ n\log_2 n,\ n^2,\ n^3,\ldots,\ 2^n,\ n!\,.$$

27. A binary search of n elements.

28. A linear search to find the smallest number in a list of n numbers.

29. An algorithm that lists all ways to put the numbers $1, 2, 3, \ldots, n$ in a row.

30. An algorithm that prints all bit strings of length n.

31. The number of print statements in the following:

$$
\begin{aligned}
&i := 1,\ j := 1\\
&\textbf{while } i \le n\\
&\quad \textbf{begin}\\
&\qquad \textbf{while } j \le i\\
&\qquad \quad \textbf{begin}\\
&\qquad \qquad \textbf{print "hello";}\\
&\qquad \qquad j := j + 1\\
&\qquad \quad \textbf{end}\\
&\qquad i := i + 1\\
&\quad \textbf{end}.
\end{aligned}
$$

32. The number of print statements in the following:

$$
\begin{aligned}
&\textbf{while } n > 1\\
&\quad \textbf{begin}\\
&\qquad \textbf{print "hello";}\\
&\qquad n := \lfloor n/2 \rfloor\\
&\quad \textbf{end}.
\end{aligned}
$$

33. An iterative algorithm to compute $n!$, (counting the number of multiplications).

34. An algorithm that finds the average of n numbers by adding them and dividing by n.

35. An algorithm that prints all subsets of size three of the set $\{1, 2, 3, \ldots, n\}$.

36. The best-case analysis of a linear search of a list of size n (counting the number of comparisons).

37. The worst-case analysis of a linear search of a list of size n (counting the number of comparisons).

38. Prove or disprove: For all integers a, b, c, d, if $a|b$ and $c|d$, then $(a + c)|(b + d)$.

39. Prove or disprove: For all integers a, b, c, if $a|b$ and $b|c$ then $a|c$.

40. Prove or disprove: For all integers a, b, c, if $a|c$ and $b|c$, then $(a + b)|c$.

41. Prove or disprove: For all integers a, b, c, d, if $a|b$ and $c|d$, then $(ac)|(b + d)$.

42. Prove or disprove: For all integers a, b, if $a|b$ and $b|a$, then $a = b$.

43. Prove or disprove: For all integers a, b, c, if $a|(b+c)$, then $a|b$ and $a|c$.

44. Prove or disprove: For all integers a, b, c, if $a|bc$, then $a|b$ or $a|c$.

45. Prove or disprove: For all integers a, b, c, if $a|c$ and $b|c$, then $ab|c^2$.

46. Find the prime factorization of 1,024.

47. Find the prime factorization of 1,025.

48. Find the prime factorization of 510,510.

49. Find the prime factorization of 8,827.

50. Find the prime factorization of 45,617.

51. Find the prime factorization of 111,111.

52. List all positive integers less than 30 that are relatively prime to 20.

53. Find gcd(20!, 12!) by directly finding the largest divisor of both numbers.

54. Find gcd($2^{89}, 2^{346}$) by directly finding the largest divisor of both numbers.

55. Find lcm(20!, 12!) by directly finding the smallest positive multiple of both numbers.

56. Find lcm($2^{89}, 2^{346}$) by directly finding the smallest positive multiple of both numbers.

57. Suppose that the lcm of two numbers is 400 and their gcd is 10. If one of the numbers is 50, find the other number.

58. Applying the division algorithm with $a = -41$ and $d = 6$ yields what value of r?

59. Find 18 **mod** 7.

60. Find -88 **mod** 13.

61. Find 289 **mod** 17.

62. Find the hexadecimal expansion of $(ABC)_{16}+(2F5)_{16}$.

63. Prove or disprove: A positive integer congruent to 1 modulo 4 cannot have a prime factor congruent to 3 modulo 4.

64. Find 50! **mod** 50.

65. Find 50! **mod** 49!.

66. Prove or disprove: The sum of two primes is a prime.

67. Prove or disprove: If p and q are primes (> 2), then $p + q$ is composite.

68. Prove or disprove: There exist two consecutive primes, each greater than 2.

69. Prove or disprove: The sum of two irrational numbers is irrational.

70. Prove or disprove: If a and b are rational numbers (not equal to zero), then a^b is rational.

71. Prove or disprove: If $f(n) = n^2 - n + 17$, then $f(n)$ is prime for all positive integers n.

72. Prove or disprove: If p and q are primes (> 2), then $pq + 1$ is never prime.

73. Find three integers m such that $13 \equiv 7 \pmod{m}$.

74. Find the smallest positive integer a such that $a + 1 \equiv 2a \pmod{11}$.

75. Find four integers b (two negative and two positive) such that $7 \equiv b \pmod{4}$.

76. Find an integer a such that $a \equiv 3a \pmod{7}$.

77. Find integers a and b such that $a + b \equiv a - b \pmod{5}$.

In 78–84 determine whether each of the following "theorems" is true or false. Assume that a, b, c, d, and m are integers with $m > 1$.

78. If $a \equiv b \pmod{m}$, and $a \equiv c \pmod{m}$, then $a \equiv b + c \pmod{m}$.

79. If $a \equiv b \pmod{m}$ and $c \equiv d \pmod{m}$, then $ac \equiv b + d \pmod{m}$.

80. If $a \equiv b \pmod{m}$, then $2a \equiv 2b \pmod{m}$.

81. If $a \equiv b \pmod{m}$, then $2a \equiv 2b \pmod{2m}$.

82. If $a \equiv b \pmod{m}$, then $a \equiv b \pmod{2m}$.

83. If $a \equiv b \pmod{2m}$, then $a \equiv b \pmod{m}$.

84. If $a \equiv b \pmod{m^2}$, then $a \equiv b \pmod{m}$.

85. Either find an integer x such that $x \equiv 2 \pmod{6}$ and $x \equiv 3 \pmod{9}$ are both true, or else prove that there is no such integer.

86. What sequence of pseudorandom numbers is generated using the pure multiplicative generator $x_{n+1} = 3x_n \bmod 11$ with seed $x_0 = 2$?

87. Encrypt the message NEED HELP by translating the letters into numbers, applying the encryption function $f(p) = (p + 3) \bmod 26$, and then translating the numbers back into letters.

88. Encrypt the message NEED HELP by translating the letters into numbers, applying the encryption function $f(p) = (3p + 7) \bmod 26$, and then translating the numbers back into letters.

89. Suppose that a computer has only the memory locations $0, 1, 2, \ldots, 19$. Use the hashing function h where $h(x) = (x + 5) \bmod 20$ to determine the memory locations in which 57, 32, and 97 are stored.

90. A message has been encrypted using the function $f(x) = (x + 5) \bmod 26$. If the message in coded form is JCFHY, decode the message.

91. Explain why $f(x) = (2x + 3) \bmod 26$ would not be a good coding function.

92. Encode the message "stop at noon" using the function $f(x) = (x + 6) \bmod 26$.

93. Explain in words the difference between $a|b$ and $\dfrac{b}{a}$.

94. Prove or disprove: if p and q are prime numbers, then $pq + 1$ is prime.

95. (a) Find two positive integers, each with exactly three positive integer factors greater than 1.
(b) Prove that there are an infinite number of positive integers, each with exactly three positive integer factors greater than 1.

96. Convert $(204)_{10}$ to base 2.

97. Convert $(11101)_2$ to base 16.

98. Convert $(11101)_2$ to base 10.

99. Convert $(2AC)_{16}$ to base 10.

100. Convert $(10000)_{10}$ to base 2.

101. Convert $(8091)_{10}$ to base 2.

102. Convert $(BC1)_{16}$ to base 2.

103. Convert $(10011010011)_2$ to base 16.

104. Take any three-digit integer, reverse its digits, and subtract. For example, $742 - 247 = 495$. The difference is divisible by 9. Prove that this must happen for all three-digit numbers abc.

105. Prove or disprove that 30! ends in exactly seven 0s.

106. Here is a sample proof that contains an error. Explain why the proof is not correct.

Theorem: If $a|b$ and $b|c$, then $a|c$.
Proof: Since $a|b$, $b = ak$.
Since $b|c$, $c = bk$.
Therefore $c = bk = (ak)k = ak^2$.
Therefore $a|c$.

107. Use the Euclidean algorithm to find $\gcd(44, 52)$.

108. Use the Euclidean algorithm to find $\gcd(144, 233)$.

109. Use the Euclidean algorithm to find $\gcd(203, 101)$.

110. Use the Euclidean algorithm to find $\gcd(300, 700)$.

111. Use the Euclidean algorithm to find $\gcd(34, 21)$.

112. Use the Euclidean Algorithm to find $\gcd(900, 140)$.

113. Use the Euclidean Algorithm to find $\gcd(580, 50)$.

114. Use the Euclidean Algorithm to find $\gcd(390, 72)$.

115. Use the Euclidean Algorithm to find $\gcd(400, 0)$.

116. Use the Euclidean Algorithm to find $\gcd(128, 729)$.

117. Find the two's complement of 12.

118. Find the two's complement of -13.

119. Find the two's complement of 9.

120. Find a 2×2 matrix $\mathbf{A} \neq \begin{pmatrix} 0 & 0 \\ 0 & 0 \end{pmatrix}$ such that $\mathbf{A}^2 = \begin{pmatrix} 0 & 0 \\ 0 & 0 \end{pmatrix}$.

121. Suppose $\mathbf{A}$ is a 6×8 matrix, $\mathbf{B}$ is an 8×5 matrix, and $\mathbf{C}$ is a 5×9 matrix. Find the number of rows, the number of columns, and the number of entries in $\mathbf{A}(\mathbf{BC})$.

122. Let $\mathbf{A} = \begin{pmatrix} 1 & m \\ 0 & 1 \end{pmatrix}$. Find $\mathbf{A}^n$ where n is a positive integer.

123. Suppose $\mathbf{A} = \begin{pmatrix} 3 & 5 \\ 2 & 4 \end{pmatrix}$ and $\mathbf{C} = \begin{pmatrix} 2 & 1 \\ 0 & 6 \end{pmatrix}$. Find a matrix $\mathbf{B}$ such that $\mathbf{AB} = \mathbf{C}$ or prove that no such matrix exists.

124. Suppose $\mathbf{B} = \begin{pmatrix} 3 & 5 \\ 2 & 4 \end{pmatrix}$ and $\mathbf{C} = \begin{pmatrix} 2 & 1 \\ 0 & 6 \end{pmatrix}$. Find a matrix $\mathbf{A}$ such that $\mathbf{AB} = \mathbf{C}$ or prove that no such matrix exists.

125. Suppose $\mathbf{B} = \begin{pmatrix} 6 & 2 \\ 3 & 1 \end{pmatrix}$ and $\mathbf{C} = \begin{pmatrix} 2 & 1 \\ 0 & 6 \end{pmatrix}$. Find a matrix $\mathbf{A}$ such that $\mathbf{AB} = \mathbf{C}$ or prove that no such matrix exists.

In 126–132 determine whether the statement is true or false.

126. If $\mathbf{AB} = \mathbf{AC}$, then $\mathbf{B} = \mathbf{C}$.

127. If $\mathbf{A} = \begin{pmatrix} 3 & 5 \\ 1 & 2 \end{pmatrix}$, then $\mathbf{A}^{-1} = \begin{pmatrix} 2 & 5 \\ 1 & -3 \end{pmatrix}$.

128. If $\mathbf{A} = \begin{pmatrix} 1 & 3 \\ -5 & 2 \end{pmatrix}$, then $\mathbf{A}^2 = \begin{pmatrix} 1 & 9 \\ 25 & 4 \end{pmatrix}$.

129. If $\mathbf{A}$ is a 6×4 matrix and $\mathbf{B}$ is a 4×5 matrix, then $\mathbf{AB}$ has 16 entries.

130. If $\mathbf{A}$ and $\mathbf{B}$ are 2×2 matrices such that $\mathbf{AB} = \begin{pmatrix} 0 & 0 \\ 0 & 0 \end{pmatrix}$, then $\mathbf{A} = \begin{pmatrix} 0 & 0 \\ 0 & 0 \end{pmatrix}$ or $\mathbf{B} = \begin{pmatrix} 0 & 0 \\ 0 & 0 \end{pmatrix}$.

131. If $\mathbf{A}$ and $\mathbf{B}$ are 2×2 matrices, then $\mathbf{A} + \mathbf{B} = \mathbf{B} + \mathbf{A}$.

132. $\mathbf{AB} = \mathbf{BA}$ for all 2×2 matrices $\mathbf{A}$ and $\mathbf{B}$.

133. What is the most efficient way to multiply the matrices $\mathbf{A}_1$, $\mathbf{A}_2$, $\mathbf{A}_3$ of sizes 20×5, 5×50, 50×5?

134. What is the most efficient way to multiply the matrices $\mathbf{A}_1$, $\mathbf{A}_2$, $\mathbf{A}_3$ of sizes 10×50, 50×10, 10×40?

135. Suppose $\mathbf{A} = \begin{pmatrix} 1 & 0 & 1 \\ 0 & 1 & 1 \\ 1 & 1 & 0 \end{pmatrix}$ and $\mathbf{B} = \begin{pmatrix} 0 & 1 & 0 \\ 0 & 1 & 1 \\ 1 & 0 & 0 \end{pmatrix}$. Find

(a) the join of $\mathbf{A}$ and $\mathbf{B}$.

(b) the meet of $\mathbf{A}$ and $\mathbf{B}$.

(c) the Boolean product of $\mathbf{A}$ and $\mathbf{B}$.

136. Suppose $\mathbf{A}$ is a 2×2 matrix with real number entries such that $\mathbf{AB} = \mathbf{BA}$ for all 2×2 matrices. What relationships must exist among the entries of $\mathbf{A}$?

137. Given that $\gcd(620, 140) = 20$, write 20 as a linear combination of 620 and 140.

138. Given that $\gcd(662, 414) = 2$, write 2 as a linear combination of 662 and 414.

139. Express $\gcd(84, 18)$ as a linear combination of 18 and 84.

140. Express $\gcd(450, 120)$ as a linear combination of 120 and 450.

141. Find an inverse of 5 modulo 12.

142. Find an inverse of 17 modulo 19.

143. Solve the linear congruence $2x \equiv 5 \pmod 9$.

144. Solve the linear congruence $5x \equiv 3 \pmod{11}$.

Answers for Chapter 2

1. **procedure** *greaterthanfive*($a_1, \ldots, a_n$: integers)
answer := 0
for $i := 1$ **to** n
  if $a_i > 5$ **then** *answer* := *answer* $+1$.

2. **procedure** *secondlargest*($a_1, \ldots, a_n$: integers)
largest := a_1
secondlargest := a_2
if $a_2 > a_1$ **then**
  begin
    secondlargest := a_1
    largest := a_2
  end
if $n = 2$ **then**
  stop
for $i := 3$ **to** n
if $a_i > $ *largest* **then**
  begin
    secondlargest := *largest*
    largest := a_i
  end
if ($a_i > $ *secondlargest* **and** $a_i \leq$ *largest*) **then**
  secondlargest := a_i.

3. **procedure** *lasteven*($a_1, \ldots, a_n$: integers)
location := 0
for $i := 1$ **to** n
if $2 \mid a_i$ **then** *location* := i.

4. **procedure** *avgmaxmin*($a_1, \ldots, a_n$: integers)
max := a_1
min := a_1
for $i := 2$ **to** n
begin
  if $a_i > $ *max* **then** *max* := a_i
  if $a_i < $ *min* **then** *min* := a_i
end
avg := (*max* + *min*)/2.

5. To search for x in an ordered list $a_1, \ldots, a_n$, find the "midpoint" of the list and choose the appropriate half of the list. Continue until the list consists of one element. Either this element is x, or else x is not in the list.

6. The consecutive choices of sublists of the original list are: 15 21 25 31, 25 31, and 25. Since $27 \neq 25$, the integer 25 is not in the list.

7. The greedy algorithm first chooses a 12-foot-long board, and then three one-foot-long boards. This requires four boards. But only three boards are needed: each five feet long.

8. $1^2 + 2^2 + \cdots + n^2 \leq n^2 + n^2 + \cdots + n^2 = n \cdot n^2 = n^3$.

9. $\dfrac{3n - 8 - 4n^3}{2n - 1} \leq \dfrac{3n^3 + 8n^3 + 4n^3}{2n - n} = \dfrac{15n^3}{n} = 15n^2$ if $n \geq 1$.

10. $1^3 + 2^3 + \cdots + n^3 \leq n^3 + n^3 + \cdots + n^3 = n \cdot n^3 = n^4$.

11. $\dfrac{6n + 4n^5 - 4}{7n^2 - 3} \leq \dfrac{6n^5 + 4n^5}{7n^2 - n^2} = \dfrac{10n^5}{6n^2} = \dfrac{5}{3}n^3$, if $n \geq 2$.

12. $1 \cdot 2 + 2 \cdot 3 + \cdots + (n-1) \cdot n \leq (n-1) \cdot n + (n-1) \cdot n + \cdots + (n-1) \cdot n = (n-1)^2 \cdot n \leq n^3$.

13. $f(n) \leq 3n^2 + 8n^2 + 7n^2 = 18n^2$ if $n \geq 1$; therefore $C = 18$ and $k = 1$ can be used.

14. n^2.

15. n^2.

16. n.

17. n^4.

18. n^2.

19. n^4.

20. $\displaystyle\sum_{j=1}^{n}(j^3 + j) \leq \sum_{j=1}^{n}(n^3 + n^3) = n \cdot 2n^3 = 2n^4$.

21. $\log_2(x^2 + 1)$ and $\log_2(x^3 + 1)$ are each $O(\log_2 x)$. Thus each term is $O(x \log_2 x)$, and hence so is the sum.

22. n^3.

23. x^2.

24. $5x^4 + 2x^3 - 1$ is $O(x^4)$ since $|5x^4 + 2x^3 - 1| \leq |5x^4 + 2x^4| \leq 7|x^4|$ (if $x \geq 1$). Also, x^4 is $O(5x^4 + 2x^3 - 1)$ since $|x^4| \leq |5x^4 + x^3| \leq |5x^4 + 2x^3 - 1|$ (if $x \geq 1$).

25. $\dfrac{x^3 + 7x^2 + 3}{2x + 1}$ is $O(x^2)$ since $\dfrac{x^3 + 7x^2 + 3}{2x + 1} \leq \dfrac{x^3 + 7x^3 + 3x^3}{2x} = \dfrac{11x^3}{2x} = \dfrac{11}{2}x^2$ (if $x \geq 1$). Also, x^2 is $O\left(\dfrac{x^3 + 7x^2 + 3}{2x + 1}\right)$ since $x^2 = \dfrac{x^3}{x} \leq \dfrac{x^3 + 7x}{2x} \leq \dfrac{x^3 + 7x + 3}{2x + 1} \leq \dfrac{x^3 + 7x^2 + 3}{2x + 1}$ (if $x \geq 1$).

26. $x^3 + 7x + 2 \geq 1 \cdot x^3$ (if $x \geq 1$).

27. $\log_2 n$.

28. n.

29. $n!$.

30. 2^n.

31. n^2.

32. $\log_2 n$.

33. n.

34. n.

35. n^2.

36. 1.

37. n.

38. False: $a = b = c = 1, d = 2$.

39. True: If $b = ak$ and $c = bl$, then $c = a(kl)$, so $a \mid c$.

40. False: $a = b = c = 1$.

41. False: $a = b = 2, c = d = 1$.

42. False: $a = 1, b = -1$.

43. False: $a = 2, b = c = 3$.

44. False: $a = 4, b = 2, c = 6$.

45. True: If $c = ak$ and $c = bl$, then $c^2 = ab(kl)$, so $ab \mid c^2$.

46. 2^{10}.

47. $5^2 \cdot 41$.

48. $2 \cdot 3 \cdot 5 \cdot 7 \cdot 11 \cdot 13 \cdot 17$.

49. $7 \cdot 13 \cdot 97$.

50. $11^2 \cdot 13 \cdot 29$.

51. $3 \cdot 7 \cdot 11 \cdot 13 \cdot 37$.

52. $1, 3, 7, 9, 11, 13, 17, 19, 21, 23, 27, 29$.

53. $12!$.

54. 2^{89}.

55. $20!$.

56. 2^{346}.

57. 80.

58. 1.

59. 4.

60. 3.

61. 0.

62. $(DB1)_{16}$.

63. False: $9 = 4 \cdot 2 + 1 = 3 \cdot 3$.

64. 0.

65. 0.

66. False; $3 + 5$ is not prime.

67. $p + q$ is even, hence composite.

68. False; one of any two consecutive integers is even, hence not prime.

69. False; $\sqrt{2} + (-\sqrt{2}) = 0$.

70. False; $(1/2)^{1/2} = \sqrt{2}/2$, which is not rational.

71. False, $f(17)$ is divisible by 17.

72. $pq + 1$ is an even number, hence not prime.

73. $2, 3, 6$.

74. 12.

75. $3, 7, 11, 15, \ldots, -1, -5, -9, \ldots$.

76. $0, \pm 7, \pm 14, \ldots$.

77. $b = 0, \pm 5, \pm 10, \pm 15, \ldots$; a any integer.

78. False.

79. False.

80. True.

81. True.

82. False.

83. True.

84. True.

85. There is no such x; if there were, then there would be integers k and l such that $x - 2 = 6k$ and $x - 3 = 9l$. Hence $1 = 6k - 9l = 3(2k - 3l)$, which is not possible.

86. The sequence $2, 6, 7, 10, 8$ repeats.

87. Encrypted form: QHHG KHOS.

88. Encrypted form: UTTQ CTOA.

89. $2, 17, 3$.

90. EXACT.

91. f is not $1 - 1$ ($f(0) = f(13)$), and hence f^{-1} is not a function.

92. YZUV GZ TUUT.

93. $a \mid b$ is a statement; $\dfrac{b}{a}$ represents a number.

94. False: $p = q = 3$.

95. (a) $8, 27$.   (b) Any integer of the form p^3 where p is prime.

96. 1100 1100.

97. 1D.

98. 29.

99. 684.

100. 10 0111 0001 0000.

101. 1 1111 1001 1011.

102. 1011 1100 0001.

103. 4C3.

104. $abc - cba = 100a + 10b + c - (100c + 10b + a) = 99a - 99c = 9(11a - 11c)$. Therefore $9 \mid abc - cba$.

105. True. When the factors 5, 10, 15, 20, and 30 are multiplied by the factor 2, each contributes one zero; when the factor 25 is multiplied by two factors 2, it contributes two zeros.

106. The proof is not correct since there is no guarantee that the multiple k will be the same in both cases.

107. 4.

108. 1.

109. 1.

110. 100.

111. 1.

112. 20.

113. 10.

114. 6.

115. 400.

116. 1.

117. 01100.

118. 10011.

119. 01001.

120. A matrix of the form $\begin{pmatrix} -2a & a \\ -4a & 2a \end{pmatrix}$ where $a \neq 0$.

121. $\mathbf{A}(\mathbf{BC})$ has 6 rows, 9 columns, and 54 entries.

122. $\mathbf{A}^n = \begin{pmatrix} 1 & mn \\ 0 & 1 \end{pmatrix}$.

123. $\begin{pmatrix} 4 & -13 \\ -2 & 8 \end{pmatrix}$.

124. $\begin{pmatrix} 3 & -7/2 \\ -6 & 9 \end{pmatrix}$.

125. None exists since $\det \mathbf{B} = 0$ and $\det \mathbf{C} \neq 0$.

126. False.

127. False.

128. False.

129. False.

130. False.

131. True.

132. False.

133. $\mathbf{A}_1(\mathbf{A}_2\mathbf{A}_3)$, 1750 multiplications.

134. $(\mathbf{A}_1\mathbf{A}_2)\mathbf{A}_3$, 9000 multiplications.

135. (a) $\begin{pmatrix} 1 & 1 & 1 \\ 0 & 1 & 1 \\ 1 & 1 & 0 \end{pmatrix}$.　(b) $\begin{pmatrix} 0 & 0 & 0 \\ 0 & 1 & 1 \\ 1 & 0 & 0 \end{pmatrix}$.　(c) $\begin{pmatrix} 1 & 1 & 0 \\ 1 & 1 & 1 \\ 0 & 1 & 1 \end{pmatrix}$.

136. $\begin{pmatrix} a & 0 \\ 0 & a \end{pmatrix}$.

137. $620 \cdot (-2) + 140 \cdot 9$.

138. $662 \cdot (-5) + 414 \cdot 8$.

139. $18 \cdot (-9) + 84 \cdot 2$.

140. $120 \cdot 4 + 450 \cdot (-1)$.

141. 5.

142. 9.

143. $7 + 9k$.

144. $5 + 11k$.

Questions for Chapter 3

1. Give a proof by cases that $x \le |x|$ for all real numbers x.

2. Prove: if n is an integer that is not a multiple of 3, then $n^2 \equiv 1 \bmod 3$.

3. Prove: if n is an integer that is not a multiple of 4, then $n^2 \equiv 0 \bmod 4$ or $n^2 \equiv 1 \bmod 4$.

4. Suppose you are allowed to give either a direct or an indirect proof of the following: if $3n + 5$ is even, then n is odd. Which type of proof would be easier to give? Explain why.

In 5–9 find a formula that generates the following sequence $a_1, a_2, a_3 \ldots$.

5. $5, 9, 13, 17, 21, \ldots$.

6. $3, 3, 3, 3, 3, \ldots$.

7. $15, 20, 25, 30, 35, \ldots$.

8. $1, 0.9, 0.8, 0.7, 0.6, \ldots$.

9. $1, 1/3, 1/5, 1/7, 1/9, \ldots$.

10. Find the sum $1/4 + 1/8 + 1/16 + 1/32 + \cdots$.

11. Find the sum $2 + 4 + 8 + 16 + 32 + \cdots + 2^{28}$.

12. Find the sum $2 - 4 + 8 - 16 + 32 - \cdots - 2^{28}$.

13. Find the sum $1 - 1/2 + 1/4 - 1/8 + 1/16 - \cdots$.

14. Find the sum $2 + 1/2 + 1/8 + 1/32 + 1/128 + \cdots$.

15. Suppose you wish to prove that the following is true for all positive integers n by using the Principle of Mathematical Induction: $1 + 3 + 5 + \cdots + (2n - 1) = n^2$.
(a) Write $P(1)$ (b) Write $P(72)$
(c) Write $P(73)$ (d) Use $P(72)$ to prove $P(73)$
(e) Write $P(k)$ (f) Write $P(k + 1)$
(g) Use the Principle of Mathematical Induction to prove that $P(n)$ is true for all positive integers n

16. Suppose you wish to use the Principle of Mathematical Induction to prove that $1 \cdot 1! + 2 \cdot 2! + 3 \cdot 3! + \cdots + n \cdot n! = (n + 1)! - 1$ for all $n \geq 1$.
(a) Write $P(1)$ (b) Write $P(5)$
(c) Write $P(k)$ (d) Write $P(k + 1)$
(e) Use the Principle of Mathematical Induction to prove that $P(n)$ is true for all $n \geq 1$

17. Use the Principle of Mathematical Induction to prove that $1 - 2 + 2^2 - 2^3 + \cdots + (-1)^n 2^n = \dfrac{2^{n+1}(-1)^n + 1}{3}$ for all positive integers n.

18. Use the Principle of Mathematical Induction to prove that $1 + 2^n \leq 3^n$ for all $n \geq 1$.

19. Use the Principle of Mathematical Induction to prove that $n^3 > n^2 + 3$ for all $n \geq 2$.

20. Use the Principle of Mathematical Induction to prove that $2 | (n^2 + n)$ for all $n \geq 0$.

21. Use the Principle of Mathematical Induction to prove that $1 + 3 + 9 + 27 + \cdots + 3^n = \dfrac{3^{n+1} - 1}{2}$ for all $n \geq 0$.

22. Use the Principle of Mathematical Induction to prove that $1 + 4 + 7 + 10 + \cdots + (3n - 2) = \dfrac{n(3n - 1)}{2}$ for all $n \geq 1$.

23. Use the Principle of Mathematical Induction to prove that $2 | (n^2 + 3n)$ for all $n \geq 1$.

24. Use the Principle of Mathematical Induction to prove that $2n + 3 \leq 2^n$ for all $n \geq 4$.

25. Use the Principle of Mathematical Induction to prove that $3 | (n^3 + 3n^2 + 2n)$ for all $n \geq 1$.

26. Use the Principle of Mathematical Induction to prove that any integer amount of postage from 18 cents on up can be made from an infinite supply of 4-cent and 7-cent stamps.

27. Suppose that the only currency were 3-dollar bills and 10-dollar bills. Show that any dollar amount greater than 17 dollars could be made from a combination of these bills.

28. Use mathematical induction to prove that every amount of postage of six cents or more can be formed using 3-cent and 4-cent stamps.

29. Prove that $\displaystyle\sum_{j=n}^{2n-1} (2j + 1) = 3n^2$ for all positive integers n.

30. Use mathematical induction to show that n lines in the plane passing through the same point divide the plane into $2n$ regions.

31. Let $a_1 = 2$, $a_2 = 9$, and $a_n = 2a_{n-1} + 3a_{n-2}$ for $n \geq 3$. Show that $a_n \leq 3^n$ for all positive integers n.

32. Floor borders one foot wide and of varying lengths are to be covered with nonoverlapping tiles that are available in two sizes: $1' \times 3'$ and $1' \times 5'$ sizes. Assuming that the supply of each size is infinite, prove that every $1' \times n'$ border ($n > 7$) can be covered with these tiles.

33. A *T-omino* is a tile pictured at the right. Prove that every $2^n \times 2^n$ $(n > 1)$ chessboard can be tiled with T-ominoes.

34. Use the Principle of Mathematical Induction to prove that $4|(9^n - 5^n)$ for all $n \geq 0$.

35. Use the Principle of Mathematical Induction to prove that $5|(7^n - 2^n)$ for all $n \geq 0$.

36. Prove that the distributive law $A_1 \cap (A_2 \cup \cdots \cup A_n) = (A_1 \cap A_2) \cup \cdots \cup (A_1 \cap A_n)$ is true for all $n \geq 3$.

37. Prove that $\dfrac{1}{2} + \dfrac{2}{4} + \dfrac{3}{8} + \cdots + \dfrac{n}{2^n} = \dfrac{2^{n+1} - 2 - n}{2^n}$ for all $n \geq 1$.

38. Find the error in the following proof of this "theorem":

"Theorem: Every positive integer equals the next largest positive integer."
"*Proof*: Let $P(n)$ be the proposition '$n = n + 1$'. To show that $P(k) \to P(k+1)$, assume that $P(k)$ is true for some k, so that $k = k + 1$. Add 1 to both sides of this equation to obtain $k + 1 = k + 2$, which is $P(k+1)$. Therefore $P(k) \to P(k+1)$ is true. Hence $P(n)$ is true for all positive integers n."

In 39–44 give a recursive definition (with initial condition(s)) of $\{a_n\}$ $(n = 1, 2, 3, \ldots)$.

39. $a_n = 2^n$.

40. $a_n = 3n - 5$.

41. $a_n = (n+1)/3$.

42. $a_n = \sqrt{2}$.

43. $a_n = 2^{1/2^n}$.

44. $a_n = n^2 + n$.

In 45–49 give a recursive definition with initial condition(s) of the set S.

45. $\{3, 7, 11, 15, 19, 23, \ldots\}$.

46. All positive integer multiples of 5.

47. $\{\ldots, -5, -3, -1, 1, 3, 5, \ldots\}$.

48. $\{0.1, 0.01, 0.001, 0.0001\}$.

49. The set of strings $1, 111, 11111, 1111111, \ldots$.

In 50–58 give a recursive definition with initial condition(s).

50. The sequence $\{a_n\}$, $n = 1, 2, 3, \ldots$ where $a_n = 2^n$.

51. The sequence $1!, 2!, 3!, \ldots$.

52. The sequence $\{a_n\}$ where $a_n = 5n + 2$.

53. The sequence $a_1 = 16$, $a_2 = 13$, $a_3 = 10$, $a_4 = 7$, $\ldots$.

54. The Fibonacci numbers $1, 1, 2, 3, 5, 8, 13, \ldots$.

55. The set $\{0, 3, 6, 9, \ldots\}$.

56. The set $\{1, 5, 9, 13, 17, \ldots\}$.

57. The set $\{1, 1/3, 1/9, 1/27, \ldots\}$.

58. The set $\{\ldots, -4, -2, 0, 2, 4, 6, \ldots\}$.

59. Find $f(2)$ and $f(3)$ if $f(n) = 2f(n-1) + 6$, $f(0) = 3$.

60. Find $f(2)$ and $f(3)$ if $f(n) = f(n-1) \cdot f(n-2) + 1$, $f(0) = 1$, $f(1) = 4$.

61. Find $f(2)$ and $f(3)$ if $f(n) = f(n-1)/f(n-2)$, $f(0) = 2$, $f(1) = 5$.

62. Suppose $\{a_n\}$ is defined recursively by $a_n = a_{n-1}^2 - 1$ and that $a_0 = 2$. Find a_3 and a_4.

63. Give a recursive algorithm for computing na, where n is a positive integer and a is a real number.

64. Describe a recursive algorithm for computing 3^{2^n} where n is a nonnegative integer.

65. Verify that the program segment

$a := 2$
$b := a + c$

is correct with respect to the initial assertion $c = 3$ and the final assertion $b = 5$.

66. Consider the following program segment:

$i := 1$
$total := 1$
while $i < n$
begin
   $i := i + 1$
   $total := total + i$
end.

Let p be the proposition "$total = \frac{i(i+1)}{2}$ and $i \le n$." Use mathematical induction to prove that p is a loop invariant.

67. Verify that the following program segment:

if $x \le y$ **then**
$max := y$
else
$max := x$.

is correct with respect to the initial assertion $\mathbf{T}$ and the final assertion $(x \le y \wedge max = y) \vee (x > y \wedge max = x)$.

Answers for Chapter 3

1. Case 1, $x \ge 0$: then $x = |x|$, so $x \le |x|$. Case 2, $x < 0$: here $x < 0$ and $0 < |x|$, so $x < |x|$.

2. Proof by cases. Suppose n is not a multiple of 3. Then $n = 3k + 1$ or $n = 3k + 2$ for some integer k.
Case 1, $n = 3k + 1$: therefore $n^2 = (3k + 1)^2 = 9k^2 + 6k + 1 = 3(3k^2 + 2k) + 1$, and hence $n^2 \equiv 1 \bmod 3$.
Case 2, $n = 3k + 2$: therefore $n^2 = (3k + 2)^2 = 9k^2 + 12k + 4 = 3(3k^2 + 4k + 1) + 1$, and hence $n^2 \equiv 1 \bmod 3$.

3. Proof by cases. Suppose n is not a multiple of 4. Then there is an integer k such that $n = 4k+1$, $n = 4k+2$, or $n = 4k + 3$.
Case 1, $n = 4k + 1$: therefore $n^2 = (4k + 1)^2 = 16k^2 + 8k + 1 = 4(4k^2 + 2k) + 1$, and hence $n^2 \equiv 1 \bmod 4$.
Case 2, $n = 4k + 2$: therefore $n^2 = (4k + 2)^2 = 16k^2 + 16k + 4 = 4(4k^2 + 4k + 1)$, and hence $n^2 \equiv 0 \bmod 4$.
Case 3, $n = 4k + 3$: therefore $n^2 = (4k + 3)^2 = 16k^2 + 24k + 9 = 4(4k^2 + 6k + 2) + 1$, and hence $n^2 \equiv 1 \bmod 4$.

4. It is easier to give an indirect proof; it is usually easier to proceed from a simple expression (such as n) to a more complex expression (such as $3n + 5$ is even). Begin by supposing that n is not odd. Therefore n is even and hence $n = 2k$ for some integer k. Therefore $3n + 5 = 3(2k) + 5 = 6k + 5 = 2(3k + 2) + 1$, which is not even. If we try a direct proof, we assume that $3n + 5$ is even; that is, $3n + 5 = 2k$ for some integer k. From this we obtain $n = (2k - 5)/3$, and it it not obvious from this form that n is even.

5. $a_n = 4n + 1$.

6. $a_n = 3$.

7. $a_n = 5(n + 2)$.

8. $a_n = 1 - (n-1)/10$.

9. $a_n = 1/(2n-1)$.

10. $1/2$.

11. $2^{29} - 2$.

12. $\frac{2}{3} + \frac{2}{3}(2^{29})$.

13. $2/3$.

14. $8/3$.

15. (a) $1 = 1^2$.
(b) $1 + 3 + 5 + \cdots + 143 = 72^2$.
(c) $1 + 3 + 5 + \cdots + 145 = 73^2$.
(d) $1 + 3 + 5 + \cdots + 145 = (1 + 3 + 5 + \cdots + 143) + 145 = 72^2 + 145 = 72^2 + 2 \cdot 72 + 1 = (72+1)^2 = 73^2$.
(e) $1 + 3 + \cdots + (2k-1) = k^2$.
(f) $1 + 3 + \cdots + (2k+1) = (k+1)^2$.
(g) $P(1)$ is true since $1 = 1^2$. $\quad P(k) \to P(k+1)$: $1 + 3 + \cdots + (2k+1) = k^2 + (2k+1) = (k+1)^2$.

16. (a) $1 \cdot 1! = 2! - 1$.
(b) $1 \cdot 1! + 2 \cdot 2! + \cdots + 5 \cdot 5! = 6! - 1$.
(c) $1 \cdot 1! + 2 \cdot 2! + \cdots + k \cdot k! = (k+1)! - 1$.
(d) $1 \cdot 1! + 2 \cdot 2! + \cdots + (k+1)(k+1)! = (k+2)! - 1$.
(e) $P(1)$ is true since $1 \cdot 1! = 1$ and $2! - 1 = 1$. $\quad P(k) \to P(k+1)$: $1 \cdot 1! + 2 \cdot 2! + \cdots + (k+1)(k+1)! = (k+1)! - 1 + (k+1)(k+1)! = (k+1)![1 + (k+1)] - 1 = (k+1)!(k+2) - 1 = (k+2)! - 1$.

17. $P(1)$: $1 - 2 = \dfrac{2^2(-1) + 1}{3}$, which is true since both sides are equal to -1. $\quad P(k) \to P(k+1)$: $1 - 2 + 2^2 + \cdots + (-1)^{k+1}2^{k+1} = \dfrac{2^{k+1}(-1)^k + 1}{3} + (-1)^{k+1}2^{k+1} = \dfrac{2^{k+1}(-1)^k + 1 + 3(-1)^{k+1}2^{k+1}}{3}$ $= \dfrac{2^{k+1}(-1)^k(1 + 3(-1)) + 1}{3} = \dfrac{2^{k+1}(-1)^k(-2) + 1}{3} = \dfrac{2^{k+2}(-1)^{k+1} + 1}{3}$.

18. $P(1)$: $1 + 2^1 \le 3^1$, which is true since both sides are equal to 3. $\quad P(k) \to P(k+1)$: $1 + 2^{k+1} = (1 + 2^k) + 2^k \le 3^k + 2^k \le 3^k + 3^k = 2 \cdot 3^k < 3 \cdot 3^k = 3^{k+1}$.

19. $P(2)$: $2^3 > 2^2 + 3$ is true since $8 > 7$. $\quad P(k) \to P(k+1)$: $(k+1)^2 + 3 = k^2 + 2k + 1 + 3 = (k^2 + 3) + 2k + 1 < k^3 + 2k + 1 \le k^3 + 3k \le k^3 + 3k^2 + 3k + 1 = (k+1)^3$.

20. $P(0)$: $2 \mid 0^2 + 0$, which is true since $2 \mid 0$. $\quad P(k) \to P(k+1)$: $(k+1)^2 + (k+1) = (k^2 + k) + 2(k+1)$, which is divisible by 2 since $2 \mid k^2 + k$ and $2 \mid 2(k+1)$.

21. $P(0)$: $1 = \dfrac{3^1 - 1}{2}$, which is true since $1 = 1$. $\quad P(k) \to P(k+1)$: $1 + 3 + \cdots + 3^{k+1} = \dfrac{3^{k+1} - 1}{2} + 3^{k+1} = \dfrac{3^{k+1} - 1 + 2 \cdot 3^{k+1}}{2} = \dfrac{3^{k+2} - 1}{2}$.

22. $P(1)$: $1 = \dfrac{1 \cdot 2}{2}$, which is true since $1 = 1$. $\quad P(k) \to P(k+1)$: $1 + 4 + \cdots + (3(k+1) - 2) = \dfrac{k(3k-1)}{2} + (3k+1) = \dfrac{k(3k-1) + 2(3k+1)}{2} = \dfrac{3k^2 + 5k + 2}{2} = \dfrac{(3k+2)(k+1)}{2} = \dfrac{(k+1)(3(k+1) - 1)}{2}$.

23. $P(1)$: $2 \mid 1^2 + 3 \cdot 1$, which is true since $2 \mid 4$. $\quad P(k) \to P(k+1)$: $(k+1)^2 + 3(k+1) = (k^2 + 3k) + 2(k+2)$, which is divisible by 2 since $2 \mid k^2 + 3k$ and $2 \mid 2(k+2)$.

24. $P(4)$: $2 \cdot 4 + 3 \le 2^4$, which is true since $11 \le 16$. $\quad P(k) \to P(k+1)$: $2(k+1) + 3 = (2k+3) + 2 \le 2^k + 2 \le 2^k + 2^k = 2^{k+1}$.

25. $P(1)$: $3 \mid 1^3 + 3 \cdot 1^2 + 2 \cdot 1$, which is true since $3 \mid 6$. $\quad P(k) \to P(k+1)$: $(k+1)^3 + 3(k+1)^2 + 2(k+1) = (k^3 + 3k^2 + 2k) + 3(k^2 + 3k + 2)$, which is divisible by 3 since each of the two terms is divisible by 3.

26. $P(18)$: use one 4-cent stamp and two 7-cent stamps. $\quad P(k) \to P(k+1)$: if a pile of stamps for k cents postage has a 7-cent stamp, replace one 7-cent stamp with two 4-cent stamps; if the pile contains only 4-cent stamps (there must be at least five of them), replace five 4-cent stamps with three 7-cent stamps.

27. $P(18)$: Eighteen dollars can be made using six 3-dollar bills. $\quad P(k) \to P(k+1)$: Suppose that k dollars

can be formed, for some $k \geq 18$. If at least two 10-dollar bills are used, replace them by seven 3-dollar bills to form $k + 1$ dollars. Otherwise (that is, at most one 10-dollar bill is used), at least three 3-dollar bills are being used, and three of them can be replaced by one 10-dollar bill to form $k + 1$ dollars.

28. $P(6)$: Six cents postage can be made from two 3-cent stamps. $P(k) \to P(k+1)$: either replace a 3-cent stamp by a 4-cent stamp or else (if there are only 4-cent stamps in the pile of stamps making k cents postage) replace two 4-cent stamps by three 3-cent stamps.

29. The basis case holds since $\sum_{j=1}^{1}(2j + 1) = 3 = 3 \cdot 1^2$. Now assume that $\sum_{j=k}^{2k-1}(2j + 1) = 3k^2$ for some k. It follows that $\sum_{j=k+1}^{2(k+1)-1}(2j + 1) = \sum_{j=k}^{2k-1}(2j + 1) - (2k + 1) + (4k + 1) + (4k + 3) = 3k^2 + 6k + 3 = 3(k + 1)^2$.

30. The basis step follows since one line divides the plane into 2 regions. Now assume that k lines passing through the same point divide the plane into $2k$ regions. Adding the $(k + 1)$st line splits exactly two of these regions into two parts each. Hence $k + 1$ concurrent lines split the plane into $2k + 2 = 2(k + 1)$ regions.

31. Let $P(n)$ be the proposition that $a_n \leq 3^n$. The proof uses the Second Principle of Mathematical Induction. The basis step follows since $a_1 = 2 \leq 3 = 3^1$ and $a_2 = 9 \leq 9 = 3^2$. Now assume that $P(k)$ is true for all k such that $1 \leq k < n$. Then $a_k \leq 3^k$ for $1 \leq k < n$. Hence $a_n = 2a_{n-1} + 3a_{n-2} \leq 2 \cdot 3^{n-1} + 3 \cdot 3^{n-2} = 2 \cdot 3^{n-1} + 3^{n-1} = 3 \cdot 3^{n-1} = 3^n$.

32. $P(8)$: use one of each type. $P(k) \to P(k+1)$: If a $1' \times 5'$ tile is used as part of the covering of a $1' \times k'$ strip, replace a $1' \times 5'$ tile with two $1' \times 3'$ tiles to cover a $1' \times (k+1)'$ strip. Otherwise, the tiles for the $1' \times k'$ strip must include three $1' \times 3'$ tiles; replace three of these with two $1' \times 5'$ tiles to cover a $1' \times (k+1)'$ strip.

33. $P(2)$: The figure at the right shows a tiling of a 4×4 board. $P(k) \to P(k+1)$: Divide the $2^{k+1} \times 2^{k+1}$ board into four quarters, each of which is a $2^k \times 2^k$ board. $P(k)$ guarantees that each of these four $2^k \times 2^k$ boards can be tiled. Put these four tiled boards together to obtain a tiling for the $2^{k+1} \times 2^{k+1}$ board.

34. $P(0)$: $4 \mid 1 - 1$ is true since $4 \mid 0$. $P(k) \to P(k+1)$: $9^{k+1} - 5^{k+1} = 9(9^k - 5^k) + 5^k(9 - 5)$. Each term is divisible by 4: $4 \mid 9^k - 5^k$ (by $P(k)$) and $4 \mid 9 - 5$.

35. $P(1)$: $5 \mid 7 - 2$ is true since $5 \mid 5$. $P(k) \to P(k+1)$: $7^{k+1} - 2^{k+1} = 7(7^k - 2^k) + 2^k(7 - 2)$. Each term is divisible by 5: $5 \mid 7^k - 2^k$ (by $P(k)$) and $5 \mid 7 - 2$.

36. The second form of mathematical induction is used. $P(3)$ is true since it is the ordinary distributive law for intersection over union. $P(3) \wedge \cdots \wedge P(n) \to P(n+1)$: $A_1 \cap (A_2 \cup \cdots \cup A_{n+1}) = A_1 \cap ((A_2 \cup \cdots \cup A_n) \cup A_{n+1}) = [A_1 \cap (A_2 \cup \cdots \cup A_n)] \cup (A_1 \cap A_{n+1}) = [(A_1 \cap A_2) \cup \cdots \cup (A_1 \cap A_n)] \cup (A_1 \cap A_{n+1}) = (A_1 \cap A_2) \cup \cdots \cup (A_1 \cap A_{n+1})$.

37. $P(1)$: $\dfrac{1}{2} = \dfrac{(2^2 - 2 - 1)}{2^1}$, which is true since the right side is equal to 1/2. $P(k) \to P(k+1)$: $\dfrac{1}{2} + \dfrac{2}{4} + \dfrac{3}{8} + \cdots + \dfrac{k+1}{2^{k+1}} = \dfrac{2^{k+1} - 2 - k}{2^k} + \dfrac{k+1}{2^{k+1}} = \dfrac{2^{k+2} - 4 - 2k + k + 1}{2^{k+1}} = \dfrac{2^{k+2} - 3 - k}{2^{k+1}} = \dfrac{2^{k+2} - 2 - (k+1)}{2^{k+1}}$.

38. No basis case has been shown.

39. $a_n = 2a_{n-1}$, $a_1 = 2$.

40. $a_n = a_{n-1} + 3$, $a_1 = -2$.

41. $a_n = a_{n-1} + 1/3$, $a_1 = 2/3$.

42. $a_n = a_{n-1}$, $a_1 = \sqrt{2}$.

43. $a_n = \sqrt{a_{n-1}}$, $a_1 = \sqrt{2}$.

44. $a_n = a_{n-1} + 2n$, $a_1 = 2$.

45. $3 \in S$; $x \in S \to x + 4 \in S$.

46. $5 \in S$; $x \in S \to x + 5 \in S$.

47. $1 \in S$; $x \in S \to x \pm 2 \in S$.

48. $0.1 \in S$; $x \in S \to x/10 \in S$.

49. $1 \in S$; $x \in S \to x11 \in S$ (or $x \in S \to 100x + 11 \in S$).

50. $a_n = 2a_{n-1}$, $a_1 = 2$.

51. $n! = n(n-1)!$, $1! = 1$.

52. $a_n = 5 + a_{n-1}$, $a_1 = 7$.

53. $a_n = a_{n-1} - 3$, $a_1 = 16$.

54. $a_n = a_{n-1} + a_{n-2}$, $a_1 = 1$, $a_2 = 1$.

55. $0 \in S$; $x \in S \to x + 3 \in S$.

56. $1 \in S$; $x \in S \to x + 4 \in S$.

57. $1 \in S$; $x \in S \to x/3 \in S$.

58. $0 \in S$; $x \in S \to x \pm 2 \in S$.

59. $f(2) = 30$, $f(3) = 66$.

60. $f(2) = 5$, $f(3) = 21$.

61. $f(2) = 5/2$, $f(3) = 1/2$.

62. $a_3 = 63$ and $a_4 = 3{,}968$.

63. The following procedure computes na:
    procedure $mult(a$: real number, n: positive integer)
    if $n = 1$ **then** $mult(a, n) := a$
    else $mult(a, n) := a + mult(a, n - 1)$.

64. The following procedure computes 3^{2^n}:
    procedure $power(n$: nonnegative integer)
    if $n = 0$ **then** $power(n) := 3$
    else $power(n) := power(n - 1) \cdot power(n - 1)$.

65. Suppose $c = 3$. The program segment assigns 2 to a and then assigns $a + c = 2 + 3 = 5$ to b.

66. Before the loop is entered p is true since $total = \frac{1 \cdot 2}{2}$ and $i \le n$. Suppose p is true and $i < n$ after an execution of the loop. Suppose that the **while** loop is executed again. The variable i is incremented by 1, and hence $i \le n$. The variable $total$ was $\frac{(i-1)i}{2}$, which now becomes $\frac{(i-1)i}{2} + i = \frac{i(i+1)}{2}$. Hence p is a loop invariant.

67. If $x < y$ initially, max is set equal to y, so $(x \le y \ \land \ max = y)$ is true. If $x = y$ initially, max is set equal to y, so $(x \le y \ \land \ max = y)$ is again true. If $x > y$, max is set equal to x, so $(x > y \ \land \ max = x)$ is true.

Questions for Chapter 4

In 1–7 suppose that a "word" is any string of seven letters of the alphabet, with repeated letters allowed.

1. How many words are there?

2. How many words have no repeated letters?

3. How many words end with the letter T?

4. How many words begin with R and end with T?

5. How many words begin with A or B?

6. How many words have no vowels?

7. How many words have exactly one vowel?

8. Find the number of words of length eight of distinct letters of the alphabet so that the words do not have both A and B in them.

In 9–13 consider all bit strings of length 12.

9. How many begin with 110?

10. How many begin with 11 and end with 10?

11. How many begin with 11 or end with 10?

12. How many have exactly four 1s?

13. How many have exactly four 1s and none of these 1s are adjacent to each other?

14. How many permutations of the seven letters A, B, C, D, E, F, G are there?

15. How many permutations of the seven letters A, B, C, D, E, F, G have E in the first position?

16. How many permutations of the seven letters A, B, C, D, E, F, G have E in one of the first two positions?

17. How many permutations of the seven letters A, B, C, D, E, F, G do not have vowels on the ends?

18. How many permutations of the seven letters A, B, C, D, E, F, G have the two vowels before the five consonants?

19. How many permutations of the seven letters A, B, C, D, E, F, G have A immediately to the left of E?

20. How many permutations of the seven letters A, B, C, D, E, F, G neither begin nor end with A?

21. How many permutations of the seven letters A, B, C, D, E, F, G do not have the vowels next to each other?

In 22–28 nine people (Ann, Ben, Cal, Dot, Ed, Fran, Gail, Hal, and Ida) are in a room. Five of them stand in a row for a picture.

22. In how many ways can this be done if Ben is to be in the picture?

23. In how many ways can this be done if both Ed and Gail are in the picture?

24. In how many ways can this be done if neither Ed nor Fran are in the picture?

25. In how many ways can this be done if Dot is on the left end and Ed is on the right end?

26. In how many ways can this be done if Hal or Ida (but not both) are in the picture?

27. In how many ways can this be done if Ed and Gail are in the picture, standing next to each other?

28. In how many ways can this be done if Ann and Ben are in the picture, but not standing next to each other?

29. In a technician's box there are 400 VLSI chips, 12 of which are faulty. How many ways are there to pick two chips, so that one is a working chip and the other is faulty?

30. How many truth tables are possible for compound propositions with the five variables p, q, r, s, t?

In 31–35 let A be the set of all bit strings of length 10.

31. How many bit strings of length 10 are there?

32. How many bit strings of length 10 begin with 1101?

33. How many bit strings of length 10 have exactly six 0s?

34. How many bit strings of length 10 have equal numbers of 0s and 1s?

35. How many bit strings of length 10 have more 0s than 1s?

In 36–39 suppose you have 30 books (15 novels, 10 history books, and 5 math books). Assume that all 30 books are different. In how many ways can you

36. In how many ways can you put the 30 books in a row on a shelf?

37. In how many ways can you get a bunch of four books to give to a friend?

38. In how many ways can you get a bunch of three history books and seven novels to give to a friend?

39. In how many ways can you put the 30 books in a row on a shelf if the novels are on the left, the math books are in the middle, and the history books are on the right?

40. A class consists of 20 sophomores and 15 freshmen. The class needs to form a committee of size five.

(a) How many committees are possible?

(b) How many committees are possible if the committee must have three sophomores and two freshmen?

In 41–44 a club with 20 women and 17 men needs to form a committee of size six.

41. How many committees are possible?

42. How many committees are possible if the committee must have three women and three men?

43. How many committees are possible if the committee must have at least two men?

44. How many committees are possible if the committee must consist of all women or all men?

45. A club with 20 women and 17 men needs to choose three different members to be president, vice president, and treasurer.

(a) In how many ways is this possible?

(b) In how many ways is this possible if women will be chosen as president and vice president and a man as treasurer?

46. A class consists of 20 sophomores and 15 freshmen. The club needs to choose four different members to be president, vice president, secretary, and treasurer.

(a) In how many ways is this possible?

(b) In how many ways is this possible if sophomores will be chosen as president and treasurer and freshmen as vice president and secretary?

47. Suppose $|A| = 4$ and $|B| = 10$. Find the number of functions $f: A \to B$.

48. Suppose $|A| = 4$ and $|B| = 10$. Find the number of 1-1 functions $f: A \to B$.

49. Suppose $|A| = 10$ and $|B| = 4$. Find the number of 1-1 functions $f: A \to B$.

In 50–53 let A be the set of all strings of decimal digits of length five. For example 00312 and 19483 are strings in A.

50. Find $|A|$.

51. How many strings in A begin with 774?

52. How many strings in A have exactly one 5?

53. How many strings in A have exactly three 5s?

54. Make up a word problem in good English whose answer is 15!/10!.

55. Make up a word problem in good English whose answer is $\binom{15}{4} \cdot \binom{7}{3}$.

56. How many subsets with an odd number of elements does a set with 10 elements have?

57. How many subsets with more than two elements does a set with 100 elements have?

58. Each user has a password 6 characters long where each character is an uppercase letter, a lowercase letter, or a digit. Each password must contain at least one digit. How long will it take to check every possible character combination, if each check takes one unit of time.

In 59–62 suppose you have a class with 30 students — 10 freshmen, 12 sophomores, and 8 juniors.

59. In how many ways can you put all 30 in a line?

60. In how many ways can you put all students in a line so that the freshmen are first, the sophomores are in the middle, and the juniors are at the end?

61. In how many ways can you get a committee of 7?

62. In how many ways can you get a committee of 4 freshmen and 3 sophomores?

63. Using the ordinary alphabet and allowing repeated letters, find the number of words of length 8.

64. Using the ordinary alphabet and allowing repeated letters, find the number of words of length 8 that begin and end with T.

65. Using the ordinary alphabet and allowing repeated letters, find the number of words of length 8 that begin and end with the same letter.

66. Using the ordinary alphabet and allowing repeated letters, find the number of words of length 8 that have exactly one B.

67. Using the ordinary alphabet and allowing repeated letters, find the number of words of length 8 that have at least one C.

68. Using the ordinary alphabet and allowing repeated letters, find the number of words of length 8 that begin with L or end with R.

69. How many ways are there to select 6 students from a class of 25 to serve on a committee?

70. How many ways are there to select 6 students from a class of 25 to hold six different executive positions on a committee?

71. Find the number of subsets of $S = \{1, 2, 3, \ldots, 10\}$ that contain the number 5.

72. Find the number of subsets of $S = \{1, 2, 3, \ldots, 10\}$ that contain neither 5 nor 6.

73. Find the number of subsets of $S = \{1, 2, 3, \ldots, 10\}$ that contain both 5 and 6.

74. Find the number of subsets of $S = \{1, 2, 3, \ldots, 10\}$ that contain no odd numbers.

75. Find the number of subsets of $S = \{1, 2, 3, \ldots, 10\}$ that contain exactly three elements.

76. Find the number of subsets of $S = \{1, 2, 3, \ldots, 10\}$ that contain exactly three elements, one of which is 3.

77. Find the number of subsets of $S = \{1, 2, 3, \ldots, 10\}$ that contain exactly five elements, all of them even.

78. Find the number of subsets of $S = \{1, 2, 3, \ldots, 10\}$ that contain exactly three elements, all of them even.

79. Find the number of subsets of $S = \{1, 2, 3, \ldots, 10\}$ with exactly five elements, two of which are 3 and 4.

80. Find the number of subsets of $S = \{1, 2, 3, \ldots, 10\}$ with exactly five elements, including 3 or 4 but not both.

81. Find the number of subsets of $S = \{1, 2, 3, \ldots, 10\}$ that contain exactly five elements, but neither 3 nor 4.

82. Find the number of subsets of $S = \{1, 2, 3, \ldots, 10\}$ that contain exactly five elements, the sum of which is even.

83. Find the number of subsets of $S = \{1, 2, 3, \ldots, 10\}$ that contain exactly four elements, the sum of which is odd.

84. Find the number of subsets of $S = \{1, 2, 3, \ldots, 10\}$ that contain exactly four elements, the sum of which is even.

85. Suppose a restaurant serves a "special dinner" consisting of soup, salad, entree, dessert, and beverage. The restaurant has five kinds of soup, three kinds of salad, ten entrees, five desserts, and four beverages. How many different special dinners are possible? (Two special dinners are different if they differ in at least one selection.)

86. The figure at the right shows a 4-block by 5-block grid of streets. Find the number of ways in which you can go from point A to point B, where at each stage you can only go right or up. (You are not allowed to go left or down.) For example, one allowable route from A to B is:

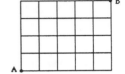

  Right, Right, Up, Right, Up, Up, Right, Right, Up.

87. Here is an incorrect solution to a problem. Find the error, explain why it is not correct, and give the correct answer.

"*Problem*: Find the number of ways to get two pairs of two different ranks (such as 2 jacks and 2 fives) in a 4-card hand from an ordinary deck of 52 cards."

"*Solution*: There are 13 ways to get a rank (such as "kings") for the first pair and $\binom{4}{2}$ ways to get a pair of that rank. Similarly, there are 12 ways to get a rank (such as "sevens") for the second pair and $\binom{4}{2}$ ways to get a pair of that rank. Therefore there are $13 \cdot \binom{4}{2} \cdot 12 \cdot \binom{4}{2}$ ways to get 2 pairs."

88. A game consisting of flipping a coin ends when the player gets two heads in a row, two tails in a row, or flips the coin four times.
(a) Draw a tree diagram to show the ways in which the game can end.
(b) In how many ways can the game end?

89. A factory makes automobile parts. Each part has a code consisting of a letter and three digits, such as C117, O076, or Z920. Last week the factory made 60,000 parts. Prove that there are at least three parts that have the same serial number.

90. A factory makes automobile parts. Each part has a code consisting of a digit, a letter, and a digit, with the digits distinct, such as 5C7, 1O6, or 3Z0. Last week the factory made 5,000 parts. Find the minimum number of parts that must have the same serial number.

91. Show that if five points are picked on or in the interior of a square of side length 2, then there are at least two of these points no farther than $\sqrt{2}$ apart.

92. A professor teaching a Discrete Math course gives a multiple choice quiz that has ten questions, each with four possible responses: a, b, c, d. What is the minimum number of students that must be in the professor's class in order to guarantee that at least three answer sheets must be identical? (Assume that no answers are left blank.)

93. Show that in a group of ten people (where any two people are either friends or enemies) there are either three mutual friends or four mutual enemies.

94. A computer network consists of six computers. Each computer is directly connected to zero or more of the other computers. Show that there are at least two computers in the network that are directly connected to the same number of computers.

95. A computer is programmed to print subsets of $\{1, 2, 3, 4, 5\}$ at random. If the computer prints 40 subsets, prove that some subset must have been printed at least twice.

96. A computer randomly prints three-digit codes, with no repeated digits in any code (for example, 387, 072, 760). What is the minimum number of codes that must be printed in order to guarantee that at least six of the codes are identical?

97. Explain how the Pigeonhole Principle can be used to show that among any 11 integers, at least two must have the same last digit.

98. Let $s_1, s_2 \ldots, s_{101}$ be 101 bit strings of length at most 9. Prove that there exist two strings, s_i and s_j, where $i \neq j$, that contain the same number of 0s and the same number of 1s. (For example, strings 001001 and 101000 contain the same number of 0s and the same number of 1s.)

99. You pick cards one at a time without replacement from an ordinary deck of 52 playing cards. What is the minimum number of cards you must pick in order to guarantee that you get
(a) a pair (for example, two kings or two 5s).
(b) three of a kind (for example, three 7s).

100. Use the binomial theorem to expand $(2a + b)^4$.

101. Use the binomial theorem to expand $(x + y)^5$.

102. Use the binomial theorem to expand $(a + 2)^6$.

103. Use the binomial theorem to expand $(2c - 3d)^4$.

104. Use the binomial theorem to expand $\left(x - \frac{3}{x}\right)^5$.

105. Use the binomial theorem to expand $\left(x^2 + \frac{1}{x}\right)^7$.

106. Use the binomial theorem to prove the following: $\binom{6}{0} + \binom{6}{1} + \cdots + \binom{6}{6} = 2^6$.

107. Use the binomial theorem to prove the following:

$$\binom{100}{0} + \binom{100}{2} + \binom{100}{4} + \binom{100}{6} + \cdots + \binom{100}{98} + \binom{100}{100} = \binom{100}{1} + \binom{100}{3} + \binom{100}{5} + \cdots + \binom{100}{97} + \binom{100}{99}.$$

108. Use the binomial theorem to prove the following:

$$3^{100} = \binom{100}{0} + \binom{100}{1} \cdot 2 + \binom{100}{2} \cdot 2^2 + \binom{100}{3} \cdot 2^3 + \cdots + \binom{100}{99} \cdot 2^{99} + \binom{100}{100} \cdot 2^{100}.$$

109. Find the coefficient of $x^7 y^5$ in the expansion of $(3x - y)^{12}$.

110. Find the coefficient of $x^5 y^6$ in the expansion of $(2x - y)^{11}$.

111. Find the coefficient of x^8 in the expansion of $(x^2 + 2)^{13}$.

112. Find the coefficient of x^9 in the expansion of $(2 + x^3)^{10}$.

113. Find the coefficient of x^5 in $(2 + x^2)^{12}$.

114. Find the number of terms in the expansion of $(5a + 8b)^{15}$.

115. Find the largest coefficient in the expansion of $(x + 1)^6$.

116. Find the largest coefficient in the expansion of $(x + 3)^5$.

117. List the derangements of $1, 2, 3, 4$.

118. Find the number of positive integers not exceeding 1000 that are not divisible by.4, 6, or 9.

119. How many permutations of 12345 are there that leave 3 in the third position but leave no other integer in its own position?

120. (a) Find the number of solutions to $x + y + z = 32$, where x, y, and z are nonnegative integers.

(b) Answer part (a), but assume that $x \geq 7$ and $y \geq 15$.

121. You have 20 pennies, 30 nickels, and 40 dimes. Assume that the pennies are identical, the nickels are identical, and the dimes are identical. In how many ways can you put all the coins in a row?

122. Find the number of permutations of the word CORRECT.

123. Find the number of permutations of the word COEFFICIENT.

124. Find the number of permutations of the word TATTERED.

125. Find the number of permutations of your last name.

126. How many different strings can be made using all the letters in the word *GOOGOL*?

127. (a) In how many ways are there to arrange the letters of the word *NONSENSE*?
(b) How many of these ways start or end with the letter *O*?

128. A doughnut shop sells 30 kinds of doughnuts. In how many ways can you
(a) get a bag of 12 doughnuts?
(b) get a bag of 12 doughnuts if you want at least 3 glazed doughnuts and at least 4 raspberry doughnuts?
(c) get a bag of 12 doughnuts if you want exactly 3 glazed doughnuts and exactly 4 raspberry doughnuts?

129. You have 50 of each of the following kinds of jellybeans: red, orange, green, yellow. The jellybeans of each color are identical.
(a) In how many ways can you put all the jellybeans in a row?
(b) How many handfuls of 12 are possible?

In 130–133 assume that you have 50 pennies and three jars, labeled A, B, and C.
130. In how many ways can you put the pennies in the jars, assuming that the pennies are distinguishable?

131. In how many ways can you put the pennies in the jars, assuming that the pennies are identical?

132. In how many ways can you put the pennies in the jars, assuming that the pennies are identical and each jar must have at least two pennies put into it?

133. In how many ways can you put the pennies in the jars, assuming that the pennies are identical and each jar must have an even number of pennies put into it?

In 134–137 assume that you have a bowl containing hard candies: 50 cherry, 50 strawberry, 40 orange, 70 lemon, and 40 pineapple. Assuming that the pieces of each flavor are identical,
134. How many handfuls of 15 are possible?

135. How many handfuls of 15 are possible with at least one piece of each flavor?

136. How many handfuls of 15 are possible with at least two pieces of each flavor?

137. How many handfuls of 15 are possible with at least three pieces of each flavor?

138. You have a pile of 20 identical blank cards. On each card you draw a circle, a plus, or a square. How many piles of 20 cards are possible?

139. You have 20 cards and 12 envelopes (labeled $1, 2, \ldots, 12$). In how many ways can you put the 20 cards into the envelopes if
(a) the cards are distinct.
(b) the cards are identical.
(c) the cards are identical and no envelope can be left empty.

140. If the permutations of $1, 2, 3, 4, 5, 6$ are written in lexicographic order, with 123456 in position #1, 123465 in position #2, etc., find the permutation immediately after 246531.

141. If the permutations of $1, 2, 3, 4, 5, 6$ are written in lexicographic order, with 123456 in position #1, 123465 in position #2, etc., find the permutation immediately before 534126.

142. If the permutations of $1, 2, 3, 4, 5, 6$ are written in lexicographic order, with 123456 in position #1, 123465 in position #2, etc., find the permutation in position #483.

143. Find the next largest permutation in lexicographic order after 1324.

144. Find the next largest permutation in lexicographic order after 52143.

145. Find the next largest permutation in lexicographic order after 6714235.

146. Find the next largest permutation in lexicographic order after 3254781.

147. Find the next four largest 4-combinations of the set $\{1, 2, 3, 4, 5, 6, 7, 8\}$ after $\{1, 2, 3, 5\}$.

Answers for Chapter 4

1. 26^7.

2. $P(26, 7)$.

3. 26^6.

4. 26^5.

5. $2 \cdot 26^6$.

6. 21^7.

7. $5 \cdot 7 \cdot 21^6$.

8. First count the number of words that contain both A and B. This number is $8 \cdot 7 \cdot P(24, 6)$. Therefore the answer is equal to total number of words of length eight minus the number of words of length eight that have both A and B: $P(26, 8) - 8 \cdot 7 \cdot P(24, 6)$.

9. 2^9.

10. 2^8.

11. $2 \cdot 2^{10} - 2^8$.

12. $\binom{12}{4}$.

13. $\binom{9}{4}$.

14. $7!$.

15. $6!$.

16. $2 \cdot 6!$.

17. $5 \cdot 4 \cdot 5!$.

18. $2 \cdot 5!$.

19. $6!$.

20. $5 \cdot 6!$.

21. $7! - 2 \cdot 6!$.

22. $5P(8, 4)$.

23. $5 \cdot 4 \cdot P(7, 3)$.

24. $P(7, 5)$.

25. $P(7, 3)$.

26. $2 \cdot 5 \cdot P(7, 4)$.

27. $2 \cdot 4 \cdot P(7, 3)$.

28. $5 \cdot 4 \cdot P(7, 3) - 2 \cdot 4 \cdot P(7, 3)$.

29. $388 \cdot 12$.

30. 2^{2^5}.

31. 2^{10}.

32. 2^6.

33. $\binom{10}{6}$.

34. $\binom{10}{5}$.

35. $\binom{10}{6} + \binom{10}{7} + \cdots + \binom{10}{10} = \frac{2^{10} - \binom{10}{5}}{2}$.

36. $30!$.

37. $\binom{30}{4}$.

38. $\binom{10}{3}\binom{15}{7}$.

39. $15! \cdot 5! \cdot 10!$.

40. (a) $\binom{35}{5}$.   (b) $\binom{20}{3}\binom{15}{2}$.

41. $\binom{37}{6}$.

42. $\binom{20}{3}\binom{17}{3}$.

43. $\binom{17}{2}\binom{20}{4} + \binom{17}{3}\binom{20}{3} + \binom{17}{4}\binom{20}{2} + \binom{17}{5}\binom{20}{1} + \binom{17}{6}\binom{20}{0}$.

44. $\binom{20}{6} + \binom{17}{6}$.

45. (a) $37 \cdot 36 \cdot 35$.   (b) $20 \cdot 19 \cdot 17$.

46. (a) $35 \cdot 34 \cdot 33 \cdot 32$.   (b) $20 \cdot 19 \cdot 15 \cdot 14$.

47. 10^4.

48. $P(10, 4)$.

49. 0.

50. 10^5.

51. 10^2.

52. $5 \cdot 9^4$.

53. $\binom{5}{3} \cdot 9^2$.

54. In how many ways can 5 out of 15 people be put in a row for a picture?

55. A class has 15 women and 7 men. In how many ways can a committee of 4 women and 3 men be formed?

56. $C(10, 1) + C(10, 3) + C(10, 5) + C(10, 7) + C(10, 9)$.

57. $2^{100} - C(100, 0) - C(100, 1) - C(100, 2)$.

58. $(26 + 26 + 10)^6 - (26 + 26)^6$ units of time.

59. $30!$.

60. $10! \cdot 12! \cdot 8!$.

61. $\binom{30}{7}$.

62. $\binom{10}{4}\binom{12}{3}$.

63. 26^8.

64. 26^6.

65. $26 \cdot 26^6$.

66. $8 \cdot 25^7$.

67. $26^8 - 25^8$.

68. $26^7 + 26^7 - 26^6$.

69. $C(25, 6)$.

70. $P(25, 6)$.

71. 2^9.

72. 2^8.

73. 2^8.

74. 2^5.

75. $C(10,3)$.

76. $C(9,2)$.

77. 1.

78. $C(5,3)$.

79. $C(8,3)$.

80. $2C(8,4)$.

81. $C(8,5)$.

82. $C(5,1)C(5,4) + C(5,3)C(5,2) + 1$.

83. $2C(5,3)C(5,1)$.

84. $2C(5,4) + C(5,2)^2$.

85. $5 \cdot 3 \cdot 10 \cdot 5 \cdot 4$.

86. $C(9,5)$.

87. The same hand is counted twice. (Getting a pair of kings first and a pair of sevens second is the same as getting a pair of sevens first and a pair of kings second.) To obtain the correct answer, divide the given answer by two.

88. (a)

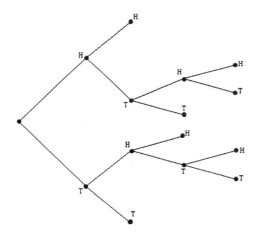

(b) 8.

89. The number of codes is $26 \cdot 10^3 = 26{,}000$. Since $\lceil 60{,}000/26{,}000 \rceil = 3$, at least three parts have the same code number.

90. The number of codes is $10 \cdot 26 \cdot 9 = 2{,}340$. Since $\lceil 6{,}000/2{,}340 \rceil = 3$, at least three parts have the same code number.

91. Divide the square into four congruent 1×1 squares. At least two of the five points lie in or on the edge of one of these 1×1 squares. The maximum distance between these two points is $\sqrt{2}$.

92. There are 4^{10} possible answer sheets. Therefore $2 \cdot 4^{10} + 1$ is the minimum number that will guarantee three identical answer sheets.

93. Let A be one of the people. A either has at least four friends or else has at least six enemies among the other nine people. Case 1: A has at least four friends, say B, C, D, E. If any two of B, C, D, E are friends, then these two together with A form a group of three mutual friends. If none of B, C, D, E are friends with

each other, then B, C, D, E are four mutual enemies. Case 2: A has at least six enemies, say B, C, D, E, F, G. Applying the Pigeonhole Principle to this set of six, there are either three mutual friends or three mutual enemies. If there are three friends, we are done. If there are three mutual enemies, then these three together with A form a group of four mutual enemies.

94. Each computer can be connected to $0, 1, 2, 3, 4$, or 5 other computers, but it is not possible in the network to have a computer connected to 0 others and a computer connected to all 5 others. Therefore there are only five possible connection numbers, which is smaller than the number of computers. By the Pigeonhole Principle at least two must have the same number of connections.

95. There are $2^5 = 32$ subsets. If 33 or more subsets are printed, at least one will have been printed twice.

96. There are $10 \cdot 9 \cdot 8 = 720$ different codes. Therefore $5 \cdot 720 + 1 = 3,601$ is the minimum number of printed codes that guarantees that at least six identical codes will be printed.

97. Use the eleven integers as the pigeons and the ten possible last digits are the pigeonholes.

98. There are ten possible lengths a bit string can have — $0, 1, 2, \ldots, 9$. Since there are 101 bit strings, there is a length number k such that at least 11 bit strings have length k. The number of 0s in these 11 bit strings must be one of the ten numbers $0, 1, 2, \ldots, 9$. Therefore, there are at least two bit strings s_i and s_j, with the same number of 0s. Since s_i and s_j have the same length, k, they both have the same number of 1s.

99. (a) 14.   (b) 27.

100. $16a^4 + 32a^3b + 24a^2b^2 + 8ab^3 + b^4$.

101. $x^5 + 5x^4y + 10x^3y^2 + 10x^2y^3 + 5xy^4 + y^5$.

102. $a^6 + 12a^5 + 60a^4 + 160a^3 + 240a^2 + 192a + 64$.

103. $16c^4 - 96c^3d + 216c^2d^2 - 216cd^3 + 81d^4$.

104. $x^5 - 15x^3 + 90x - 270/x + 405/x^3 - 243/x^5$.

105. $x^{14} + 7x^{11} + 21x^8 + 35x^5 + 35x^2 + 21/x + 7/x^4 + 1/x^7$.

106. In $(a + b)^n$ use $n = 6$, $a = b = 1$.

107. In $(a + b)^n$ use $n = 100$, $a = 1$, $b = -1$.

108. In $(a + b)^n$ use $n = 100$, $a = 1$, $b = 2$.

109. $-\binom{12}{7}3^7$.

110. $\binom{11}{5}2^5$

111. $\binom{13}{9}2^9$.

112. $\binom{10}{3}2^7$.

113. 0.

114. 16.

115. 20.

116. 405.

117. 2143, 2341, 2413, 3142, 3412, 3421, 4123, 4312, 4321.

118. 611.

119. 9.

120. (a) $\binom{34}{2}$.   (b) $\binom{12}{2}$.

121. $\frac{90!}{20! \cdot 30! \cdot 40!}$.

122. (a) $\frac{7!}{2! \cdot 2!}$.

123. $\frac{11!}{(2!)^4}$.

124. $\frac{8!}{3! \cdot 2!}$.

125. Depends on last name.

126. $\frac{6!}{3! 2! 1!}$.

127. (a) $\frac{8!}{3!2!2!1!}$.   (b) $\frac{2\cdot 7!}{3!2!2!}$.

128. (a) $\binom{41}{29}$.   (b) $\binom{34}{29}$.   (c) $\binom{32}{27}$.

129. (a) $\frac{200!}{50!^4}$.   (b) $\binom{15}{3}$.

130. 3^{50}.

131. $\binom{52}{2}$.

132. $\binom{46}{2}$.

133. $\binom{27}{2}$.

134. (a) $\binom{19}{4}$.

135. $\binom{14}{4}$.

136. $\binom{9}{4}$.

137. $\binom{4}{4}$.

138. $\binom{22}{2}$.

139. (a) 12^{20}.   (b) $\binom{31}{11}$.   (c) $\binom{19}{11}$.

140. 251346.

141. 532641.

142. 512436.

143. 1342.

144. 52314.

145. 6714253.

146. 3254817.

147. $\{1,2,3,6\}, \{1,2,3,7\}, \{1,2,3,8\}, \{1,2,4,5\}$.

Questions for Chapter 5

1. What is the probability that a card chosen from an ordinary deck of 52 cards is an ace?

2. What is the probability that a randomly selected integer chosen from the first 100 positive integers is odd?

3. What is the probability that a randomly selected day of the year (366 days) is in May?

4. What is the probability that the sum of the numbers on two dice is even when they are rolled?

5. What is the probability that a fair coin lands Heads 6 times in a row?

6. What is the probability that a fair coin lands Heads 4 times out of 5 flips?

7. Three coins are tossed.
(a) List the elements in the sample space.
(b) Find the probability that exactly two heads show.

8. Suppose you pick two cards, one at a time, at random from an ordinary deck of 52 cards. Find
(a) p(both cards are diamonds).
(b) p(the cards form a pair).

9. Suppose you and a friend each choose at random an integer between 1 and 8. For example, some possibilities are $(3,7), (7,3), (4,4), (8,1)$, where your number is written first and your friend's number second. Find

(a) p(you pick 5 and your friend picks 8).
(b) p(sum of the two numbers picked is < 4).
(c) p(both numbers match).

10. Prove or disprove: $p(E \cup F) = p(E) + p(F)$ for all events E and F.

11. Find and correct the error in the solution to the following problem:

Problem: You flip two coins and want to find the probability that both coins show heads.
Solution: There are three possible outcomes: 2 heads, 2 tails, or 1 head and 1 tail. Since a "success" is one of these three outcomes, p(both heads) $= 1/3$.

12. Let A be the set of all strings of decimal digits of length 5. For example 00312 and 19483 are two strings in A. You pick a string from A at random. What is the probability that
(a) the string begins with 7575.
(b) the string has no 4 in it.

In 13–16 suppose you have 40 different books (20 math books, 15 history books, and 5 geography books).

13. You pick one book at random. What is the probability that the book is a history book?

14. You pick one book at random. What is the probability that the book is not a geography book?

15. You pick two books at random, one at a time. What is the probability that both books are history books?

16. You pick two books at random, one at a time. What is the probability that the two books are from different disciplines?

In 17–19 suppose you have a class with 30 students — 10 freshmen, 12 sophomores, and 8 juniors.

17. You pick one student at random. What is the probability that the student is not a junior?

18. You pick two students at random, one at a time. What is the probability that both are freshmen?

19. You pick two students at random, one at a time. What is the probability that the second student is a freshman, given that the first is a freshman?

20. In a certain lottery game, three distinct numbers between 10 and 25 (inclusive) are chosen as the winning numbers. What is the probability that the winning numbers are all composite numbers.

21. In a certain lottery game you choose a set of six numbers out of 54 numbers. Find the probability that none of your numbers match the six winning numbers.

In 22–27 you pick a bit string from the set of all bit strings of length ten.
22. What is the probability that the bit string has exactly two 1s?

23. What is the probability that the bit string has exactly two 1s, given that the string begins with a 1?

24. What is the probability that the bit string begins and ends with 0?

25. What is the probability that the bit string has more 0s than 1s?

26. What is the probability that the bit string has the sum of its digits equal to seven?

27. What is the probability that the bit string begins with 111?

28. A group of ten women and ten men are in a room. If five of the 20 are selected at random and put in a row for a picture, what is the probability that the five are of the same sex?

29. A group of ten women and ten men are in a room. A committee of four is chosen at random. Find the probability that the committee consists only of women?

30. You pick a word at random from the set of all words of length six of letters of the alphabet with no repeated letters. What is the probability that the word has exactly one vowel?

31. You pick a word at random from the set of all words of length six of letters of the alphabet with no repeated letters. What is the probability that the word begins and ends with a vowel?

32. A red and a green die are rolled. What is the probability of getting a sum of sis, given that the number on the red die is even.

33. A red and a green die are rolled. What is the probability of getting a sum of six, given that the number on the green die is odd?

In 34–39 an experiment consists of picking at random a bit string of length five. Consider the following events:
   E_1: the bit string chosen begins with 1;
   E_2: the bit string chosen ends with 1;
   E_3: the bit string chosen has exactly three 1s.

34. Find $p(E_1|E_3)$.

35. Find $p(E_3|E_2)$.

36. Find $p(E_2|E_3)$.

37. Find $p(E_3|E_1 \cap E_2)$.

38. Determine whether E_1 and E_2 are independent.

39. Determine whether E_2 and E_3 are independent.

In 40–42 you flip an unfair coin, where $p(\text{heads}) = 3/4$ and $p(\text{tails}) = 1/4$, ten times.
40. Find $p(\text{exactly 9 heads})$.

41. Find $p(\text{exactly 7 heads})$.

42. Find $p(\text{at least 7 heads})$.

In 43–45 a bowl has eight ping pong balls numbered 1,2,2,3,4,5,5,5. You pick a ball at random.
43. Find $p(\text{the number on the ball drawn is} \geq 3)$.

44. Find $p(\text{the number on the ball drawn is even})$.

45. Find $E(X)$, where $X =$ the number on the ball you draw.

46. A die has the numbers $1, 2, 2, 3, 3, 3$ on its six sides. If the die is rolled, what is the expected value and variance of the number showing?

47. A pair of dice, each with the numbers $1, 2, 2, 3, 3, 3$ on its six sides are rolled.

(a) What is the expected value of the sum of the numbers showing?

(b) What is the expected value of the product of the numbers showing in part (a)?

48. You have seven cards, numbered 3 through 9, and you pick one at random. If you pick a card with a prime number, you get 1 point; if you pick a card with a composite number, you lose 1 point. Find the expected value of the number of points you get.

49. You flip a coin. If it lands heads, you lose 1 point. If it lands tails, you flip the coin again, and lose 1 point if it lands heads and get 3 points if it lands tails. What is the expected value of the number of points you get when you play this game.

50. Each of 26 cards has a different letter of the alphabet on it. You pick one card at random. A vowel is worth 3 points and a consonant is worth 0 points. Let $X =$ the value of the card picked. Find $E(X)$, $V(X)$, and the standard deviation of X.

51. You have two decks of 26 cards. Each card in each of the two decks has a different letter of the alphabet on it. You pick at random one card from each of the two decks. A vowel is worth 3 points and a consonant is worth 0 points. Let $X =$ the sum of the values of the two cards picked. Find $E(X)$, $V(X)$, and the standard deviation of X.

Answers for Chapter 5

1. 4/52.

2. 50/100.

3. 31/366.

4. 18/36.

5. $1/2^6$.

6. $C(5,4)/2^5 = 5/32$.

7. (a) HHH, HHT, HTH, THH, HTT, THT, TTH, TTT.   (b) 3/8.

8. (a) (13/52)(12/51).   (b) 3/51.

9. (a) 1/64.   (b) 3/64.   (c) 8/64.

10. False. Choose one card at random from a deck of 52 cards. Let E = choose a diamond, F = choose a king. Then $p(E \cup F) = 16/52$ while $p(E) + p(F) = 17/52$.

11. The probabilities of the three outcomes are not equal. Using {HH, HT, TH, TT} as the sample space, the correct answer, 1/4, is obtained.

12. (a) $10/10^5$.   (b) $9^5/10^5$.

13. 15/40.

14. 35/40.

15. $(15 \cdot 14)/(40 \cdot 39)$.

16. $1 - \dfrac{20 \cdot 19 + 15 \cdot 14 + 5 \cdot 4}{40 \cdot 39}$.

17. 22/30.

18. $(10 \cdot 9)/(30 \cdot 29)$.

19. 9/29.

20. $\binom{11}{3}/\binom{16}{3}$.

21. $\binom{48}{6}/\binom{54}{6}$.

22. $\binom{10}{2}/2^{10}$.

23. $9/2^{10}$.

24. $2^8/2^{10}$.

25. $\left(\binom{10}{6} + \binom{10}{7} + \binom{10}{8} + \binom{10}{9} + \binom{10}{10}\right)/2^{10}$.

26. $\binom{10}{7}/2^{10}$.

27. $2^7/2^{10}$.

28. $\left(\binom{10}{5} + \binom{10}{5}\right)/\binom{20}{5}$.

29. $\binom{10}{4}/\binom{20}{4}$.

30. $5 \cdot 6 \cdot P(21,5)/P(26,6)$.

31. $5 \cdot 4 \cdot P(24,4)/P(26,6)$.

32. 1/9.

33. 1/6.

34. 6/10.

35. 6/16.

36. 6/10.

37. 3/8.

38. Yes.

39. No.

40. $\binom{10}{9} \left(\frac{3}{4}\right)^9 \frac{1}{4}$.

41. $\binom{10}{7} \left(\frac{3}{4}\right)^7 \left(\frac{1}{4}\right)^3$.

42. $\binom{10}{7} \left(\frac{3}{4}\right)^7 \left(\frac{1}{4}\right)^3 + \binom{10}{8} \left(\frac{3}{4}\right)^8 \left(\frac{1}{4}\right)^2 + \binom{10}{9} \left(\frac{3}{4}\right)^9 \frac{1}{4} + \binom{10}{10} \left(\frac{3}{4}\right)^{10}$.

43. 5/8.

44. 3/8.

45. 27/8.

46. 7/3, 5/9.

47. (a) 14/3.   (b) 49/9.

48. −1/7.

49. 0.

50. 15/26, 1.38, 1.18.

51. $2 \cdot \frac{15}{26}$, $2 \cdot 1.38$, 1.66.

Questions for Chapter 6

In 1–16, describe each sequence recursively. Include initial conditions and assume that the sequences begin with a_1.

1. $a_n = 5^n$.

2. The Fibonacci numbers.

3. $0, 1, 0, 1, 0, 1, \ldots$.

4. $a_n = 1 + 2 + 3 + \cdots + n$.

5. $3, 2, 1, 0, -1, -2, \ldots$.

6. $a_n = n!$.

7. $1/2, 1/3, 1/4, 1/5, \ldots$.

8. $0.1, 0.11, 0.111, 0.1111, \ldots$.

9. $1^2, 2^2, 3^3, 4^2, \ldots$.

10. $1, 111, 11111, 1111111, \ldots$.

11. a_n = the number of subsets of a set of size n.

12. $1, 101, 10101, 1010101, \ldots$.

13. a_n = the number of bit strings of length n with an even number of 0s.

14. a_n = the number of bit strings of length n that begin with 1.

15. a_n = the number of bit strings of length n that contain a pair of consecutive 0s.

16. a_n = the number of ways to go down an n-step staircase if you go down 1, 2, or 3 steps at a time.

17. Verify that $a_n = 6$ is a solution to the recurrence relation $a_n = 4a_{n-1} - 3a_{n-2}$.

18. Verify that $a_n = 3^n$ is a solution to the recurrence relation $a_n = 4a_{n-1} - 3a_{n-2}$.

19. Verify that $a_n = 3^{n+4}$ is a solution to the recurrence relation $a_n = 4a_{n-1} - 3a_{n-2}$.

20. Verify that $a_n = 3^n + 1$ is a solution to the recurrence relation $a_n = 4a_{n-1} - 3a_{n-2}$.

21. Verify that $a_n = 7 \cdot 3^n - \pi$ is a solution to the recurrence relation $a_n = 4a_{n-1} - 3a_{n-2}$.

In 22–26 find a recurrence relation with initial condition(s) satisfied by the sequence. Assume a_0 is the first term of the sequence.

22. $a_n = 2^n$.

23. $a_n = 2^n + 1$.

24. $a_n = (-1)^n$.

25. $a_n = 3n - 1$.

26. $a_n = \sqrt{2}$.

27. You take a job that pays $25,000 annually.

(a) How much do you earn n years from now if you receive a three percent raise each year?

(b) How much do you earn n years from now if you receive a five percent raise each year?

(c) How much do you earn n years from now if each year you receive a raise of $1000 plus two percent of your previous year's salary.

28. Suppose inflation continues at three percent annually. (That is, an item that costs $1.00 now will cost $1.03 next year.) Let a_n = the value (that is, the purchasing power) of one dollar after n years.

(a) Find a recurrence relation for a_n.

(b) What is the value of $1.00 after 20 years?

(c) What is the value of $1.00 after 80 years?

(d) If inflation were to continue at ten percent annually, find the value of $1.00 after 20 years.

(e) If inflation were to continue at ten percent annually, find the value of $1.00 after 80 years.

In 29–34 determine whether the recurrence relation is a linear homogeneous recurrence relation with constant coefficients.

29. $a_n = 0.7a_{n-1} - 0.3a_{n-2}$.

30. $a_n = na_{n-1}$.

31. $a_n = 5a_{n-1}^2 - 3a_{n-2}^2$.

32. $a_n = a_{n-3}$.

33. $a_n - 7a_{n-2} + a_{n-5} = 0$.

34. $a_n + a_{n-1} = 1$.

35. A vending machine dispensing books of stamps accepts only $1 coins, $1 bills, and $2 bills. Let a_n denote the number of ways of depositing n dollars in the vending machine, where the order in which the coins and bills are deposited matters.

(a) Find a recurrence relation for a_n and give the necessary initial condition(s).

(b) Find an explicit formula for a_n by solving the recurrence relation in part (a).

36. Find the solution of the recurrence relation $a_n = 3a_{n-1}$ with $a_0 = 2$.

In 37–45 solve the recurrence relation either by using the characteristic equation or by discovering a pattern formed by the terms.

37. $a_n = 5a_{n-1} - 4a_{n-2}$, $a_0 = 1$, $a_1 = 0$.

38. $a_n = 5a_{n-1} - 4a_{n-2}$, $a_0 = 0$, $a_1 = 1$.

39. $a_n = -10a_{n-1} - 21a_{n-2}$, $a_0 = 2$, $a_1 = 1$.

40. $a_n = a_{n-2}$, $a_0 = 2$, $a_1 = -1$.

41. $a_n = 2a_{n-1} + 2a_{n-2}$, $a_0 = 0$, $a_1 = 1$.

42. $a_n = 3na_{n-1}$, $a_0 = 2$.

43. $a_n = a_{n-1} + 3n$, $a_0 = 5$.

44. $a_n = 2a_{n-1} + 5$, $a_0 = 3$.

45. $a_n = a_{n-1} + 2n + 1$, $a_0 = 5$.

46. The solutions to $a_n = -3a_{n-1} + 18a_{n-2}$ have the form $a_n = c \cdot 3^n + d \cdot (-6)^n$. Which of the following are solutions to the given recurrence relation?

(a) $a_n = 3^{n+1} + (-6)^n$.

(b) $a_n = 5(-6)^n$.

(c) $a_n = 3c - 6d$.

(d) $a_n = 3^{n-2}$.

(e) $a_n = \pi(3^n + (-6)^n)$.

(f) $a_n = -3^n$.

(g) $a_n = 3^n(1 + (-2)^n)$.

(h) $a_n = 3^n + 6^n$.

47. Assume that the characteristic equation for a homogeneous linear recurrence relation with constant coefficients is $(r - 5)^3 = 0$. Describe the form for the general solution to the recurrence relation.

48. Assume that the characteristic equation for a homogeneous linear recurrence relation with constant coefficients is $(r + 2)(r + 4)^2 = 0$. Describe the form for the general solution to the recurrence relation.

49. Assume that the characteristic equation for a homogeneous linear recurrence relation with constant coefficients is $(r + 1)^4(r - 1)^4 = 0$. Describe the form for the general solution to the recurrence relation.

50. Assume that the characteristic equation for a homogeneous linear recurrence relation with constant coefficients is $(r - 3)^2(r - 4)^3(r + 7)^2 = 0$. Describe the form for the general solution to the recurrence relation.

51. The Catalan numbers C_n also count the number of strings of n +'s and n −'s with the following property: as each string is read from left to right, the number of +'s encountered is always at least as large as the number of −'s.

(a) Verify this by listing these strings of lengths 2, 4, and 6 and showing that there are C_1, C_2, and C_3 of these, respectively.

(b) Explain how counting these strings is the same as counting the number of ways to correctly parenthesize strings of variables.

52. What form does a particular solution of the linear nonhomogeneous recurrence relation $a_n = 4a_{n-1} - 4a_{n-2} + F(n)$ have when $F(n) = 2^n$?

53. What form does a particular solution of the linear nonhomogeneous recurrence relation $a_n = 4a_{n-1} - 4a_{n-2} + F(n)$ have when $F(n) = n2^n$?

54. What form does a particular solution of the linear nonhomogeneous recurrence relation $a_n = 4a_{n-1} - 4a_{n-2} + F(n)$ have when $F(n) = n^2 \cdot 4^n$?

55. What form does a particular solution of the linear nonhomogeneous recurrence relation $a_n = 4a_{n-1} - 4a_{n-2} + F(n)$ have when $F(n) = (n^2 + 1)2^n$?

56. Consider the recurrence relation $a_n = 2a_{n-1} + 3n$.

(a) Write the associated homogeneous recurrence relation.

(b) Find the general solution to the associated homogeneous recurrence relation.

(c) Find a particular solution to the given recurrence relation.

(d) Write the general solution to the given recurrence relation.

(e) Find the particular solution to the given recurrence relation when $a_0 = 1$.

57. Consider the recurrence relation $a_n = -a_{n-1} + n$.

(a) Write the associated homogeneous recurrence relation.

(b) Find the general solution to the associated homogeneous recurrence relation.

(c) Find a particular solution to the given recurrence relation.

(d) Write the general solution to the given recurrence relation.

(e) Find the particular solution to the given recurrence relation when $a_0 = 1$.

58. Consider the recurrence relation $a_n = 3a_{n-1} + 5^n$.

(a) Write the associated homogeneous recurrence relation.

(b) Find the general golution to the associated homogeneous recurrence relation.

(c) Find a particular solution to the given recurrence relation.

(d) Write the general solution to the given recurrence relation.

(e) Find the particular solution to the given recurrence relation when $a_0 = 1$.

59. Consider the recurrence relation $a_n = 2a_{n-1} + 1$.

(a) Write the associated homogeneous recurrence relation.

(b) Find the general golution to the associated homogeneous recurrence relation.

(c) Find a particular solution to the given recurrence relation.

(d) Write the general solution to the given recurrence relation.

(e) Find the particular solution to the given recurrence relation when $a_0 = 1$.

60. Suppose $f(n) = 3f(n/2) + 1$, $f(1) = 1$. Find $f(8)$.

61. Suppose $f(n) = f(n/3) + 2n$, $f(1) = 1$. Find $f(27)$.

62. Suppose $f(n) = 2f(n/2)$, $f(8) = 2$. Find $f(1)$.

63. Suppose $f(n) = 2f(n/2) + 3$, $f(16) = 51$. Find $f(2)$.

64. Suppose $f(n) = 4f(n/2) + n + 2$, $f(1) = 2$. Find $f(8)$.

65. Use generating functions to solve $a_n = 3a_{n-1} + 2^n$, $a_0 = 5$.

66. Use generating functions to solve $a_n = 5a_{n-1} + 1$, $a_0 = 1$.

In 67–76 write the first seven terms of the sequence determined by the generating function.

67. $(x + 3)^2$.

68. $(1 + x)^5$.

69. $(1 + x)^9$.

70. $\dfrac{1}{1 - 3x}$.

71. $\dfrac{x^2}{1 - x}$.

72. $\dfrac{1 + x}{1 - x}$.

73. 5.

74. $e^x + e^{-x}$.

75. $\cos x$.

76. $\dfrac{1}{1-x} - x^2 - x^3$.

In 77–87 find the coefficient of x^8 in the power series of each of the function.

77. $(1 + x^2 + x^4)^3$.

78. $(1 + x^2 + x^4 + x^6)^3$.

79. $(1 + x^2 + x^4 + x^6 + x^8)^3$.

80. $(1 + x^2 + x^4 + x^6 + x^8 + x^{10})^3$.

81. $(1 + x^3)^{12}$.

82. $(1 + x)(1 + x^2)(1 + x^3)(1 + x^4)(1 + x^5)$.

83. $\frac{1}{1-2x}$.

84. $\frac{x^3}{1-3x}$.

85. $\frac{1}{(1-x)^2}$.

86. $\frac{x^2}{(1+2x)^2}$.

87. $\frac{1}{1-3x^2}$.

In 88–100 find a closed form for the generating function for the sequence.

88. $4, 8, 16, 32, 64, \ldots$.

89. $1, 0, 1, 0, 1, 0, 1, 0, \ldots$.

90. $2, 0, 0, 2, 0, 0, 2, 0, 0, 2, \ldots$.

91. $2, 4, 6, 8, 10, 12, \ldots$.

92. $0, 0, 0, 1, 1, 1, 1, 0, 0, 0, 0, 0, 0, 0, 0, 0, \ldots$.

93. $2, 3, 4, 5, 6, 7, \ldots$.

94. $0, 1, 1, 0, 1, 1, 0, 1, 1, 0, 1, 1, 0, 1 \ldots$.

95. $1, -1, \frac{1}{2!}, -\frac{1}{3!}, \frac{1}{4!}, -\frac{1}{5!}, \ldots$.

96. $1, \frac{1}{2!}, \frac{1}{4!}, \frac{1}{6!}, \frac{1}{8!} \ldots$.

97. $1, -1, 1, -1, 1, -1, 1, -1, \ldots$.

98. $1, 0, -1, 0, 1, 0, -1, 0, 1, 0, -1, \ldots$.

99. $\binom{50}{50}, \binom{50}{49}, \binom{50}{48}, \ldots, \binom{50}{1}, \binom{50}{0}, 0, 0, 0, \ldots$.

100. $\binom{50}{1}, 2\binom{50}{2}, 3\binom{50}{3}, \ldots, 50\binom{50}{50}, 0, 0, 0, \ldots$.

101. Set up a generating function and use it to find the number of ways in which eleven identical coins can be put in three distinct envelopes if each envelope has at least two coins in it.

102. Set up a generating function and use it to find the number of ways in which eleven identical coins can be put in three distinct envelopes if each envelope has most six coins in it.

103. Set up a generating function and use it to find the number of ways in which eleven identical coins can be put in three distinct envelopes if no envelope is empty.

104. Set up a generating function and use it to find the number of ways in which eleven identical coins can be put in three distinct envelopes if each envelope has an even number of coins in it.

105. Set up a generating function and use it to find the number of ways in which eleven identical coins can be put in three distinct envelopes if each envelope has at least two but no more than five coins in it.

106. Set up a generating function and use it to find the number of ways in which eleven identical coins can be put in three distinct envelopes (labeled A, B, C) if envelope A has at least three coins in it.

107. Set up a generating function and use it to find the number of ways in which eleven identical coins can be put in three distinct envelopes (labeled A, B, C) envelopes A and B have the same number of coins in them.

108. Set up a generating function and use it to find the number of ways in which nine identical blocks can be given to four children if each child gets at least one block.

109. Set up a generating function and use it to find the number of ways in which nine identical blocks can be given to four children, if each child gets at least two blocks.

110. Set up a generating function and use it to find the number of ways in which nine identical blocks can be given to four children, if each child gets at most five blocks.

111. Set up a generating function and use it to find the number of ways in which nine identical blocks can be given to four children, if the oldest child gets three blocks.

112. Set up a generating function and use it to find the number of ways in which nine identical blocks can be given to four children, if the oldest child gets at most three blocks.

113. Set up a generating function and use it to find the number of ways in which nine identical blocks can be given to four children, if the oldest child gets either 2 or 3 blocks.

114. If $G(x)$ is the generating function for $a_0, a_1, a_2, a_3, \ldots$, describe in terms of $G(x)$ the generating function for $0, 0, 0, a_0, a_1, a_2, \ldots$.

115. If $G(x)$ is the generating function for $a_0, a_1, a_2, a_3, \ldots$, describe in terms of $G(x)$ the generating function for $0, 0, 0, a_3, a_4, a_5, \ldots$.

116. If $G(x)$ is the generating function for $a_0, a_1, a_2, a_3, \ldots$, describe in terms of $G(x)$ the generating function for $a_3, a_4, a_5, a_6, \ldots$.

117. If $G(x)$ is the generating function for $a_0, a_1, a_2, a_3, \ldots$, describe in terms of $G(x)$ the generating function for $a_0, 0, a_1, 0, a_2, 0, a_3, 0, a_4, \ldots$.

118. If $G(x)$ is the generating function for $a_0, a_1, a_2, a_3, \ldots$, describe in terms of $G(x)$ the generating function for $a_0, 3a_1, 9a_2, 27a_3, 81a_4, \ldots$.

119. If $G(x)$ is the generating function for $a_0, a_1, a_2, a_3, \ldots$, describe in terms of $G(x)$ the generating function for $a_0, 0, 0, a_1, 0, 0, a_2, 0, 0, a_3, \ldots$.

120. If $G(x)$ is the generating function for $a_0, a_1, a_2, a_3, \ldots$, describe in terms of $G(x)$ the generating function for $5, a_1, 0, a_3, a_4, a_5, \ldots$.

121. Use generating functions to solve $a_n = 5a_{n-1} + 3$, $a_0 = 2$.

122. Use generating functions to solve $a_n = 7a_{n-1} - 10a_{n-2}$, $a_0 = 1$, $a_1 = 1$.

123. Use generating functions to solve $a_n = 3a_{n-1} + 2^n + 5$, $a_0 = 1$.

124. Find $|A_1 \cup A_2 \cup A_3 \cup A_4|$ if each set A_i has 100 elements, each intersection of two sets has 60 elements, each intersection of three sets has 20 elements, and there are 10 elements in all four sets.

125. Find $|A_1 \cup A_2 \cup A_3 \cup A_4|$ if each set A_i has 150 elements, each intersection of two sets has 80 elements, each intersection of three sets has 20 elements, and there are no elements in all four sets.

126. Find the number of terms in the formula for the number of elements in the union of four sets given by the principle of inclusion-exclusion.

127. Find the number of positive integers ≤ 1000 that are multiples of at least one of $3, 5, 11$.

128. Find the number of positive integers ≤ 1000 that are multiples of at least one of $2, 6, 12$.

129. Find the number of positive integers ≤ 1000 that are multiples of at least one of $3, 4, 12$.

130. Suppose $|A| = |B| = |C| = 100$, $|A \cap B| = 60$, $|A \cap C| = 50$, $|B \cap C| = 40$, and $|A \cup B \cup C| = 175$. How many elements are in $A \cap B \cap C$?

131. How many positive integers not exceeding 1000 are not divisible by either 4 or 6?

132. A doughnut shop sells 20 kinds of doughnuts. You want to buy 30 doughnuts. How many possibilities are there if you want at most six of any one kind?

133. A doughnut shop sells 20 kinds of doughnuts. You want to buy 30 doughnuts. How many possibilities are there if you want at most 12 of any one kind?

134. A market sells ten kinds of soda. You want to buy 12 bottles. How many possibilities are there? if you want

(a) at least one of each kind   (b) at most seven bottles of any kind?

135. A market sells ten kinds of soda. You want to buy 12 bottles. How many possibilities are there? if you want at most three bottles of any kind?

136. Suppose you have 100 identical marbles and five jars (labeled A, B, C, D, E). In how many ways can you put the marbles in the jars if:

(a) each jar has at least six marbles in it?   (b) each jar has at most forty marbles in it?

137. How many ways are there to choose five donuts if there are eight varieties and only the type of each donut matters?

138. A market sells 40 kinds of candy bars. You want to buy 15 candy bars.

(a) How many possibilities are there?

(b) How many possibilities are there if you want at least three peanut butter bars and at least five almond bars?

(c) How many possibilities are there if you want exactly three peanut butter bars and exactly five almond bars?

(d) How many possibilities are there if you want at most four toffee bars and at most six mint bars?

139. How many permutations of all 26 letters of the alphabet are there that contain at least one of the words DOG, BIG, OIL?

140. How many permutations of all 26 letters of the alphabet are there that contain at least one of the words CART, SHOW, LIKE?

141. How many permutations of all 26 letters of the alphabet are there that contain at least one of the words SWORD, PLANT, CARTS?

142. How many permutations of all 26 letters of the alphabet are there that contain none of the words: SAVE, PLAY, SNOW?

143. How many permutations of all 26 letters of the alphabet are there that contain at least one of the words: CAR, CARE, SCAR, SCARE?

144. How many permutations of the 26 letters of the alphabet are there that do not contain any of the following strings: LOP, SLOP, SLOPE, LOPE.

145. You have ten cards, numbered 1 through 10. In how many ways can you put the ten cards in a row so that card i is not in spot i, for $i = 1, 2, \ldots, 10$?

146. Suppose $|A| = 8$ and $|B| = 4$. Find the number of functions $f : A \to B$ that are onto B.

147. An office manager has four employees and nine reports to be done. In how many ways can the reports be assigned to the employees so that each employee has at least one report to do.

148. An office manager has five employees and 12 projects to be completed. In how many ways can the projects be assigned to the employees so that each employee works on at least one project.

149. Find the number of ways to put eight different books in five boxes, if no box is allowed to be empty.

150. Find the number of bit strings of length eight that contain a pair of consecutive 0s.

151. Find the number of ways to climb a 12-step staircase, if you go up either one or three steps at a time.

152. Find the number of strings of 0s, 1s, and 2s of length six that have no consecutive 0s.

Answers for Chapter 6

1. $a_n = 5a_{n-1}, a_0 = 1$.
2. $a_n = a_{n-1} + a_{n-2}, a_1 = a_2 = 1$.
3. $a_n = a_{n-2}, a_1 = 0, a_2 = 1$.
4. $a_n = a_{n-1} + n, a_1 = 1$.
5. $a_n = a_{n-1} - 1, a_1 = 3$.
6. $a_n = na_{n-1}, a_1 = 1$.
7. $a_n = \dfrac{a_{n-1}}{1 + a_{n-1}}, a_1 = 1/2$.
8. $a_n = a_{n-1} + 1/10^n, a_1 = 0.1$.
9. $a_n = a_{n-1} + 2n - 1, a_1 = 1$.
10. $a_n = 100a_{n-1} + 11$.
11. $a_n = 2 \cdot a_{n-1}, a_1 = 2$.
12. $a_n = 100a_{n-1} + 1, a_1 = 1$.
13. $a_n = a_{n-1} + 2^{n-2}, a_1 = 1$.
14. $a_n = 2a_{n-1}, a_1 = 1$.
15. $a_n = a_{n-1} + a_{n-2} + 2^{n-2}, a_1 = 0, a_2 = 1$.
16. $a_n = a_{n-1} + a_{n-2} + a_{n-3}, a_1 = 0, a_2 = 1, a_3 = 1$.
17. $4 \cdot 6 - 3 \cdot 6 = 1 \cdot 6 = 6$.
18. $4 \cdot 3^{n-1} - 3 \cdot 3^{n-2} = 4 \cdot 3^{n-1} - 3^{n-1} = 3 \cdot 3^{n-1} = 3^n$.
19. $4 \cdot 3^{n+3} - 3 \cdot 3^{n+2} = 4 \cdot 3^{n+3} - 3^{n+3} = 3 \cdot 3^{n+3} = 3^{n+4}$.
20. $4(3^{n-1} + 1) - 3(3^{n-2} + 1) = 4 \cdot 3^{n-1} - 3^{n-1} + 4 - 3 = 3^{n-1}(4 - 1) + 1 = 3^n + 1$.
21. $4(7 \cdot 3^{n-1} - \pi) - 3(7 \cdot 3^{n-2} - \pi) = 28 \cdot 3^{n-1} - 7 \cdot 3^{n-1} - 4\pi + 3\pi = 7 \cdot 3^n - \pi$.
22. $a_n = 2a_{n-1}, a_0 = 1$.
23. $a_n = 2a_{n-1} - 1, a_0 = 2$.
24. $a_n = -a_{n-1}, a_0 = 1$.
25. $a_n = a_{n-1} + 3, a_0 = -1$.

26. $a_n = a_{n-1}$, $a_0 = \sqrt{2}$.

27. (a) $25,000 \cdot 1.03^n$.   (b) $25,000 \cdot 1.05^n$.   (c) $25,000 \cdot 1.02^n + 1,000\left(\frac{1.02^n-1}{0.02}\right)$.

28. (a) $a_n = a_{n-1}/1.03$.   (b) $a_{20} = 1/1.03^{20} \approx 0.55$.   (c) $a_{80} = 1/1.03^{80} \approx 0.09$.   (d) $1/1.1^{20} \approx 0.15$.
(e) $1/1.1^{80} \approx 0.00$.

29. Yes.

30. No.

31. No.

32. Yes.

33. Yes.

34. No.

35. (a) $a_n = 2a_{n-1} + a_{n-2}$, $a_0 = 1$, $a_1 = 2$.   (b) $a_n = \alpha(1+\sqrt{2})^n + \beta(1-\sqrt{2})^n$ where $\alpha = (1 + \frac{1}{\sqrt{2}})/2$ and
$\beta = (1 - \frac{1}{\sqrt{2}})/2$.

36. $a_n = 2 \cdot 3^n$

37. $a_n = (-1/3) \cdot 4^n + (4/3) \cdot 1^n$.

38. $a_n = (1/3) \cdot 4^n - (1/3) \cdot 1^n$.

39. $a_n = (-7/4)(-7)^n + (15/4) \cdot (-3)^n$.

40. $a_n = (1/2) \cdot 1^n + (3/2) \cdot (-1)^n$.

41. $a_n = (\sqrt{3}/6)(1+\sqrt{3})^n - (\sqrt{3}/6)(1-\sqrt{3})^n$.

42. $a_n = 2 \cdot 3^n \cdot n!$.

43. $a_n = 5 + 3\frac{n(n+1)}{2}$.

44. $a_n = 3 \cdot 2^n + 5(2^n - 1) = 2^{n+3} - 5$.

45. $a_n = 5 + n(n+1) + n = n^2 + 2n + 5$.

46. (a) Yes.   (b) Yes.   (c) No.   (d) Yes.   (e) Yes.   (f) Yes.   (g) Yes.   (h) No.

47. $a_n = c5^n + dn5^n + en^25^n$.

48. $a_n = c(-2)^n + d(-4)^n + en(-4)^n$.

49. $a_n = c(-1)^n + dn(-1)^n + en^2(-1)^n + fn^3(-1)^n + g + hn + in^2 + jn^3$.

50. $a_n = c3^n + dn3^n + en^23^n + f4^n + gn4^n + hn^24^n + i(-7)^n + jn(-7)^n$.

51. (a) C_1: $+-$, C_2: $+-+-, ++--$, C_3: $+-+-+-, +++---, ++-+--, ++--+-, +-++--$.
(b) Treat each $+$ as a left parenthesis and each $-$ as a right parenthesis.

52. $p_0n^22^n$.

53. $n^2(p_1n + p_0)2^n$.

54. $(p_2n^2 + p_1n + p_0)4^n$.

55. $n^2(p_2n^2 + p_1n + p_0)2^n$.

56. (a) $a_n = 2a_{n-1}$.   (b) $a_n = c2^n$.   (c) $a_n = -3n - 6$.   (d) $a_n = -3n - 6 + c2^n$.   (e) $a_n = -3n - 6 + 7 \cdot 2^n$.

57. (a) $a_n = -a_{n-1}$.   (b) $a_n = c(-1)^n$.   (c) $a_n = \frac{n}{2} + \frac{1}{4}$.   (d) $a_n = \frac{n}{2} + \frac{1}{4} + c(-1)^n$.   (e) $a_n = \frac{n}{2} + \frac{1}{4} + \frac{3}{4}(-1)^n$.

58. (a) $a_n = 3a_{n-1}$ (b) $a_n = c3^n$ (c) $a_n = \frac{5^{n+1}}{2}$ (d) $a_n = \frac{5^{n+1}}{2} + c3^n$ (e) $a_n = \frac{5^{n+1}}{2} - \frac{3^{n+1}}{2}$

59. (a) $a_n = 2a_{n-1}$.   (b) $a_n = c2^n$.   (c) $a_n = -1$.   (d) $a_n = c2^n - 1$.   (e) $a_n = 2^{n+1} - 1$.

60. 40.

61. 79.

62. 1/4.

63. 15/4.

64. 226.

65. $a_n = 7 \cdot 3^n - 2 \cdot 2^n$.

66. $a_n = \frac{5^{n+1}}{4} - \frac{1}{4}$.

67. (a) $9, 6, 1, 0, 0, 0, 0$.

68. $1, 5, 10, 10, 5, 1, 0$.

69. $1, 9, 36, 84, 126, 126, 84$.

70. $1, 3, 9, 27, 81, 243, 729$.

71. $0, 0, 1, 1, 1, 1, 1$.

72. $1, 2, 2, 2, 2, 2, 2$.

73. $5, 0, 0, 0, 0, 0, 0$.

74. $2, 0, 1, 0, \frac{1}{12}, 0, \frac{1}{360}$.

75. $1, 0, \frac{-1}{2!}, 0, \frac{1}{4!}, 0, \frac{-1}{6!}$.

76. $1, 1, 0, 0, 1, 1, 1$.

77. 6.

78. 12.

79. 15.

80. 15.

81. 0.

82. 3.

83. 2^8.

84. 3^5.

85. 9.

86. $7 \cdot 2^6$.

87. 3^4.

88. $\dfrac{4}{1 - 2x}$.

89. $\dfrac{1}{1 - x^2}$.

90. $\dfrac{2}{1 - x^3}$.

91. $\dfrac{2}{(1 - x)^2}$.

92. $x^3(1 + x + x^2 + x^3)$.

93. $\dfrac{1}{(1 - x)^2} + \dfrac{1}{1 - x} = \dfrac{2 - x}{(1 - x)^2}$.

94. $\dfrac{1}{1 - x} - \dfrac{1}{1 - x^3}$.

95. e^{-x}.

96. e^{x^2}.

97. $\dfrac{1}{1 + x}$.

98. $\dfrac{1}{1 + x^2}$.

99. $(1 + x)^{50}$.

100. $50(1 + x)^{49}$.

101. $(x^2 + x^3 + x^4 + \cdots)^3$, 21.

102. $(1 + x + x^2 + \cdots + x^6)^3$, 33.

103. $(x + x^2 + x^3 + \cdots)^3$, 45.

104. $(1 + x^2 + x^4 + x^6 + \cdots)^3$, 0.

105. $(x^2 + x^3 + x^4 + x^5)^3$, 12.

106. $(x^3 + x^4 + x^5 + x^6 + \cdots)(1 + x + x^2 + x^3 + \cdots)^2$, 45.

107. $(1 + x^2 + x^4 + x^6 + x^8 + x^{10})(1 + x + x^2 + x^3 + \cdots)$, 6.

108. $(x + x^2 + x^3 + \cdots)^4$, 56.

109. $(x^2 + x^3 + x^4 + \cdots)^4$, 4.

110. $(1 + x + x^2 + x^3 + x^4 + x^5)^4$, 140.

111. $x^3(1 + x + x^2 + x^3 + \cdots)^3$, 28.

112. $(1 + x + x^2 + x^3)(1 + x + x^2 + x^3 + \cdots)^3$, 164.

113. $(x^2 + x^3)(1 + x + x^2 + x^3 + \cdots)^3$, 64.

114. $x^3 G(x)$.

115. $G(x) - a_0 - a_1 x - a_2 x^2$.

116. $\dfrac{1}{x^3}(G(x) - a_0 - a_1 x - a_2 x^2)$.

117. $G(x^2)$.

118. $G(3x)$.

119. $G(x^3)$.

120. $G(x) - a_0 - a_2 x^2 + 5$.

121. $a_n = -\frac{3}{4} + \frac{11}{4} \cdot 5^n$.

122. $a_n = -\frac{1}{3} \cdot 5^n + \frac{4}{3} \cdot 2^n$.

123. $a_n = \frac{11}{2} \cdot 3^n - 2^{n+1} - \frac{5}{2}$.

124. 110.

125. 200.

126. 15.

127. 515.

128. 500.

129. 542.

130. 25.

131. 667.

132. $\binom{49}{19} - \binom{20}{1}\binom{42}{19} + \binom{20}{2}\binom{35}{19} - \binom{20}{3}\binom{28}{19} + \binom{20}{4}\binom{21}{19}$.

133. $\binom{49}{19} - \binom{20}{1}\binom{36}{19} + \binom{20}{2}\binom{23}{19}$.

134. (a) $\binom{11}{2}$ (b) $\binom{21}{9} - \binom{10}{1}\binom{13}{9}$.

135. $\binom{21}{9} - \binom{10}{1}\binom{17}{9} + \binom{10}{2}\binom{13}{9} - \binom{10}{3}\binom{9}{9}$.

136. (a) $\binom{74}{4}$.   (b) $\binom{104}{4} - \binom{5}{1}\binom{63}{4} + \binom{5}{2}\binom{22}{4}$.

137. $\binom{12}{7}$.

138. (a) $\binom{54}{39}$.   (b) $\binom{46}{39}$.   (c) $\binom{44}{37}$.   (d) $\binom{54}{39} - \binom{49}{39} - \binom{47}{39} + \binom{42}{39}$.

139. $24! \cdot 3$.

140. $3 \cdot 23! - 3 \cdot 20! + 17!$.

141. $3 \cdot 22! - 18!$.

142. $26! - 3 \cdot 23! + 20!$.

143. $24!$.

144. $26! - 24!$.

145. $D_{10} = 10! - \binom{10}{1}9! + \binom{10}{2}8! - \binom{10}{3}7! + \cdots + \binom{10}{10}0!$.

146. $4^8 - \binom{4}{1}3^8 + \binom{4}{2}2^8 - \binom{4}{3}1^8$.

147. $4^9 - \binom{4}{1}3^9 + \binom{4}{2}2^9 - \binom{4}{3}1^9$.

148. $5^{12} - \binom{5}{1}4^{12} + \binom{5}{2}3^{12} - \binom{5}{3}2^{12} + \binom{5}{4}1^{12}$.

149. $5^8 - \binom{5}{1}4^8 + \binom{5}{2}3^8 - \binom{5}{3}2^8 + \binom{5}{4}1^8$.

150. $a_n = a_{n-1} + a_{n-2} + 2^{n-2}$, $a_1 = 0$, $a_2 = 1$. Hence $a_8 = 201$.

151. $a_n = a_{n-1} + a_{n-3}$, $a_1 = a_2 = 1$, $a_3 = 2$. Hence $a_{12} = 60$.

152. $a_n = 2a_{n-1} + 2a_{n-2}$, $a_1 = 3$, $a_2 = 8$. Hence $a_6 = 448$.

Questions for Chapter 7

1. List all the binary relations on the set $\{0, 1\}$.

2. List the reflexive relations on the set $\{0, 1\}$.

3. List the irreflexive relations on the set $\{0, 1\}$.

4. List the symmetric relations on the set $\{0, 1\}$.

5. List the transitive relations on the set $\{0, 1\}$.

6. List the antisymmetric relations on the set $\{0, 1\}$.

7. List the asymmetric relations on the set $\{0, 1\}$.

8. List the relations on the set $\{0, 1\}$ that are reflexive and symmetric.

9. List the relations on the set $\{0, 1\}$ that are neither reflexive nor irreflexive.

In 10–23 determine whether the binary relation is:

(1) reflexive,   (2) symmetric,   (3) antisymmetric,   (4) transitive.

10. The relation R on $\{1, 2, 3, \ldots\}$ where $a\,R\,b$ means $a|b$.

11. The relation R on $\{w, x, y, z\}$ where $R = \{(w, w), (w, x), (x, w), (x, x), (x, z), (y, y), (z, y), (z, z)\}$.

12. The relation R on $\mathcal{Z}$ where $a\,R\,b$ means $|a - b| \leq 1$.

13. The relation R on $\mathcal{Z}$ where $a\,R\,b$ means $a^2 = b^2$.

14. The relation R on $\{a, b, c\}$ where $R = \{(a, a), (b, b), (c, c), (a, b), (a, c), (c, b)\}$.

15. The relation R on $A = \{x, y, z\}$ where $R = \{(x, x), (y, z), (z, y)\}$.

16. The relation R on $\mathcal{Z}$ where $a\,R\,b$ means $a \neq b$.

17. The relation R on $\mathcal{Z}$ where aRb means that the units digit of a is equal to the units digit of b.

18. The relation R on $\mathcal{N}$ where aRb means that a has the same number of digits as b.

19. The relation R on the set of all subsets of $\{1, 2, 3, 4\}$ where SRT means $S \subseteq T$.

20. The relation R on the set of all people where aRb means that a is at least as tall as b.

21. The relation R on the set of all people where aRb means that a is younger than b.

22. The relation R on the set $\{(a, b) \mid a, b \in \mathcal{Z}\}$ where $(a, b)R(c, d)$ means $a = c$ or $b = d$.

23. The relation R on $\mathcal{R}$ where aRb means $a - b \in \mathcal{Z}$.

24. A company makes four kinds of products. Each product has a size code, a weight code, and a shape code. The following table shows these codes:

	Size Code	Weight Code	Shape Code
#1	42	27	42
#2	27	38	13
#3	13	12	27
#4	42	38	38

Find which of the three codes is a primary key. If none of the three codes is a primary key, explain why.

25. If $X =$(Fran Williams, 617885197, MTH 202, 248B West), find the projections $P_{1,3}(X)$ and $P_{1,2,4}(X)$.

In 26–31 suppose R and S are relations on $\{a, b, c, d\}$, where $R = \{(a, b), (a, d), (b, c), (c, c), (d, a)\}$ and $S = \{(a, c), (b, d), (d, a)\}$. Find the combination of relations.

26. R^2.

27. R^3.

28. S^2.

29. S^3.

30. $R \circ S$.

31. $S \circ R$.

In 32–41 find the matrix that represents the given relation. Use elements in the order given to determine rows and columns of the matrix.

32. R on $\{1, 2, 3, 4\}$ where aRb means $|a - b| \leq 1$.

33. R on $\{w, x, y, z\}$ where $R = \{(w, w), (w, x), (x, w), (x, x), (x, z), (y, y), (z, y), (z, z)\}$.

34. R on $\{-2, -1, 0, 1, 2, \}$ where aRb means $a^2 = b^2$.

35. R on $\{1, 2, 3, 4, 6, 12\}$ where aRb means $a|b$.

36. R on $\{1, 2, 4, 8, 16\}$ where aRb means $a|b$.

37. R on $\{1, 2, 4, 8, 16\}$ where aRb means $a \leq b$.

38. R^2, where R is the relation on on $\{1, 2, 3, 4\}$ such that aRb means $|a - b| \leq 1$.

39. R^2, where R is the relation $\{(w, w), (w, x), (x, w), (x, x), (x, z), (y, y), (z, y), (z, z)\}$ on $\{w, x, y, z\}$.

40. R^{-1}, where R is the relation on $\{1, 2, 3, 4\}$ such that aRb means $|a - b| \leq 1$.

41. $\overline{R}$, where R is the relation $\{(w, w), (w, x), (x, w), (x, x), (x, z), (y, y), (z, y), (z, z)\}$ on $\{w, x, y, z\}$.

42. If $M_R = \begin{pmatrix} 1 & 0 & 1 & 0 \\ 1 & 1 & 0 & 1 \\ 1 & 1 & 1 & 0 \\ 1 & 1 & 0 & 1 \end{pmatrix}$, determine if R is: (a) reflexive (b) symmetric (c) antisymmetric (d) transitive.

43. If $M_R = \begin{pmatrix} 1 & 1 & 1 & 1 \\ 0 & 1 & 1 & 1 \\ 0 & 0 & 1 & 1 \\ 0 & 0 & 0 & 1 \end{pmatrix}$, determine if R is: (a) reflexive (b) symmetric (c) antisymmetric (d) transitive.

44. Draw the directed graph for the relation defined by the matrix $\begin{pmatrix} 1 & 0 & 1 & 0 \\ 1 & 1 & 0 & 1 \\ 1 & 1 & 1 & 0 \\ 1 & 1 & 0 & 1 \end{pmatrix}$,

45. Draw the directed graph for the relation defined by the matrix $\begin{pmatrix} 1 & 1 & 1 & 1 \\ 0 & 1 & 1 & 1 \\ 0 & 0 & 1 & 1 \\ 0 & 0 & 0 & 1 \end{pmatrix}$.

46. Draw the Hasse diagram for the relation R on $A = \{2, 3, 4, 6, 10, 12, 16\}$ where aRb means $a|b$.

47. Draw the Hasse diagram for the relation R on $A = \{2, 3, 4, 5, 6, 8, 10, 40\}$ where aRb means $a|b$.

48. Suppose $A = \{2, 3, 6, 9, 10, 12, 14, 18, 20\}$ and R is the partial order relation defined on A where xRy means x is a divisor of y.
(a) Draw the Hasse diagram for R.
(b) Find all maximal elements.
(c) Find all minimal elements.
(d) Find lub($\{2, 9\}$).
(e) Find lub($\{3, 10\}$).
(f) Find glb($\{14, 10\}$).

49. The diagram at the right is the Hasse diagram for a partially ordered set. Referring to this diagram:
(a) List the maximal elements
(b) List the minimal elements
(c) Find all upper bounds for f, g
(d) Find all lower bounds for d, f
(e) Find lub($\{g, j, m\}$)
(f) Find glb($\{d, e\}$)
(g) Find the greatest element
(h) Find the least element
(i) Use a topological sort to order the elements of the poset represented by this Hasse diagram.

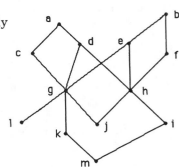

50. Find the transitive closure of R if M_R is $\begin{pmatrix} 1 & 0 & 0 \\ 0 & 1 & 1 \\ 1 & 0 & 1 \end{pmatrix}$.

51. Find the transitive closure of R if M_R is $\begin{pmatrix} 1 & 0 & 1 & 0 \\ 1 & 0 & 0 & 1 \\ 0 & 1 & 1 & 0 \\ 0 & 1 & 0 & 0 \end{pmatrix}$.

52. If $R = \{(1, 2), (1, 4), (2, 3), (3, 1), (4, 2)\}$, find the reflexive closure of R.

53. If $R = \{(1,2), (1,4), (2,3), (3,1), (4,2)\}$, find the symmetric closure of R.

54. If $R = \{(x,y) \mid x$ and y are bit strings containing the same number of 0s $\}$, find the equivalence classes of

(a) 1.

(b) 00.

(c) 101.

55. Find the smallest equivalence relation on $\{1,2,3\}$ that contains $(1,2)$ and $(2,3)$.

56. Find the smallest partial order relation on $\{1,2,3\}$ that contains $(1,1)$, $(3,2)$, $(1,3)$.

57. What is the covering relation of the partial ordering $\{(a,b) \mid a$ divides $b\}$ on the set $\{1,2,3,4,6,8,12,24\}$?

58. What is the covering relation of the partial ordering $\{(a,b) \mid a$ divides $b\}$ on the set $\{2,4,6,8,10,12\}$?

59. Find the join of the 3-ary relation

   $\{$(Lewis,MS410,N507), (Rosen,CS540,N525), (Michaels,CS518,N504), (Michaels,MS410,N510)$\}$

and the 4-ary relation

   $\{$(MS410,N507,Monday,6:00), (MS410,N507,Wednesday,6:00), (CS540,N525,Monday,7:30),
   (CS518,N504,Tuesday,6:00), (CS518,N504,Thursday,6:00)$\}$

with respect to the last two fields of the first relation and the first two fields of the second relation.

60. Find the transitive closure of $R = \{(a,a), (b,a), (b,c), (c,a), (c,c), (c,d), (d,a), (d,c)\}$ on $\{a,b,c,d\}$.

61. Which of the following are partitions of $\{1,2,3,\ldots,10\}$?

(a) $\{2,4,6,8\}$, $\{1,3,5,9\}$, $\{7,10\}$.   (b) $\{1,2,4,8\}$, $\{2,5,7,10\}$, $\{3,6,9\}$.

(c) $\{3,8,10\}$, $\{1,2,5,9\}$, $\{4,7,8\}$.   (d) $\{1\}, \{2\}, \ldots, \{10\}$.

(e) $\{1,2,\ldots,10\}$.

62. Suppose R is the relation on $\mathcal{N}$ where aRb means that a ends in the same digit in which b ends. Determine whether R is an equivalence relation on $\mathcal{N}$.

63. Suppose the relation R is defined on the set $\mathcal{Z}$ where aRb means that $ab \leq 0$. Determine whether R is an equivalence relation on $\mathcal{Z}$.

64. Suppose A is the set composed of all ordered pairs of positive integers. Let R be the relation defined on A where $(a,b)R(c,d)$ means that $a + d = b + c$.

(a) Prove that R is an equivalence relation.

(b) Find $[(2,4)]$.

65. Suppose that R and S are equivalence relations on a set A. Prove that the relation $R \cap S$ is also an equivalence relation on A.

66. Let R be the relation on $A = \{1,2,3,4,5\}$ where $R = \{(1,1), (1,3), (1,4), (2,2), (3,1), (3,3), (3,4), (4,1),$ $(4,3), (4,4), (5,5)\}$. Write the matrix for R.

67. Let R be the relation on $A = \{1,2,3,4,5\}$ where $R = \{(1,1), (1,3), (1,4), (2,2), (3,1), (3,3), (3,4), (4,1),$ $(4,3), (4,4), (5,5)\}$. Draw the directed graph for R.

68. Let R be the relation on $A = \{1,2,3,4,5\}$ where $R = \{(1,1), (1,3), (1,4), (2,2), (3,1), (3,3), (3,4), (4,1),$ $(4,3), (4,4), (5,5)\}$. Find the equivalence classes for the partition of A given by R.

In 69–71 give an example or else prove that there are none.

69. A relation on $\{a,b,c\}$ that is reflexive and transitive, but not antisymmetric.

70. A relation on $\{1,2\}$ that is symmetric and transitive, but not reflexive.

71. A relation on $\{1,2,3\}$ that is reflexive and transitive, but not symmetric.

72. Suppose $|A| = n$. Find the number of binary relations on A.

73. Suppose $|A| = n$. Find the number of symmetric binary relations on A.

74. Suppose $|A| = n$. Find the number of reflexive, symmetric binary relations on A.

Answers for Chapter 7

1. There are 16 binary relations:

$\{\ \}$;	$\{(0,0)\}$;	$\{(0,1)\}$;	$\{(1,0)\}$;
$\{(1,1)\}$;	$\{(0,0),(0,1)\}$;	$\{(0,0),(1,0)\}$;	$\{(0,0),(1,1)\}$;
$\{(0,1),(1,0)\}$;	$\{(0,1),(1,1)\}$;	$\{(1,0),(1,1)\}$;	$\{(0,0),(0,1),(1,0)\}$;
$\{(0,0),(0,1),(1,1)\}$;	$\{(0,0),(1,0),(1,1)\}$;	$\{(0,1),(1,0),(1,1)\}$;	$\{(0,0),(0,1),(1,0),(1,1)\}$.

2. 8, 13, 14, 16.

3. 1, 3, 4, 9.

4. 1, 2, 5, 8, 9, 12, 15, 16.

5. 1, 2, 3, 4, 5, 6, 7, 8, 10, 11, 13, 14, 16.

6. 1, 2, 3, 4, 5, 6, 7, 8, 10, 11, 13, 14.

7. 1, 3, 4.

8. 8, 16.

9. 2, 5, 6, 7, 10, 11, 12, 15.

10. 1, 3, 4.

11. 1.

12. 1, 2.

13. 1, 2, 4.

14. 1, 3, 4.

15. 2.

16. 2.

17. 1, 2, 4.

18. 1, 2, 4.

19. 1, 3, 4.

20. 1, 4.

21. 3, 4, 5, 6.

22. 1, 2.

23. 1, 2, 4.

24. Shape code.

25. $P_{1,3}(X) = $ (Fran Williams, MTH 202) $\quad P_{1,2,4}(X) = $ (Fran Williams, 617885197, 248B West).

26. $\{(a,a),(a,c),(b,c),(c,c),(d,b),(d,d)\}$.

27. $\{(a,b),(a,c),(a,d),(b,c),(c,c),(d,a),(d,c)\}$.

28. $\{(b,a),(d,c)\}$.

29. $\{(b,c)\}$.

30. $\{(a,c),(b,a),(d,b),(d,d)\}$.

31. $\{(a,a),(a,d),(d,c)\}$.

32. $\begin{pmatrix} 1 & 1 & 0 & 0 \\ 1 & 1 & 1 & 0 \\ 0 & 1 & 1 & 1 \\ 0 & 0 & 1 & 1 \end{pmatrix}$.

33. $\begin{pmatrix} 1 & 1 & 0 & 0 \\ 1 & 1 & 0 & 1 \\ 0 & 0 & 1 & 0 \\ 0 & 0 & 1 & 1 \end{pmatrix}$.

34. $\begin{pmatrix} 1 & 0 & 0 & 0 & 1 \\ 0 & 1 & 0 & 1 & 0 \\ 0 & 0 & 1 & 0 & 0 \\ 0 & 1 & 0 & 1 & 0 \\ 1 & 0 & 0 & 0 & 1 \end{pmatrix}$.

35. $\begin{pmatrix} 1 & 1 & 1 & 1 & 1 & 1 \\ 0 & 1 & 0 & 1 & 1 & 1 \\ 0 & 0 & 1 & 0 & 1 & 1 \\ 0 & 0 & 0 & 1 & 0 & 1 \\ 0 & 0 & 0 & 0 & 1 & 1 \\ 0 & 0 & 0 & 0 & 0 & 1 \end{pmatrix}$.

36. $\begin{pmatrix} 1 & 1 & 1 & 1 & 1 \\ 0 & 1 & 1 & 1 & 1 \\ 0 & 0 & 1 & 1 & 1 \\ 0 & 0 & 0 & 1 & 1 \\ 0 & 0 & 0 & 0 & 1 \end{pmatrix}$.

37. $\begin{pmatrix} 1 & 1 & 1 & 1 & 1 \\ 0 & 1 & 1 & 1 & 1 \\ 0 & 0 & 1 & 1 & 1 \\ 0 & 0 & 0 & 1 & 1 \\ 0 & 0 & 0 & 0 & 1 \end{pmatrix}$.

38. $\begin{pmatrix} 1 & 1 & 1 & 0 \\ 1 & 1 & 1 & 1 \\ 1 & 1 & 1 & 1 \\ 0 & 1 & 1 & 1 \end{pmatrix}$.

39. $\begin{pmatrix} 1 & 1 & 0 & 1 \\ 1 & 1 & 1 & 1 \\ 0 & 0 & 1 & 0 \\ 0 & 0 & 1 & 1 \end{pmatrix}$.

40. $\begin{pmatrix} 1 & 1 & 0 & 0 \\ 1 & 1 & 1 & 0 \\ 0 & 1 & 1 & 1 \\ 0 & 0 & 1 & 1 \end{pmatrix}$.

41. $\begin{pmatrix} 0 & 0 & 1 & 1 \\ 0 & 0 & 1 & 0 \\ 1 & 1 & 0 & 1 \\ 1 & 1 & 0 & 0 \end{pmatrix}$.

42. (a) Yes.   (b) No.   (c) No.   (d) No.

43. (a) Yes.   (b) No.   (c) Yes.   (d) Yes.

44.

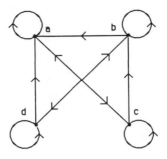

45.

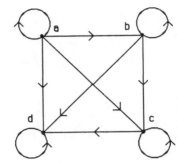

46.

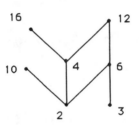

47.

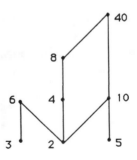

48. (a)

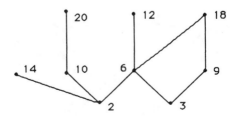

(b) 12, 14, 18, 20.   (c) 2, 3.   (d) 18.   (e) Does not exist.   (f) 2.

49. (a) a, b. (b) l, m. (c) b. (d) h, i, j, m. (e) g. (f) None. (g) None. (h) None.
(i) For example: $m, k, i, j, l, h, g, f, e, c, d, b, a$.

50. $\begin{pmatrix} 1 & 0 & 0 \\ 1 & 1 & 1 \\ 1 & 0 & 1 \end{pmatrix}$.

51. $\begin{pmatrix} 1 & 1 & 1 & 1 \\ 1 & 1 & 1 & 1 \\ 1 & 1 & 1 & 1 \\ 1 & 1 & 1 & 1 \end{pmatrix}$.

52. $\{(1,1), (1,2), (1,4), (2,2), (2,3), (3,1), (3,3), (4,2), (4,4)\}$.

53. $\{(1,2), (1,3), (1,4), (2,1), (2,3), (2,4), (3,1), (3,2), (4,1), (4,2)\}$.

54. (a) All strings that contain no 0s (including the empty string). (b) All strings with exactly two 0s.
(c) All strings with exactly one 0.

55. $\{(1,1), (1,2), (1,3), (2,1), (2,2), (2,3), (3,1), (3,2), (3,3)\}$.

56. $\{(1,1), (2,2), (3,3), (3,2), (1,3), (1,2)\}$.

57. $\{(1,2), (1,3), (2,4), (2,6), (3,6), (4,8), (4,12), (6,12), (8,24), (12,24)\}$.

58. $\{(2,4), (2,6), (2,10), (4,8), (4,12), (6,12)\}$.

59. $\{$(Lewis,MS410,N507,Monday,6:00), (Lewis,MS410,N507,Wednesday,6:00),
    (Rosen,CS540,N525,Monday,7:30), (Michaels,CS518,N504,Tuesday,6:00),
    (Michaels,CS518,N504,Thursday,6:00)$\}$.

60. $\{(a,a), (b,a), (b,c), (b,d), (c,a), (c,c), (c,d), (d,a), (d,c), (d,d)\}$.

61. a, d, e.

62. Yes.

63. No (not reflexive, not transitive).

64. (a) Reflexive: $a + b = b + a$; Symmetric: if $a + d = b + c$, then $c + b = d + a$; Transitive: if
$a + d = b + c$ and $c + f = d + e$, then $a + d - (d + e) = (b + c) - (c + f)$, therefore $a - e = b - f$, or $a + f = b + e$.
(b) $[(2,4)] = \{ (a,b) \mid b = a + 2 \}$.

65. Reflexive: for all $a \in A$, aRa and aSa; hence for all $a \in A$, $a(R \cap S)a$. Symmetric: suppose $a(R \cap S)b$;
then aRb and aSb; by symmetry of R and S, bRa and bSa; therefore $b(R \cap S)a$. Transitive: suppose
$a(R \cap S)b$ and $b(R \cap S)c$; then aRb, aSb, bRc, and bSc; by transitivity of R and S, aRc and aSc; therefore
$a(R \cap S)c$.

66. $\begin{pmatrix} 1 & 0 & 1 & 1 & 0 \\ 0 & 1 & 0 & 0 & 0 \\ 1 & 0 & 1 & 1 & 0 \\ 1 & 0 & 1 & 1 & 0 \\ 0 & 0 & 0 & 0 & 1 \end{pmatrix}$.

67.

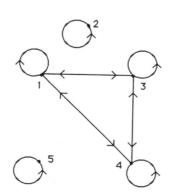

68. $\{1, 3, 4\}, \{2\}, \{5\}$.

69. $\{(a, a), (b, b), (c, c), (a, b), (b, a)\}$.

70. $\{(1, 1)\}$.

71. $\{(1, 1), (2, 2), (3, 3), (1, 2)\}$.

72. 2^{n^2}.

73. $2^{n(n+1)/2}$.

74. $2^{n(n-1)/2}$.

Questions for Chapter 8

In 1–5 find an ordered pair, an adjacency matrix, and a graph representation for the graph.

1. K_6.

2. C_4.

3. W_5.

4. $K_{4,5}$.

5. Q_3.

In 6–46 fill in the blanks.

6. K_n has _____ edges and _____ vertices.

7. $K_{m,n}$ has _____ edges and _____ vertices.

8. W_n has _____ edges and _____ vertices.

9. Q_n has _____ edges and _____ vertices.

10. The length of the longest simple circuit in K_5 is _____.

11. The length of the longest simple circuit in W_{10} is _____.

12. The length of the longest simple circuit in $K_{4,10}$ is _____.

13. List all positive integers n such that C_n is bipartite _____.

14. The adjacency matrix for $K_{m,n}$ has _____ columns.

15. The adjacency matrix for K_n has _____ 1s and _____ 0s.

16. There are _____ 0s and _____ 1s in the adjacency matrix for C_n.

17. The adjacency matrix for Q_4 has _____ entries.

18. The incidence matrix for W_n has _____ rows and _____ columns.

19. The incidence matrix for Q_5 has _____ rows and _____ columns.

20. There are _____ non-isomorphic simple undirected graphs with 5 vertices and 3 edges.

21. There are _____ non-isomorphic simple digraphs with 3 vertices and 2 edges.

22. There are _____ non-isomorphic simple graphs with 3 vertices.

23. List all positive integers n such that K_n has an Euler circuit. _____

24. List all positive integers n such that Q_n has an Euler circuit. _____

25. List all positive integers n such that W_n has an Euler circuit. _____

26. Every Euler circuit for K_9 has length _____.

27. List all positive integers n such that K_n has a Hamilton circuit. _____

28. List all positive integers n such that W_n has a Hamilton circuit. _____

29. List all positive integers n such that Q_n has a Hamilton circuit. _____

30. List all positive integers m and n such that $K_{m,n}$ has a Hamilton circuit. _____

31. Every Hamilton circuit for W_n has length _____.

32. List all positive integers n such that K_n has a Hamilton circuit but no Euler circuit. _____

33. List all positive integers m and n such that $K_{m,n}$ has a Hamilton path but no Hamilton circuit. _____

34. The largest value of n for which K_n is planar is _____.

35. The largest value of n for which $K_{6,n}$ is planar is _____.

36. List all the positive integers n such that $K_{2,n}$ is planar. _____

37. The Euler formula for planar connected graphs states that _____.

38. If G is a connected graph with 12 regions and 20 edges, then G has _____ vertices.

39. If G is a planar connected graph with 20 vertices, each of degree 3, then G has _____ regions.

40. If a regular graph G has 10 vertices and 45 edges, then each vertex of G has degree _____.

41. The edge-chromatic number for $K_{2,5} = $ _____.

42. The vertex-chromatic number for $K_{7,7} = $ _____.

43. The vertex-chromatic number for $C_{15} = $ _____.

44. The vertex-chromatic number for $W_9 = $ _____.

45. The region-chromatic number for $W_9 = $ _____.

46. The vertex-chromatic number for $K_n = $ _____.

In 47–71 either give an example or prove that there are none.

47. A simple graph with 6 vertices, whose degrees are $2, 2, 2, 3, 4, 4$.

48. A simple graph with 8 vertices, whose degrees are $0, 1, 2, 3, 4, 5, 6, 7$.

49. A simple graph with degrees $1, 2, 2, 3$.

50. A simple graph with degrees $2, 3, 4, 4, 4$.

51. A simple graph with degrees $1, 1, 2, 4$.

52. A simple digraph with indegrees $0, 1, 2$ and outdegrees $0, 1, 2$.

53. A simple digraph with indegrees $1, 1, 1$ and outdegrees $1, 1, 1$.

54. A simple digraph with indegrees $0, 1, 2, 2$ and outdegrees $0, 1, 1, 3$.

55. A simple digraph with indegrees $0, 1, 2, 4, 5$ and outdegrees $0, 3, 3, 3, 3$.

56. A simple digraph with indegrees $0, 1, 1, 2$ and outdegrees $0, 1, 1, 1$.

57. A simple digraph with indegrees: $0, 1, 2, 2, 3, 4$ and outdegrees: $1, 1, 2, 2, 3, 4$.

58. A simple graph with 6 vertices and 16 edges.

59. A graph with 7 vertices that has a Hamilton circuit but no Euler circuit.

60. A graph with 6 vertices that has an Euler circuit but no Hamilton circuit.

61. A graph with a Hamilton path but no Hamilton circuit.

62. A graph with a Hamilton circuit but no Hamilton path.

63. A connected simple planar graph with 5 regions and 8 vertices, each of degree 3.

64. A graph with 4 vertices that is not planar.

65. A planar graph with 10 vertices.

66. A graph with vertex-chromatic number equal to 6.

67. A graph with 9 vertices with edge-chromatic number equal to 2.

68. A graph with region-chromatic number equal to 6.

69. A planar graph with 8 vertices, 12 edges, and 6 regions.

70. A planar graph with 7 vertices, 9 edges, and 5 regions.

71. A bipartite graph with an odd number of vertices that has a Hamilton circuit.

72. Are these two graphs isomorphic?

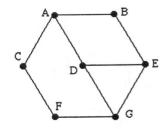 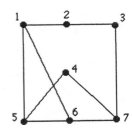

73. Are these two graphs isomorphic?

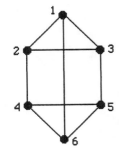 

74. Are these two digraphs isomorphic?

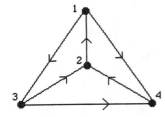 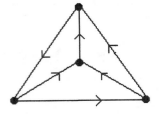

75. Are these two graphs isomorphic?

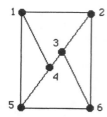 

76. Suppose you have a graph G with vertices $v_1, v_2, \ldots, v_{17}$. Explain how you would use the adjacency matrix A to find

(a) The number of paths from v_5 to v_3 of length 12.

(b) The length of a shortest path from v_5 to v_3.

77. A simple graph is *regular* if every vertex has the same degree.

(a) For which positive integers n are the following graphs regular: C_n, W_n, K_n, Q_n?

(b) For which positive integers m and n is $K_{m,n}$ regular?

78. If a simple graph G has v vertices and e edges, how many edges does $\overline{G}$ have?

79. Draw the digraph with adjacency matrix $\begin{pmatrix} 0 & 0 & 0 & 0 \\ 0 & 0 & 1 & 0 \\ 1 & 1 & 0 & 1 \\ 1 & 1 & 1 & 0 \end{pmatrix}$.

80. Draw the undirected graph with adjacency matrix $\begin{pmatrix} 0 & 1 & 3 & 0 & 4 \\ 1 & 2 & 1 & 3 & 0 \\ 3 & 1 & 1 & 0 & 1 \\ 0 & 3 & 0 & 0 & 2 \\ 4 & 0 & 1 & 2 & 3 \end{pmatrix}$.

81. Suppose G is a graph with vertices a, b, c, d, e, f with adjacency matrix $\begin{pmatrix} 0 & 1 & 0 & 1 & 0 & 0 \\ 1 & 0 & 0 & 1 & 1 & 1 \\ 0 & 0 & 0 & 0 & 1 & 1 \\ 1 & 1 & 0 & 0 & 1 & 0 \\ 0 & 1 & 1 & 1 & 0 & 1 \\ 0 & 1 & 1 & 0 & 1 & 0 \end{pmatrix}$ (where

alphabetical order is used to determine the rows and columns of the adjacency matrix). Find

(a) the number of vertices in G.

(b) the number of edges in G.

(c) the degree of each vertex.

(d) the number of loops.

(e) the length of the longest simple path in G.

(f) the number of components in G.

(g) the distance between vertex a and vertex c.

In 82–84 a graph is a *cubic* graph if it is simple and every vertex has degree 3.

82. Draw a cubic graph with 7 vertices, or else prove that there are none.

83. Draw a cubic graph with 6 vertices that is not isomorphic to $K_{3,3}$, or else prove that there are none.

84. Draw a cubic graph with 8 edges, or else prove that there are none.

85. In K_5 find the number of paths of length 2 between every pair of vertices.

86. In K_5 find the number of paths of length 3 between every pair of vertices.

87. In K_5 find the number of paths of length 6 between every pair of vertices.

88. In $K_{3,3}$ let a and b be any two adjacent vertices. Find the number of paths between a and b of length 3.

89. In $K_{3,3}$ let a and b be any two adjacent vertices. Find the number of paths between a and b of length 4.

90. In $K_{3,3}$ let a and b be any two adjacent vertices. Find the number of paths between a and b of length 5.

91. How many different channels are needed for six television stations (A, B, C, D, E, F) whose distances (in miles) from each other are shown in the following table? Assume that two stations cannot use the same channel when they are within 150 miles of each other?

	A	B	C	D	E	F
A	–	85	175	100	50	100
B	85	–	125	175	100	130
C	175	125	–	100	200	250
D	100	175	100	–	210	220
E	50	100	200	210	–	100
F	100	130	250	220	100	–

92. Consider the graph at the right.

(a) Does it have an Euler circuit?

(b) Does it have an Euler path?

(c) Does it have a Hamilton circuit?

(d) Does it have a Hamilton path?

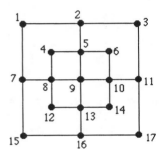

93. Consider the graph at the right.

(a) Does it have an Euler circuit?

(b) Does it have an Euler path?

(c) Does it have a Hamilton circuit?

(d) Does it have a Hamilton path?

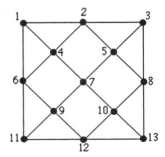

94. Consider the graph at the right.
(a) Does it have an Euler circuit?
(b) Does it have an Euler path?
(c) Does it have a Hamilton circuit?
(d) Does it have a Hamilton path?

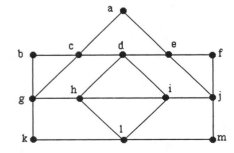

95. Use Dijkstra's Algorithm to find the shortest path length between the vertices a and z in this weighted graph.

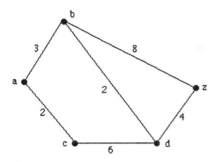

96. Use Dijkstra's Algorithm to find the shortest path length between the vertices a and z in this weighted graph.

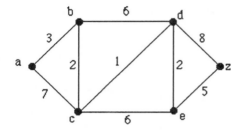

97. The Math Department has 6 committees that meet once a month. How many different meeting times must be used to guarantee that no one is scheduled to be at 2 meetings at the same time, if committees and their members are: $C_1 = \{$Allen, Brooks, Marg$\}$, $C_2 = \{$Brooks, Jones, Morton$\}$, $C_3 = \{$Allen, Marg, Morton$\}$, $C_4 = \{$Jones, Marg, Morton$\}$, $C_5 = \{$Allen, Brooks$\}$, $C_6 = \{$Brooks, Marg, Morton$\}$.

98. Determine whether this graph is planar.

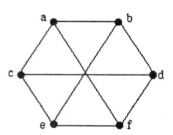

99. Determine whether this graph is planar.

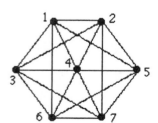

100. Determine whether this graph is planar.

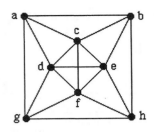

101. The picture at the right shows the floor plan of an office. Use graph theory ideas to prove that it is impossible to plan a walk that passes through each doorway exactly once, starting and ending at A.

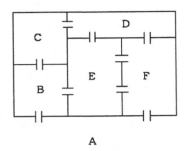

102. Find the vertex-chromatic number, the edge-chromatic number, and the region-chromatic number for $K_{3,2}$.

103. Find the vertex-chromatic number, the edge-chromatic number, and the region-chromatic number for K_4.

104. Find the vertex-chromatic number, the edge-chromatic number, and the region-chromatic number for C_7.

105. Find the vertex-chromatic number, the edge-chromatic number, and the region-chromatic number for Q_3.

106. Find the vertex-chromatic number, the edge-chromatic number, and the region-chromatic number for W_5.

107. Give a recurrence relation for $e_n = $ the number of edges of the graph K_n.

108. Give a recurrence relation for $v_n = $ number of vertices of the graph Q_n.

109. Give a recurrence relation for $e_n = $ number of edges of the graph Q_n.

110. Give a recurrence relation for $e_n = $ the number of edges of the graph W_n.

111. Solve the traveling salesman problem for the graph at the right by finding the total weight of all Hamilton circuits and determining a circuit with minimum total weight.

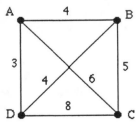

112. Solve the traveling salesman problem for the graph at the right by finding the total weight of all Hamilton circuits and determining a circuit with minimum total weight.

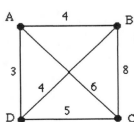

In 113–122 the *grid graph* $G_{m,n}$ refers to the graph obtained by taking an $m \times n$ rectangular grid of streets $(m \leq n)$ with m north/south blocks and n east/west blocks. For example:

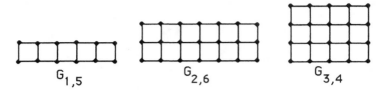

113. Find a formula for the number of vertices of $G_{m,n}$.

114. Find a formula for the number of edges of $G_{m,n}$.

115. Find a formula for the number of regions (including the infinite region) of $G_{m,n}$.

116. For which positive integers m and n does $G_{m,n}$ have an Euler circuit?

117. For which positive integers m and n does $G_{m,n}$ have an Euler path but no Euler circuit?

118. For which positive integers m and n does $G_{m,n}$ have a Hamilton circuit?

119. For which positive integers m and n does $G_{m,n}$ have a Hamilton path but no Hamilton circuit?

120. Find the vertex-chromatic number for $G_{m,n}$.

121. Find the edge-chromatic number for $G_{m,n}$.

122. Find the region-chromatic number for $G_{m,n}$ (including the infinite face).

Answers for Chapter 8

1. Vertices $= \{1, 2, 3, 4, 5, 6\}$; Edges $= \{\{a, b\} \mid 1 \leq a \leq 6, 1 \leq b \leq 6, \ a \neq b\}$;
$$\begin{pmatrix} 0 & 1 & 1 & 1 & 1 & 1 \\ 1 & 0 & 1 & 1 & 1 & 1 \\ 1 & 1 & 0 & 1 & 1 & 1 \\ 1 & 1 & 1 & 0 & 1 & 1 \\ 1 & 1 & 1 & 1 & 0 & 1 \\ 1 & 1 & 1 & 1 & 1 & 0 \end{pmatrix}.$$

2. Vertices $= \{1, 2, 3, 4\}$; Edges $= \{\{1, 2\}, \{2, 3\}, \{3, 4\}, \{4, 1\}\}$;
$$\begin{pmatrix} 0 & 1 & 0 & 0 \\ 0 & 0 & 1 & 0 \\ 0 & 0 & 0 & 1 \\ 1 & 0 & 0 & 0 \end{pmatrix}.$$

3. Vertices $= \{1, 2, 3, 4, 5, 6\}$; Edges $= \{\{1, 2\}, \{1, 3\}, \{1, 4\}, \{1, 5\}, \{1, 6\}, \{2, 3\}, \{3, 4\}, \{4, 5\}, \{5, 6\}, \{6, 2\}\}$;

$$\begin{pmatrix} 0 & 1 & 1 & 1 & 1 & 1 \\ 1 & 0 & 1 & 0 & 0 & 1 \\ 1 & 1 & 0 & 1 & 0 & 0 \\ 1 & 0 & 1 & 0 & 1 & 0 \\ 1 & 0 & 0 & 1 & 0 & 1 \\ 1 & 1 & 0 & 0 & 1 & 0 \end{pmatrix}.$$

4. Vertices $= \{a_1, a_2, a_3, a_4, b_1, b_2, b_3, b_4, b_5\}$, Edges $= \{\{a_i, b_j\} \mid i = 1, 2, 3, 4, \ j = 1, 2, 3, 4, 5\}$;

$$\begin{pmatrix} 0 & 0 & 0 & 0 & 1 & 1 & 1 & 1 & 1 \\ 0 & 0 & 0 & 0 & 1 & 1 & 1 & 1 & 1 \\ 0 & 0 & 0 & 0 & 1 & 1 & 1 & 1 & 1 \\ 0 & 0 & 0 & 0 & 1 & 1 & 1 & 1 & 1 \\ 1 & 1 & 1 & 1 & 0 & 0 & 0 & 0 & 0 \\ 1 & 1 & 1 & 1 & 0 & 0 & 0 & 0 & 0 \\ 1 & 1 & 1 & 1 & 0 & 0 & 0 & 0 & 0 \\ 1 & 1 & 1 & 1 & 0 & 0 & 0 & 0 & 0 \\ 1 & 1 & 1 & 1 & 0 & 0 & 0 & 0 & 0 \end{pmatrix}.$$

5. Vertices $= \{(0,0,0),(0,0,1),(0,1,0),(0,1,1),(1,0,0),(1,0,1),(1,1,0),(1,1,1)\};$

Edges $= \{\,\{(a_1,a_2,a_3),(b_1,b_2,b_3)\} : |a_1 - b_1| + |a_2 - b_2| + |a_3 - b_3| = 1\,\};$ $\begin{pmatrix} 0 & 1 & 1 & 0 & 1 & 0 & 0 & 0 \\ 1 & 0 & 0 & 1 & 0 & 1 & 0 & 0 \\ 1 & 0 & 0 & 1 & 0 & 0 & 1 & 0 \\ 0 & 1 & 1 & 0 & 0 & 0 & 0 & 1 \\ 1 & 0 & 0 & 0 & 0 & 1 & 1 & 0 \\ 0 & 1 & 0 & 0 & 1 & 0 & 0 & 1 \\ 0 & 0 & 1 & 0 & 1 & 0 & 0 & 1 \\ 0 & 0 & 0 & 1 & 0 & 1 & 1 & 0 \end{pmatrix}.$

Graphs for 1-5:

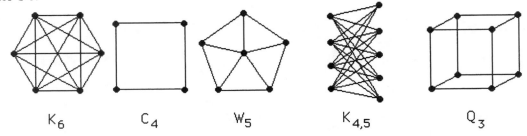

$K_6 \qquad C_4 \qquad W_5 \qquad K_{4,5} \qquad Q_3$

6. $n(n-1)/2$, n.

7. mn, $m+n$.

8. $2n$, $n+1$.

9. $n2^{n-1}$, 2^n.

10. 10.

11. 15.

12. 40.

13. n even.

14. $m+n$.

15. $n(n-1)$, n.

16. $n^2 - 2n$, $2n$.

17. 256.

18. $n+1$, $2n$.

19. 32, 80.

20. 4.

21. 4.

22. 4.

23. n odd.

24. n even.

25. None.

26. 36.

27. All n except $n = 2$.

28. All n.

29. All n except $n = 1$.

30. $m = n > 1$.

31. $n + 1$.

32. n even ($\neq 2$).

33. $m = n + 1$ or $n = m + 1$.

34. 4.

35. 2.

36. All n.

37. $v - e + r = 2$.

38. 10.

39. 12.

40. 9.

41. 5.

42. 2.

43. 3.

44. 4 (if the infinite region is colored).

45. 4.

46. n.

47. None. It is not possible to have one vertex of odd degree.

48. None. It is not possible to have a vertex of degree 7 and a vertex of degree 0 in this graph.

49.

50. None. It is not possible to have a graph with one vertex of odd degree.

51. None. In a simple graph with 4 vertices, the largest degree a vertex can have is 3.

52.

53.

54.

55. None. In a simple graph with five vertices, there cannot be a vertex with indegree 5.

56. None. The sum of the outdegrees must equal the sum of the indegrees.

57. None. The sum of the outdegrees must equal the sum of the indegrees.

58. None. The largest number of edges in a simple graph with six vertices is 15.

59. W_6.

60.

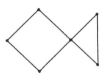

61. $K_{1,1}$.

62. None. Every Hamilton circuit is a Hamilton path.

63. None. The graph would have 12 edges, and hence $v - e + r = 8 - 12 + 5 = 1$, which is not possible.

64. None. The largest such graph, K_4, is planar.

65. C_{10}.

66. K_6.

67. C_9 with one edge removed.

68. None. The 4-color theorem rules this out.

69. Q_3.

70.

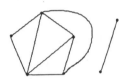

71. None. Any bipartite Hamilton graph must have an even number of vertices.

72. The graphs are isomorphic: A–7, B–4, C–3, D–6, E–5, F–2, G–1.

73. The graphs are not isomorphic: the graph on the left is planar, but the graph on the right is isomorphic to $K_{3,3}$.

74. The digraphs are isomorphic: label the center vertex 4, the top vertex 2, the left vertex 1, and the right vertex 3.

75. The graphs are isomorphic: label the graph clockwise from the top with $2, 3, 6, 5, 4, 1$.

76. (a) Use the 5,3-entry of A^{12}.

(b) Examine the 5,3-entry of $A, A^2, A^3, \ldots, A^{16}$. The smallest positive integer i such that the 5,3-entry of A^i is not zero is the length of a shortest path from v_5 to v_3. If the 5,3-entry is always zero, there is no path from v_5 to v_3.

77. (a) All $n \geq 3$, $n = 3$, all $n \geq 1$, all $n \geq 0$.   (b) $m = n$.

78. $\frac{v(v-1)}{2} - e$.

79.

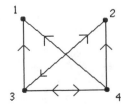

80. The numbers on the edges of the graph indicate the multiplicities of the edges.

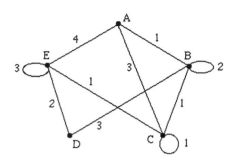

81. (a) 6.

(b) 9.

(c) $2, 4, 2, 3, 4, 3$.

(d) 0.

(e) 9 (G has an Euler circuit).

(f) 1.

(g) 3.

82. None, since the number of vertices of odd degree must be even.

83. This graph is planar, whereas $K_{3,3}$ is not.

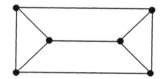

84. None. If $e = 8$, then $3v = 2e = 16$, which is not possible.

85. 3.

86. 13.

87. 819.

88. 9.

89. 0.

90. 81.

91. 4. Stations A, B, E, and F require different channels. Stations C and A can be assigned the same channel. Stations D and B can be assigned the same channel.

92. (a) No.   (b) No.   (c) No.   (d) No.

93. (a) No.   (b) No.   (c) Yes.   (d) Yes.

94. (a) Yes.   (b) Yes.   (c) No.   (d) Yes.

95. First iteration: distinguished vertices a; labels a:0, b:3, c:2, d,z:∞; second iteration: distinguished vertices a, c; labels a:0, b:3, c:2, d:8, z:∞; third iteration: distinguished vertices a, b, c, labels a:0, b:3, c:2, d:5, z:11; fourth iteration: distinguished vertices a, b, c, d, labels a:0, b:3, c:2, d:5, z:9. Since z now becomes a distinguished vertex, the length of a shortest path is 9.

96. First iteration: distinguished vertices a; labels a:0, b:3, c:7, d,e,z:∞; second iteration: distinguished vertices a, b; labels a:0, b:3, c:5, d:9, e,z:∞; third iteration: distinguished vertices a, b, c, labels a:0, b:3, c:5, d:6, e:11, z:∞; fourth iteration: distinguished vertices a, b, c, d; labels: a:0, b:3, c:5, d:6, e:8, z:14; fifth iteration: distinguished vertices a, b, c, d, e; labels a:0, b:3, c:5, d:6, e:8, z:13. Since z now becomes a distinguished vertex, the length of a shortest path is 13.

97. 5. Only C_4 and C_5 can meet at the same time.

98. The graph is not planar. The graph is isomorphic to $K_{3,3}$.

99. The graph is not planar. The graph contains a subgraph isomorphic to $K_{3,3}$, using $\{1,3,5\}$ and $\{2,4,6\}$ as the two vertex sets.

100. The graph is not planar. The graph contains a subgraph homeomorphic to K_5, using vertices b, c, d, e, f.

101. Use vertices for rooms and edges for doorways. A walk would be an Euler circuit in this multigraph, which does not exist since B and D have odd degree.

102. vertex-chromatic number = 2; edge-chromatic number = 3; region-chromatic number = 3.

103. vertex-chromatic number = 4; edge-chromatic number = 3; region-chromatic number = 4.

104. vertex-chromatic number = 3; edge-chromatic number = 3; region-chromatic number = 2.

105. vertex-chromatic number = 2; edge-chromatic number = 3; region-chromatic number = 3.

106. vertex-chromatic number = 4; edge-chromatic number = 5; region-chromatic number = 4 (assuming that the infinite region is colored).

107. $e_n = e_{n-1} + n - 1$.

108. $v_n = 2v_{n-1}$.

109. $e_n = 2e_{n-1} + 2^{n-1}$.

110. $e_n = e_{n-1} + 2$.

111. A–D–B–C–A (weight 18).

112. A–B–D–C–A (weight 19).

113. $(m+1)(n+1)$.

114. $n(m+1) + m(n+1)$.

115. $mn + 1$.

116. $m = n = 1$.

117. $m = 1, n = 2$.

118. m or n odd.

119. m and n even.

120. 2.

121. 4.

122. 3.

Questions for Chapter 9

In 1–26 fill in the blanks.

1. If T is a tree with 999 vertices, then T has _____ edges.

2. There are _____ non-isomorphic trees with four vertices.

3. There are _____ non-isomorphic rooted trees with four vertices.

4. There are _____ full binary trees with six vertices.

5. The minimum number of weighings with a pan balance scale needed to guarantee that you find the single counterfeit coin and determine whether it is heavier or lighter than the other coins in a group of five coins is _____.

6. The value of the arithmetic expression whose prefix representation is $- \; 5 \; / \; \cdot \; 6 \; 2 \; - \; 5 \; 3$ is _____.

7. Write $3n - (k + 5)$ in prefix notation: _____.

8. C_7 has _____ spanning trees.

9. If each edge of Q_4 has weight 1, then the cost of any spanning tree of minimum cost is _____.

10. The best comparison-based sorting algorithms for a list of n items have complexity $O(\underline{\hspace{1cm}})$.

11. The bubble sort has complexity $O(\underline{\hspace{1cm}})$.

12. If T is a binary tree with 100 vertices, its minimum height is _____.

13. If T is a full binary tree with 101 vertices, its minimum height is _____.

14. If T is a full binary tree with 101 vertices, its maximum height is _____.

15. If T is a full binary tree with 50 leaves, its minimum height is _____.

16. Every full binary tree with 61 vertices has _____ leaves.

17. Every full binary tree with 50 leaves has _____ vertices.

18. If T is a full binary tree of height h, then the minimum number of leaves in T is _____ and the maximum number of leaves in T is _____.

19. Every 3-ary tree with 13 vertices has _____ leaves.

20. If T is a full binary tree with 50 internal vertices, then T has _____ vertices.

21. Every full 3-ary tree of height 2 has at least _____ vertices and at most _____ vertices.

22. The largest number of leaves in a binary tree of height 5 is _____.

23. Every full binary tree with 45 vertices has _____ internal vertices.

24. A full 3-ary tree with 13 internal vertices has _____ vertices.

25. There are _____ full 3-ary trees with 6 vertices.

26. If T is a tree, then its vertex-chromatic number is _____ and its region-chromatic number is _____.

In 27–36 mark the statement TRUE or FALSE.

27. If T is a tree with 17 vertices, then there is a simple path in T of length 17.

28. Every tree is bipartite.

29. There is a tree with degrees $3, 2, 2, 2, 1, 1, 1, 1, 1$.

30. There is a tree with degrees $3, 3, 2, 2, 1, 1, 1, 1$.

31. If two trees have the same number of vertices and the same degrees, then the two trees are isomorphic.

32. If T is a tree with 50 vertices, the largest degree that any vertex can have is 49.

33. In a rooted binary tree with 16 vertices, there must be a path of length 4.

34. Every tree is planar.

35. No tree has a Hamilton path.

36. If T is a rooted binary tree of height 5, then T has at most 25 leaves.

37. Draw all nonisomorphic trees with 5 vertices.

38. Draw all nonisomorphic rooted trees with 4 vertices.

39. Suppose T is a full m-ary tree with i internal vertices. Prove that T has $1 + (m-1)i$ leaves.

40. Prove that if T is a full m-ary tree with l leaves, then T has $(ml-1)/(m-1)$ vertices.

41. Suppose T is a full m-ary tree with l leaves. Prove that T has $(l-1)/(m-1)$ internal vertices.

42. Prove that if T is a full m-ary tree with v vertices, then T has $((m-1)v+1)/m$ leaves.

43. Suppose that the universal address set address of a vertex v in an ordered rooted tree is 3.2.5.1.5. Find

(a) the level of v.

(b) the minimum number of siblings of v.

(c) the address of the parent of v.

(d) the minimum number of vertices in the tree.

44. Suppose you have 50 coins, one of which is counterfeit (either heavier or lighter than the others). You use a pan balance scale to find the bad coin. Prove that 4 weighings is not enough to guarantee that you find the bad coin and determine whether it is heavier or lighter than the other coins.

45. Suppose you have 5 coins, one of which is counterfeit (either heavier or lighter than the other four). You use a pan balance scale to find the bad coin and determine whether it is heavier or lighter.

(a) Prove that 2 weighings are not enough to guarantee that you find the bad coin and determine whether it is heavier or lighter.

(b) Draw a decision tree for weighing the coins to determine the bad coin (and whether it is heavier or lighter) in the minimum number of weighings.

46. Suppose you have 5 coins, one of which is heavier than the other four. Draw the decision tree for using a pan balance scale to find the heavy coin.

47. (a) Set up a binary tree for the following list, in the given order, using alphabetical ordering: STOP, LET, THERE, TAPE, NONE, YOU, ANT, NINE, OAT, NUT.

(b) Explain step by step how you would search for the word TEST in your tree.

(c) What is the height of the shortest binary search tree that can hold all 10 words?

(d) Write the preorder traversal of the tree.

(e) Write the postorder traversal of the tree.

(f) Write the inorder traversal of the tree.

48. (a) Set up a binary tree for the following list, in the given order, using alphabetical ordering: SHE, SELLS, SEA, SHELLS, BY, THE, SEASHORE.

(b) How many comparisons with words in the tree are needed to determine if the word SHARK is in the tree?

(c) How many comparisons with words in the tree are needed to determine if the word SEAWEED is in the tree?

(d) How many comparisons with words in the tree are needed to determine if the word CONCH is in the tree?

49. Draw a parsing tree for $(a - (3 + 2b))/(c^2 + d)$.

50. Find the preorder traversal of the parsing tree for $(8x - y)^5 - 7\sqrt{4z - 3}$.

51. Find the postorder traversal of the parsing tree for $(8x - y)^5 - 7\sqrt{4z - 3}$.

52. Find the inorder traversal of the parsing tree for $(8x - y)^5 - 7\sqrt{4z - 3}$.

In 53–55 refer to the tree at the right.

53. Find the preorder traversal.

54. Find the inorder traversal.

55. Find the postorder traversal.

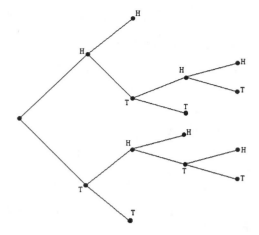

56. The algebraic expression $/ - \uparrow - a \cdot 7\, c\, 3\, 4 \cdot 3\, b$ is written in prefix notation. Write the expression in postfix notation.

57. Write the compound proposition $(\neg p) \to (q \vee (r \wedge \neg s))$ in postfix notation.

58. Write the compound proposition $(\neg p) \to (q \vee (r \wedge \neg s))$ in prefix notation.

59. Write the compound proposition $(\neg p) \to (q \vee (r \wedge \neg s))$ in infix notation.

60. The string $2\, 3\, a \cdot x + 4 \uparrow + 7 \uparrow$ is postfix notation for an algebraic expression. Write the expression in prefix notation.

61. The string $2\, 3\, a \cdot x + 4 \uparrow + 7 \uparrow$ is postfix notation for an algebraic expression. Write the expression in infix notation.

62. The string $- \cdot 2 - x\, a + 4\, y$ is prefix notation for an algebraic expression. Write the expression in postfix notation.

63. The string $- \cdot 2 - x\, a + 4\, y$ is prefix notation for an algebraic expression. Write the expression in infix notation.

64. The string $p\, r\, q \to \neg\, q \triangle p \to \wedge$ is postfix notation for a logic expression, however there is a misprint. The triangle should be one of these three: r, $\vee$, or $\neg$. Determine which of these three it must be and explain your reasoning.

65. Find the value of $- \uparrow x \cdot 5\, t\, / 4 - 7\, c$ (in prefix notation) if $c = 5$, $x = 2$, and $t = 1$.

In 66–73 refer to this graph.

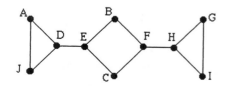

66. Using alphabetical ordering, find a spanning tree for this graph by using a depth-first search.

67. Using alphabetical ordering, find a spanning tree for this graph by using a breadth-first search.

68. Using the ordering C, D, E, F, G, H, I, J, A, B, C find a spanning tree for this graph by using a depth-first search.

69. Using the ordering C, D, E, F, G, H, I, J, A, B, C find a spanning tree for this graph by using a breadth-first search.

70. Using reverse alphabetical ordering, find a spanning tree for the graph by using a depth-first search.

71. Using reverse alphabetical ordering, find a spanning tree for the graph by using a breadth-first search.

72. Using the ordering B, G, J, A, C, I, F, H, D, E, find a spanning tree for this graph by using a depth-first search.

73. Using the ordering B, G, J, A, C, I, F, H, D, E, find a spanning tree for this graph by using a breadth-first search.

In 74–81 refer to this graph.

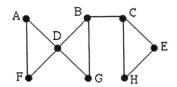

74. Using alphabetical ordering, find a spanning tree for this graph by using a depth-first search.

75. Using alphabetical ordering, find a spanning tree for this graph by using a breadth-first search.

76. Using the ordering C, D, E, F, G, H, I, J, A, B, C find a spanning tree for this graph by using a depth-first search.

77. Using the ordering C, D, E, F, G, H, I, J, A, B, C find a spanning tree for this graph by using a breadth-first search.

78. Using reverse alphabetical ordering, find a spanning tree for the graph by using a depth-first search.

79. Using reverse alphabetical ordering, find a spanning tree for the graph by using a breadth-first search.

80. Using the ordering B, G, J, A, C, I, F, H, D, E, find a spanning tree for this graph by using a depth-first search.

81. Using the ordering B, G, J, A, C, I, F, H, D, E, find a spanning tree for this graph by using a breadth-first search.

82. Find a spanning tree for the graph $K_{3,4}$ using a depth-first search. (Assume that the vertices are labeled u_1, u_2, u_3 in one set and v_1, v_2, v_3, v_4 in the other set, and that alphabetical ordering is used in the search, with numerical ordering on the subscripts used to break ties.)

83. Find a spanning tree for the graph $K_{3,4}$ using a breadth-first search. (Assume that the vertices are labeled u_1, u_2, u_3 in one set and v_1, v_2, v_3, v_4 in the other set, and that alphabetical ordering is used in the search, with numerical ordering on the subscripts used to break ties.)

84. Is the following code a prefix code: A: 11, B: 10, C: 0?

85. Use the bubble sort to sort the list 5, 2, 3, 1, 4 in increasing order.

86. Use the merge sort to sort the list 4, 8, 6, 1, 5, 7, 3, 2 in increasing order.

87. Use the bubble sort to sort the list 5, 4, 3, 2, 1 in increasing order.

88. Use the merge sort to sort the list 3, 8, 12, 4, 1, 5, 9, 6 in increasing order.

89. Use backtracking to find a sum of integers in the set $\{18, 19, 23, 25, 31\}$ that equals 44.

90. Find a minimal spanning tree for this weighted graph using Prim's algorithm.

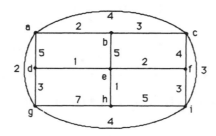

91. Use Prim's algorithm to find a minimal spanning tree for this weighted graph. Use alphabetical order to break ties.

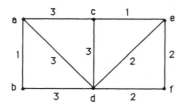

92. Find a spanning tree of minimum cost for this graph.

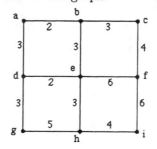

93. Describe the difference between Prim's algorithm and Kruskal's algorithm for finding a spanning tree of minimum cost.

Answers for Chapter 9

1. 998.

2. 2.

3. 4.

4. 0.

5. 3.

6. -1.

7. $- \cdot 3\, n + k\, 5$.

8. 7.

9. 15.

10. $n \log_2 n$.

11. n^2.

12. 6.

13. 6.

14. 50.

15. 6.

16. 31.

17. 99.

18. $h + 1$, 2^h.

19. 9.

20. 101.

21. 7, 13.

22. 32.

23. 22.

24. 40.

25. 0.

26. 2, 1.

27. False.

28. True.

29. False.

30. True.

31. False.

32. True.

33. True.

34. True.

35. False.

36. False.

37.

38.

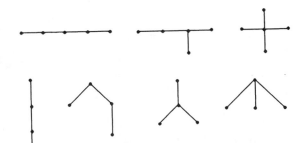

39. $mi + 1 = v = i + l$. Therefore $l = mi + 1 - i = 1 + (m - 1)i$.

40. $mi + 1 = v$ and $i = v - l$. Therefore $m(v - l) + 1 = v$. Solve for v to obtain the formula.

41. $i + l = v = mi + 1$. Therefore $i + l = mi + 1$. Solve for i to obtain the result.

42. $i + l = v$ and $mi + 1 = v$. Therefore $v - l = i$ and $i = (v - 1)/m$. Therefore, $v - l = (v - 1)/m$. Solve for l to obtain the result.

43. (a) 5.   (b) 4.   (c) 3.2.5.1.   (d) 17.

44. Four weighings yield a 3-ary tree of height 4, which has at most 81 leaves. Fifty coins require a tree with 100 leaves.

45. (a) Two weighings yield a 3-ary tree of height 2, which has at most 9 leaves, but 5 coins require a tree with 10 leaves.

(b) Use the weighing 1 and 2 against 3 and 4 as the root. If the four coins have the same weight, weigh 1 against 5 to determine whether 5 is heavy or light. If 1 and 2 are lighter or heavier than 3 and 4, weigh 1 against 2. If 1 and 2 balance, weight 3 against 4 to find out which of these coins is heavier or lighter; if 1 and 2 do not balance, then immediate information is obtained regarding coins 1 or 2.

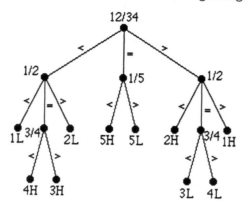

46. Weigh 1 and 2 against 3 and 4. If they balance, 5 is the bad coin. If 1 and 2 weigh less than 3 and 4, weigh 3 against 4 to find which of 3 or 4 is bad. If 1 and 2 weigh more than 3 and 4, weigh 1 against 2 to find out which of 1 or 2 is bad.

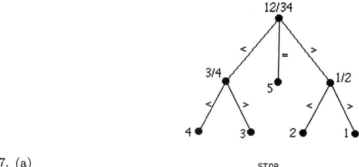

47. (a)

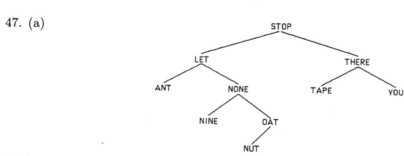

(b) In sequence, TEST would be compared with STOP, THERE, TAPE, and inserted as the right child of TAPE.   (c) 3.   (d) STOP, LET, ANT, NONE, NINE, OAT, NUT, THERE, TAPE, YOU.   (e) ANT, NINE, NUT, OAT, NONE. LET, TAPE, YOU, THERE, STOP.   (f) ANT, LET, NINE, NONE, NUT, OAT, STOP, TAPE, THERE, YOU.

48. (a)

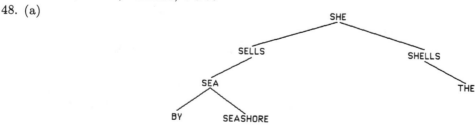

(b) 2.   (c) 4.   (d) 4.

49.

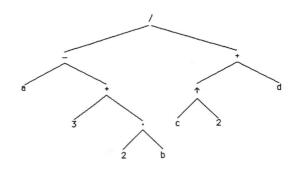

50. $- \uparrow - \cdot 8 \ x \ y \ 5 \ \cdot \ 7 \ \sqrt{} \ - \ \cdot 4 \ z \ 3$

51. $8 \ x \ \cdot \ y \ - \ 5 \ \uparrow \neg 4 \ z \ \cdot \ 3 \ - \ \sqrt{} \ \cdot \ -$

52. $8 \ \cdot \ x \ - \ y \ \uparrow 5 \ - \ 7 \ \cdot \ 4 \ \cdot \ z \ - \ 3 \ \sqrt{}.$

53. $d \ b \ a \ c \ e \ f \ g \ h \ i \ l \ j \ m \ k \ n \ o \ p$

54. $a \ b \ c \ f \ e \ g \ d \ i \ h \ j \ l \ k \ m \ n \ o \ p$

55. $a \ c \ f \ g \ e \ b \ i \ j \ k \ n \ m \ o \ p \ l \ h \ d$

56. $a \ 7 \ c \ \cdot \ - \ 3 \ \uparrow \ 4 \ - \ 3 \ b \ \cdot \ /$

57. $p \ \neg \ q \ r \ s \ \neg \ \wedge \ \vee \ \rightarrow$

58. $\rightarrow \ \neg \ p \ \vee \ q \ \wedge \ r \ \neg \ s$

59. $p \ \neg \ \rightarrow \ q \ \vee \ r \ \wedge \ s \ \neg$

60. $\uparrow + 2 \uparrow + \cdot 3 \ a \ x \ 4 \ 7$

61. $2 + 3 \cdot a + x \uparrow 4 \uparrow 7$

62. $2 \ x \ a \ - \ \cdot \ 4 \ y \ + \ -$

63. $2 \cdot x - a - 4 + y$

64. The triangle should be $\vee$. Using either r or $\neg$ makes the parsing tree impossible to draw.

65. 30.

66.

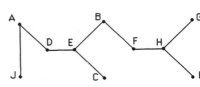

67.

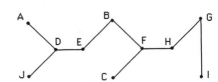

68.

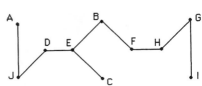

69.

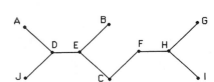

70.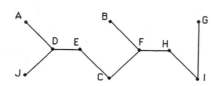

71.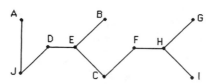

72.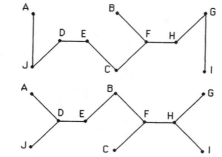

73.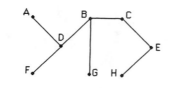

74.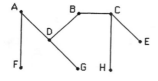

75.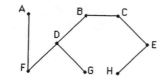

76.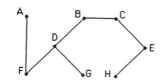

77.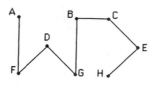

78.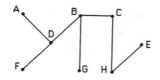

79.

80.

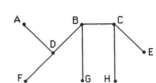

81.

82.

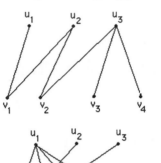

83.

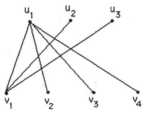

84. Yes

85. $2, 5, 3, 1, 4$, $2, 3, 5, 1, 4$, $2, 3, 1, 5, 4$, $2, 3, 1, 4, 5$; $2, 3, 1, 4, 5$, $2, 1, 3, 4, 5$, $2, 1, 3, 4, 5$; $1, 2, 3, 4, 5$, $1, 2, 3, 4, 5$; $1, 2, 3, 4, 5$.

86. After splitting the list into eight lists of 1 element each, the lists are merged into four sorted lists of 2 elements each: $4, 8$; $1, 6$; $5, 7$; $2, 3$. These are merged into two sorted lists of 4 elements: $1, 4, 6, 8$ and $2, 3, 5, 7$. Finally, these are merged into the final sorted list $1, 2, 3, 4, 5, 6, 7, 8$.

87. $5, 4, 3, 2, 1$, $4, 5, 3, 2, 1$, $4, 3, 5, 2, 1$, $4, 3, 2, 5, 1$, $4, 3, 2, 1, 5$; $3, 4, 2, 1, 5$, $3, 2, 4, 1, 5$, $3, 2, 1, 4, 5$; $2, 3, 1, 4, 5$, $2, 1, 3, 4, 5$; $1, 2, 3, 4, 5$.

88. $3, 8$; $4, 12$; $1, 5$; $6, 9$. $3, 4, 8, 12$; $1, 5, 6, 9$. $1, 3, 4, 5, 6, 8, 9, 12$.

89. The following tree is obtained using backtracking; it yields $44 = 19 + 25$.

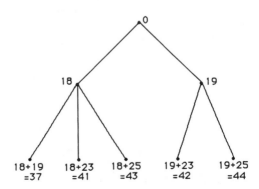

90. In order, the following edges are added: $\{d, e\}$, $\{e, h\}$, $\{e, f\}$, $\{d, g\}$, $\{g, a\}$, $\{a, b\}$, $\{b, c\}$, $\{c, i\}$. The weight of the minimal spanning tree is 17.

91. In order, the following edges are added: $\{a, b\}$. $\{a, c\}$, $\{c, e\}$, $\{d, e\}$. $\{d, f\}$. The weight is 9.

92. The minimum weight is 24. One example of a tree is

93. Using Prim's algorithm, at each stage the edges selected will form a tree, whereas in Kruskal's algorithm this need not happen.

Questions for Chapter 10

In 1–8 fill in the blanks.

1. The idempotent laws in a Boolean algebra state that _____ and _____.

2. There are _____ Boolean functions with 2 variables.

3. There are _____ Boolean functions with 3 variables.

4. There are _____ Boolean functions with 4 variables.

5. Using "↓" for "nor", $(x \downarrow y) \downarrow (x \downarrow y)$ can be written in terms of $\neg$, $\vee$, and $\wedge$ as _____.

6. Using "↓" for "nor", $(x \downarrow x) \downarrow (y \downarrow y)$ can be written in terms of $\neg$, $\vee$, and $\wedge$ as _____.

7. When written as a sum of minterms (in the variables x and y), $x + \overline{x}\,y = $ _____.

8. When written as a product of maxterms (in the variables x and y), $(x + y)\,z = $ _____.

In 9–22 mark each statement TRUE or FALSE.

9. When written as a sum of minterms in the variables x and y, $x + \overline{y} = x\,y + x\,\overline{y} + \overline{x}\,\overline{y}$.

10. When written as a sum of minterms in the variables x and y, $1 = x\,y + x\,\overline{y} + \overline{x}\,y + \overline{x}\,\overline{y}$.

11. If $f(z, y, z) = x\,y\,z$, then $\overline{f(z, y, z)} = \overline{x}\,\overline{y}\,\overline{z}$.

12. $x\,x\,x + x\,y + y\,y = x\,y$.

13. Every Boolean function can be written using only the operators $^{-}$, $+$, and $\cdot$.

14. There are n^2 minterms in the variables $x_1, x_2, \ldots, x_n$.

15. $\overline{x}\,\overline{y} = ((x|x)|(y|y)) \mid ((x|x)|(y|y))$.

16. $x + y = \overline{x} \mid \overline{y}$.

17. $x \downarrow y = \overline{x + y}$.

18. $\overline{x \downarrow y} = \overline{x} \mid \overline{y}$.

19. $\overline{x \mid y} = x \downarrow y$.

20. $\{+, \cdot\}$ is a functionally complete set of operators.

21. The circuit diagrams for $x + \overline{x}\,y$ and $y + x\,\overline{y}$ produce the same output.

22. The circuit diagrams for $\overline{\overline{x}\,\overline{y} + \overline{x}\,y}$ and $x + y$ produce the same output.

23. Write $x + y$ as a sum-of-products in the variables x and y.

24. Write $x(y + 1)$ as a sum-of-products in the variables x and y.

25. Write $(x + y)(\overline{x} + \overline{y})$ as a sum-of-products in the variables x and y.

26. Write 1 as a sum-of-products in the variables x and y.

27. Write $x + y + z$ as a sum-of-products in the variables x, y, and z.

28. Write $x\,y + x\,y\,\overline{z}$ as a sum-of-products in the variables x, y, and z.

29. Write $(x + y\,z)(\overline{x} + y\,z)$ as a sum-of-products in the variables x, y, and z.

30. Write $x + z$ as a sum-of-products in the variables x, y, and z.

31. Write $x\,\overline{y}\,z$ as a sum-of-products in the variables x, y, and z.

32. Find the sum-of-products expansion of the Boolean function $f(x, y)$ that is 1 if and only if either $x = 0$ and $y = 1$, or $x = 1$ and $y = 0$.

33. Find the sum-of-products expansion of the Boolean function $f(x, y, z)$ that is 1 if and only if exactly two of the three variables have value 1.

34. Find the sum-of-products expansion of the Boolean function $f(x, y, z)$ that is 1 if and only if either $x = z = 1$ and $y = 0$, or $x = 0$ and $y = z = 1$.

35. Find a Boolean function $F : \{0, 1\}^2 \to \{0, 1\}$ such that $F(0, 0) = F(0, 1) = F(1, 1) = 1$ and $F(1, 0) = 0$.

36. (a) Find a Boolean function $f : \{0, 1\}^3 \to \{0, 1\}$ such that $f(1, 1, 0) = 1$, $f(0, 1, 1) = 1$, and $f(x, y, z) = 0$ otherwise.

(b) Write f using only $\cdot$ and $^{-}$

37. If $f(w, x, y, z) = \overline{(\overline{x} + y\,\overline{z})} + (\overline{w}\,x)$, find $f(1, 1, 1, 1)$.

38. If $f(w, x, y, z) = \overline{(\overline{x} + y\,\overline{z})} + (\overline{w}\,x)$, find $f(0, 1, 0, 1)$.

39. If $f(w, x, y, z) = \overline{(\overline{x} + y\,\overline{z})} + (\overline{w}\,x)$, find $f(1, 0, 1, 1)$.

40. If $f(w, x, y, z) = \overline{(\overline{x} + y\,\overline{z})} + (\overline{w}\,x)$, find $f(0, 0, 0, 0)$.

41. If $f(w, x, y, z) = \overline{(\overline{x} + y\,\overline{z})} + (\overline{w}\,x)$, find $f(1, 1, 0, 0)$.

42. If $f(w, x, y, z) = \overline{(\overline{x} + y\,\overline{z})} + (\overline{w}\,x)$, find $f(0, 0, 1, 0)$.

43. Prove that $F = G$, where $F(x, y) = \overline{(x + \overline{x}\,y)}\,\overline{y}$ and $G(x, y) = \overline{x} + y$.

44. Show that the Boolean function F given by $F(x, y, z) = x(z + y\,z) + y\,\overline{(\overline{x}\,\overline{z}\,x)}$ simplifies to $x\,z + \overline{x}\,y$, by using only the definition of a Boolean algebra.

45. Show that the Boolean function F given by $F(x, y, z) = \overline{\overline{x} + y} + xy + \overline{x + y}$ simplifies to $x + \overline{y}$, by using only the definition of a Boolean algebra.

46. Using only the five properties associative laws, commutative laws, distributive laws, identity laws, and complement laws, prove that $x\,x = x$ is true in all Boolean algebras.

47. Using only the five properties associative laws, commutative laws, distributive laws, identity laws, and complement laws, prove that $x + x = x$ is true in all Boolean algebras.

48. Using only the five properties associative laws, commutative laws, distributive laws, identity laws, and complement laws, prove that $x + (x\,y) = x$ is true in all Boolean algebras.

49. Using only the five properties associative laws, commutative laws, distributive laws, identity laws, and complement laws, prove that $x + 1 = 1$ is true in all Boolean algebras.

In 50–61 determine whether the statement is TRUE or FALSE. Assume that x, y, and z represent Boolean variables.

50. $x + x\,y\,z = x$.

51. $x + x\,y + x = x$.

52. $\overline{x + y} = \overline{x} + \overline{y}$.

53. $x(x + y) = x + y\,x$.

54. $\overline{x}\,z + x\,z = z$.

55. $x + y + z = x\,y\,z$.

56. $x + x\,\overline{y} = x\,y\,z + x(\overline{z} + \overline{y}\,z)$.

57. $(x\,x + 1) = (x + 1)(x + 1)$.

58. $\overline{z + x\,y} = \overline{z} + \overline{x\,y}$.

59. $\overline{y + x\,z} = \overline{y}\,\overline{x} + \overline{y}\,\overline{z}$.

60. $\overline{y\,z + \overline{x}} = \overline{y}\,\overline{z}\,x$.

61. $(0 + x)(1 + x) = x\,x$.

62. Prove that the set of real numbers, with addition and multiplication of real numbers as $+$ and $\cdot$, negation as complementation, and the real numbers 0 and 1 as the 0 and the 1 respectively, is not a Boolean algebra.

63. Give a reason for each step in the proof that $x + x = x$ is true in Boolean algebras. Your reasons should come from the following: associative laws for addition and multiplication, commutative laws for addition and multiplication, distributive law for multiplication over addition and distributive law for addition over multiplication, identity laws, unit property, and zero property.

$$x = x + 0 = x + (x\,\overline{x}) = (x + x)(x + \overline{x}) = (x + x) \cdot 1 = 1 \cdot (x + x) = x + x.$$

64. Give a reason for each step in the proof that $x + 1 = x$ is true in Boolean algebras. Your reasons should come from the following: associative laws for addition and multiplication, commutative laws for addition and multiplication, distributive law for multiplication over addition and distributive law for addition over multiplication, identity laws, unit property, and zero property.

$$1 = x + \overline{x} = x + \overline{x} \cdot 1 = (x + \overline{x})(x + 1) = 1 \cdot (x + 1) = x + 1.$$

65. Give a reason for each step in the proof that $x + xy = x$ is true in Boolean algebras. Your reasons should come from the following: associative laws for addition and multiplication, commutative laws for addition and multiplication, distributive law for multiplication over addition and distributive law for addition over multiplication, identity laws, unit property, zero property, and idempotent laws.

$$x + x\,y = x \cdot 1 + x\,y = x(y + \overline{y}) + x\,y = (x\,y + x\,\overline{y}) + x\,y = x\,y + (x\,y + x\,\overline{y}) = (x\,y + x\,y) + x\,\overline{y} = x\,y + x\,\overline{y} = x(y + \overline{y}) = x \cdot 1 = x.$$

66. Draw a logic gate diagram for the Boolean function $F(x, y, z) = \overline{(x\,\overline{y})} + x\,\overline{z}$.

67. Let $F(x, y, z) = \overline{y}\,\overline{(\overline{x}\,z)} + y\,x + y\,\overline{z}$. Draw a logic gate diagram for F.

68. Let $F(x, y, z) = \overline{y}\,\overline{(\overline{x}\,z)} + y\,x + y\,\overline{z}$. Use a Karnaugh map to simplify the function F.

69. Use a Karnaugh map to minimize the sum-of-products expression $x\,y\,z + x\,\overline{y}\,z + x\,\overline{y}\,\overline{z} + \overline{x}\,\overline{y}\,z$.

70. Use a Karnaugh map to minimize the sum-of-products expression $x\,y\,z + x\,\overline{y}\,z + \overline{x}\,\overline{y}\,z + x\,\overline{y}\,\overline{z} + \overline{x}\,y\,z + \overline{x}\,\overline{y}\,\overline{z}$.

71. Construct a circuit using inverters, OR gates, and AND gates that gives an output of 1 if and only if three people on a committee do not all vote the same.

72. Let $F(x, y, z) = \overline{(\overline{y}\,z)}(x + \overline{x}\,y)$. Draw a logic gate diagram for F.

73. Let $F(x, y, z) = \overline{(\overline{y}\,z)}(x + \overline{x}\,y)$. Show that F can be simplified to give $y + x\,\overline{z}$.

74. A circuit is to be built that takes the numbers 0 through 9 as inputs $(1 = 0001, 2 = 0010, \ldots, 9 = 1001)$. Let $F(w, x, y, z)$ be the Boolean function that produces an output of 1 if and only if the input is an even number. Find a Karnaugh map for F and use the map and don't care conditions to find a simple expression for F.

75. A circuit is to be built that takes the numbers 0 through 9 as inputs $(1 = 0001, 2 = 0010, \ldots, 9 = 1001)$. Let $G(w, x, y, z)$ be the Boolean function that produces as output of 1 if and only if the input is an odd number. Find a Karnaugh map for G and use the map and don't care conditions to find a simple expression for G.

76. Use the Quine-McCluskey method to simplify the Boolean expression $\overline{x}\,y\,z + \overline{x}\,y\,\overline{z} + \overline{x}\,\overline{y}\,z + \overline{x}\,\overline{y}\,\overline{z} + x\,y\,z$.

77. Use the Quine-McCluskey method to simplify the Boolean expression $w\,x\,y\,z + w\,x\,y\,\overline{z} + w\,\overline{x}\,y\,z + w\,\overline{x}\,y\,\overline{z} + \overline{w}\,\overline{x}\,y\,z + w\,\overline{x}\,\overline{y}\,z + \overline{w}\,\overline{x}\,\overline{y}\,z$

Answers for Chapter 10

1. $x + x = x$, $x \cdot x = x$.
2. 2^4.
3. 2^8.
4. 2^{16}.
5. $x + y$.
6. $x\,y$.
7. $x\,y + x\,\overline{y} + \overline{x}\,y$.
8. $(x + y + z)(x + \overline{y} + z)(x + y + \overline{z})(\overline{x} + y + z)(\overline{x} + \overline{y} + z)$.
9. True.
10. True.
11. False.
12. False.
13. True.
14. False.
15. True.
16. True.
17. True.
18. True.
19. False.
20. False.
21. True.
22. False.
23. $x\,y + x\,\overline{y} + \overline{x}\,y$.
24. $x\,y + x\,\overline{y}$.
25. $x\,\overline{y} + \overline{x}\,y$.
26. $x\,y + \overline{x}\,y + x\,\overline{y} + \overline{x}\,\overline{y}$.
27. $x\,y\,z + \overline{x}\,y\,z + x\,\overline{y}\,z + x\,y\,\overline{z} + \overline{x}\,\overline{y}\,z + \overline{x}\,y\,\overline{z} + x\,\overline{y}\,\overline{z}$.
28. $x\,y\,z + x\,y\,\overline{z}$.

29. $x\,y\,z + \overline{x}\,y\,\overline{z}$.

30. $x\,y\,z + x\overline{y}z + x\,y\overline{z} + x\,\overline{y}\,\overline{z} + \overline{x}\,y\,z + \overline{x}\,\overline{y}\,z$.

31. $x\,\overline{y}\,z$.

32. $\overline{x}\,y + x\,\overline{y}$.

33. $\overline{x}\,y\,z + x\,\overline{y}\,z + x\,y\,\overline{z}$.

34. $x\,\overline{y}\,z + \overline{x}\,y\,z$.

35. $\overline{x\,\overline{y}}$.

36. (a) $x\,y\,\overline{z} + \overline{x}\,y\,z$ (b) $\overline{\overline{x\,y\,\overline{z}} \cdot \overline{\overline{x}\,y\,z}}$.

37. 1.

38. 1.

39. 0.

40. 0.

41. 0.

42. 0.

43. $F = \overline{(x + \overline{x}\,y)}\,\overline{y} = (\overline{x}\,(\overline{\overline{x}\,y}))\,\overline{y} = \overline{x}\,(x + \overline{y})\,\overline{y} = (\overline{x}\,x + \overline{x}\,\overline{y})\,\overline{y} = \overline{x}\,x\,\overline{y} + \overline{x}\,\overline{y}\,\overline{y} = 0 + \overline{x}\,\overline{y} = \overline{x}\,\overline{y} = \overline{x + y} = G$.

44. $x\,(z + y\,z) + y\,(\overline{\overline{x\,\overline{z}}\,x}) = x\,z + x\,y\,z + y\,(\overline{\overline{x\,\overline{z}}} + \overline{x}) = x\,z + x\,y\,z + x\,y\,z + \overline{x}\,y = x\,z + x\,y\,z + \overline{x}\,y = x\,z + \overline{x}\,y$.

45. $\overline{\overline{x + y}} + x\,y + \overline{x + y} = \overline{\overline{x}}\,\overline{y} + x\,y + \overline{x}\,\overline{y} = x\,\overline{y} + x\,y + \overline{x}\,\overline{y} = x\,\overline{y} + x\,\overline{y} + x\,y + \overline{x}\,\overline{y} = x\,\overline{y} + x\,y + x\,\overline{y} + \overline{x}\,\overline{y} = x\,(y + \overline{y}) + (x + \overline{x})\overline{y} = x\,(y + \overline{y}) + \overline{y}(x + \overline{x}) = x1 + \overline{y}1 = x + \overline{y}$.

46. $x = x \cdot 1 = x\,(x + \overline{x}) = x\,x + x\,\overline{x} = x\,x + 0 = x\,x$.

47. $x = x + 0 = x + x\,\overline{x} = (x + x)(x + \overline{x}) = (x + x) \cdot 1 = x + x$.

48. $x + (x\,y) = x \cdot 1 + x\,y = x\,(y + \overline{y}) + x\,y = x\,y + x\,y + x\,\overline{y} =^* x\,y + x\,\overline{y} = x\,(y + \overline{y}) = x \cdot 1 = x$ [*using idempotent law].

49. $x + 1 = (x + 1) \cdot 1 = (x + 1)(x + \overline{x}) = x + 1\overline{x} = x + \overline{x} = 1$.

50. True.

51. True.

52. False.

53. True.

54. True.

55. False.

56. True.

57. True.

58. False.

59. False.

60. True.

61. True.

62. The following laws fail: distributive law for addition over multiplication and the two complement laws.

63. Additive property of 0, multiplicative property of complement, distributive law for addition over multiplication, additive property of complement, commutative law for multiplication, multiplicative property of 1.

64. Multiplicative property of 1, additive property of 1, distributive law for multiplication over addition, multiplicative property of complement, additive property of 0.

65. Additive property of complement, multiplicative property of 1, distributive law for addition over multiplication, additive property of complement, multiplicative property of 1.

66. Multiplicative property of 1, additive property of complement, distributive law for multiplication over addition, associative law for addition, additive idempotent law, distributive law for multiplication over addition,

additive property of complement, multiplicative property of 1.

67.

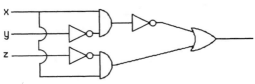

68.

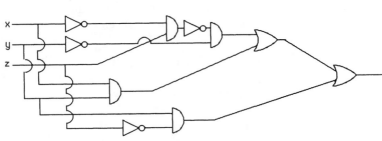

69. The following Karnaugh map yields $x + \overline{z}$.

70. The following Karnaugh map yields $x\,\overline{y} + x\,z + \overline{y}\,z$.

71. The following Karnaugh map yields $\overline{y} + z$.

72. The function $f(x, y, z) = \overline{(x\,y\,z + \overline{x}\,\overline{y}\,\overline{z})}$, with the following gate diagram, gives the desired output.

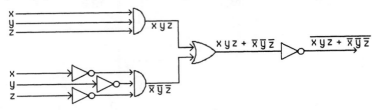

73. (a)

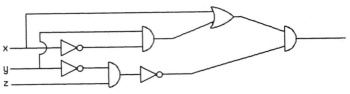

(b) $(\overline{\overline{y}\,z})(x + \overline{x}\,y) = (y + \overline{z})(x + \overline{x}\,z) = x\,z + x\,\overline{z} + y\,\overline{x}\,y + \overline{x}\,y\,\overline{z} = x\,y + x\,\overline{z} + \overline{x}\,y + \overline{x}\,y\,\overline{z} = x\,y + \overline{x}\,y + x\,\overline{z} + \overline{x}\,y\,\overline{z} = (x + \overline{x})\,y + x\,\overline{z} + \overline{x}\,y\,\overline{z} = y + \overline{x}\,y\,\overline{z} + x\,\overline{z} = y + x\,\overline{z}.$

74. The Karnaugh map for F is drawn here, with "d" used for the don't care conditions (that is, the bit strings representing the numbers 10 through 15). All 1s are covered by one oval in this map, and hence $F(w, x, y, z) = \overline{z}$.

75. The Karnaugh map for G is drawn here, with "d" used for the don't care conditions (that is, the bit strings representing the numbers 10 through 15). All 1s are covered by one oval, and hence $G(w, x, y, z) = z$.

76.

1 $x\,y\,z$ 111	(1,2) $y\,z$ –11	(2,3,4,5) $\overline{x}$ 0––
2 $\overline{x}\,y\,z$ 011	(2,3) $\overline{x}\,y$ 01–	
3 $\overline{x}\,y\,\overline{z}$ 010	(2,4) $\overline{x}\,z$ 0–1	
4 $\overline{x}\,\overline{y}\,z$ 001	(3,5) $\overline{x}\,\overline{z}$ 0–0	
5 $\overline{x}\,\overline{y}\,\overline{z}$ 000	(4,5) $\overline{x}\,\overline{y}$ 00–	

The products that were not used to form products in fewer variables are $y\,z$ and x. This yields

	$\overline{x}\,y\,z$	$\overline{x}\,y\,\overline{z}$	$\overline{x}\,\overline{y}\,z$	$\overline{x}\,\overline{y}\,\overline{z}$	$x\,y\,z$
$y\,z$	×		×		×
$\overline{x}$	×	×	×	×	

To cover the original five minterms, we use $\overline{x} + y\,z$.

77.

1 $w\,x\,y\,z$ 1111	(1,2) $w\,x\,y$ 111–	(1,2,3,4) $w\,y$ 1–1–
2 $w\,x\,y\,\overline{z}$ 1110	(1,3) $w\,y\,z$ 1–11	(1,2,3,4) $w\,y$ 1–1–
3 $w\,\overline{x}\,y\,z$ 1011	(2,4) $w\,y\,\overline{z}$ 1–10	(3,5,6,7) $\overline{x}\,z$ –0–1
4 $w\,\overline{x}\,y\,\overline{z}$ 1010	(3,4) $w\,\overline{x}\,y$ 101–	(3,5,6,7) $\overline{x}\,z$ –0–1
5 $\overline{w}\,\overline{x}\,y\,z$ 0011	(3,5) $\overline{x}\,y\,z$ –011	
6 $w\,\overline{x}\,\overline{y}\,z$ 1001	(3,6) $w\,\overline{x}\,z$ 10–1	
7 $\overline{w}\,\overline{x}\,\overline{y}\,z$ 0001	(5,7) $\overline{w}\,\overline{x}\,z$ 00–1	
	(6,7) $\overline{x}\,\overline{y}\,z$ –001	

The products that were not used to form products in fewer variables are $w\,y$ and $\overline{x}\,z$. This yields

	$w\,x\,y\,z$	$w\,x\,y\,\overline{z}$	$w\,\overline{x}\,y\,z$	$w\,\overline{x}\,y\,\overline{z}$	$\overline{w}\,\overline{x}\,y\,z$	$w\,\overline{x}\,\overline{y}\,z$	$\overline{w}\,\overline{x}\,\overline{y}\,z$
$w\,y$	×	×	×	×			
$\overline{x}\,z$			×		×	×	×

To cover the original seven minterms, use $w\,y + \overline{x}\,z$.

Questions for Chapter 11

1. Suppose $A = \{0, 1\}$. Describe all strings belonging to A^*.

2. Suppose a phrase-structure grammar has productions $S \to S0$, $S \to A1$, $A \to 0$. Find a derivation of 01.

3. Suppose a phrase-structure grammar has productions $S \to S0$, $S \to A1$, $A \to 0$. Find a derivation of 0100.

4. Suppose a phrase-structure grammar has productions $S \to S0$, $S \to A1$, $A \to 0$. Find a derivation of 010.

5. Suppose a phrase-structure grammar has productions $S \to 1S0$, $S \to 0A$, $A \to 0$. Find a derivation of 00.

6. Suppose a phrase-structure grammar has productions $S \to 1S0$, $S \to 0A$, $A \to 0$. Find a derivation of 1000.

7. Suppose a phrase-structure grammar has productions $S \to 1S0$, $S \to 0A$, $A \to 0$. Find a derivation of 110000.

8. Suppose a phrase-structure grammar has productions $S \to S11$, $S \to 0A$, $S \to A1$, $A \to 0$. Find a derivation of 01.

9. Suppose a phrase-structure grammar has productions $S \to S11$, $S \to 0A$, $S \to A1$, $A \to 0$. Find a derivation of 0011.

10. Suppose a phrase-structure grammar has productions $S \to S11$, $S \to 0A$, $S \to A1$, $A \to 0$. Find a derivation of 011111.

11. Find a production of the form "$A \to$___" such that $S \to 0A$, $A \to$___ produces $\{00\}$.

12. Find a production of the form "$A \to$___" such that $S \to 1S$, $S \to 0A$, $A \to$___ produces $\{1^n00 \mid n \geq 0\}$.

13. Find a set of two productions that produces $\{1^{2n} \mid n > 0\}$.

14. Let G be the phrase-structure grammar with vocabulary $V = \{A, B, a, b, S\}$, terminal element set $T = \{a, b\}$, start symbol S, and production set $P = \{S \to ABa, S \to Ba, A \to aB, AB \to b, B \to ab\}$. Which of these are derivable from ABa? (1) *ba*, (2) *abb*, (3) *aba*, (4) *b*, (5) *aababa*.

15. Let G be the phrase-structure grammar with vocabulary $V = \{A, B, a, b, S\}$, terminal element set $T = \{a, b\}$, start symbol S, and production set $P = \{S \to ABa, S \to Ba, A \to aB, AB \to b, B \to ab\}$. Which of these are derivable from A? (1) *babaa*, (2) *aab*, (3) *bba*.

16. Let G be the phrase-structure grammar with vocabulary $V = \{A, B, a, b, S\}$, terminal element set $T = \{a, b\}$, start symbol S, and production set $P = \{S \to ABa, S \to Ba, A \to aB, AB \to b, B \to ab\}$. Which of these are derivable from S? (1) *ba*, (2) *ab*, (3) *baab*, (4) *aababa*, (5) *aba*.

17. Let G be the phrase-structure grammar with vocabulary $V = \{A, B, 0, 1, S\}$, terminal elements $T = \{0, 1\}$, start symbol S, productions $P = \{S \to AB0, AB \to 1, A \to 0, B \to AB\}$. Which of these are derivable from S? (1) 000, (2) 11, (3) 010, (4) 0000, (5) 0001, (6) 110, (7) 0010.

18. Suppose $V = \{S, A, a, b\}$, $T = \{a, b\}$, and S is the start symbol. Find a set of productions that includes $S \to Aa$ and $A \to a$ and generates the language $\{a, aa\}$.

19. Suppose $V = \{S, A, a, b\}$, $T = \{a, b\}$, and S is the start symbol. Find a set of productions that includes $S \to Aa$ and $A \to a$ and generates the language $\{a, b, ba, baa\}$.

20. The productions of a phrase-structure grammar are $S \to S1$, $S \to 0A$, $A \to 1$. Find a derivation of 0111.

21. What language is generated by the phrase-structure grammar if the productions are $S \to S11$, $S \to \lambda$, where S is the start symbol?

22. What is the language generated by the grammar with productions $S \to SA$, $S \to 0$, $A \to 1A$, and $A \to 1$, where S is the start symbol?

23. Find a grammar for the set $\{0^{2n}1^n \mid n \geq 0\}$.

In 24–29 let $V = \{S, A, B, 0, 1\}$ and $T = \{0, 1\}$. For each set of productions determine whether the resulting grammar G is

    (i) type 0 grammar, but not type 1,   (ii) type 1 grammar, but not type 2,

    (iii) type 2 grammar, but not type 3,   (iv) type 3 grammar.

24. $S \to A10$, $AB \to 0$.

25. $S \to B$, $A \to B$, $B \to A$.

26. $S \to AB$, $A \to 0B1$, $0B1 \to 0$.

27. $S \to 1A$, $A \to 1$, $S \to \lambda$.

28. $S \to 1AB$, $AB \to 0B$, $B \to 0$, $A \to 1B$.

29. $S \to 0B$, $B \to 1A$, $B \to 0$, $A \to 0B$.

30. Construct a finite-state machine that models a vending machine accepting only quarters that gives a container of orange juice when 50 cents has been deposited, followed by a button being pushed. (The possible inputs are quarters and the button, and the possible outputs are nothing, orange juice, and a quarter. The machine returns any extra quarters.)

31. What is the output produced by this finite-state machine when the input string is 11101?

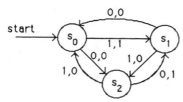

32. Construct a finite-state machine with output that produces a 1 if and only if the last 3 input bits read are 0s.

33. Suppose that $A = \{1, 11, 01\}$ and $B = \{0, 10\}$. Find AB.

34. Suppose that $A = \{1, 11, 01\}$ and $B = \{0, 10\}$. Find BA.

In 35–38 determine the output for each input string, using this state table.

35. 1111.

36. 10111.

37. 000.

38. 11000.

	f		g	
	input:		input:	
	0	1	0	1
s_0	s_1	s_2	1	1
s_1	s_2	s_0	0	0
s_2	s_1	s_3	1	1
s_3	s_3	s_1	0	1

39. Let $A = \{1, 10\}$. Which strings belong to A^*?

40. Find the set recognized by this deterministic finite-state machine.

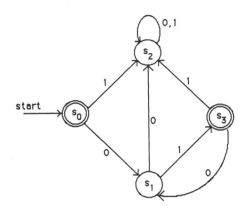

41. Find all strings recognized by this deterministic finite-state automaton.

42. Find all strings recognized by this deterministic finite-state automaton.

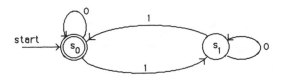

43. Find the language recognized by this nodeterministic finite-state automaton.

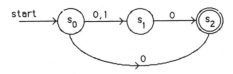

44. Find the language recognized by this nodeterministic finite-state automaton.

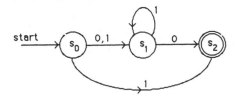

45. Let $A = \{0, 11\}$. Find A^2.

46. Let $A = \{0, 11\}$. Find A^3.

47. Find the Kleene closure of $A = \{1\}$.

48. Find the Kleene closure of $A = \{00\}$.

49. Find the Kleene closure of $A = \{0, 1, 2\}$.

50. Which strings belong to the set represented by the regular expression $0^* \cup 11$?

51. Construct a finite-state automaton that recognizes all strings that end with 11.

52. Construct a finite-state automaton that recognizes the set represented by the regular expression **10***.

53. Find a deterministic finite-state automaton equivalent to the following nondeterministic finite-state machine.

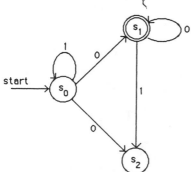

54. Which strings belong to the regular set represented by the regular expression **(1*01*0)** ?

55. Determine if 1101 belongs to the regular set **1*0*1**.

56. Determine if 1101 belongs to the regular set **(0∪1)*1**.

57. Determine if 1101 belongs to the regular set **(11)*0*(11)***.

58. Determine if 1101 belongs to the regular set **1(10)*1***.

59. Determine if 1101 belongs to the regular set **(01)*(11)*(01)***.

60. Determine if 1101 belongs to the regular set **11(00)*(10)***.

61. Determine if 1101 belongs to the regular set **(111)*(01)***.

62. Which strings are recognized by the following finite-state automaton?

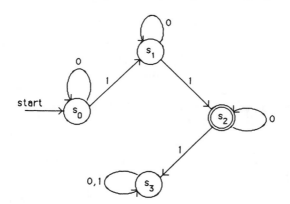

63. For the following Turing machines T, find the final tape when T is run on the following tape, beginning in the initial position (the first nonzero entry from the left):

$$\cdots \boxed{B}\boxed{B}\boxed{0}\boxed{0}\boxed{0}\boxed{1}\boxed{B}\boxed{0}\boxed{B}\boxed{B} \cdots$$

$(s_0, 0, s_0, 0, R)$, $(s_0, 1, s_1, 0, R)$, $(s_1, 0, s_1, 1, R)$, $(s_1, 1, s_2, 1, L)$, $(s_1, B, s_1, 1, L)$.

64. For the following Turing machine T, find the final tape when T is run on the following tape, beginning in the initial position (the first nonzero entry from the left):

$$\cdots \boxed{B}\boxed{B}\boxed{0}\boxed{0}\boxed{0}\boxed{1}\boxed{B}\boxed{0}\boxed{B}\boxed{B} \cdots$$

$(s_0, 0, s_0, 1, R)$, $(s_0, 1, s_1, 0, R)$, $(s_1, 1, s_2, 1, R)$, $(s_1, B, s_0, 0, R)$.

65. For the following Turing machine T, find the final tape when T is run on the following tape, beginning in the initial position (the first nonzero entry from the left):

| | $\cdots$ | B | B | 0 | 0 | 0 | 1 | B | 0 | B | B | $\cdots$ | |

$(s_0, 0, s_1, 1, R), (s_0, 1, s_1, 1, L), (s_1, 0, s_0, 1, L).$

66. For the following Turing machine T, find the final tape when T is run on the following tape, beginning in the initial position (the first nonzero entry from the left):

| | $\cdots$ | B | B | 0 | 0 | 0 | 1 | B | 0 | B | B | $\cdots$ | |

$(s_0, 0, s_2, 0, R), (s_0, B, s_0, 1, R), (s_1, 0, s_2, 1, R), (s_2, 0, s_1, 1, L), (s_2, 1, s_0, 1, R) .$

67. Consider the Turing machine T: $(s_0, 0, s_1, 1, R), (s_0, 1, s_1, 1, R), (s_1, 0, s_0, 1, L), (s_1, 1, s_0, 0, R),$ $(s_0, B, s_1, 1, R)$. For the following tape, determine the final tape when T halts, assuming that T begins in state s_0 at the leftmost nonblank symbol.

| | $\cdots$ | B | B | 1 | 1 | 0 | B | B | $\cdots$ | |

68. Consider the Turing machine T: $(s_0, 0, s_1, 1, R), (s_0, 1, s_1, 1, R), (s_1, 0, s_0, 1, L), (s_1, 1, s_0, 0, R),$ $(s_0, B, s_1, 1, R)$. For the following tape, determine the final tape when T halts, assuming that T begins in state s_0 at the leftmost nonblank symbol.

| | $\cdots$ | B | B | 0 | 0 | 0 | B | B | $\cdots$ | |

69. Consider the Turing machine T: $(s_0, 0, s_1, 1, R), (s_0, 1, s_1, 1, R), (s_1, 0, s_0, 1, L), (s_1, 1, s_0, 0, R),$ $(s_0, B, s_1, 1, R)$. For the following tape, determine the final tape when T halts, assuming that T begins in state s_0 at the leftmost nonblank symbol.

| | $\cdots$ | B | B | 1 | 0 | 1 | B | B | $\cdots$ | |

70. Construct a Turing machine that computes $f(n) = n + 2$, where $n \geq 0$.

71. Construct a Turing machine that computes $f(n_1, n_2) = n_2 + 1$, where $n_1, n_2 \geq 0$.

Answers for Chapter 11

1. A^* consists of all strings of 0s and 1s, including the empty string.

2. $S \Rightarrow A1 \Rightarrow 01.$

3. $S \Rightarrow S0 \Rightarrow S00 \Rightarrow A100 \Rightarrow 0100.$

4. $S \Rightarrow S0 \Rightarrow A10 \Rightarrow 010.$

5. $S \Rightarrow 0A \Rightarrow 00.$

6. $S \Rightarrow 1S0 \Rightarrow 10A0 \Rightarrow 1000.$

7. $S \Rightarrow 1S0 \Rightarrow 11S00 \Rightarrow 110A00 \Rightarrow 110000.$

8. $S \Rightarrow A1 \Rightarrow 01.$

9. $S \Rightarrow S11 \Rightarrow 0A11 \Rightarrow 0011.$

10. $S \Rightarrow S11 \Rightarrow S1111 \Rightarrow A11111 \Rightarrow 011111.$

11. $A \rightarrow 0.$

12. $A \rightarrow 0.$

13. $S \rightarrow S11, S \rightarrow 11.$

14. $(1), (5).$

15. (2).

16. (1), (4), (5).

17. (3), (7).

18. $S \rightarrow Aa$, $A \rightarrow a$, $S \rightarrow a$.

19. $S \rightarrow Aa$, $A \rightarrow a$, $S \rightarrow aA$, $A \rightarrow ab$.

20. Apply the production $S \rightarrow S1$ twice to obtain $S11$. Then apply $S \rightarrow 0A$ to obtain $0A11$. Then apply $A \rightarrow 1$ to obtain 0111.

21. The language generated is the set of all strings consisting of an even number of 1s and no other symbols.

22. The set of all bit strings that consist of a 0 followed by an arbitrary number of 1s.

23. Use the grammar with productions $S \rightarrow 00S1$ and $S \rightarrow \lambda$, where S is the start symbol.

24. *i*.

25. *iii*.

26. *i*.

27. *iv*.

28. *ii*.

29. *iv*.

30.

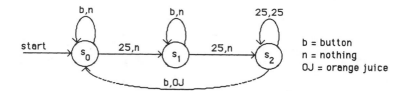

31. 10000.

32.

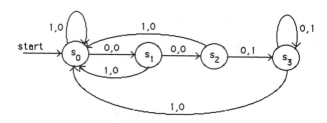

33. $AB = \{10, 110, 1110, 010, 0110\}$.

34. $BA = \{01, 011, 001, 101, 1011, 1001\}$.

35. 1110.

36. 11011.

37. 101.

38. 11000.

39. The strings in A^* are those in which each 0 is preceded by at least one 1.

40. The set represented by $(\mathbf{01})^*$.

41. All bit strings with no 1s.

42. All bit strings with an even number of 1s.

43. $\{0, 00, 10\}$.

44. $\{1, 01^n0, 1^n0 \mid n \geq 0\}$.

45. $\{00, 011, 110, 1111\}$.

46. $\{000, 0011, 01111, 0110, 1100, 11011, 11110, 111111\}$.

47. $\{1^n \mid n = 0, 1, 2, \ldots\}$.

48. $\{0^{2n} \mid n = 0, 1, 2, \ldots\}$.

49. All strings of 0s, 1s, and 2s.

50. The bit strings consisting of all 0s (including the empty string) and the string 11.

51.

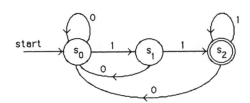

52.

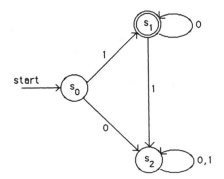

53.

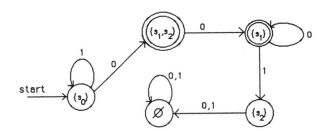

54. The strings containing an even number of 0s and not ending with a 1.

55. Yes.

56. Yes.

57. No.

58. Yes.

59. Yes.

60. No.

61. No.

62. Strings containing exactly two 1s.

63. $\cdots$ | B | B | 0 | 0 | 0 | 1 | 1 | 0 | B | B | $\cdots$

64. $\cdots$ | B | B | 1 | 1 | 1 | 0 | 0 | 1 | B | B | $\cdots$

65. $\cdots$ | B | B | 1 | 1 | 0 | 1 | B | 0 | B | B | $\cdots$

66. $\cdots$ | B | B | 1 | 1 | 0 | 1 | 1 | 0 | B | B | $\cdots$

67. $\cdots$ | B | B | 1 | 0 | 1 | B | B | $\cdots$

68. $\cdots$ | B | B | 1 | 1 | 1 | B | B | $\cdots$

69. $\cdots$ | B | B | 1 | 0 | 1 | B | B | $\cdots$

70. $(s_0, 1, s_1, 1, R), (s_1, 1, s_1, 1, R), (s_1, B, s_2, 1, R), (s_2, B, s_3, 1, R)$.

71. $(s_0, 1, s_1, B, R), (s_1, 1, s_1, B, R), (s_1, *, s_2, 1, R)$.